NIOSH POCKET GUIDE TO CHEMICAL HAZARDS

U.S. DEPARTMENT OF HEALTH AND HUMAN SERVICES
Public Health Service
Centers for Disease Control and Prevention
National Institute for Occupational Safety and Health

June 1997

D0904734

ii

DISCLAIMER

Mention of the name of any company or product does not constitute endorsement by the National Institute for Occupational Safety and Health.

To receive other information about occupational safety and health problems, call
1-800-35NIOSH (1-800-356-4674), or
visit the NIOSH Home Page on the World Wide Web at
http://www.cdc.gov/niosh/homepage.html

DHHS (NIOSH) Publication No. 97-140

COPYING AND REPRINTING

This document is in the public domain and may be freely copied or reprinted.

Printed and Distributed By:

J. J. Keller & Associates, Inc.
3003 W. Breezewood Lane, P.O. Box 368
Neenah, Wisconsin 54957-0368
USA
Phone: (800) 327-6868

PREFACE

The *NIOSH Pocket Guide to Chemical Hazards* presents information taken from the *NIOSH/OSHA Occupational Health Guidelines for Chemical Hazards*, from National Institute for Occupational Safety and Health (NIOSH) criteria documents and Current Intelligence Bulletins, and from recognized references in the fields of industrial hygiene, occupational medicine, toxicology, and analytical chemistry. The information is presented in tabular form to provide a quick, convenient source of information on general industrial hygiene practices. The information in the *Pocket Guide* includes chemical structures or formulas, identification codes, synonyms, exposure limits, chemical and physical properties, incompatibilities and reactivities, measurement methods, respirator selections, signs and symptoms of exposure, and procedures for emergency treatment.

The information assembled in the original 1978 printing of the *Pocket Guide* was the result of the Standards Completion Program, a joint effort by NIOSH and the Department of Labor to develop supplemental requirements for the approximately 380 workplace environmental exposure standards adopted by the Occupational Safety and Health Administration (OSHA) in 1971.

This revision of the *Pocket Guide* includes updated sampling and analytical methods, updated Department of Transportation (DOT) identification and guide numbers, revised conversion factors, current exposure limits, guidelines for selecting "Part 84" respirators in Table 4, the new NIOSH carcinogen policy in Appendix A, an expanded synomyn and trade name index, and minor technical changes since the June 1994 Edition.

CONTENTS

ACKNOWLEDGMENTS

The Education and Information Division (EID), National Institute for Occupational Safety and Health (NIOSH), had primary responsibility for the development of the *Pocket Guide*. I would like to express my appreciation to the following people within EID for their assistance in preparing the *Pocket Guide*: Howard Ludwig (former Technical Editor) for general guidance; David Case and Rolland Rogers for reformatting and computerization; Richard Niemeier, John Whalen, Ralph Zumwalde, Barb Dames, Laurence Reed, and Heinz Ahlers for policy review; Susan Cairelli and Kent Hatfield for consultation on toxicology issues; David Votaw, Joann Wess, Crystal Ellison, Faye Rice, John Palassis, Charles Bryant, Walter Ruch, Leela Murthy, Henryka Nagy, Clayton Doak, Sherry Medley, and Eileen Kuempel for assistance in updating and adding new information; Ronald Schuler, Vicki Reuss, Lucy Schoolfield, and Lawrence Foster for data acquisition; Sharon Cheesman for administrative support; Anne Hamilton and Vanessa Becks for editorial review; Vivian Morgan for electronic database negotiations; Charlene Maloney for publication dissemination; Shirley Carr for printing procurement; Pauline Elliott for graphic design; and Midwest Publications Consultants (Sherri Diana, Gary Litfin, Rob Schattauer, and Carla Brooks) for answering requests and mailing thousands of copies of the *Pocket Guide*.

In addition, the following people from other Divisions in NIOSH also contributed greatly to the *Pocket Guide*: Mary Ellen Cassinelli, Donald Dollberg, and Peter Eller from the Division of Physical Sciences and Engineering (DPSE) for the development of the measurement methods section; Shiro Tanaka from the Division of Surveillance, Hazard Evaluations, and Field Studies (DSHEFS) for medical terminology; and Donald Campbell, Chris Coffey, and John Dower, from the Division of Safety Research (DSR) for the development of the respirator recommendations.

Also, thanks are due to those individuals who reviewed and constructively commented on the *Pocket Guide* during its initial development and subsequent revisions.

Henry Chan (Technical Editor)

INTRODUCTION

The *NIOSH Pocket Guide to Chemical Hazards* is intended as a source of general industrial hygiene information for workers, employers, and occupational health professionals. The *Pocket Guide* presents key information and data in abbreviated tabular form for 677 chemicals or substance groupings (e.g., manganese compounds, tellurium compounds, inorganic tin compounds, etc.) that are found in the work environment. The industrial hygiene information found in the *Pocket Guide* should help users recognize and control occupational chemical hazards. The chemicals or substances contained in this revision include all substances for which the National Institute for Occupational Safety and Health (NIOSH) has recommended exposure limits (RELs) and those with permissible exposure limits (PELs) as found in the Occupational Safety and Health Administration (OSHA) General Industry Air Contaminants Standard (29 CFR 1910.1000).

Background

In 1974, NIOSH (which is responsible for recommending health and safety standards) joined OSHA (whose jurisdictions include promulgation and enforcement activities) in developing a series of occupational health standards for substances with existing PELs. This joint effort was labeled the Standards Completion Program and involved the cooperative efforts of several contractors and personnel from various divisions within NIOSH and OSHA. The Standards Completion Program developed 380 substance-specific draft standards with supporting documentation that contained technical information and recommendations needed for the promulgation of new occupational health regulations. The *Pocket Guide* was developed to make the technical information in those draft standards more conveniently available to workers, employers, and occupational health professionals. The *Pocket Guide* is updated periodically to reflect new data regarding the toxicity of various substances and any changes in exposure standards or recommendations.

Data Collection and Application

The data collected for this revision were derived from a variety of sources, including NIOSH policy documents such as criteria documents and Current Intelligence Bulletins (CIBs), and recognized references in the fields of industrial hygiene, occupational medicine, toxicology, and analytical chemistry.

NIOSH RECOMMENDATIONS

Acting under the authority of the Occupational Safety and Health Act of 1970 (29 USC Chapter 15) and the Federal Mine Safety and Health Act of 1977 (30 USC Chapter 22), NIOSH develops and periodically revises recommended exposure limits (RELs) for hazardous substances or conditions in the workplace. NIOSH also recommends appropriate preventive measures to reduce or eliminate the adverse health and safety effects of these hazards. To formulate these recommendations, NIOSH evaluates all known and available medical, biological, engineering, chemical, trade, and other information relevant to the hazard. These recommendations are then published and transmitted to OSHA and the Mine Safety and Health Administration (MSHA) for use in promulgating legal standards.

NIOSH recommendations are published in a variety of documents. Criteria documents recommend workplace exposure limits and appropriate preventive measures to reduce or eliminate adverse health effects and accidental injuries.

Current Intelligence Bulletins (CIBs) are issued to disseminate new scientific information about occupational hazards. A CIB may draw attention to a formerly unrecognized hazard, report new data on a known hazard, or present information on hazard control.

Alerts, Special Hazard Reviews, Occupational Hazard Assessments, and Technical Guidelines support and complement the other standards development activities of the Institute. Their purpose is to assess the safety and health problems associated with a given agent or hazard (e.g., the potential for injury or for carcinogenic, mutagenic, or teratogenic effects) and to recommend appropriate control and surveillance methods. Although these documents are not intended to supplant the more comprehensive criteria documents, they are prepared to assist OSHA and MSHA in the formulation of regulations.

In addition to these publications, NIOSH periodically presents testimony before various Congressional committees and at OSHA and MSHA rulemaking hearings.

A complete list of occupational safety and health issues for which NIOSH has formal policies (e.g., recommendations for occupational exposure to chemical and physical hazards, engineering controls, work practices, safety considerations, etc.) can be found in *NIOSH Recommendations for Occupational Safety and Health: Compendium of Policy Documents and Statements* [DHHS (NIOSH) Publication No. 92-100].

HOW TO USE THIS POCKET GUIDE

The *Pocket Guide* has been designed to provide chemical-specific data to supplement general industrial hygiene knowledge. To maximize the amount of data provided in this limited space, abbreviations and codes have been used extensively. These abbreviations and codes, which have been designed to permit rapid comprehension by the regular user, are discussed for each column in the following subsections.

Chemical Name and Structure/Formula, CAS and RTECS Numbers, and DOT ID and Guide Numbers

Chemical Name and Structure/Formula. — The chemical name found in the OSHA General Industry Air Contaminants Standard (29 CFR* 1910.1000) is listed first. The chemical structure or formula is also provided; carbon-carbon double bonds (-C=C-) and carbon-carbon triple bonds (-C≡C-) have been indicated where applicable. A page index for synonyms and trade names is included at the back of the *Pocket Guide* to help the user locate a specific substance.

CAS and RTECS Numbers. — Below the chemical struc-

Code of Federal Regulations.

ture/formula is the Chemical Abstracts Service (CAS) registry number. This number, in the format xxx-xx-x, is unique for each chemical and allows efficient searching on computerized data bases. A page index for all CAS registry numbers listed is included at the back of the *Pocket Guide* to help the user locate a specific substance.

Immediately below the CAS number is the *NIOSH Registry of Toxic Effects of Chemical Substances* (RTECS) number, in the format ABxxxxxxx. RTECS may be useful for obtaining additional toxicologic information on a specific substance.

DOT ID and GUIDE Number. — Under the RTECS number are the U.S. Department of Transportation (DOT) identification number and the corresponding guide number. Their format is xxxx xxx. The Identification number (xxxx) indicates that the chemical is regulated by DOT. The Guide number (xxx) refers to actions to be taken to stabilize an emergency situation; this information can be found in the 1996 *North American Emergency Response Guidebook*, (Office of Hazardous Materials Transportation [DHM-51], U.S. Department of Transportation, 400 Seventh Street S.W., Washington, D.C. 20590-0001). A page index for all DOT ID numbers listed is included at the back of the *Pocket Guide* to help the user locate a specific substance; please note however, that many DOT numbers are NOT unique for specific substances.

Synonyms, Trade Names, and Conversion Factors

Common synonyms and trade names are listed alphabetically for each chemical. Factors for the conversion of ppm (parts of vapor or gas per million parts of contaminated air by volume) to mg/m^3 (milligrams of vapor or gas per cubic meter of contaminated air) at 25°C and 1 atmosphere are listed for chemicals with exposure limits expressed in ppm.

Exposure Limits

The NIOSH recommended exposure limits (RELs) are listed first in this column. Unless noted otherwise, RELs are time-weighted average (TWA) concentrations for up to a 10-hour workday during a 40-hour workweek. A short-term exposure limit (STEL) is designated by "ST" preceding the value; unless noted otherwise, the STEL is a 15-minute TWA exposure that should not be exceeded at any time during a workday. A ceiling REL is designated by "C" preceding the value; unless noted otherwise, the ceiling value should not be exceeded at any time. Any substance that NIOSH considers to be a potential occupational carcinogen is designated by the notation "Ca" (see Appendix A, which contains a brief discussion of potential occupational carcinogens).

The OSHA permissible exposure limits (PELs), as found in Tables Z-1, Z-2, and Z-3 of the OSHA General Industry Air Contaminants Standard (29 CFR 1910.1000), that were effective on July 1, 1993* and which are currently enforced by OSHA are listed next. [*Note: In July 1992, the 11th Circuit Court of Appeals in its decision in *AFL-CIO v. OSHA*, 965 F.2d 962 (11th Cir., 1992) vacated more protective PELs set by OSHA in 1989 for 212 substances, moving them back to PELs established in 1971. The appeals court also vacated new PELs for 164 substances that were not previously regulated. Although OSHA is currently enforcing exposure limits in Tables Z-1, Z-2, and Z-3 of 29 CFR 1910.1000 which were in effect before 1989, violations of the "general duty clause" as contained in Section 5(a)(1) of the Occupational Safety and Health Act may be considered when worker exposures exceed the 1989 PELs for the 164 substances that were not previously regulated. The substances for which OSHA PELs were vacated on June 30, 1993 are indicated by the symbol "†" following OSHA in this column and previous values are listed in Appendix G.] Unless

x

noted otherwise, PELs are TWA concentrations that must not be exceeded during any 8-hour workshift of a 40-hour workweek. A STEL is designated by "ST" preceding the value and is measured over a 15-minute period unless noted otherwise. OSHA ceiling concentrations (designated by "C" preceding the value) must not be exceeded during any part of the workday; if instantaneous monitoring is not feasible, the ceiling must be assessed as a 15-minute TWA exposure. In addition, there are a number of substances from Table Z-2 (e.g., beryllium, ethylene dibromide, and methylene chloride) that have PEL ceiling values that must not be exceeded except for a maximum peak over a specified period (e.g., a 5-minute maximum peak in any 2 hours). Appendix B contains a brief discussion of substances regulated as carcinogens by OSHA.

Concentrations are given in ppm, mg/m^3, mppcf (millions of particles per cubic foot of air as determined from counting an impinger sample), or $fibers/cm^3$ (fibers per cubic centimeter). The "[skin]" designation indicates the potential for dermal absorption; skin exposure should be prevented as necessary through the use of good work practices and gloves, coveralls, goggles, and other appropriate equipment. The "(total)" designation indicates that the REL or PEL listed is for "total particulate" versus the "(resp)" designation which refers to the "re-

spirable fraction" of the airborne particulate. Appendix C contains more detailed discussions of the specific exposure limits for certain low-molecular-weight aldehydes, asbestos, various dyes (benzidine-, o-tolidine-, and o-dianisidine-based), carbon black, the various chromium compounds (chromic acid and chromates, chromium(II) and chromium(III) compounds, and chromium metal), coal tar pitch volatiles, coke oven emissions, cotton dust, lead, NIAX Catalyst ESN, trichloroethylene, and tungsten carbide (cemented). Appendix D contains a brief discussion of substances included in the *Pocket Guide* with no established RELs at this time and Appendix F contains miscellaneous notes regarding the OSHA PELs. Appendix G lists the OSHA PELS that were vacated on June 30, 1993.

IDLH

For the June 1994 Edition of the *Pocket Guide*, immediately dangerous to life or health concentrations (IDLHs) were reviewed and, in many cases, were revised and made more protective. As a consequence of the IDLH changes, many of the respirator recommendations for these substances were also revised. The criteria utilized to determine the adequacy of existing IDLH values were a combination of those used during the Standards Completion Program and a newer methodology developed by NIOSH. These "interim" criteria form a tiered approach with acute human toxicity data being used preferentially, followed next by acute animal inhalation toxicity data, and then finally by acute animal oral toxicity data to determine an updated IDLH value. When relevant acute toxicity data were insufficient or unavailable, the use of chronic toxicity data or an analogy to a chemically similar substance was considered. The criteria and information sources for both the original and revised IDLH values are given in Documentation for Immediately Dangerous to Life and Health Concentrations (IDLHs) (NTIS Publication No. PB-94-195047). NIOSH is currently assessing the various uses of IDLHs and whether the original criteria used to derive the IDLH values are valid or if other information or criteria should be utilized. Based on this assessment, NIOSH will develop a new strategy for revising the IDLH values currently listed, as well as for developing new IDLH values for the more than 300 substances listed in the Pocket Guide without IDLHs.

The definition of IDLH that was derived during the Standards Completion Program was based on the Mine Safety and Health Administration (MSHA) definition stipulated in 30 CFR 11.3(t). The purpose for establishing an IDLH value in the Standards Completion Program was to ensure that a worker could escape without injury or irreversible health effects from an IDLH exposure in the event of the failure of respiratory protection equipment. The IDLH was considered a maximum concentration above which only a highly reliable breathing apparatus providing maximum worker protection was permitted. In determining IDLH values, the ability of a worker to escape without loss of life or irreversible health effects was considered along with severe eye or respiratory irritation and other deleterious effects (e.g., disorientation or incoordination) that could prevent escape. As a safety margin, the Standards Completion Program IDLH values were based on the effects that might occur as a consequence of a 30-minute exposure. However, the 30-minute period was NOT meant to imply that workers should stay in the work environment any longer than necessary, in fact, EVERY EFFORT SHOULD BE MADE TO EXIT IMMEDIATELY!

The current NIOSH definition for an IDLH exposure condition, as stipulated in the NIOSH Respirator Decision Logic (DHHS [NIOSH] Publication No. 87-108, NTIS Publication No. PB-91-151183), is a condition "that poses a threat of exposure to airborne contaminants when that exposure is likely to cause death or immediate or delayed permanent adverse health effects or prevent escape from such an environment." The purpose of establishing an IDLH exposure concentration is to "ensure that the worker can escape from a given contaminated environment in the event of failure of the respiratory protection equipment." The *NIOSH Respirator Decision Logic* uses these IDLH values as one of several respirator selection criteria. Under the *NIOSH Respirator Decision Logic*, the most protective respirators (e.g., a self-contained breathing apparatus equipped with a full facepiece and operated in a pressure-demand or other positive-pressure mode) would be selected for firefighting, exposure to carcinogens, entry into oxygen-deficient atmospheres, in emergency situations, during entry into an atmosphere that contains a substance at a concentration greater than 2,000 times the NIOSH REL or OSHA PEL, and for entry into IDLH atmospheres.

IDLH values are listed for over 380 substances. The notation "Ca" appears in this column for all substances that NIOSH considers to be potential occupational carcinogens. However, IDLH values that were originally determined in the Standards Completion Program or were recently revised are shown in brackets following the "Ca" designations. "10%LEL" indicates that the IDLH was based on 10% of the lower explosive limit for safety considerations even though the relevant toxicological data indicated that irreversible health effects or impairment of escape existed only at higher concentrations. "N.D." indicates that an IDLH has not as yet been determined.

Physical Description

This column provides a brief description of the appearance and odor of each substance. Notations are made as to whether a substance can be shipped as a liquefied compressed gas or whether it has major use as a pesticide.

Chemical and Physical Properties

The following abbreviations are used for the chemical and physical properties given for each substance. "NA" indicates that a property is not applicable, and a question mark (?) indicates that it is unknown.

MW .... Molecular weight
BP .... Boiling point at 1 atmosphere, °F

xiv

Sol .... Solubility in water at 68°F*, % by weight (i.e., g/100 ml)

Fl.P .... Flash point (i.e., the temperature at which the liquid phase gives off enough vapor to flash when exposed to an external ignition source), closed cup (unless annotated "(oc)" for open cup),°F

IP** .... Ionization potential, eV (electron volts)

VP .... Vapor pressure at 68°F*, mm Hg; "approx" indicates approximately

MLT .... Melting point for solids, °F

FRZ .... Freezing point for liquids and gases, °F

UEL .... Upper explosive (flammable) limit in air, % by volume (at room temperature*)

LEL .... Lower explosive (flammable) limit in air, % by volume (at room temperature*)

MEC .... Minimum explosive concentration, g/m^3 (when available)

Sp.Gr .... Specific gravity at 68°F* referenced to water at 39.2°F(4°C)

RGasD .... Relative density of gases referenced to air = 1 (indicates how many times a gas is heavier than air at the same temperature)

When possible, the flammability/combustibility of a substance was determined and listed after the specific gravity. The following OSHA criteria (29 CFR 1910.106) were used to classify flammable or combustible liquids:

Class IA flammable liquid .... Fl.P. below 73°F and BP below 100°F.

Class IB flammable liquid .... Fl.P. below 73°F and BP at or above 100°F.

Class IC flammable liquid .... Fl.P. at or above 73°F and below 100°F.

Class II combustible liquid .... Fl.P. at or above 100°F and below 140°F.

Class IIIA combustible liquid .... Fl.P. at or above 140°F and below 200°F.

Class IIIB combustible liquid .... Fl.P. at or above 200°F.

---

*If noted after a specific entry, these properties may be reported at other temperatures.

**Ionization potentials are given as a guideline for the selection of photoionization detector lamps used in some direct-reading instruments.

Incompatibilities and Reactivities

This column lists important hazardous incompatibilities or reactivities of each substance.

Measurement Method

This column provides a brief, key word description of the suggested sampling and analysis method. Each description comprises four components: (1) the collection method, (2) the sample work-up, (3) the analytical method, and (4) the method number. The method number is usually from the 4th edition of the *NIOSH Manual of Analytical Methods* (DHHS [NIOSH] Publication No. 94-113) and is indicated by "IV" following the sample work-up. If a different edition of the *NIOSH Manual of Analytical Methods* is cited, the appropriate edition (and, for the 2nd edition only, the volume number) would be noted [e.g., II(4)]. In a number of instances, the table cites the *OSHA Analytical Methods Manual* (or the OSHA web site, http://www.osha-slc.gov/) and applicable method number (e.g., OSHA [#21]). When a method for a particular substance is not included in the latest NIOSH or OSHA analytical methods manuals or at the OSHA web site, "None available" is listed. The codes listed are explained in Table 1. Table 2 presents ordering information for the measurement methods cited.

Personal Protection and Sanitation

This column presents a summary of recommended practices for each toxic substance. These recommendations supplement general work practices (e.g., no eating, drinking, or smoking where chemicals are used). Table 3 explains the codes used. Each category is described as follows:

SKIN: Recommends the need for personal protective clothing.

EYES: Recommends the need for eye protection.

WASH SKIN: Recommends when workers should wash the spilled chemical from the body in addition to normal washing (e.g., before eating).

REMOVE: Advises workers when to remove clothing that has accidentally become wet or significantly contaminated.

CHANGE: Recommends whether the routine changing of clothing is needed.

PROVIDE: Recommends the need for eyewash fountains and/or quick drench facilities.

Recommendations for Respirator Selection

This column provides a condensed table of allowable respirator use for those substances for which IDLH values have been determined. NIOSH is currently reevaluating the IDLH values, and as new or revised IDLH values are developed, respirator selection recommendations will be incorporated into subsequent editions of the *Pocket Guide*. In the interim no respirator recommendations will be made for substances without IDLH values (these will be noted by "TBAL" -- to be added later).

NIOSH has developed a new set of regulations in 42 CFR 84 (also referred to as "Part 84") for testing and certifying nonpowered, air-purifying, particulate-filter respirators. The new Part 84 respirators have passed a more demanding certification test than the old respirators (e.g.; dust [D]; dust and mist [DM]; dust, mist, and fume [DMFu]; spray paint; pesticide; etc.) certified under 30 CFR 11 (also referred to as "Part 11"). Under Part 84, NIOSH is allowing manufacturers to continue selling and shipping Part 11 particulate filters as NIOSH-certified until July 10, 1998. It is important to see Table 4 (pages xxxi-xxxii) for substitution of Part 84 respirators for Part 11 respirators. Also see the *NIOSH Guide to the Selection and*

Use of Particulate Respirators (DHHS [NIOSH] publication 96-101).

The first line in the column indicates whether the "NIOSH" or the "OSHA" exposure limit is used on which to base the respirator recommendations. The more protective limit between the NIOSH REL or the OSHA PEL is always used. "NIOSH/OSHA" indicates that the limits are equivalent.

Each subsequent line lists a maximum use concentration (MUC) followed by a series of codes representing classes of respirators that are acceptable for use below the MUC. Individual respirator class codes are separated by diagonal lines (/). More protective respirators may be worn. Emergency or planned entry into unknown concentrations or entry into IDLH conditions are designated by the symbol § and followed by the codes for classes of respirators acceptable for these conditions. "Escape" indicates that the respirators are to be used only for escape purposes. For each MUC or condition the table lists only those respirators with the required protection factor and other use restrictions based on the *NIOSH Respirator Decision Logic*.

All respirators selected must be approved by NIOSH and MSHA under the provisions of 30 CFR 11 or by NIOSH under 42 CFR 84. The current listing of NIOSH/MSHA certified respirators can be found in the *NIOSH Certified Equipment List* (DHHS [NIOSH] Publication No. 94-104). A list of Part 84 respirators can be found on the NIOSH Home Page (http://www.cdc.gov/niosh/homepage.html) or obtained by calling 1-800-35-NIOSH.

A complete respiratory protection program must be implemented and must fulfill all requirements of 29 CFR 1910.134. A respiratory protection program must include a written standard operating procedure covering regular training, fit-testing, fit-checking, periodic environmental monitoring, maintenance, medical monitoring, inspection, cleaning, storage, and periodic program evaluation. Selection of a specific respirator within a given class of recommended respirators depends on the particular situation; this choice should be made only by a knowledgeable person. *REMEMBER:* Air-purifying respirators will not protect users against oxygen-deficient atmospheres, and they are not to be used in IDLH conditions. The only respirators recommended for fire fighting are self-contained breathing apparatuses that have full facepieces and are operated in a pressure-demand or other positive-pressure modes. Additional information on the selection and use of respirators can be found in the *NIOSH Respirator Decision Logic* and the *NIOSH Guide to Industrial Respiratory Protection* (DHHS [NIOSH] Publication No. 87-116).

Codes for the various categories of respirators are defined in Table 4. In addition, the assigned protection factor (APF) is indicated for each respirator class.

Route of Health Hazard

This column lists the toxicologically important routes of entry for each substance and whether contact with the skin or eyes is potentially hazardous, abbreviated as follows:

Inh .... Inhalation
Abs .... Skin absorption
Ing .... Ingestion
Con .... Skin and/or eye contact
(liq) .... Liquid
(sol) .... Solid
(soln) ..... Solution

Symptoms

This column lists the potential symptoms of exposure. Their abbreviations are defined in Table 5.

First Aid

    This column lists emergency procedures for eye and skin contact, inhalation, and ingestion of the toxic substance. Abbreviations are defined in Table 6.

Target Organs

    This column lists the organs that are affected by exposure to each substance. Abbreviations are defined in Table 5.

Table 1. — Codes for measurement methods

Code	Method/reagent	Code	Method/reagent
Collection method:*		T-Sorb	Thermosorb® tube
Ambersorb	Ambersorb® XE-347 tube	Vertical elut	Vertical elutriator
Anasorb	Anasorb tube	XAD	XAD® tube
Bag	Gas collection bag		
Bub	Bubbler	Sample work-up	
Carbo-B	Carbosieve® B tube	CCl_4	Carbon tetrachloride
Char	Charcoal tube	$CHCl_3$	Chloroform
Char (low-Ni)	Charcoal tube (low nickel content)	CH_2Cl_2	Methylene chloride
Char (pet)	Charcoal tube (petroleum-based)	CH_3CN	Acetonitrile
Chrom	Chromosorb tube	CH_3COOH	Acetic acid
Dry tube	Drying tube	CS_2	Carbon disulfide
Filter	Particulate filter	DCE	1,2-Dichloroethane
Florisil	Florisil® tube	DMF	Dimethylformamide
G-chrom P	Gas-chrom P® tube	DMSO	Dimethyl sulfoxide
Hydrar	Hydrar® sorbent tube	EDTA	Ethylenedinitrilo-tetraacetic acid
Imp	Impinger	$FeCl_3$	Ferric chloride
Mol-sieve	Molecular sieve tube	HCl	Hydrochloric acid
OVS	OSHA versatile sampler	HCOOH	Formic acid
Pad/Pre-filter	Treated pad with a pre-filter	HNO_3	Nitric acid
Porapak	Porapak® tube	H_2O_2	Hydrogen peroxide
Si gel	Silica gel tube	HPLC	High-pressure liquid chromatography
Soda lime	Soda lime sorbent tube	H_3PO_4	Phosphoric acid
TD	Thermal desorption tube	HSA	Hexanesulfonic acid
Tenax GC	Tenax® GC tube		(Continued)

xix

In the chemical listing, an asterisk following an adsorbent tube code (e.g., Char, Si gel*, XAD-2*, etc.) indicates that a special coating must be added. The figure "2" in parentheses following a collection device (e.g., Filter(2), Imp(2), Char(2), etc.) indicates that two are used in series.

Table 1. — Codes for measurement methods (Continued)

Code	Method/reagent	Code	Method/reagent
H_2SO_4	Sulfuric acid	GC/ECD	GC with electron capture detection
KI	Potassium iodide	GC/EConD	GC with electrolytic conductivity detection
KOH	Potassium hydroxide		
LTA	Low-temperature ashing	GC/FID	GC with flame ionization detection
Na_2CO_3	Sodium carbonate	GC/FPD	GC with flame photometric detection for sulfur, nitrogen, or phosphorus
$NaHCO_3$	Sodium bicarbonate		
NaOH	Sodium hydroxide		
$Na_2S_2O_3$	Sodium thiosulfate	GC/NPD	GC with nitrogen/phosphorus detection
NH_4OH	Ammonium hydroxide		
Pho-acid	Phosphomolybdic acid	GC/PID	GC with photoionization detection
Thermal desorp	Thermal desorption apparatus	GC/TCD	GC with thermal conductivity detection
THF	Tetrahydrofuran		
		GC/TEA	GC with thermal energy analyzer detection
Analytical method:			
		GC/TEA-EAP	GC/TEA with explosives package
DPCSP	Differential pulse cathodic stripping polarography	GFAAS	Graphite furnace atomic absorption spectrometry
ECA	Electrochemical analysis	Grav	Gravimetric
EGA	Evolved gas analysis	HPLC/GFAAS	High-pressure liquid chromatography with GFAAS
FAAS	Flame atomic absorption spectrometry		
GC	Gas chromatography	HPLC/FLD	High-pressure liquid chromatography with fluorescence detection
GC/AlkFID	GC with alkaline flame ionization detection		

(Continued)

Table 1. — Codes for measurement methods (Continued)

Code	Method/reagent	Code	Method/reagent
HPLC/UVD	High-pressure liquid chromatography with ultraviolet detection	R	Infrared spectrometry
		ISE	Ion-specific electrode
HPLC/UV/ECD	High-pressure liquid chromatography with ultraviolet and electrochemical detection	PCM	Phase contrast microscopy
		PES	Plasma emission spectroscopy
		PLR	Polarography
HPLC/UV/FLD	High-pressure liquid chromatography with ultraviolet and fluorescence detection	TEM	Transmission electron microscopy
		TOA	Thermal optical analyzer
		Titrate	Titration
HYAAS	Hydride generation atomic absorption spectrometry	UV-vis	Ultraviolet-visible spectrophotometry
		Vis	Visible spectrophotometry
IC	Ion chromatography	XRF	X-ray fluorescence spectrometry
ICP	Inductively coupled plasma	XRD	X-ray diffraction spectrometry

Table 2. — Ordering information for measurement methods

Manual	Publication No.	Ordering No.	Manual	Publication No.	Ordering No.
NIOSH Manual of Analytical Methods, 2nd edition (II):			1st supplement to 3rd edition	NIOSH 85-117	PB-86-116-266
Vol. 1	NIOSH 77-157-A	PB-274-845			
Vol. 2	NIOSH 77-157-B	PB-276-624	2nd supplement to 3rd edition	NIOSH 87-117	PB-88-204-722
Vol. 3	NIOSH 77-157-C	PB-276-838			
Vol. 4	NIOSH 78-175	PB-83-105-437	3rd supplement to 3rd edition	NIOSH 89-127	PB-90-162-470
Vol. 5	NIOSH 79-141	PB-83-105-445			
Vol. 6	NIOSH 80-125	PB-82-157-728			
Vol. 7	NIOSH 82-100	PB-83-105-452	4th supplement to 3rd edition	NIOSH 90-121	PB-91-152-660
NIOSH Manual of Analytical Methods (NMAM), 3rd edition (III)	NIOSH 84-100	PB-85-179-018	OSHA Analytical Methods Manual, 1990 & 1993	---	4542*
			NIOSH Manual of Analytical Methods (NMAM), 4th edition (IV)	NIOSH 94-113	017-011-00007-9**

*Denotes ordering number of the American Conference of Governmental Industrial Hygienists (ACGIH), 1330 Kemper Meadow Drive, Cincinnati, OH 45240 (513-742-2020). All other ordering numbers are for the National Technical Information Service (NTIS), Springfield, VA 22161 (703-487-4650).

** Printed copies of the NMAM are available from the U. S. Government Printing Office, Superintendent of Documents, Washington, DC 20402.
The computerized version of the NIOSH Manual of Analytical Methods (NMAM) is available on diskette from the Canadian Centre for Occupational Health and Safety, 250 Main Street East, Hamilton, Ontario CANADA L8N 1H6; Telephone 905-570-8094; Toll Free 1-800-668-4284 and WindowChem Software, Inc., 420-F Executive Court North, Fairfield, CA 94585; Telephone 707-864-0845; Toll Free 1-800-536-0404.

Table 3. — Personal protection and sanitation codes

Code	Definition	Code	Definition
SKIN		**WASH SKIN**	
Prevent skin contact .	Wear appropriate personal protective clothing to prevent skin contact.	When contam	The worker should immediately wash the skin when it becomes contaminated.
Frostbite	Wear appropriate personal protective clothing to prevent the skin from becoming frozen from contact with the liquid or from contact with vessels containing the liquid.	Daily	The worker should wash daily at the end of each work shift.
N.R	No recommendation is made specifying the need for personal protective equipment for the body.	N.R	No recommendation is made specifying the need for washing the substance from the skin (either immediately or at the end of the work shift).
EYES		**REMOVE**	
Prevent eye contact ..	Wear appropriate eye protection to prevent eye contact.	When wet or contam .	Work clothing that becomes wet or significantly contaminated should be removed and replaced.
Frostbite	Wear appropriate eye protection to prevent eye contact with the liquid that could result in burns or tissue damage from frostbite.	When wet (flamm)	Work clothing that becomes wet should be immediately removed due to its flammability hazard (i.e., for liquids with a flash point <100°F).
N.R	No recommendation is made specifying the need for eye protection.	N.R.	No recommendation is made specifying the need for removing clothing that becomes wet or contaminated.
			(Continued)

xxiii

Table 3. — Personal protection and sanitation codes (Continued)

Code	Definition	Code	Definition
CHANGE			body areas likely to be exposed. The actual determination of what constitutes an adequate quick drench facility depends on the specific circumstances. In certain instances, a deluge shower should be readily available, whereas in others, the availability of water from a sink or hose could be considered adequate.]
Daily	Workers whose clothing may have become contaminated should change into uncontaminated clothing before leaving the work premises.		
N.R	No recommendation is made specifying the need for the worker to change clothing after the workshift.		
PROVIDE		Frostbite	Quick drench facilities and/or eyewash fountains should be provided within the immediate work area for emergency use where there is any possibility of exposure to liquids that are extremely cold or rapidly evaporating.
Eyewash	Eyewash fountains should be provided in areas where there is any possibility that workers could be exposed to the substance; this is irrespective of the recommendation involving the wearing of eye protection.		
Quick drench	Facilities for quickly drenching the body should be provided within the immediate work area for emergency use where there is a possibility of exposure. [Note: It is intended that these facilities provide a sufficient quantity or flow of water to quickly remove the substance from any	**OTHER CODES**	
		Liq. .... Liquid	
		Molt. ....Molten	
		N.R. ....No recommendation applies in this category	
		Sol. .... Solid	
		Soln. ....Solution containing the contaminant	
		Vap. ....Vapor	

xxiv

Table 4. — Symbols, code components, and codes used for respirator selection

Item	Definition	Item	Definition
Symbol:		PAPR	Powered, air-purifying respirator
¥	At concentrations above the NIOSH REL, or where there is no REL, at any detectable concentration	SA	Supplied-air respirator
		SCBA ...	Self-contained breathing apparatus
§	Emergency or planned entry into unknown concentrations or IDLH conditions	AG	Acid gas cartridge or canister
		CF	Continuous flow mode
*	Substance reported to cause eye irritation or damage; may require eye protection	HiE	Air-purifying respirator with a high-efficiency particulate filter (if an independent code); or a high-efficiency particulate filter
£	Substance causes eye irritation or damage; eye protection needed	HiEF	Air-purifying, full-facepiece respirator with a high-efficiency particulate filter
^	If not present as a fume	OV	Organic vapor cartridge or canister
¿	Only nonoxidizable sorbents allowed (not charcoal)	PD,PP ..	Pressure-demand or other positive-pressure mode
†	End of service life indicator (ESLI) required	S	Chemical cartridge or canister providing protection against the compound of concern
APF	Assigned protection factor		
TBAL ...	To be added later	T	Tight-fitting facepiece
		XS	Except single-use respirator
Code component:		XSQ	Except single-use and quarter-mask respirator
CCR	Chemical cartridge respirator	**Code:**	
D	Dust respirator (if an independent code); or a dust filter	CCRFAGHiE (APF = 50)	Any chemical cartridge respirator with a full facepiece and acid gas cartridge(s) in combination with a high-efficiency particulate filter
F	Full facepiece		
Fu	Fume filter		
GMF	Air-purifying, full-facepiece respirator (gas mask) with a chin-style, front- or back-mounted canister		
M	Mist filter		(Continued)

Table 4. — Symbols, code components, and codes used for respirator selection (Continued)

Item	Definition	Item	Definition
Code (continued)		CCROV (APF = 10)	Any chemical cartridge respirator with organic vapor cartridge(s)
CCRFOV (APF = 50)	Any chemical cartridge respirator with a full facepiece and organic vapor cartridge(s)	CCROVAG (APF = 10)	Any chemical cartridge respirator with organic vapor and acid gas cartridge(s)
CCRFOVDMFu (APF = 50)	Any chemical cartridge respirator with a full facepiece and organic vapor cartridge(s) in combination with a dust, mist, and fume filter	CCROVDM (APF = 10)	Any chemical cartridge respirator with organic vapor cartridge(s) in combination with a dust and mist filter
CCRFOVHiE (APF = 50) ...	Any chemical cartridge respirator with a full facepiece and organic vapor cartridge(s) in combination with a high-efficiency particulate filter	CCROVDMFu (APF = 10) .	Any chemical cartridge respirator with organic vapor cartridge(s) in combination with a dust, mist, and fume filter
CCRFS (APF = 50)	Any chemical cartridge respirator with a full facepiece and cartridge(s) providing protection against the compound of concern	CCROVHiE (APF = 10)	Any chemical cartridge respirator with organic vapor cartridge(s) in combination with a high-efficiency particulate filter
CCRFSHiE (APF = 50)	Any chemical cartridge respirator with a full facepiece and cartridge(s) providing protection against the compound of concern and having a high-efficiency particulate filter	CCRS (APF = 10)	Any chemical cartridge respirator with cartridge(s) providing protection against the compound of concern
		D (APF = 5)	Any dust respirator
		DM (APF = 5)	Any dust and mist respirator
			(Continued)

Table 4. — Symbols, code components, and codes used for respirator selection (Continued)

Item	Definition	Item	Definition
Code (continued)		GMFOV (APF = 50)	Any air-purifying, full-facepiece respirator (gas mask) with a chin-style, front- or back-mounted organic vapor canister
DMF (APF = 10)	Any dust and mist respirator with a full facepiece		
DMFu (APF = 10)	Any dust, mist, and fume respirator		
DMXSQ (APF = 10)	Any dust and mist respirator except single-use and quarter-mask respirators	GMFOVAG (APF = 50)	Any air-purifying, full-facepiece respirator (gas mask) with a chin-style, front- or back-mounted organic vapor and acid gas canister
DXSQ (APF = 10)	Any dust respirator except single-use and quarter-mask respirators	GMFOVAGHiE (APF = 50)	Any air-purifying, full-facepiece respirator (gas mask) with a chin-style, front- or back-mounted organic vapor and acid gas canister having a high efficiency particulate filter
GMFAG (APF = 50)	Any air-purifying, full-facepiece respirator (gas mask) with a chin-style, front- or back-mounted acid gas canister		
GMFAGHiE (APF = 50)	Any air-purifying, full-facepiece respirator (gas mask) with a chin-style, front- or back-mounted acid gas canister having a high-efficiency particulate filter	GMFOVDMFu (APF = 50) .	Any air-purifying, full-facepiece respirator (gas mask) with a chin-style, front- or back-mounted organic vapor canister in combination with a dust, mist, and fume filter
			(Continued)

Table 4. — Symbols, code components, and codes used for respirator selection (Continued)

Item	Definition	Item	Definition
Code (continued)		HiEF (APF = 50)	Any air-purifying, full-facepiece respirator with a high-efficiency particulate filter
GMFOVHiE (APF = 50)	Any air-purifying, full-facepiece respirator (gas mask) with a chin-style, front- or back-mounted organic vapor canister having a high-efficiency particulate filter	PAPRAG (APF = 25)	Any powered, air-purifying respirator with acid gas cartridge(s)
GMFS (APF = 50)	Any air-purifying, full-facepiece respirator (gas mask) with a chin-style, front- or back-mounted canister providing protection against the compound of concern	PAPRAGHiE (APF = 25)	Any powered, air-purifying respirator with acid gas cartridge(s) in combination with a high-efficiency particulate filter
		PAPRD (APF = 25)	Any powered, air-purifying respirator with a dust filter
GMFSHiE (APF = 50)	Any air-purifying, full-facepiece respirator (gas mask) with a chin-style, front- or back-mounted canister providing protection against the compound of concern and having a high-efficiency particulate filter	PAPRDM (APF = 25)	Any powered, air-purifying respirator with a dust and mist filter
		PAPRDMFu (APF = 25)	Any powered, air-purifying respirator with a dust, mist, and fume filter
		PAPRHiE (APF = 25)	Any powered, air-purifying respirator with a high-efficiency particulate filter
HiE (APF = 10)	Any air-purifying respirator with a high-efficiency particulate filter	PAPROV (APF = 25)	Any powered, air-purifying respirator with organic vapor cartridge(s)

(Continued)

xxviii

Table 4. — Symbols, code components, and codes used for respirator selection (Continued)

Item	Definition	Item	Definition
Code (continued)		PAPRTOVHiE (APF = 50)...	Any powered, air-purifying respirator with a tight-fitting facepiece and organic vapor cartridge(s) in combination with a high-efficiency particulate filter
PAPROVAG (APF = 25).....	Any powered, air-purifying respirator with organic vapor and acid gas cartridge(s)		
PAPROVDM (APF = 25) ...	Any powered, air-purifying respirator with organic vapor cartridge(s) in combination with a dust and mist filter		
PAPROVDMFu (APF = 25)	Any powered, air-purifying respirator with organic vapor cartridge(s) in combination with a dust, mist, and fume filter	PAPRTS (APF = 50)	Any powered, air-purifying respirator with a tight-fitting facepiece and cartridge(s) providing protection against the compound of concern
PAPRS (APF = 25)	Any powered, air-purifying respirator with cartridge(s) providing protection against the compound of concern	SA (APF = 10)	Any supplied-air respirator
		SA:CF (APF = 25)	Any supplied-air respirator operated in a continuous-flow mode
PAPRTHiE (APF = 50)	Any powered, air-purifying respirator with a tight-fitting facepiece and a high-efficiency particulate filter	SAF (APF = 50)	Any supplied-air respirator with a full facepiece
PAPRTOV (APF = 50)	Any powered, air-purifying respirator with a tight-fitting facepiece and organic vapor cartridge(s)	SAF:PD,PP (APF = 2000) ..	Any supplied-air respirator that has a full facepiece and is operated in a pressure-demand or other positive-pressure mode

(Continued)

xxix

Table 4. — Symbols, code components, and codes used for respirator selection (Continued)

Item	Definition	Item	Definition
Code (continued) SAF:PD,PP:ASCBA (APF = 10,000)	Any supplied-air respirator that has a full facepiece and is operated in a pressure-demand or other positive-pressure mode in combination with an auxiliary self-contained breathing apparatus operated in pressure-demand or other positive-pressure mode	SAT:CF (APF = 50)	Any supplied-air respirator that has a tight-fitting facepiece and is operated in a continuous-flow mode
		SCBAE	Any appropriate escape-type, self-contained breathing apparatus
SA:PD,PP (APF = 1000) ...	Any supplied-air respirator operated in a pressure-demand or other positive-pressure mode	SCBAF (APF = 50)	Any self-contained breathing apparatus with a full facepiece
		SCBAF:PD,PP (APF = 10,000)	Any self-contained breathing apparatus that has a full facepiece and is operated in a pressure- demand or other positive-pressure mode

(Continued)

Table 4. — Symbols, code components, and codes used for respirator selection (Continued)

SUBSTITUTION OF PART 84 RESPIRATORS FOR PART 11 RESPIRATORS ALREADY IN USE

The following selection guidelines are intended for those who are currently using a Part 11 respirator that has been properly selected (see the "Recommendations for Respirator Selection" section on page xvi). In this context, a properly selected respirator means one that has been selected based on knowledge of the contaminant and its concentration in a particular work setting, the exposure limit of the contaminant, and the general principles of respirator selection.

Following these recommendations is the simplest approach to making the transition from Part 11 filters to Part 84 filters.

1. If you are currently using a D, DM or DMFu filter:

In a work setting free of oil aerosols, the minimally protective filter would be an N95.

In a work setting that may contain or does contain oil aerosols, the minimally protective filter would be an R95 or P95.

2. If you are currently using a HiE filter:

In a work setting free of oil aerosols, an N100 filter would be protective.

In a work setting that contains or may contain oil aerosols, an R100 or P100 filter would be protective.

3. If you are currently using a paint-lacquer-enamel combination cartridge:

In a work setting free of oil aerosols, a combination respirator consisting of an organic vapor cartridge and an N95 particulate filter with an optional prefilter (to prevent rapid clogging by paint aerosols) would be minimally protective.

In a work setting that may contain or does contain oil aerosols, a combination respirator consisting of an organic vapor cartridge and an R95 or P95 particulate filter with a prefilter (to prevent rapid clogging by paint aerosols) would be minimally protective.

4. **If you are currently using a pesticide respirator for protection against a particulate and an organic vapor:** A combination respirator consisting of an organic vapor cartridge and an N95 (non-oil aerosols) or an R95 or P95 particulate filter would be minimally protective. As another example, a particular pesticide may have such low vapor pressure that only a particulate filter may be needed. Thus in certain situations, there may be no need for a combination particulate filter and organic vapor cartridge as recommended above.	

Table 5. — Abbreviations for symptoms of exposure and target organs

Abbreviation	Symptom/organ	Abbreviation	Symptom/organ
abdom	Abdominal	constip	Constipation
abnor	Abnormal/Abnormalities	convuls	Convulsions
album	Albuminuria	corn	Corneal
anes	Anesthesia	CVS	Cardiovascular system
anor	Anorexia	cyan	Cyanosis
anos	Anosmia (loss of the sense of smell)	decr	Decrease(d)
appre	Apprehension	depres	Depressant/Depression
arrhy	Arrhythmias	derm	Dermatitis
aspir	Aspiration	diarr	Diarrhea
asphy	Asphyxia	dist	Disturbance
BP	Blood pressure	dizz	Dizziness
breath	Breathing	drow	Drowsiness
bron	Bronchitis	dysfunc	Dysfunction
broncopneu	Bronchopneumonia	dysp	Dyspnea (breathing difficulty)
bronspas	Bronchospasm	emphy	Emphysema
BUN	Blood urea nitrogen	eosin	Eosinophilia
[carc]	Potential occupational carcinogen	epilep	Epileptiform
card	Cardiac	epis	Epistaxis (nosebleed)
chol	Cholinesterase	equi	Equilibrium
cirr	Cirrhosis	eryt	Erythema (skin redness)
CNS	Central nervous system	euph	Euphoria
conc	Concentration	fail	Failure
conf	Confusion	fasc	Fasiculation
conj	Conjunctivitis		(Continued)

xxxiii

Abbreviation	Symptom/organ	Abbreviation	Symptom/organ
FEV	Forced expiratory volume	jaun	Jaundice
fib	Fibrosis	kera	Keratitis (inflammation of the cornea)
fibrl	Fibrillation	lac	Lacrimation (discharge of tears)
ftg	Fatigue	lar	Laryngeal
func	Function	lass	Lassitude (weakness, exhaustion)
GI	Gastrointestinal	leth	Lethargy (drowsiness or indifference)
gidd	Giddiness	leucyt	Leukocytosis (increased blood leukocytes)
halu	Hallucinations		
head	Headache	leupen	Leukopenia (reduced blood leukocytes)
hema	Hematuria (blood in the urine)	li-head	Lightheadedness
hemato	Hematopoietic	liq	Liquid
hemog	Hemoglobinuria	local	Localized
hemorr	Hemorrhage	low-wgt	Weight loss
hyperpig	Hyperpigmentation	mal	Malaise (vague feeling of discomfort)
hypox	Hypoxemia (reduced oxygen in the blood)	malnut	Malnutrition
inco	Incoordination	methemo	Methemoglobinemia
incr	Increase(d)	monocy	Monocytosis (increased blood monocytes)
inebri	Inebriation		
inflamm	Inflammation	molt	Molten
inj	Injury	muc memb	Mucous membrane
insom	Insomnia	musc	Muscle
irreg	Irregular/Irregularities	narco	Narcosis
irrit	Irritation	nau	Nausea
irrity	Irritability		(Continued)

xxxiv

Table 5. — Abbreviations for symptoms of exposure and target organs (Continued)

Abbreviation	Symptom/organ	Abbreviation	Symptom/organ
nec	Necrosis	retster	Retrosternal (occurring behind the sternum)
neph	Nephritis	rhin	Rhinorrhea (discharge of thin nasal mucus)
ner	Nervousness		
numb	Numbness	salv	Salivation
opac	Opacity	sens	Sensitization
palp	Palpitations	sez	Seizure
para	Paralysis	short	Shortness
pares	Paresthesia	sneez	Sneezing
perf	Perforation	sol	Solid
peri neur	Peripheral neuropathy	soln	Solution
periorb	Periorbital (situated around the eye)	som	Somnolence (sleepiness, unnatural drowsiness)
phar	Pharyngeal		
photo	Photophobia (abnormal visual intolerance to light)	subs	Substernal (occurring beneath the sternum)
pneu	Pneumonia	sweat	Sweating
pneuitis	Pneumonitis	swell	Swelling
PNS	Peripheral nervous system	sys	System
polyneur	Polyneuropathy	tacar	Tachycardia
prot	Proteinuria	tend	Tenderness
pulm	Pulmonary	terato	Teratogenic
RBC	Red blood cell	throb	Throbbing
repro	Reproductive	tight	Tightness
resp	Respiratory		
restless	Restlessness		(Continued)

Table 5. — Abbreviations for symptoms of exposure and target organs (Continued)

Abbreviation	Symptom/organ	Abbreviation	Symptom/organ
trachbronc	Tracheobronchitis	verti	Vertigo (an illusion of movement)
twitch	Twitching	vesic	Vesiculation
uncon	Unconsciousness	vis dist	Visual disturbance
vap	Vapor	vomit	Vomiting
venfib	Ventricular fibrillation	weak	Weakness
		wheez	Wheezing

Table 6. — Codes for first aid data

Code	Definition	Code	Definition
Eye:			soon as possible.
Irr immed.	If this chemical contacts the eyes, immediately wash the eyes with large amounts of water, occasionally lifting the lower and upper lids. Get medical attention immediately. Contact lenses should not be worn when working with this chemical.	Medical attention	Self-explanatory
		Skin:	
		Blot/brush away	If irritation occurs, gently blot or brush away excess.
		Dust off solid;	
Irr prompt	If this chemical contacts the eyes, promptly wash the eyes with large amounts of water, occasionally lifting the lower and upper lids. Get medical attention if any discomfort continues. Contact lenses should not be worn when working with this chemical.	water flush.	If this solid chemical contacts the skin, dust it off immediately and then flush the contaminated skin with water. If this chemical or liquids containing this chemical penetrate the clothing, promptly remove the clothing and flush the skin with water. Get medical attention immediately.
Frostbite	If eye tissue is frozen, seek medical attention immediately; if tissue is not frozen, immediately and thoroughly flush the eyes with large amounts of water for at least 15 minutes, occasionally lifting the lower and upper eyelids. If irritation, pain, swelling, lacrimation, or photophobia persist, get medical attention as	Frostbite	If frostbite has occurred, seek medical attention immediately; do NOT rub the affected areas or flush them with water. In order to prevent further tissue damage, do NOT attempt to remove frozen clothing from frostbitten areas. If frostbite (Continued)

xxxvii

Table 6. — Codes for first aid data (Continued)

Code	Definition	Code	Definition
Skin (continued)			immediately remove the clothing and flush the skin with water. If irritation persists after washing, get medical attention.
	has NOT occurred, immediately and thoroughly wash contaminated skin with soap and water.		
Molten flush immed/sol-liq soap wash prompt	If this molten chemical contacts the skin, immediately flush the skin with large amounts of water. Get medical attention immediately. If this chemical (or liquids containing this chemical) contacts the skin, promptly wash the contaminated skin with soap and water. If this chemical or liquids containing this chemical penetrate the clothing, immediately remove the clothing and wash the skin with soap and water. If irritation persists after washing, get medical attention.	Soap flush prompt ..	If this chemical contacts the skin, promptly flush the contaminated skin with soap and water. If this chemical penetrates the clothing, promptly remove the clothing and flush the skin with water. If irritation persists after washing, get medical attention.
Soap flush immed ..	If this chemical contacts the skin, immediately flush the contaminated skin with soap and water. If this chemical penetrates the clothing,	Soap prompt/ molten flush immed	If this solid chemical or a liquid containing this chemical contacts the skin, promptly wash the contaminated skin with soap and water. If irritation persists after washing, get medical attention. If this molten chemical contacts the skin or nonimpervious clothing, immediately flush the affected area with large amounts of water to remove heat. Get medical attention immediately.

Table 6. — Codes for first aid data (Continued)

Code	Definition	Code	Definition
Skin (continued)			immediately flush the contaminated skin with water. If this chemical penetrates the clothing, immediately remove the clothing and flush the skin with water. Get medical attention promptly.
Soap wash.............	If this chemical contacts the skin, wash the contaminated skin with soap and water.		
Soap wash immed ..	If this chemical contacts the skin, immediately wash the contaminated skin with soap and water. If this chemical penetrates the clothing, immediately remove the clothing, wash the skin with soap and water, and get medical attention promptly.	Water flush prompt .	If this chemical contacts the skin, flush the contaminated skin with water promptly. If this chemical penetrates the clothing, immediately remove the clothing and flush the skin with water promptly. If irritation persists after washing, get medical attention.
Soap wash prompt .	If this chemical contacts the skin, promptly wash the contaminated skin with soap and water. If this chemical penetrates the clothing, promptly remove the clothing and wash the skin with soap and water. Get medical attention promptly.	Water wash	If this chemical contacts the skin, wash the contaminated skin with water.
Water flush.............	If this chemical contacts the skin, flush the contaminated skin with water. Where there is evidence of skin irritation, get medical attention.	Water wash immed	If this chemical contacts the skin, immediately wash the contaminated skin with water. If this chemical penetrates the clothing, immediately remove the clothing and wash the skin with water. If symptoms occur
Water flush immed .	If this chemical contacts the skin,		(Continued)

Table 6. — Codes for first aid data (Continued)

Code	Definition	Code	Definition
Skin (continued)		Fresh air	If a person breathes large amounts of this chemical, move the exposed person to fresh air at once. Other measures are usually unnecessary.
	after washing, get medical attention immediately.		
Water wash prompt	If this chemical contacts the skin, promptly wash the contaminated skin with water. If this chemical penetrates the clothing, promptly remove the clothing and wash the skin with water. If irritation persists after washing, get medical attention.	Fresh air; 100% O_2	If a person breathes large amounts of this chemical, move the exposed person to fresh air at once. If breathing has stopped, perform artificial respiration. When breathing is difficult, properly trained personnel may assist the affected person by administering 100% oxygen. Keep the affected person warm and at rest. Get medical attention as soon as possible.
Breath:			
Resp support	If a person breathes large amounts of this chemical, move the exposed person to fresh air at once. If breathing has stopped, perform mouth-to-mouth resuscitation. Keep the affected person warm and at rest. Get medical attention as soon as possible.	Swallow:	
		Medical attention immed	If this chemical has been swallowed, get medical attention immediately.

xl

CHEMICAL LISTING

Chemical name, structure/formula, CAS and RTECS Nos., and DOT ID and guide Nos.	Synonyms, trade names, and conversion factors	Exposure limits (TWA unless noted otherwise)	IDLH	Physical description	Chemical and physical properties		Incompatibilities and reactivities	Measurement method (See Table 1)
					MW, BP, SOL Fl.P, IP, Sp, Gr, flammability	VP, FRZ UEL, LEL		
Acetaldehyde CH₃CHO 75-07-0 AB1925000 1089 129	Acetic aldehyde, Ethanal, Ethyl aldehyde 1 ppm = 1.80 mg/m³	NIOSH Ca See Appendix A See Appendix C (Aldehydes) OSHA† 200 ppm (360 mg/m³)	Ca [2000 ppm]	Colorless liquid or gas (above 69°F) with a pungent, fruity odor.	MW: 44.1 BP: 69°F Sol: Miscible Fl.P: -36°F IP: 10.22 eV Sp.Gr. 0.79 Class IA Flammable Liquid	VP: 740 mm FRZ: -190°F UEL: 60% LEL: 4.0%	Strong oxidizers, acids, bases, alcohols, ammonia & amines, phenols, ketones, HCN, H₂S [Note: Prolonged contact with air may cause formation of peroxides that may explode and burst containers; easily undergoes polymerization.]	XAD-2*; Toluene; GC/FID; IV [#2538]
Acetic acid CH₃COOH 64-19-7 AF1225000 2790 153 (10-80% acid) 2789 132 (>80% acid)	Acetic acid (aqueous), Ethanoic acid, Glacial acetic acid (pure compound), Methanecarboxylic acid [Note: Can be found in concentrations of 5-8% in vinegar.] 1 ppm = 2.46 mg/m³	NIOSH 10 ppm (25 mg/m³) ST 15 ppm (37 mg/m³) OSHA 10 ppm (25 mg/m³)	50 ppm	Colorless liquid or crystals with a sour, vinegar-like odor. [Note: Pure compound is a solid below 62°F. Often used in an aqueous solution.]	MW: 60.1 BP: 244°F Sol: Miscible Fl.P: 103°F IP: 10.66 eV Sp.Gr. 1.05 Class II Combustible Liquid	VP: 11 mm FRZ: 62°F UEL(200°F): 19.9% LEL: 4.0%	Strong oxidizers (especially chromic acid, sodium peroxide & nitric acid), strong caustics [Note: Corrosive to metals.]	Char; HCOOH; GC/FID; IV [#1603]
Acetic anhydride (CH₃CO)₂O 108-24-7 AK1925000 1715 137	Acetic acid anhydride, Acetic oxide, Acetyl oxide, Ethanoic anhydride 1 ppm = 4.18 mg/m³	NIOSH C 5 ppm (20 mg/m³) OSHA† 5 ppm (20 mg/m³)	200 ppm	Colorless liquid with a strong, pungent, vinegar-like odor.	MW: 102.1 BP: 282°F Sol: 12% Fl.P: 120°F IP: 10.00 eV Sp.Gr. 1.08 Class II Combustible Liquid	VP: 4 mm FRZ: -99°F UEL: 10.3% LEL: 2.7%	Water, alcohols, strong oxidizers (especially chromic acid), amines, strong caustics [Note: Corrosive to iron, steel & other metals. Reacts with water to form acetic acid.]	Bub; Reagent; Vis; IV [#3506]
Acetone (CH₃)₂CO 67-64-1 AL3150000 1090 127	Dimethyl ketone, Ketone propane, 2-Propanone 1 ppm = 2.38 mg/m³	NIOSH 250 ppm (590 mg/m³) OSHA† 1000 ppm (2400 mg/m³)	2500 ppm [10%LEL]	Colorless liquid with a fragrant, mint-like odor.	MW: 58.1 BP: 133°F Sol: Miscible Fl.P: 0°F IP: 9.69 eV Sp.Gr. 0.79 Class IB Flammable Liquid	VP: 180 mm FRZ: -140°F UEL: 12.8% LEL: 2.5%	Oxidizers, acids	Char; CS₂; GC/FID; IV [#1300, Ketones I]

Personal protection and sanitation (See Table 3)	Recommendations for respirator selection — maximum concentration for use (MUC) (See Table 4)	Health hazards			
		Route	Symptoms (See Table 5)	First aid (See Table 6)	Target organs (See Table 5)
Skin: Prevent skin contact Eyes: Prevent eye contact Wash skin: When contam Remove: When wet (flamm) Change: N.R. Provide: Eyewash, Quick drench	NIOSH ¥: SCBAF:PD,PP/SAF:PD,PP:ASCBA Escape: GMFOV/SCBAE	Inh Ing Con	Irrit eyes, nose, throat; eye, skin burns; derm; conj; cough; CNS depres; delayed pulm edema; in animals: kidney, repro, terato effects; [carc]	Eye: Irr immed Skin: Water flush prompt Breath: Resp support Swallow: Medical attention immed	Eyes, skin, resp sys, kidneys, CNS, repro sys [in animals: nasal cancer]
[Acetaldehyde]					
Skin: Prevent skin contact (>10%) Eyes: Prevent eye contact Wash skin: When contam (>10%) Remove: When wet or contam (>10% Change: N.R. Provide: Eyewash (>5%), Quick drench (>50%)	NIOSH/OSHA 50 ppm: SA:CF^E/PAPROV^E/CCRFOV/ GMFOV/SCBAF/SAF §: SCBAF:PD,PP/SAF:PD,PP:ASCBA Escape: GMFOV/SCBAE	Inh Con	Irrit eyes, skin, nose, throat; eye, skin burns; skin sens; dental erosion; black skin, hyperkeratosis; conj, lac; phar edema, chronic bron	Eye: Irr immed Skin: Water flush immed Breath: Resp support Swallow: Medical attention immed	Eyes, skin, resp sys, teeth
[Acetic acid]					
Skin: Prevent skin contact Eyes: Prevent eye contact Wash skin: When contam Remove: When wet or contam Change: N.R Provide: Eyewash, Quick drench	NIOSH/OSHA 125 ppm: SA:CF^E/PAPROV^E 200 ppm: CCRFOV/GMFOV/PAPRTOV^E/ SCBAF/SAF §: SCBAF:PD,PP/SAF:PD,PP:ASCBA Escape: GMFOV/SCBAE	Inh Ing Con	Conj, lac, corn edema, opac, photo; nasal, phar irrit; cough, dysp, bron; skin burns, vesic, sens derm	Eye: Irr immed Skin: Water flush immed Breath: Resp support Swallow: Medical attention immed	Eyes, skin, resp sys
[Acetic anhydride]					
Skin: Prevent skin contact Eyes: Prevent eye contact Wash skin: When contam Remove: When wet (flamm) Change: N.R.	NIOSH 2500 ppm: CCROV*/PAPROV*/GMFOV/ SA*/SCBAF §: SCBAF:PD,PP/SAF:PD,PP:ASCBA Escape: GMFOV/SCBAE	Inh Ing Con	Irrit eyes, nose, throat; head, dizz, CNS depres; derm	Eye: Irr immed Skin: Soap wash immed Breath: Resp support Swallow: Medical attention immed	Eyes, skin, resp sys, CNS
[Acetone]					

3

Chemical name, structure/formula, CAS and RTECS Nos., and DOT ID and guide Nos.	Synonyms, trade names, and conversion factors	Exposure limits (TWA unless noted otherwise)	IDLH	Physical description	Chemical and physical properties		Incompatibilities and reactivities	Measurement method (See Table 1)
					MW, BP, SOL Fl.P, IP, Sp, Gr, flammability	VP, FRZ UEL, LEL		
Acetone cyanohydrin CH₃C(OH)CNCH₃ 75-86-5 OD9275000 1541 155 (stabilized)	Cyanohydrin-2-propanone, 2-Cyano-2-propanol, α-Hydroxyisobutyronitrile, 2-Hydroxy-2-methyl-propionitrile, 2-Methyllactonitrile 1 ppm = 3.48 mg/m³	NIOSH C 1 ppm (4 mg/m³) [15-min] OSHA none	N.D.	Colorless liquid with a faint odor of bitter almond. [Note: Forms cyanide in the body.]	MW: 85.1 BP: 203°F Sol: Miscible Fl.P: 165°F IP: ? Sp.Gr(77°F): 0.93 Class IIIA Combustible Liquid	VP: 0.8 mm FRZ: -4°F UEL: 12.0% LEL: 2.2%	Sulfuric acid, caustics [Note: Slowly decomposes to acetone & HCN at room temperatures; rate is accelerated by an increase in pH, water content, or temperature.]	Porapak; Ethyl acetate; GC/NPD; IV [#2506]
Acetonitrile CH₃CN 75-05-8 AL7700000 1648 131	Cyanomethane, Ethyl nitrile, Methyl cyanide 1 ppm = 1.68 mg/m³	NIOSH 20 ppm (34 mg/m³) OSHA† 40 ppm (70 mg/m³)	500 ppm	Colorless liquid with an aromatic odor. [Note: Forms cyanide in the body.]	MW: 41.1 BP: 179°F Sol: Miscible Fl.P(oc): 42°F IP: 12.20 eV Sp.Gr: 0.78 Class IB Flammable Liquid	VP: 73 mm FRZ: -49°F UEL: 16.0% LEL: 3.0%	Strong oxidizers	Char; Benzene; GC/FID; IV [#1606]
2-Acetylaminofluorene C₁₅H₁₃NO 53-96-3 AB9450000	AAF, 2-AAF, 2-Acetaminofluorene, N-Acetyl-2-aminofluorene, FAA, 2-FAA, 2-Fluorenylacetamide	NIOSH Ca See Appendix A OSHA [1910.1014] See Appendix B	Ca [N.D.]	Tan, crystalline powder.	MW: 223.3 BP: ? Sol: Insoluble Fl.P: ? IP: ? Sp.Gr: ? Combustible Solid	VP: ? MLT: 381°F UEL: ? LEL: ?	None reported	None available
Acetylene HC≡CH 74-86-2 AO9600000 1001 116	Ethine, Ethyne [Note: A compressed gas used in the welding & cutting of metals.] 1 ppm = 1.06 mg/m³	NIOSH C 2500 ppm (2662 mg/m³) OSHA none	N.D.	Colorless gas with a faint, ethereal odor. [Note: Commercial grade has a garlic-like odor. Shipped under pressure dissolved in acetone.]	MW: 26.0 BP: Sublimes Sol: 2% Fl.P: NA (Gas) IP: 11.40 eV RGasD: 0.91 Flammable Gas	VP: 44.2 atm FRZ: -119°F (Sublimes) UEL: 100% LEL: 2.5%	Zinc; oxygen & other oxidizing agents such as halogens [Note: Forms explosive acetylide compounds with copper, mercury, silver & brasses (containing more than 66% copper).]	Bag; none; GC/FID; NIOSH Acetylene Crit. Doc.

Personal protection and sanitation (See Table 3)		Recommendations for respirator selection — maximum concentration for use (MUC) (See Table 4)	Health hazards					
			Route	Symptoms (See Table 5)	First aid (See Table 6)		Target organs (See Table 5)	

Personal protection and sanitation (See Table 3)	Recommendations for respirator selection — maximum concentration for use (MUC) (See Table 4)	Route	Symptoms (See Table 5)	First aid (See Table 6)	Target organs (See Table 5)
Skin: Prevent skin contact Eyes: Prevent eye contact Wash skin: When contam Remove: When wet or contam Change: N.R. Provide: Eyewash, Quick drench	NIOSH 10 ppm: SA 25 ppm: SA:CF 50 ppm: SCBAF/SAF 250 ppm: SAF:PD,PP §: SCBAF:PD,PP/SAF:PD,PP:ASCBA Escape: GMFOV/SCBAE	Inh Abs Ing Con	Irrit eyes, skin, resp sys; dizz, weak, head, conf, convuls; liver, kidney inj; pulm edema, asphy	Eye: Irr immed Skin: Water flush immed Breath: Resp support Swallow: Medical attention immed	Eyes, skin, resp sys, CNS, CVS, liver, kidneys, GI tract
[Acetone cyanohydrin]					
Skin: Prevent skin contact Eyes: Prevent eye contact Wash skin: When contam Remove: When wet (flamm) Change: N.R. Provide: Quick drench	NIOSH 200 ppm: CCROV/SA 500 ppm: SA:CF/PAPROV/CCRFOV/ GMFOV/SCBAF/SAF §: SCBAF:PD,PP/SAF:PD,PP:ASCBA Escape: GMFOV/SCBAE	Inh Abs Ing Con	Irrit nose, throat; asphy; nau, vomit; chest pain; weak; stupor, convuls; in animals: liver, kidney damage	Eye: Irr immed Skin: Water flush immed Breath: Resp support Swallow: Medical attention immed	Resp sys, CVS, CNS, liver, kidneys
[Acetonitrile]					
Skin: Prevent skin contact Eyes: Prevent eye contact Wash skin: When contam/Daily Remove: When wet or contam Change: Daily Provide: Eyewash, Quick drench	NIOSH ¥: SCBAF:PD,PP/SAF:PD,PP:ASCBA Escape: HiEF/SCBAE	Inh Abs Ing Con	Reduced function of liver, kidneys, bladder, pancreas; [carc]	Eye: Irr immed Skin: Soap wash immed Breath: Resp support Swallow: Medical attention immed	Liver, bladder, kidneys, lungs, pancreas, skin [in animals: tumors of the liver, bladder, lungs, skin & pancreas]
[2-Acetylaminofluorene]					
Skin: Frostbite Eyes: Frostbite Wash skin: N.R. Remove: When wet (flamm) Change: N.R. Provide: Frostbite	TBAL	Inh Con (liq)	Head, dizz; asphy; liq: frostbite	Eye: Frostbite Skin: Frostbite Breath: Fresh air	CNS, resp sys
[Acetylene]					

Chemical name, structure/formula, CAS and RTECS Nos., and DOT ID and guide Nos.	Synonyms, trade names, and conversion factors	Exposure limits (TWA unless noted otherwise)	IDLH	Physical description	Chemical and physical properties		Incompatibilities and reactivities	Measurement method (See Table 1)
					MW, BP, SOL Fl.P, IP, Sp, Gr, flammability	VP, FRZ UEL, LEL		
Acetylene tetrabromide CHBr$_2$CHBr$_2$ 79-27-6 KI8225000 2504 159	Symmetrical tetrabromo-ethane; TBE; Tetrabromoacetylene; Tetrabromoethane; 1,1,2,2-Tetrabromoethane 1 ppm = 14.14 mg/m^3	NIOSH See Appendix D OSHA 1 ppm (14 mg/m^3)	8 ppm	Pale-yellow liquid with a pungent odor similar to camphor or iodoform. [Note: A solid below 32°F.]	MW: 345.7 BP: 474°F (Decomposes) Sol: 0.07% Fl.P: NA IP: ? Sp.Gr: 2.97 Noncombustible Liquid	VP: 0.02 mm FRZ: 32°F UEL: NA LEL: NA	Strong caustics; hot iron; reducing metals such as aluminum, magnesium & zinc	Si gel; THF; GC/FID; IV [#2003]
Acetylsalicylic acid CH$_3$COOC$_6$H$_4$COOH 50-78-2 VO0700000	Acetal, o-Acetoxybenzoic acid, 2-Acetoxybenzoic acid, Aspirin	NIOSH 5 mg/m^3 OSHA† none	N.D.	Odorless, colorless to white, crystal-line powder. [aspirin] [Note: Develops the vinegar-like odor of acetic acid on contact with moisture.]	MW: 180.2 BP: 284°F (Decomposes) Sol(77°F): 0.3% Fl.P: NA IP: NA Sp.Gr: 1.35 Combustible Powder; explosion hazard if dispersed in air.	VP: 0 mm (approx) MLT: 275°F UEL: NA LEL: NA MEC: 40 g/m^3	Solutions of alkali hydroxides or carbonates, strong oxidizers, moisture [Note: Slowly hydrolyzes in moist air to salicylic & acetic acids.]	Filter; none; Grav; IV [#0500, Particulates NOR (total)]
Acrolein CH$_2$=CHCHO 107-02-8 AS1050000 1092 131P (inhibited)	Acraldehyde, Acrylaldehyde, Acrylic aldehyde, Allyl aldehyde, Propenal, 2-Propenal 1 ppm = 2.29 mg/m^3	NIOSH 0.1 ppm (0.25 mg/m^3) ST 0.3 ppm (0.8 mg/m^3) See Appendix C (Aldehydes) OSHA† 0.1 ppm (0.25 mg/m^3)	2 ppm	Colorless or yellow liquid with a piercing, disagreeable odor.	MW: 56.1 BP: 127°F Sol: 40% Fl.P: -15°F IP: 10.13 eV Sp.Gr: 0.84 Class IB Flammable Liquid	VP: 210 mm FRZ: -126°F UEL: 31% LEL: 2.8%	Oxidizers, acids, alkalis, ammonia, amines [Note: Polymerizes readily unless inhibited—usually with hydroquinone. May form shock-sensitive peroxides over time.]	XAD-2*; Toluene; GC/NPD; IV [#2501]
Acrylamide CH$_2$=CHCONH$_2$ 79-06-1 AS3325000 2074 153P	Acrylamide monomer, Acrylic amide, Propenamide, 2-Propenamide	NIOSH Ca 0.03 mg/m^3 [skin] See Appendix A OSHA† 0.3 mg/m^3 [skin]	Ca [60 mg/m^3]	White crystalline, odorless solid.	MW: 71.1 BP: 347-572°F (Decomposes) Sol(86°F): 216% Fl.P: 280°F IP: 9.50 eV Sp.Gr: 1.12 Combustible Solid (may also be dissolved in flammable liquids).	VP: 0.007 mm MLT: 184°F UEL: ? LEL: ?	Strong oxidizers [Note: May polymerize violently upon melting.]	Filter/ Si gel; Methanol; GC/NPD; OSHA [#21]

Personal protection and sanitation (See Table 3)	Recommendations for respirator selection — maximum concentration for use (MUC) (See Table 4)	Route	Symptoms (See Table 5)	First aid (See Table 6)	Target organs (See Table 5)
Skin: Prevent skin contact Eyes: Prevent eye contact Wash skin: When contam Remove: When wet or contam Change: N.R.	OSHA 8 ppm: SA/SCBAF §: SCBAF:PD,PP/SAF:PD,PP:ASCBA Escape: GMFOV/SCBAE	Inh Ing Con	Irrit eyes, nose; anor, nau; severe head; abdom pain; jaun; monocy; CNS depres	Eye: Irr immed Skin: Water flush prompt Breath: Resp support Swallow: Medical attention immed	Eyes, resp sys, liver, CNS

[Acetylene tetrabromide]

| | | | | | | 7 |

Personal protection and sanitation (See Table 3)	Recommendations for respirator selection — maximum concentration for use (MUC) (See Table 4)	Route	Symptoms (See Table 5)	First aid (See Table 6)	Target organs (See Table 5)
Skin: Prevent skin contact Eyes: Prevent eye contact Wash skin: When contam Remove: N.R. Change: Daily Provide: Eyewash, Quick drench	TBAL	Inh Ing Con	Irrit eyes, skin, upper resp sys; incr blood clotting time; nau, vomit; liver, kidney inj	Eye: Irr immed Skin: Soap wash Breath: Resp support Swallow: Medical attention immed	Eyes, skin, resp sys, blood, liver, kidney

[Acetylsalicylic acid]

| Skin: Prevent skin contact
Eyes: Prevent eye contact
Wash skin: When contam
Remove: When wet (flamm)
Change: N.R.
Provide: Eyewash, Quick drench | NIOSH/OSHA
2 ppm: SA:CF*/PAPROV*/CCRFOV/
GMFOV/SCBAF/SAF
§: SCBAF:PD,PP/SAF:PD,PP:ASCBA
Escape: GMFOV/SCBAE | Inh
Ing
Con | Irrit eyes, skin, muc memb; decr pulm func; delayed pulm edema; chronic resp disease | Eye: Irr immed
Skin: Water flush immed
Breath: Resp support
Swallow: Medical attention immed | Eyes, skin, resp sys, heart |

[Acrolein]

| Skin: Prevent skin contact
Eyes: Prevent eye contact
Wash skin: When contam/Daily
Remove: When wet or contam
Change: Daily
Provide: Eyewash, Quick drench | NIOSH
¥: SCBAF:PD,PP/SAF:PD,PP:ASCBA
Escape: GMFOV/SCBAE | Inh
Abs
Ing
Con | Irrit eyes, skin; ataxia, numb limbs, pares; musc weak; absent deep tendon reflex; hand sweat; ftg, leth; repro effects; [carc] | Eye: Irr immed
Skin: Water flush immed
Breath: Resp support
Swallow: Medical attention immed | Eyes, skin, CNS, PNS repro sys
[in animals: tumors of the lungs, testes, thyroid & adrenal glands] |

[Acrylamide]

Chemical name, structure/formula, CAS and RTECS Nos., and DOT ID and guide Nos.	Synonyms, trade names, and conversion factors	Exposure limits (TWA unless noted otherwise)	IDLH	Physical description	Chemical and physical properties		Incompatibilities and reactivities	Measurement method (See Table 1)
					MW, BP, SOL FI.P, IP, Sp, Gr, flammability	VP, FRZ UEL, LEL		
Acrylic acid $CH_2=CHCOOH$ 79-10-7 AS4375000 2218 132P (inhibited)	Acroleic acid, Aqueous acrylic acid (technical grade is 94%), Ethylenecarboxylic acid, Glacial acrylic acid (98% in aqueous solution), 2-Propenoic acid 1 ppm = 2.95 mg/m³	NIOSH 2 ppm (6 mg/m³) [skin] OSHA† none	N.D.	Colorless liquid or solid (below 55°F) with a distinctive, acrid odor. [Note: Shipped with an inhibitor (e.g., hydroquinone) since it readily polymerizes.]	MW: 72.1 BP: 286°F Sol: Miscible FI.P: 121°F IP: ? Sp.Gr: 1.05 Class II Combustible Liquid	VP: 3 mm FRZ: 55°F UEL: 8.02% LEL: 2.4%	Oxidizers, amines, alkalis, ammonium hydroxide, chlorosulfonic acid, oleum, ethylene diamine, ethyleneimine, 2-aminoethanol [Note: Corrosive to many metals.]	XAD(2); Methanol/ Water; HPLC/UVD; OSHA [#28]
Acrylonitrile $CH_2=CHCN$ 107-13-1 AT5250000 1093 131P (inhibited)	Acrylonitrile monomer, AN, Cyanoethylene, Propenenitrile, 2-Propenenitrile, VCN, Vinyl cyanide 1 ppm = 2.17 mg/m³	NIOSH Ca 1 ppm C 10 ppm [15-min] [skin] See Appendix A OSHA[1910.1045] 2 ppm C 10 ppm [15-min] [skin]	Ca [85 ppm]	Colorless to pale-yellow liquid with an unpleasant odor. [Note: Odor can only be detected above the PEL.]	MW: 53.1 BP: 171°F Sol: 7% FI.P: 30°F IP: 10.91 eV Sp.Gr: 0.81 Class IB Flammable Liquid	VP: 83 mm FRZ: -116°F UEL: 17% LEL: 3.0%	Strong oxidizers, acids & alkalis; bromine; amines [Note: Unless inhibited (usually with methylhydroquinone) may polymerize spontaneously or when heated or in presence of strong alkali. Attacks copper.]	Char; Acetone/ CS₂; GC/FID; IV [#1604]
Adiponitrile $NC(CH_2)_4CN$ 111-69-3 AV2625000 2205 153	1,4-Dicyanobutane; Hexanedinitrile; Tetramethylene cyanide 1 ppm = 4.43 mg/m³	NIOSH 4 ppm (18 mg/m³) OSHA none	N.D.	Water-white, practically odorless, oily liquid. [Note: A solid below 34°F. Forms cyanide in the body.]	MW: 108.2 BP: 563°F Sol: 4.5% FI.P(o.c.): 199°F IP: ? Sp.Gr: 0.97 Class IIIA Combustible Liquid	VP: 0.002 mm FRZ: 34°F UEL: 5.0% LEL:1.7%	Oxidizers (e.g., perchlorates, nitrates), strong acids (e.g., sulfuric acid) [Note: Decomposes above 194°F, forming hydrogen cyanide.]	Char; Toluene; GC/FID; NIOSH Nitriles Crit. Doc.
Aldrin $C_{12}H_8Cl_6$ 309-00-2 IO2100000 2761 151	1,2,3,4,10,10-Hexachloro- 1,4,4a,5,8,8a-hexahydro- endo-1,4-exo-5,8- dimethanonaphthalene; HHDN; Octalene	NIOSH Ca 0.25 mg/m³ [skin] See Appendix A OSHA 0.25 mg/m³ [skin]	Ca [25 mg/m³]	Colorless to dark-brown crystalline solid with a mild chemical odor. [Note: Formerly used as an insecticide.]	MW: 364.9 BP: Decomposes Sol: 0.003% FI.P: NA IP: ? Sp.Gr: 1.60 Noncombustible Solid, but may be dissolved in flammable liquids.	VP: 0.00008 mm MLT: 219°F UEL: NA LEL: NA	Concentrated mineral acids, active metals, acid catalysts, acid oxidizing agents, phenol	Filter/Bub; Isooctane; GC/EConD; III [#5502]

Personal protection and sanitation (See Table 3)		Recommendations for respirator selection — maximum concentration for use (MUC) (See Table 4)	Health hazards				
			Route	Symptoms (See Table 5)	First aid (See Table 6)		Target organs (See Table 5)
Skin:	Prevent skin contact	TBAL	Inh	Irrit eyes, skin, resp sys;	Eye:	Irr immed	Eyes, skin, resp sys
Eyes:	Prevent eye contact		Abs	eye, skin burns; skin sens;	Skin:	Water flush immed	
Wash skin:	When contam		Ing	in animals: lung, liver,	Breath:	Resp support	
Remove:	When wet or contam		Con	kidney inj	Swallow:	Medical attention	
Change:	N.R.					immed	
Provide:	Eyewash, Quick drench						

[Acrylic acid]

Skin:	Prevent skin contact	NIOSH	Inh	Irrit eyes, skin; asphy;	Eye:	Irr immed	Eyes, skin, CVS
Eyes:	Prevent eye contact	¥: SCBAF:PD,PP/SAF:PD,PP:ASCBA	Abs	head; sneez; nau, vomit;	Skin:	Water wash immed	liver, kidneys, CNS
Wash skin:	When contam	Escape: GMFOV/SCBAE	Ing	weak, li-head; skin vesic;	Breath:	Resp support	[brain tumors,
Remove:	When wet (flamm)		Con	scaling derm; [carc]	Swallow:	Medical attention	lung & bowel
Change:	N.R.					immed	cancer]
Provide:	Eyewash, Quick drench						

[Acrylonitrile]

Skin:	Prevent skin contact	NIOSH	Inh	Irrit eyes, skin, resp sys;	Eye:	Irr immed	Eyes, skin, resp sys,
Eyes:	Prevent eye contact	40 ppm: SA	Abs	head, dizz, weak, gidd, conf,	Skin:	Soap wash immed	CNS, CVS
Wash skin:	When contam	100 ppm: SA:CF	Ing	convuls; blurred vision;	Breath:	Resp support	
Remove:	When wet or contam	200 ppm: SCBAF/SAF	Con	dysp; abdom pain, nau, vomit	Swallow:	Medical attention	
Change:	Daily	250 ppm: SAF:PD,PP				immed	
		§: SCBAF:PD,PP/SAF:PD,PP:ASCBA					
		Escape: GMFOV/SCBAE					

[Adiponitrile]

Skin:	Prevent skin contact	NIOSH	Inh	Head, dizz; nau, vomit,	Eye:	Irr immed	Cancer, CNS,
Eyes:	Prevent eye contact	¥: SCBAF:PD,PP/SAF:PD,PP:ASCBA	Abs	mal; myoclonic jerks of	Skin:	Soap wash immed	liver, kidneys,
Wash skin:	When contam/Daily	Escape: GMFOVHiE/SCBAE	Ing	limbs; clonic, tonic	Breath:	Resp support	skin
Remove:	When wet or contam		Con	convuls; coma; hema,	Swallow:	Medical attention	[in animals:
Change:	Daily			azotemia; [carc]		immed	tumors of the
Provide:	Eyewash, Quick drench						lungs, liver,
							thyroid &
							adrenal glands]

[Aldrin]

Chemical name, structure/formula, CAS and RTECS Nos., and DOT ID and guide Nos.	Synonyms, trade names, and conversion factors	Exposure limits (TWA unless noted otherwise)	IDLH	Physical description	Chemical and physical properties		Incompatibilities and reactivities	Measurement method (See Table 1)
					MW, BP, SOL Fl.P, IP, Sp, Gr, flammability	VP, FRZ UEL, LEL		
Allyl alcohol CH₂=CHCH₂OH 107-18-6 BA5075000 1098 131	AA, Allylic alcohol, Propenol, 1-Propen-3-ol, 2-Propenol, Vinyl carbinol 1 ppm = 2.38 mg/m³	NIOSH 2 ppm (5 mg/m³) ST 4 ppm (10 mg/m³) [skin] OSHA† 2 ppm (5 mg/m³)	20 ppm	Colorless liquid with a pungent, mustard-like odor.	MW: 58.1 BP: 205°F Sol: Miscible Fl.P: 70°F IP: 9.63 eV Sp.Gr: 0.85 Class IB Flammable Liquid	VP: 17 mm FRZ: -200°F UEL: 18.0% LEL: 2.5%	Strong oxidizers, acids, carbon tetrachloride [Note: Polymerization may be caused by elevated temperatures, oxidizers, or peroxides.]	Char; 2-Propanol/ CS₂; GC/FID; IV [#1402, Alcohols III]
Allyl chloride CH₂=CHCH₂Cl 107-05-1 UC7350000 1100 131	3-Chloropropene, 1-Chloro-2-propene, 3-Chloropropylene 1 ppm = 3.13 mg/m³	NIOSH 1 ppm (3 mg/m³) ST 2 ppm (6 mg/m³) OSHA† 1 ppm (3 mg/m³)	250 ppm	Colorless, brown, yellow, or purple liquid with a pungent, unpleasant odor.	MW: 76.5 BP: 113°F Sol: 0.4% Fl.P: -25°F IP: 10.05 eV Sp.Gr: 0.94 Class IB Flammable Liquid	VP: 295 mm MLT: -210°F UEL: 11.1% LEL: 2.9%	Strong oxidizers, acids, amines, iron & aluminum chlorides, magnesium, zinc	Char; Benzene; GC/FID; IV [#1000]
Allyl glycidyl ether C₆H₁₀O₂ 106-92-3 RR0875000 2219 129	AGE; 1-Allyloxy-2,3-epoxypropane; Glycidyl allyl ether; [(2-Propenyloxy)methyl] oxirane 1 ppm = 4.67 mg/m³	NIOSH 5 ppm (22 mg/m³) ST 10 ppm (44 mg/m³) [skin] OSHA† C 10 ppm (45 mg/m³)	50 ppm	Colorless liquid with a pleasant odor.	MW: 114.2 BP: 309°F Sol: 14% Fl.P: 135°F IP: ? Sp.Gr: 0.97 Class II Combustible Liquid	VP: 2 mm FRZ: -148°F [forms glass] UEL: ? LEL: ?	Strong oxidizers	Tenax GC; Diethyl ether; GC/FID; IV [#2545]
Allyl propyl disulfide H₂C=CHCH₂S₂CH₂CH₂CH₃ 2179-59-1 JO0350000	4,5-Dithia-1-octene; Onion oil; 2-Propenyl propyl disulfide; Propyl allyl disulfide 1 ppm = 6.07 mg/m³	NIOSH 2 ppm (12 mg/m³) ST 3 ppm (18 mg/m³) OSHA† 2 ppm (12 mg/m³)	N.D.	Pale-yellow liquid with a strong & irritating onion-like odor. [Note: The chief volatile component of onion oil.]	MW: 148.3 BP: ? Sol: Insoluble Fl.P: ? IP: ? Sp.Gr(59°F): 0.93 Combustible Liquid	VP: ? FRZ: 5°F UEL: ? LEL: ?	Oxidizers	None available

Personal protection and sanitation (See Table 3)		Recommendations for respirator selection — maximum concentration for use (MUC) (See Table 4)	Health hazards			
			Route	Symptoms (See Table 5)	First aid (See Table 6)	Target organs (See Table 5)
Skin:	Prevent skin contact	NIOSH/OSHA	Inh	Eye irrit, tissue damage;	Eye: Irr immed	Eyes, skin, resp sys
Eyes:	Prevent eye contact	20 ppm: SA:CF*/PAPROV*/CCRFOV/	Abs	irrit upper resp sys,	Skin: Water flush immed	
Wash skin:	When contam	GMFOV/SCBAF/SAF	Ing	skin; pulm edema	Breath: Resp support	
Remove:	When wet (flamm)	§: SCBAF:PD,PP/SAF:PD,PP:ASCBA	Con		Swallow: Medical attention	
Change:	N.R.	Escape: GMFOV/SCBAE			immed	
Provide:	Quick drench					

[Allyl alcohol]

Skin:	Prevent skin contact	NIOSH/OSHA	Inh	Irrit eyes, skin, nose,	Eye: Irr immed	Eyes, skin, resp sys,
Eyes:	Prevent eye contact	25 ppm: SA:CF*	Abs	muc memb; pulm edema;	Skin: Soap wash immed	liver, kidneys
Wash skin:	When contam	50 ppm: SCBAF/SAF	Ing	in animals: liver, kidney inj	Breath: Resp support	
Remove:	When wet (flamm)	250 ppm: SAF:PD,PP	Con		Swallow: Medical attention	
Change:	N.R.	§: SCBAF:PD,PP/SAF:PD,PP:ASCBA			immed	
Provide:	Quick drench	Escape: GMFOV/SCBAE				

11

[Allyl chloride]

Skin:	Prevent skin contact	NIOSH	Inh	Irrit eyes, skin, nose,	Eye: Irr immed	Eyes, skin, resp sys,
Eyes:	Prevent eye contact	50 ppm: CCROV/PAPROV/GMFOV/	Abs	resp sys; derm; pulm edema;	Skin: Water flush prompt	blood, repro sys
Wash skin:	When contam	SA/SCBAF	Ing	narco; possible hemato,	Breath: Resp support	
Remove:	When wet or contam	§: SCBAF:PD,PP/SAF:PD,PP:ASCBA	Con	repro effects	Swallow: Medical attention	
Change:	N.R.	Escape: GMFOV/SCBAE			immed	
Provide:	Eyewash					

[Allyl glycidyl ether]

Skin:	N.R.	TBAL	Inh	Irrit eyes, nose, resp sys; lac	Eye: Irr immed	Eyes, resp sys
Eyes:	Prevent eye contact		Ing		Skin: Soap wash immed	
Wash skin:	N.R.		Con		Breath: Resp support	
Remove:	When wet or contam				Swallow: Medical attention	
Change:	N.R.				immed	

[Allyl propyl disulfide]

Chemical name, structure/formula, CAS and RTECS Nos., and DOT ID and guide Nos.	Synonyms, trade names, and conversion factors	Exposure limits (TWA unless noted otherwise)	IDLH	Physical description	Chemical and physical properties		Incompatibilities and reactivities	Measurement method (See Table 1)
					MW, BP, SOL FI.P, IP, Sp, Gr, flammability	VP, FRZ UEL, LEL		
α-Alumina Al_2O_3 1344-28-1 BD1200000	Alumina, Aluminum oxide, Aluminum trioxide [Note: α-Alumina is the main component of technical grade alumina. Corundum is natural Al_2O_3. Emery is an impure crystalline variety of Al_2O_3.]	NIOSH See Appendix D OSHA† 15 mg/m³ (total) 5 mg/m³ (resp)	N.D.	White, odorless, crystalline powder.	MW: 101.9 BP: 5396°F Sol: Insoluble FI.P: NA IP: NA Sp.Gr: 4.0 Noncombustible solid, but dusts may form explosive mixtures in air.	VP: 0 mm (approx) MLT: 3632°F UEL: NA LEL: NA	Chlorine trifluoride, hot chlorinated rubber, acids, oxidizers [Note: Hydrogen gas may be formed when finely divided iron contacts moisture during crushing & milling operations.]	Filter; none; Grav; IV [Particulates NOR: #0500 (total), #0600 (resp)]
Aluminum Al 7429-90-5 BD0330000 1309 170 (powder, coated) 1396 138 (powder, uncoated) 9260 169 (molten)	Aluminium, Aluminum metal, Aluminum powder, Elemental aluminum	NIOSH 10 mg/m³ (total) 5 mg/m³ (resp) OSHA 15 mg/m³ (total) 5 mg/m³ (resp)	N.D.	Silvery-white, malleable, ductile, odorless metal.	MW: 27.0 BP: 4221°F Sol: Insoluble FI.P: NA IP: NA Sp.Gr: 2.70 Combustible Solid, finely divided dust is easily ignited; may cause explosions.	VP: 0 mm (approx) MLT: 1220°F UEL: NA LEL: NA	Strong oxidizers & acids, halogenated hydrocarbons [Note: Corrodes in contact with acids & other metals. Ignition may occur if powders are mixed with halogens, carbon disulfide, or methyl chloride.]	Filter; HNO_3; FAAS; IV [#7013] [Also #7300, Elements]
Aluminum (pyro powders and welding fumes, as Al) 1383 135 (powder, pyrophoric)	Synonyms vary depending upon the specific aluminum compound.	NIOSH 5 mg/m³ OSHA† none	N.D.	Appearance and odor vary depending upon the specific aluminum compound.	Properties vary depending upon the specific aluminum compound.		Varies	Filter; HNO_3; ICP; IV [#7300, Elements]
Aluminum (soluble salts and alkyls, as Al) 3051 135 (alkyls)	Synonyms vary depending upon the specific aluminum compound.	NIOSH 2 mg/m³ OSHA† none	N.D.	Appearance and odor vary depending upon the specific aluminum compound.	Properties vary depending upon the specific aluminum compound.		Varies	Filter; HNO_3; FAAS; IV [#7013, Aluminum] [Also #7300, Elements]

Personal protection and sanitation (See Table 3)		Recommendations for respirator selection — maximum concentration for use (MUC) (See Table 4)	Health hazards				
			Route	Symptoms (See Table 5)	First aid (See Table 6)		Target organs (See Table 5)
Skin:	N.R.	TBAL	Inh Ing Con	Irrit eyes, skin, resp sys	Eye: Skin: Breath: Swallow:	Irr immed Blot/brush away Fresh air Medical attention immed	Eyes, skin, resp sys
Eyes:	N.R.						
Wash skin:	N.R.						
Remove:	N.R.						
Change:	N.R.						

[α-Alumina]

Skin:	N.R.	TBAL	Inh Con	Irrit eyes, skin, resp sys	Eye: Breath:	Irr immed Fresh air	Eyes, skin, resp sys
Eyes:	N.R.						
Wash skin:	N.R.						
Remove:	N.R.						
Change:	N.R.						

[Aluminum]

Skin:	N.R.	TBAL	Inh Ing Con	Irrit skin, resp sys; pulm fib	Eye: Skin: Breath: Swallow:	Irr immed Water flush immed Resp support Medical attention immed	Skin, resp sys
Eyes:	N.R.						
Wash skin:	N.R.						
Remove:	N.R.						
Change:	N.R.						

[Aluminum (pyro powders and welding fumes, as Al]

Skin:	Prevent skin contact	TBAL	Inh Ing Con	Irrit skin, resp sys; skin burns	Eye: Skin: Breath: Swallow:	Irr immed Water flush immed Resp support Medical attention immed	Skin, resp sys
Eyes:	Prevent eye contact						
Wash skin:	When contam						
Remove:	When wet or contam						
Change:	Daily						

[Aluminum (soluble salts and alkyls, as Al)]

Chemical name, structure/formula, CAS and RTECS Nos., and DOT ID and guide Nos.	Synonyms, trade names, and conversion factors	Exposure limits (TWA unless noted otherwise)	IDLH	Physical description	Chemical and physical properties		Incompatibilities and reactivities	Measurement method (See Table 1)
					MW, BP, SOL Fl.P, IP, Sp, Gr, flammability	VP, FRZ UEL, LEL		
4-Aminodiphenyl $C_6H_5C_6H_4NH_2$ 92-67-1 DU8925000	4-Aminobiphenyl, p-Aminobiphenyl, p-Aminodiphenyl, 4-Phenylaniline	NIOSH Ca See Appendix A OSHA[1910.1011] See Appendix B	Ca [N.D.]	Colorless crystals with a floral odor. [Note: Turns purple on contact with air.]	MW: 169.2 BP: 576°F Sol: Slight Fl.P: ? IP: ? Sp.Gr. 1.16 Combustible Solid, but must be preheated before ignition possible.	VP(227°F): 1 mm MLT: 127°F UEL: ? LEL: ?	Oxidized by air	Filter/ Si gel; 2-Propanol; GC/FID; II(4) [P&CAM #269]
2-Aminopyridine $NH_2C_5H_4N$ 504-29-0 US1575000 2671 153	α-Aminopyridine, α-Pyridylamine	NIOSH/OSHA 0.5 ppm (2 mg/m³) 1 ppm = 3.85 mg/m³	5 ppm	White powder, leaflets, or crystals with a characteristic odor.	MW: 94.1 BP: 411°F Sol: >100% Fl.P: 154°F IP: 8.00 eV Sp.Gr: ? Combustible Solid	VP(77°F): 0.8 mm MLT: 137°F UEL: ? LEL: ?	Strong oxidizers	Tenax GC(2); Thermal desorp; GC/FID; II(4) [#S158]
Amitrole $C_2H_4N_4$ 61-82-5 XZ3850000	Aminotriazole; 3-Aminotriazole; 2-Amino-1,3,4-triazole; 3-Amino-1,2,4-triazole	NIOSH Ca 0.2 mg/m³ See Appendix A OSHA† none	Ca [N.D.]	Colorless to white, crystalline powder. [herbicide] [Note: Odorless when pure.]	MW: 84.1 BP: ? Sol(77°F): 28% Fl.P: NA IP: ? Sp.Gr. 1.14 Noncombustible Solid, but may be dissolved in flammable liquids.	VP: <0.000008 mm MLT: 318°F UEL: NA LEL: NA	Light (decomposes), strong oxidizers [Note: Corrosive to iron, aluminum & copper.]	Filter; none; Grav; IV [#0500, Particulates NOR (total)]
Ammonia NH_3 7664-41-7 BO0875000 1005 125 (anhydrous) 2672 154 (10-35% soln.) 2073 125 (>35-50% soln.) 1005 125 (>50% soln.)	Anhydrous ammonia, Aqua ammonia, Aqueous ammonia [Note: Often used in an aqueous solution.] 1 ppm = 0.70 mg/m³	NIOSH 25 ppm (18 mg/m³) ST 35 ppm (27 mg/m³) OSHA† 50 ppm (35 mg/m³)	300 ppm	Colorless gas with a pungent, suffo-cating odor. [Note: Shipped as a liquefied compressed gas. Easily liquefied under pressure.]	MW: 17.0 BP: -28°F Sol: 34% Fl.P: NA (Gas) IP: 10.18 eV RGasD: 0.60 [Note: Although NH_3 does not meet the DOT definition of a Flammable Gas (for labeling purposes), it should be treated as one.]	VP: 8.5 atm FRZ: -108°F UEL: 28% LEL:15%	Strong oxidizers, acids, halogens, salts of silver & zinc [Note: Corrosive to copper & galvanized surfaces.]	Si gel*; Water; Vis; IV [#6015] [Also #6016]

Personal protection and sanitation (See Table 3)		Recommendations for respirator selection — maximum concentration for use (MUC) (See Table 4)	Health hazards				
			Route	Symptoms (See Table 5)	First aid (See Table 6)		Target organs (See Table 5)
Skin:	Prevent skin contact	NIOSH	Inh	Head, dizz, leth, dysp;	Eye:	Irr immed	Bladder, skin
Eyes:	Prevent eye contact	¥: SCBAF:PD,PP/SAF:PD,PP:ASCBA	Abs	ataxia, weak; methemo;	Skin:	Soap wash immed	[bladder cancer]
Wash skin:	When contam/Daily	Escape: HiEF/SCBAE	Ing	urinary burning; acute	Breath:	Resp support	
Remove:	When wet or contam		Con	hemorrhagic cystitis; [carc]	Swallow:	Medical attention	
Change:	Daily					immed	
Provide:	Eyewash, Quick drench						

[4-Aminodiphenyl]

Skin:	Prevent skin contact	NIOSH/OSHA	Inh	Irrit eyes, nose, throat;	Eye:	Irr immed	CNS, resp sys
Eyes:	Prevent eye contact	5 ppm: SA*/SCBAF	Abs	head, dizz; excitement;	Skin:	Water flush immed	
Wash skin:	When contam	§: SCBAF:PD,PP/SAF:PD,PP:ASCBA	Ing	nau; high BP; resp	Breath:	Resp support	
Remove:	When wet or contam	Escape: GMFOVHiE/SCBAE	Con	distress; weak; convuls;	Swallow:	Medical attention	
Change:	Daily			stupor		immed	
Provide:	Quick drench						

[2-Aminopyridine]

Skin:	Prevent skin contact	NIOSH	Inh	Irrit eyes, skin; dysp,	Eye:	Irr immed	Eyes, skin, thyroid
Eyes:	Prevent eye contact	¥: SCBAF:PD,PP/SAF:PD,PP:ASCBA	Ing	musc spasms, ataxia, anor,	Skin:	Water wash immed	[in animals: liver,
Wash skin:	Daily	Escape: GMFOVHiE/SCBAE	Con	salv, incr body temperature;	Breath:	Resp support	thyroid & pituitary
Remove:	When wet or contam			lass, skin dryness, depres	Swallow:	Medical attention	gland tumors]
Change:	Daily			(thyroid func suppression)		immed	
Provide:	Eyewash, Quick drench						

[Amitrole]

Skin:	Prevent skin contact	NIOSH	Inh	Irrit eyes, nose, throat;	Eye:	Irr immed (soln/liq)	Eyes, skin, resp sys
Eyes:	Prevent eye contact	250 ppm: CCRS*/SA*	Ing	dysp, bronspas, chest	Skin:	Water flush immed	
Wash skin:	When contam (soln)	300 ppm: SA:CF*/PAPRS*/CCRFS/	(soln)	pain; pulm edema; pink		(soln/liq)	
Remove:	When wet or contam (soln)	GMFS/SCBAF/SAF	Con	frothy sputum; skin burns,	Breath:	Resp support	
Change:	N.R.	§: SCBAF:PD,PP/SAF:PD,PP:ASCBA	(soln/	vesic; liq: frostbite	Swallow:	Medical attention	
Provide:	Eyewash (>10%),	Escape: GMFS/SCBAE	liq)			immed (soln)	
	Quick drench (>10%)						

[Ammonia]

Chemical name, structure/formula, CAS and RTECS Nos., and DOT ID and guide Nos.	Synonyms, trade names, and conversion factors	Exposure limits (TWA unless noted otherwise)	IDLH	Physical description	Chemical and physical properties		Incompatibilities and reactivities	Measurement method (See Table 1)
					MW, BP, SOL Fl.P, IP, Sp, Gr, flammability	VP, FRZ UEL, LEL		
Ammonium chloride fume NH₄Cl 12125-02-9 BP4550000	Ammonium chloride, Ammonium muriate fume, Sal ammoniac fume	NIOSH 10 mg/m³ ST 20 mg/m³ OSHA† none	N.D.	Finely divided, odorless, white particulate dispersed in air.	MW: 53.5 BP: Sublimes Sol: 37% Fl.P: NA IP: NA Sp.Gr. 1.53 Noncombustible Solid	VP(321°F): 1 mm MLT: 662°F (Sublimes) UEL: NA LEL: NA	Alkalis & their carbonates, lead & silver salts, strong oxidizers, ammonium nitrate, potassium chlorate, bromine trifluoride [Note: Corrodes most metals at high (i.e., fire) temperatures.]	Filter; Water; IC; OSHA [#ID188]
Ammonium sulfamate NH₄OSO₂NH₂ 7773-06-0 WO6125000 9089 171	Ammate® herbicide, Ammonium amidosulfonate, AMS, Monoammonium salt of sulfamic acid, Sulfamate	NIOSH 10 mg/m³ (total) 5 mg/m³ (resp) OSHA† 15 mg/m³ (total) 5 mg/m³ (resp)	1500 mg/m³	Colorless to white crystalline, odorless solid. [herbicide]	MW: 114.1 BP: 320°F (Decomposes) Sol: 200% Fl.P: NA IP: ? Sp.Gr. 1.77 Noncombustible Solid	VP: 0 mm (approx) MLT: 268°F UEL: NA LEL: NA	Acids, hot water [Note: Elevated temperatures cause a highly exothermic reaction with water.]	Filter; Water; IC; II(5) [#S348]
n-Amyl acetate CH₃COO[CH₂]₄CH₃ 628-63-7 AJ1925000 1104 129	Amyl acetic ester, Amyl acetic ether, 1-Pentanol acetate, Pentyl ester of acetic acid, Primary amyl acetate 1 ppm = 5.33 mg/m³	NIOSH/OSHA 100 ppm (525 mg/m³)	1000 ppm	Colorless liquid with a persistent, banana-like odor.	MW: 130.2 BP: 301°F Sol: 0.2% Fl.P: 77°F IP: ? Sp.Gr. 0.88 Class IC Flammable Liquid	VP: 4 mm FRZ: -95°F UEL: 7.5% LEL: 1.1%	Nitrates; strong oxidizers, alkalis & acids	Char; CS₂; GC/FID; IV [#1450, Esters I] [Also #2549, VOCs (screening)]
sec-Amyl acetate CH₃COOCH(CH₃)C₃H₇ 626-38-0 AJ2100000 1104 129	1-Methylbutyl acetate, 2-Pentanol acetate, 2-Pentyl ester of acetic acid 1 ppm = 5.33 mg/m³	NIOSH/OSHA 125 ppm (650 mg/m³)	1000 ppm	Colorless liquid with a mild odor.	MW: 130.2 BP: 249°F Sol: Slight Fl.P: 89°F IP: ? Sp.Gr. 0.87 Class IC Flammable Liquid	VP: 7 mm FRZ: -109°F UEL: 7.5% LEL: 1%	Nitrates; strong oxidizers, alkalis & acids	Char; CS₂; GC/FID; IV [#1450, Esters I] [Also #2549, VOCs (screening)]

16

Personal protection and sanitation (See Table 3)		Recommendations for respirator selection — maximum concentration for use (MUC) (See Table 4)	Health hazards				
			Route	Symptoms (See Table 5)		First aid (See Table 6)	Target organs (See Table 5)
Skin:	Prevent skin contact	TBAL	Inh	Irrit eyes, skin, resp sys;	Eye:	Irr immed	Eyes, skin, resp sys
Eyes:	Prevent eye contact		Con	cough, dysp, pulm sens	Skin:	Soap wash immed	
Wash skin:	When contam				Breath:	Resp support	
Remove:	When wet or contam						
Change:	Daily						
Provide:	Eyewash, Quick drench						

[Ammonium chloride fume]

Personal protection and sanitation (See Table 3)		Recommendations for respirator selection — maximum concentration for use (MUC) (See Table 4)	Health hazards				
Skin:	N.R.	NIOSH	Inh	Irrit eyes, nose, throat;	Eye:	Irr immed	Eyes, resp sys
Eyes:	N.R.	50 mg/m³: DM	Con	cough, dysp	Skin:	Soap wash prompt	
Wash skin:	N.R.	100 mg/m³: DMXSQ/SA			Breath:	Resp support	
Remove:	N.R.	250 mg/m³: SA:CF/PAPRDM			Swallow:	Medical attention	
Change:	N.R.	500 mg/m³: SAT:CF/PAPRTHiE/HiEF/				immed	
		SCBAF/SAF					
		1500 mg/m³: SA:PD,PP					
		§: SCBAF:PD,PP/SAF:PD,PP:ASCBA					
		Escape: HiEF/SCBAE					

[Ammonium sulfamate]

Personal protection and sanitation (See Table 3)		Recommendations for respirator selection — maximum concentration for use (MUC) (See Table 4)	Health hazards				
Skin:	Prevent skin contact	NIOSH/OSHA	Inh	Irrit eyes, nose; derm;	Eye:	Irr immed	Eyes, skin, resp sys,
Eyes:	Prevent eye contact	1000 ppm: CCROV*/GMFOV/PAPROV*/	Ing	possible CNS depres,	Skin:	Water flush prompt	CNS
Wash skin:	When contam	SA*/SCBAF	Con	narco	Breath:	Resp support	
Remove:	When wet (flamm)	§: SCBAF:PD,PP/SAF:PD,PP:ASCBA			Swallow:	Medical attention	
Change:	N.R.	Escape: GMFOV/SCBAE				immed	

[n-Amyl acetate]

Personal protection and sanitation (See Table 3)		Recommendations for respirator selection — maximum concentration for use (MUC) (See Table 4)	Health hazards				
Skin:	Prevent skin contact	NIOSH/OSHA	Inh	Irrit eyes, skin, nose;	Eye:	Irr immed	Eyes, skin, resp sys,
Eyes:	Prevent eye contact	1000 ppm: CCROV*/GMFOV/PAPROV*/	Ing	narco; derm; possible kidney,	Skin:	Water flush prompt	kidneys, liver, CNS
Wash skin:	When contam	SA*/SCBAF	Con	liver inj; possible CNS	Breath:	Resp support	
Remove:	When wet (flamm)	§: SCBAF:PD,PP/SAF:PD,PP:ASCBA		depres	Swallow:	Medical attention	
Change:	N.R.	Escape: GMFOV/SCBAE				immed	

[sec-Amyl acetate]

Chemical name, structure/formula, CAS and RTECS Nos., and DOT ID and guide Nos.	Synonyms, trade names, and conversion factors	Exposure limits (TWA unless noted otherwise)	IDLH	Physical description	Chemical and physical properties		Incompatibilities and reactivities	Measurement method (See Table 1)
					MW, BP, SOL FI.P, IP, Sp, Gr, flammability	VP, FRZ UEL, LEL		
Aniline (and homologs) C₆H₅NH₂ 62-53-3 BW6650000 1547 153	Aminobenzene, Aniline oil, Benzenamine, Phenylamine	NIOSH Ca See Appendix A OSHA† 5 ppm (19 mg/m³) [skin] 1 ppm = 3.81 mg/m³	Ca [100 ppm]	Colorless to brown, oily liquid with an aromatic amine-like odor. [Note: A solid below 21°F.]	MW: 93.1 BP: 363°F Sol: 4% Fl.P: 158°F IP: 7.70 eV Sp.Gr. 1.02 Class IIIA Combustible Liquid	VP: 0.6 mm FRZ: 21°F UEL:11% LEL: 1.3%	Strong oxidizers, strong acids, tcluene diIsocyanate, alkalis	Si gel; Ethanol; GC/FID; IV [#2002, Aromatic Amines]
o-Anisidine NH₂C₆H₄OCH₃ 90-04-0 BZ5410000 2431 153	ortho-Aminoanisole, 2-Anisidine, o-Methoxyaniline [Note: o-Anisidine has been used as a basis for many dyes.]	NIOSH Ca 0.5 mg/m³ [skin] See Appendix A OSHA 0.5 mg/m³ [skin]	Ca [50 mg/m³]	Red or yellow, oily iquid with an amine-like odor. [Note: A solid below 41°F.]	MW: 123.2 BP: 437°F Sol(77°F): 1% Fl.P(oc): 244°F IP: 7.44 eV Sp.Gr. 1.10 Class IIIB Combustible Liquid	VP: <0.1 mm FRZ: 41°F UEL: ?: LEL: ?	Strong oxidizers	XAD-2; Methanol; HPLC/UVD; IV [#2514]
p-Anisidine NH₂C₆H₄OCH₃ 104-94-9 BZ5450000 2431 153	para-Aminoanisole, 4-Anisidine, p-Methoxyaniline	NIOSH/OSHA 0.5 mg/m³ [skin]	50 mg/m³	Yellow to brown, crystalline solid with an amine-like odor.	MW: 123.2 BP: 475°F Sol: Moderate Fl.P: ? IP: 7.44 eV Sp.Gr. 1.07 Combustible Solid	VP(77°F): 0.006 mm MLT: 135°F UEL: ? LEL: ?	Strong oxidizers	XAD-2; Methanol; HPLC/UVD; IV [#2514]
Antimony Sb 7440-36-0 CC4025000 1549 157 (inorganic, n.o.s.) 2871 170 (powder) 3141 157 (inorganic liquid compounds, n.o.s.)	Antimony metal, Antimony powder, Stibium	NIOSH*/OSHA* 0.5 mg/m³ [*Note: The REL and PEL also apply to other Antimony compounds (as Sb).]	50 mg/m³ (as Sb)	Silver-white, lustrous, hard, brittle solid; scale-like crystals; or a dark-gray, lustrous powder.	MW: 121.8 BP: 2975°F Sol: Insoluble Fl.P: NA IP: NA Sp.Gr. 6.69 Noncombustible Solid in bulk form, but a moderate explosion hazard in the form of dust when exposed to flame.	VP: 0 mm (approx) MLT: 1166°F UEL: NA LEL: NA	Strong oxidizers, acids, halogenated acids [Note: Stibine is formed when antimony is exposed to nascent (freshly formed) hydrogen.]	Filter; Acid; FAAS; II(4) [P&CAM #261]

Personal protection and sanitation (See Table 3)	Recommendations for respirator selection — maximum concentration for use (MUC) (See Table 4)	Health hazards			
		Route	Symptoms (See Table 5)	First aid (See Table 6)	Target organs (See Table 5)
Skin: Prevent skin contact Eyes: Prevent eye contact Wash skin: When contam Remove: When wet or contam Change: N.R. Provide: Quick drench	NIOSH ¥: SCBAF:PD,PP/SAF:PD,PP:ASCBA Escape: GMFOV/SCBAE	Inh Abs Ing Con	Head, weak, dizz; cyan; ataxia; dysp on effort; tacar; irrit eyes; methemo; cirr; [carc]	Eye: Irr immed Skin: Soap wash prompt Breath: Resp support Swallow: Medical attention immed	Blood, CVS, eyes, liver, kidneys, resp sys [bladder cancer]

[Aniline (and homologs)]

Skin: Prevent skin contact Eyes: Prevent eye contact Wash skin: When contam Remove: When wet or contam Change: Daily Provide: Eyewash, Quick drench	NIOSH ¥: SCBAF:PD,PP/SAF:PD,PP:ASCBA Escape: GMFOV/SCBAE	Inh Abs Ing Con	Head, dizz; cyan; RBC Heinz bodies; [carc]	Eye: Irr immed Skin: Soap wash immed Breath: Resp support Swallow: Medical attention immed	Blood, kidneys, liver, CVS, CNS [In animals: tumors of the thyroid gland, bladder & kidneys]

[o-Anisidine]

Skin: Prevent skin contact Eyes: Prevent eye contact Wash skin: When contam Remove: When wet or contam Change: Daily Provide: Quick drench	NIOSH/OSHA 5 mg/m^3: DMXSQ/SA 12.5 mg/m^3: SA:CF/PAPRDM 25 mg/m^3: HiEF/PAPRTHiE*/SCBAF/SAF 50 mg/m^3: SA:PD,PP* §: SCBAF:PD,PP/SAF:PD,PP:ASCBA Escape: HiEF/SCBAE	Inh Abs Ing Con	Head, dizz; cyan; RBC Heinz bodies; [carc]	Eye: Irr immed Skin: Soap wash immed Breath: Resp support Swallow: Medical attention immed	Blood, kidneys, liver, CVS, CNS

[p-Anisidine]

Skin: Prevent skin contact Eyes: Prevent eye contact Wash skin: When contam Remove: When wet or contam Change: Daily	NIOSH/OSHA 5 mg/m^3: DMXSQ^/SA 12.5 mg/m^3: SA:CF/PAPRDM^ 25 mg/m^3: HiEF/SAT:CF/PAPRTHiE/ SCBAF/SAF 50 mg/m^3: SA:PD,PP §: SCBAF:PD,PP/SAF:PD,PP:ASCBA Escape: HiEF/SCBAE	Inh Ing Con	Irrit eyes, skin, nose, throat, mouth; cough; dizz; head; nau, vomit, diarr; stomach cramps; insom; anor; unable to smell properly	Eye: Irr immed Skin: Soap wash immed Breath: Resp support Swallow: Medical attention immed	Eyes, skin, resp sys, CVS

[Antimony]

Chemical name, structure/formula, CAS and RTECS Nos., and DOT ID and guide Nos.	Synonyms, trade names, and conversion factors	Exposure limits (TWA unless noted otherwise)	IDLH	Physical description	Chemical and physical properties		Incompatibilities and reactivities	Measurement method (See Table 1)
					MW, BP, SOL Fl.P, IP, Sp, Gr, flammability	VP, FRZ UEL, LEL		
ANTU $C_{10}H_7NHC(NH_2)S$ 86-88-4 YT9275000 1651 153	α-Naphthyl thiocarbamide, 1-Naphthyl thiourea, α-Naphthyl thiourea	NIOSH/OSHA 0.3 mg/m³	100 mg/m³	White crystalline or gray, odorless powder. [rodenticide]	MW: 202.3 BP: Decomposes Sol: 0.06% Fl.P: NA IP: ? Sp.Gr: ? Noncombustible Solid	VP: Low UEL: NA LEL: NA	Strong oxidizers, silver nitrate	Filter; Methanol; HPLC/UVD; II(5) [#S276]
Arsenic (inorganic compounds, as As) As (Metal) 7440-38-2 (Metal) CG0525000 (Metal) 1558 152 (metal) 1562 152 (dust)	Arsenic metal: Arsenia Other synonyms vary depending upon the specific As compound. [Note: OSHA considers "Inorganic Arsenic" to mean copper acetoarsenite & all inorganic compounds containing arsenic except Arsine.]	NIOSH Ca C 0.002 mg/m³ [15-min] See Appendix A OSHA[1910.1018] 0.010 mg/m³	Ca [5 mg/m³ (as As)]	Metal: Silver-gray or tin-white, brittle, odorless solid.	MW: 74.9 BP: Sublimes Sol: Insoluble Fl.P: NA IP: NA Sp.Gr: 5.73 (Metal) Metal: Noncombustible Solid in bulk form, but a slight explosion hazard in the form of dust when exposed to flame.	VP: 0 mm (approx) MLT: 1135°F (Sublimes) UEL: NA LEL: NA	Strong oxidizers, bromine azide [Note: Hydrogen gas can react with inorganic arsenic to form the highly toxic gas arsine.]	Filter; Acid; HYAAS; IV [#7900] [Also #7300, Elements]
Arsenic (organic compounds, as As)	Synonyms vary depending upon the specific organic arsenic compound.	NIOSH none OSHA 0.5 mg/m³	N.D.	Appearance and odor vary depending upon the specific organic arsenic compound.	Properties vary depending upon the specific organic arsenic compound.		Varies	Filter; Reagent; IC/HYAAS; IV [#5022, Arsenic, Organo-]
Arsine AsH_3 7784-42-1 CG6475000 2188 119	Arsenic hydride, Arsenic trihydride, Arseniuretted hydrogen, Arsenous hydride, Hydrogen arsenide 1 ppm = 3.19 mg/m³	NIOSH Ca C 0.002 mg/m³ [15-min] See Appendix A OSHA 0.05 ppm (0.2 mg/m³)	Ca [3 ppm]	Colorless gas with a mild, garlic-like odor. [Note: Shipped as a liquefied compressed gas.]	MW: 78.0 BP: -81°F Sol: 20% Fl.P: NA (Gas) IP: 9.89 eV RGasD: 2.69 Flammable Gas	VP(70°F): 14.9 atm FRZ: -179°F UEL: 78% LEL: 5.1%	Strong oxidizers, chlorine, nitric acid [Note: Decomposes above 446°F. There is a high potential for the generation of arsine gas when inorganic arsenic is exposed to nascent (freshly formed) hydrogen.]	Char; HNO₃; GFAAS; IV [#6001]

Personal protection and sanitation (See Table 3)		Recommendations for respirator selection — maximum concentration for use (MUC) (See Table 4)	Health hazards				
			Route	Symptoms (See Table 5)	First aid (See Table 6)		Target organs (See Table 5)

Skin:
Eyes:
Wash skin:
Remove:
Change:
	N.R.
	N.R.
	N.R.
	N.R.
	Daily
		NIOSH/OSHA
		3 mg/m³: CCROVDMFu/SA
		7.5 mg/m³: SA:CF/PAPROVDMFu
		15 mg/m³: CCRFOVHiE/GMFOVHiE/
		    PAPRTOVHiE/SAT:CF/
		    SCBAF/SAF
		100 mg/m³: SA:PD,PP
		§: SCBAF:PD,PP/SAF:PD,PP:ASCBA
		Escape: GMFOVHiE/SCBAE
			Inh
			Ing
				After ingestion of large doses: vomit, dysp, cyan, coarse pulm rales; liver damage	Eye:
					Skin:
					Breath:
					Swallow:
						Irr immed
						Soap wash prompt
						Resp support
						Medical attention immed
							Resp sys, blood, liver

[ANTU]							
Skin: Eyes: Wash skin: Remove: Change: Provide:	Prevent skin contact Prevent eye contact When contam/Daily When wet or contam Daily Eyewash, Quick drench	NIOSH ¥: SCBAF:PD,PP/SAF:PD,PP:ASCBA Escape: GMFAGHiE/SCBAE	Inh Abs Con Ing	Ulceration of nasal septum, derm, GI disturbances, peri neur, resp irrit, hyperpig of skin, [carc]	Eye: Skin: Breath: Swallow:	Irr immed Soap wash immed Resp support Medical attention immed	Liver, kidneys, skin, lungs, lymphatic sys [lung & lymphatic cancer]
[Arsenic (inorganic compounds, as As)]							
Recommendations vary depending upon the specific compound.		TBAL	Inh Ing Con	In animals: irrit skin, possible derm; resp distress; diarr; kidney damage; musc tremor, sez; possible GI tract, terato, repro effects; possible liver damage	Eye: Skin: Breath: Swallow:	Irr immed Soap wash immed Resp support Medical attention immed	Skin, resp sys, kidneys, CNS, liver, GI tract, repro sys
[Arsenic (organic compounds, as As]]							
Skin: Eyes: Wash skin: Remove: Change: Provide:	Frostbite Frostbite N.R. When wet (flamm) N.R. Frostbite	NIOSH ¥: SCBAF:PD,PP/SAF:PD,PP:ASCBA Escape: GMFS/SCBAE	Inh Con (liq)	Head, mal, weak, dizz; dysp; abdom, back pain; nau, vomit; bronze skin; hema; jaun; peri neur; liq: frostbite; [carc]	Eye: Skin: Breath:	Frostbite Frostbite Resp support	Blood, kidneys, liver [lung & lymphatic cancer]
[Arsine]							

Chemical name, structure/formula, CAS and RTECS Nos., and DOT ID and guide Nos.	Synonyms, trade names, and conversion factors	Exposure limits (TWA unless noted otherwise)	IDLH	Physical description	Chemical and physical properties — MW, BP, SOL, Fl.P, IP, Sp, Gr, flammability	VP, FRZ UEL, LEL	Incompatibilities and reactivities	Measurement method (See Table 1)
Asbestos Hydrated mineral silicates 1332-21-4 CI6475000 2212 171 (blue, brown) 2590 171 (white)	Actinolite, Actinolite asbestos, Amosite (cummingtonite-grunerite), Anthophyllite, Anthophyllite asbestos, Chrysotile, Crocidolite (Riebeckite), Tremolite, Tremolite asbestos	NIOSH Ca See Appendix A See Appendix C OSHA [1910.1001] [1910.1101] See Appendix C	Ca [N.D.]	White or greenish (chrysotile), blue (crocidolite), or gray-green (amosite) fibrous, odorless solids.	MW: Varies BP: Decomposes Sol: Insoluble Fl.P: NA IP: NA Sp.Gr: ? Noncombustible Solids	VP: 0 mm (approx) MLT: 1112°F (Decomposes) UEL: NA LEL: NA	None reported	Filter; Acetone/ Triacetin; PCM; IV [#7400, Fibers] [Also #7402 (TEM)]

Asphalt fumes
 	
8052-42-4
CI9900000
 	
1999 130 (Asphalt)
	Asphalt:
	  Asphaltum,
	  Bitumen (European term),
	  Petroleum asphalt,
	  Petroleum bitumen,
	  Road asphalt,
	  Roofing asphalt
		NIOSH
		Ca
		C 5 mg/m³
		[15-min]
		See Appendix A
		
		OSHA
		none
			Ca
			[N.D.]
				Fumes generated during the production or application of asphalt (a dark-brown to black cement-like substance manufactured by the vacuum distillation of crude petroleum oil).	Properties vary depending upon the specific asphalt formulation or mixture.
					
					Asphalt: Combustible Solid
							None reported
							[Note: Asphalt becomes molten at about 200°F.]
								Filter;
								none;
								Grav;
								NIOSH
								Asphalt
								Fumes
								Crit. Doc.

Atrazine C₉H₁₄CIN₅ 1912-24-9 XY5600000 2763 151 (triazine pesticide)	2-Chloro-4-ethylamino-6-isopropylamino-s-triazine; 6-Chloro-N-ethyl-N'-(1-methylethyl)-1,3,5-triazine-2,4-diamine	NIOSH 5 mg/m³ OSHA† none	N.D.	Colorless or white, odorless, crystalline powder. [herbicide]	MW: 215.7 BP: Decomposes Sol: 0.003% Fl.P: NA IP: NA Sp.Gr: 1.19 Noncombustible Solid, but may be mixed with flammable liquids.	VP: 0.0000003 mm MLT: 340°F UEL: NA LEL: NA	Strong acids, strong bases	Filter; none; Grav; IV [#0500, Particulates NOR (total)]
Azinphos-methyl C₁₀H₁₂O₃PS₂N₃ 86-50-0 TE1925000 2783 152	O,O-Dimethyl-S-4-oxo-1,2,3-benzotriazin-3(4H)-ylmethyl phosphoro-dithioate; Guthion®; Methyl azinphos [(CH₃O)₂P(S)SCH₂(N₃C₇H₄O)]	NIOSH/OSHA 0.2 mg/m³ [skin]	10 mg/m³	Colorless crystals or a brown, waxy solid. [insecticide]	MW: 317.3 BP: Decomposes Sol: 0.003% Fl.P: NA IP: ? Sp.Gr: 1.44 Noncombustible Solid	VP: 8 x 10⁻⁹ mm MLT: 163°F UEL: NA LEL: NA	Strong oxidizers, acids	OVS-2; Toluene/ Acetone; GC/FPD; IV [#5600, Organic Pesticides]

Personal protection and sanitation (See Table 3)		Recommendations for respirator selection — maximum concentration for use (MUC) (See Table 4)	Health hazards				
			Route	Symptoms (See Table 5)	First aid (See Table 6)		Target organs (See Table 5)
Skin:	Prevent skin contact	NIOSH	Inh	Asbestosis (chronic exposure): dysp, interstitial fib, restricted pulm function, finger clubbing; irrit eyes; [carc]	Eye:	Irr immed	Resp sys, eyes [lung cancer]
Eyes:	Prevent eye contact	¥: SCBAF:PD,PP/SAF:PD,PP:ASCBA	Ing		Breath:	Fresh air	
Wash skin:	Daily	Escape: HiEF/SCBAE	Con				
Remove:	N.R.						
Change:	Daily						

[Asbestos]

Skin:	Prevent skin contact	NIOSH	Inh	Irrit eyes, resp sys; [carc]	Eye:	Irr immed	Eyes, resp sys [in animals: skin tumors]
Eyes:	Prevent eye contact	¥: SCBAF:PD,PP/SAF:PD,PP:ASCBA	Abs		Breath:	Resp support	
Wash skin:	Daily	Escape: GMFOVHiE/SCBAE	Con				
Remove:	N.R.						
Change:	Daily						

[Asphalt fumes]

Skin:	Prevent skin contact	TBAL	Inh	Irrit eyes, skin; derm, sens skin; dysp, weak, inco, salv; hypothermia; liver inj	Eye:	Irr immed	Eyes, skin, resp sys, CNS, liver
Eyes:	Prevent eye contact		Ing		Skin:	Soap wash immed	
Wash skin:	When contam		Con		Breath:	Resp support	
Remove:	When wet or contam				Swallow:	Medical attention immed	
Change:	Daily						
Provide:	Eyewash, Quick drench						

[Atrazine]

Skin:	Prevent skin contact	NIOSH/OSHA	Inh	Miosis; ache eyes; blurred vision, lac, rhin; head; tight chest, wheez, lar spas; salv; cyan; anor; nau, vomit, diarr; sweat; twitch, para, convuls; low BP, card irreg	Eye:	Irr immed	Resp sys, CNS, CVS, blood chol
Eyes:	Prevent eye contact	2 mg/m³: CCROVDMFu/SA	Abs		Skin:	Soap wash immed	
Wash skin:	When contam	5 mg/m³: SA:CF/PAPROVDMFu	Ing		Breath:	Resp support	
Remove:	When wet or contam	10 mg/m³: CCRFOVHiE/GMFOVHiE/ PAPRTOVHiE/SAT:CF/ SCBAF/SAF	Con		Swallow:	Medical attention immed	
Change:	Daily	§: SCBAF:PD,PP/SAF:PD,PP:ASCBA					
Provide:	Quick drench	Escape: GMFOVHiE/SCBAE					

[Azinphos-methyl]

23

Chemical name, structure/formula, CAS and RTECS Nos., and DOT ID and guide Nos.	Synonyms, trade names, and conversion factors	Exposure limits (TWA unless noted otherwise)	IDLH	Physical description	Chemical and physical properties		Incompatibilities and reactivities	Measurement method (See Table 1)
					MW, BP, SOL Fl.P, IP, Sp, Gr, flammability	VP, FRZ UEL, LEL		
Barium chloride (as Ba) BaCl₂ 10361-37-2 CQ8750000 1564 154 (barium compound, n.o.s.)	Barium dichloride	NIOSH*/OSHA* 0.5 mg/m³ [*Note: The REL and PEL also apply to other soluble barium compounds (as Ba) except Barium sulfate.]	50 mg/m³ (as Ba)	White, odorless solid.	MW: 208.2 BP: 2840°F SOL:38% Fl.P: NA IP: ? Sp.Gr. 3.86 Noncombustible Solid	VP: Low MLT:1765°F UEL: NA LEL: NA	Acids, oxidizers	Filter; Water; FAAS; IV [#7056, Barium, soluble cmpds]
Barium nitrate (as Ba) Ba(NO₃)₂ 10022-31-8 CQ9625000 1446 141	Barium dinitrate, Barium(II) nitrate (1:2), Barium salt of nitric acid	NIOSH*/OSHA* 0.5 mg/m³ [*Note: The REL and PEL also apply to other soluble barium compounds (as Ba except Barium sulfate.]	50 mg/m³ (as Ba)	White, odorless solid.	MW: 261.4 BP: Decomposes SOL:9% Fl.P: NA IP: ? Sp.Gr. 3.24 Noncombustible Solid, but will accelerate the burning of combustible materials.	VP: Low MLT:1094°F UEL: NA LEL: NA	Acids, oxidizers, aluminum-magnesium alloys, (barium dioxide + zinc) [Note: Contact with combustible material may cause fire.]	Filter; Water; FAAS; IV [#7056, Barium, soluble cmpds]
Barium sulfate BaSO₄ 7727-43-7 CR0600000 1564 154 (barium compound, n.o.s.)	Artificial barite, Barite, Barium salt of sulfuric acid, Barytes (natural)	NIOSH 10 mg/m³ (total) 5 mg/m³ (resp) OSHA† 15 mg/m³ (total) 5 mg/m³ (resp)	N.D.	White or yellowish, odorless powder.	MW: 233.4 BP: 2912°F (Decomposes) Sol(64°F): 0.0002% Fl.P: NA IP: NA Sp.Gr: 4.25-4.5 Noncombustible Solid	VP: 0 mm (approx) MLT: 2876°F UEL: NA LEL: NA	Phosphorus, aluminum [Note: Aluminum in the presence of heat can cause an explosion.]	Filter; none; Grav; IV [Particulates NOR: #0500 (total), #0600 (resp)]
Benomyl C₁₄H₁₈N₄O₃ 17804-35-2 DD6475000 2757 151 (carbamate pesticide, solid)	Methyl 1- (butylcarbamoyl)- 2-benzimidazolecarbamate	NIOSH See Appendix D OSHA† 15 mg/m³ (total) 5 mg/m³ (resp)	N.D.	White crystalline solid with a faint, acrid odor. [fungicide] [Note: Decomposes without melting above 572°F.]	MW: 290.4 BP: Decomposes Sol: 0.0004% Fl.P: NA IP: NA Sp.Gr: ? Noncombustible Solid	VP: <0.00001 mm MLT: >572°F (Decomposes) UEL: NA LEL: NA	Heat, strong acids, strong alkalis	Filter; none; Grav; IV [Particulates NOR: #0500 (total), #0600 (resp)]

Personal protection and sanitation (See Table 3)		Recommendations for respirator selection — maximum concentration for use (MUC) (See Table 4)	Health hazards			
			Route	Symptoms (See Table 5)	First aid (See Table 6)	Target organs (See Table 5)
Skin:	Prevent skin contact	NIOSH/OSHA	Inh	Irrit eyes, skin, upper	Eye: Irr immed	Eyes, skin, resp sys,
Eyes:	Prevent eye contact	5 mg/m³: DMXSQ/SA	Ing	resp sys; skin burns,	Skin: Water flush immed	heart, CNS
Wash skin:	When contam	12.5 mg/m³: SA:CF/PAPRDM	Con	gastroenteritis; musc	Breath: Resp support	
Remove:	When wet or contam	25 mg/m³: HiEF/SAT:CF/PAPRTHiE/		spasm; slow pulse,	Swallow: Medical attention	
Change:	Daily	SCBAF/SAF		extrasystoles; hypokalemia	immed	
		50 mg/m³: SAF:PD,PP				
		§: SCBAF:PD,PP/SAF:PD,PP:ASCBA				
		Escape: HiEF/SCBAE				
[Barium chloride (as Ba)]						
Skin:	Prevent skin contact	NIOSH/OSHA	Inh	Irrit eyes, skin, upper	Eye: Irr immed	Eyes, skin, resp sys,
Eyes:	Prevent eye contact	5 mg/m³: DMXSQ/SA	Ing	resp sys; skin burns,	Skin: Water flush immed	heart, CNS
Wash skin:	When contam	12.5 mg/m³: SA:CF/PAPRDM	Con	gastroenteritis; musc	Breath: Resp support	
Remove:	When wet or contam	25 mg/m³: HiEF/SAT:CF/PAPRTHiE/		spasm; slow pulse,	Swallow: Medical attention	
Change:	Daily	SCBAF/SAF		extrasystoles; hypokalemia	immed	
		50 mg/m³: SAF:PD,PP				
		§: SCBAF:PD,PP/SAF:PD,PP:ASCBA				
		Escape: HiEF/SCBAE				
[Barium nitrate (as Ba)]						
Skin:	Prevent skin contact	TBAL	Inh	Irrit eyes, nose, upper	Eye: Irr immed	Eyes, resp sys
Eyes:	Prevent eye contact		Con	resp sys; benign	Skin: Soap wash	
Wash skin:	Daily			pneumoconiosis (baritosis)	Breath: Resp support	
Remove:	N.R.				Swallow: Medical attention	
Change:	N.R.				immed	
Provide:	Eyewash, Quick drench					
[Barium sulfate]						
Skin:	Prevent skin contact	TBAL	Inh	Irrit eyes, skin, upper	Eye: Irr immed	Eyes, skin, resp sys,
Eyes:	Prevent eye contact		Ing	resp sys; skin sens;	Skin: Soap wash immed	repro sys
Wash skin:	When contam		Con	possible repro, terato	Breath: Resp support	
Remove:	When wet or contam			effects	Swallow: Medical attention	
Change:	Daily				immed	
Provide:	Eyewash, Quick drench					
[Benomyl]						

Chemical name, structure/formula, CAS and RTECS Nos., and DOT ID and guide Nos.	Synonyms, trade names, and conversion factors	Exposure limits (TWA unless noted otherwise)	IDLH	Physical description	Chemical and physical properties		Incompatibilities and reactivities	Measurement method (See Table 1)
					MW, BP, SOL FI.P, IP, Sp, Gr, flammability	VP, FRZ UEL, LEL		
Benzene C_6H_6 71-43-2 CY1400000 1114 130	Benzol, Phenyl hydride 1 ppm = 3.19 mg/m³	NIOSH Ca 0.1 ppm ST 1 ppm See Appendix A OSHA [1910.1028] 1 ppm ST 5 ppm See Appendix F	Ca [500 ppm]	Colorless to light-yellow liquid with an aromatic odor. [Note: A solid below 42°F.]	MW: 78.1 BP: 176°F Sol: 0.07% FI.P: 12°F IP: 9.24 eV Sp.Gr. 0.88 Class IB Flammable Liquid	VP: 75 mm FRZ: 42°F UEL: 7.8% LEL: 1.2%	Strong oxidizers, many fluorides & perchlorates, nitric acid	Char; CS_2; GC/FID; IV [#1500, Hydro-carbons] [Also #3700; #1501]
Benzenethiol C_6H_5SH 108-98-5 DC0525000 2337 131	Mercaptobenzene, Phenyl mercaptan, Thiophenol 1 ppm = 4.51 mg/m³	NIOSH C 0.1 ppm (0.5 mg/m³) [15-min] OSHA† none	N.D.	Water-white liquid with an offensive, garlic-like odor. [Note: A solid below 5°F.]	MW: 110.2 BP: 336°F Sol(77°F): 0.08% FI.P: 132°F IP: 8.33 eV Sp.Gr. 1.08 Class II Combustible Liquid	VP(65°F): 1 mm FRZ: 5°F UEL: ? LEL: ?	Strong acids & bases, calcium hypochlorite, alkali metals [Note: Oxidizes on exposure to air.]	None available
Benzidine $NH_2C_6H_4C_6H_4NH_2$ 92-87-5 DC9625000 1885 153	Benzidine-based dyes; 4,4'-Bianiline; 4,4'-Biphenyldiamine; 1,1'-Biphenyl-4,4'-diamine; 4,4'-Diaminobiphenyl; p-Diaminodiphenyl [Note: Benzidine has been used as a basis for many dyes.]	NIOSH Ca See Appendix A See Appendix C OSHA [1910.1010] See Appendix B See Appendix C	Ca [N.D.]	Grayish-yellow, reddish-gray, or white crystalline powder. [Note: Darkens on exposure to air and light.]	MW: 184.3 BP: 752°F Sol(54°F): 0.04% FI.P: ? IP: ? Sp.Gr. 1.25 Combustible Solid, but difficult to burn.	VP: Low MLT: 239°F UEL: ? LEL: ?	Red fuming nitric acid	Filter; Reagent; HPLC/UVD; IV [#5509]
Benzoyl peroxide $(C_6H_5CO)_2O_2$ 94-36-0 DM8575000 2085/2087 146 2088/2090 146 2089 145	Benzoperoxide, Dibenzoyl peroxide	NIOSH/OSHA 5 mg/m³	1500 mg/m³	Colorless to white crystals or a granular powder with a faint, benzaldehyde-like odor.	MW: 242.2 BP: Decomposes explosively Sol: <1% FI.P: 176°F IP: ? Sp.Gr. 1.33 Combustible Solid (easily ignited and burns very rapidly).	VP: <1 mm MLT: 217°F UEL: ? LEL: ?	Combustible substances (wood, paper, etc.), acids, alkalis, alcohols, amines, ethers [Note: Containers may explode when heated. Extremely explosion-sensitive to shock, heat, and friction.]	Filter; Diethyl ether; HPLC/UVD; IV [#5009]

Personal protection and sanitation (See Table 3)	Recommendations for respirator selection — maximum concentration for use (MUC) (See Table 4)	Route	Symptoms (See Table 5)	First aid (See Table 6)	Target organs (See Table 5)
Skin: Prevent skin contact Eyes: Prevent eye contact Wash skin: When contam Remove: When wet (flamm) Change: N.R. Provide: Eyewash, Quick drench	NIOSH ¥: SCBAF:PD,PP/SAF:PD,PP:ASCBA Escape: GMFOV/SCBAE	Inh Abs Ing Con	Irrit eyes, skin, nose, resp sys; gidd; head, nau, staggered gait; ftg, anor, lass; derm; bone marrow depres; [carc]	Eye: Irr immed Skin: Soap wash immed Breath: Resp support Swallow: Medical attention immed	Eyes, skin, resp sys, blood, CNS, bone marrow [leukemia]
[Benzene]					
Skin: Prevent skin contact Eyes: Prevent eye contact Wash skin: When contam Remove: When wet or contam Change: N.R. Provide: Eyewash, Quick drench	NIOSH 1 ppm: CCROV/SA 2.5 ppm: SA:CF/PAPROV 5 ppm: CCRFOV/GMFOV/PAPRTOV/SCBAF/SAF §: SCBAF:PD,PP/SAF:PD,PP:ASCBA Escape: GMFOV/SCBAE	Inh Abs Ing Con	Irrit eyes, skin, resp sys; derm; cyan; cough, wheez, dysp, pulm edema, pneuitis; head, dizz, CNS depres; nau, vomit; kidney, liver, spleen damage	Eye: Irr immed Skin: Soap wash immed Breath: Resp support Swallow: Medical attention immed	Eyes, skin, resp sys, CNS, kidneys, liver, spleen
[Benzenethiol]					
Skin: Prevent skin contact Eyes: Prevent eye contact Wash skin: When contam/Daily Remove: When wet or contam Change: Daily Provide: Eyewash, Quick drench	NIOSH ¥: SCBAF:PD,PP/SAF:PD,PP:ASCBA Escape: HiEF/SCBAE	Inh Abs Ing Con	Hema; secondary anemia from hemolysis; acute cystitis; acute liver disorders; derm; painful, irreg urination; [carc]	Eye: Irr immed Skin: Soap wash immed Breath: Resp support Swallow: Medical attention immed	Bladder, skin, kidneys, liver, blood [liver, kidney & bladder cancer]
[Benzidine]					
Skin: Prevent skin contact Eyes: Prevent eye contact Wash skin: When contam Remove: When wet or contam Change: Daily	NIOSH/OSHA 50 mg/m³: DMXSQ*/SA* 125 mg/m³: SA:CF*/PAPRDM* 250 mg/m³: HiEF/PAPRTHiE*/SCBAF/SAF 1500 mg/m³: SAF:PD,PP §: SCBAF:PD,PP/SAF:PD,PP:ASCBA Escape: HiEF/SCBAE	Inh Ing Con	Irrit eyes, skin, muc memb; sens derm	Eye: Irr immed Skin: Soap wash prompt Breath: Resp support Swallow: Medical attention immed	Eyes, skin, resp sys
[Benzoyl peroxide]					

27

Chemical name, structure/formula, CAS and RTECS Nos., and DOT ID and guide Nos.	Synonyms, trade names, and conversion factors	Exposure limits (TWA unless noted otherwise)	IDLH	Physical description	Chemical and physical properties		Incompatibilities and reactivities	Measurement method (See Table 1)
					MW, BP, SOL FI.P, IP, Sp, Gr, flammability	VP, FRZ UEL, LEL		
Benzyl chloride $C_6H_5CH_2Cl$ 100-44-7 XS8925000 1738 156	Chloromethylbenzene, α-Chlorotoluene 1 ppm = 5.18 mg/m³	NIOSH C 1 ppm (5 mg/m³) [15-min] OSHA 1 ppm (5 mg/m³)	10 ppm	Colorless to slightly yellow liquid with a pungent, aromatic odor.	MW: 126.6 BP: 354°F Sol: 0.05% FI.P: 153°F IP: ? Sp.Gr: 1.10 Class IIIA Combustible Liquid	VP: 1 mm FRZ: -38°F UEL: ? LEL: 1.1%	Oxidizers, acids, copper, aluminum, magnesium, iron, zinc, tin [Note: Can polymerize when in contact with all common metals except nickel & lead. Hydrolyzes in H_2O to benzyl alcohol.]	Char; CS_2; GC/FID; IV [#1003, Halogenated Hydrocarbons]
Beryllium & beryllium compounds (as Be) Be (Metal) 7440-41-7 (Metal) DS1750000 (Metal) 1566 154 (compounds) 1567 134 (powder)	Beryllium metal: Beryllium Other synonyms vary depending upon the specific beryllium compound.	NIOSH Ca Not to exceed 0.0005 mg/m³ See Appendix A OSHA 0.002 mg/m³ C 0.005 mg/m³ 0.025 mg/m³ [30-min maximum peak]	Ca [4 mg/m³ (as Be)]	Metal: A hard, brittle, gray-white solid.	MW: 9.0 BP: 4532°F Sol: Insoluble FI.P: NA IP: NA Sp.Gr: 1.85 (Metal) Metal: Noncombustible Solid in bulk form, but a slight explosion hazard in the form of a powder or dust.	VP: 0 mm (approx) MLT: 2349°F UEL: NA LEL: NA	Acids, caustics, chlorinated hydrocarbons, oxidizers, molten lithium	Filter; Acid; GFAAS; IV [#7102] [Also #7300, Elements]
Bismuth telluride, doped with Selenium sulfide (as Bi_2Te_3)	Doped bismuth sesquitelluride, Doped bismuth telluride, Doped bismuth tritelluride, Doped tellurobismuthite [Note: Doped with selenium sulfide. Commercial mix may contain 80% Bi_2Te_3, 20% stannous telluride, plus some tellurium.]	NIOSH 5 mg/m³ OSHA† none	N.D.	Gray, crystalline solid that has been enhanced (doped) with a small amount of selenium sulfide (SeS). [Note: Doping alters the conductivity of a semiconductor.]	Properties are unavailable but should be similar to Bismuth telluride, undoped. Sp.Gr: ? Noncombustible Solid		Strong oxidizers, moisture	Filter; none; Grav; IV [#0500, Particulates NOR (total)]
Bismuth telluride, undoped Bi_2Te_3 1304-82-1 EB3110000	Bismuth sesquitelluride, Bismuth telluride, Bismuth tritelluride, Tellurobismuthite	NIOSH 10 mg/m³ (total) 5 mg/m³ (resp) OSHA 15 mg/m³ (total) 5 mg/m³ (resp)	N.D.	Gray, crystalline solid.	MW: 800.8 BP: ? Sol: Insoluble FI.P: NA IP: NA Sp.Gr: 7.7 Noncombustible Solid	VP: 0 mm (approx) MLT: 1063°F UEL: NA LEL: NA	Strong oxidizers (e.g., bromine, chlorine, or fluorine), moisture, nitric acid (decomposes)	Filter; none; Grav; IV [Particulates NOR: #0500 (total), #0600 (resp)]

Personal protection and sanitation (See Table 3)		Recommendations for respirator selection — maximum concentration for use (MUC) (See Table 4)	Health hazards				
			Route	Symptoms (See Table 5)	First aid (See Table 6)		Target organs (See Table 5)
Skin:	Prevent skin contact	NIOSH/OSHA	Inh	Irrit eyes, skin, nose;	Eye:	Irr immed	Eyes, skin, resp sys,
Eyes:	Prevent eye contact	10 ppm: CCROVAG*/GMFOVAG/	Ing	weak; irrity; head; skin	Skin:	Soap wash immed	CNS
Wash skin:	When contam	PAPROVAG*/SA*/SCBAF	Con	eruption; pulm edema	Breath:	Resp support	
Remove:	When wet or contam	§: SCBAF:PD,PP/SAF:PD,PP:ASCBA			Swallow:	Medical attention	
Change:	N.R.	Escape: GMFOVAG/SCBAE				immed	
Provide:	Eyewash, Quick drench						

[Benzyl chloride]

Personal protection							
Skin:	Prevent skin contact	NIOSH	Inh	Berylliosis (chronic	Eye:	Irr immed	Eyes, skin, resp sys
Eyes:	Prevent eye contact	¥: SCBAF:PD,PP/SAF:PD,PP:ASCBA	Con	exposure): anor, low-wgt,	Breath:	Fresh air	[lung cancer]
Wash skin:	Daily	Escape: HiEF/SCBAE		weak, chest pain, cough,			
Remove:	When wet or contam			clubbing of fingers, cyan,			
Change:	Daily			pulm insufficiency; irrit			
Provide:	Eyewash			eyes; derm; [carc]			

[Beryllium & beryllium compounds (as Be)]

Skin:	Prevent skin contact	TBAL	Inh	Irrit eyes, skin, upper	Eye:	Irr immed	Eyes, skin, resp sys
Eyes:	Prevent eye contact		Con	resp sys; garlic breath;	Skin:	Soap wash immed	
Wash skin:	When contam			in animals: pulm lesions	Breath:	Resp support	
Remove:	When wet or contam			(nonfibrotic)	Swallow:	Medical attention	
Change:	N.R.					immed	
Provide:	Eyewash, Quick drench						

[Bismuth telluride, doped with Selenium sulfide (as Bi_2Te_3)]

Skin:	Prevent skin contact	TBAL	Inh	Irrit eyes, skin, upper	Eye:	Irr immed	Eyes, skin, resp sys
Eyes:	Prevent eye contact		Con	resp sys; garlic breath	Skin:	Soap wash immed	
Wash skin:	When contam				Breath:	Resp support	
Remove:	When wet or contam				Swallow:	Medical attention	
Change:	N.R.					immed	
Provide:	Eyewash, Quick drench						

[Bismuth telluride, undoped]

Chemical name, structure/formula, CAS and RTECS Nos., and DOT ID and guide Nos.	Synonyms, trade names, and conversion factors	Exposure limits (TWA unless noted otherwise)	IDLH	Physical description	Chemical and physical properties		Incompatibilities and reactivities	Measurement method (See Table 1)
					MW, BP, SOL FL.P, IP, Sp, Gr, flammability	VP, FRZ UEL, LEL		
Borates, tetra, sodium salts (Anhydrous) Na₂B₄O₇ 1330-43-4 ED4588000	Anhydrous borax, Borax dehydrated, Disodium salt of boric acid, Disodium tetrabromate, Fused borax, Sodium borate (anhydrous), Sodium tetraborate	NIOSH 1 mg/m³ OSHA† none	N.D.	White to gray, odorless powder. [herbicide] [Note: Becomes opaque on exposure to air.]	MW: 201.2 BP: 2867°F (Decomposes) Sol: 3% FL.P: NA IP: NA Sp.Gr: 2.37 Noncombustible Solid	VP: 0 mm (approx) MLT: 1366°F UEL: NA LEL: NA	Moisture [Note: Forms partial hydrate in moist air.]	Filter; none; Grav; IV [#0500, Particulates NOR (total)]
Borates, tetra, sodium salts (Decahydrate) Na₂B₄O₇·10H₂O 1303-96-4 VZ2275000	Borax, Borax decahydrate, Sodium borate decahydrate, Sodium tetraborate decahydrate	NIOSH 5 mg/m³ OSHA† none	N.D.	White, odorless, crystalline solid. [herbicide] [Note: Becomes anhydrous at 608°F.]	MW: 381.4 BP: 608°F Sol: 6% FL.P: NA IP: NA Sp.Gr: 1.73 Noncombustible Solid (an inherent fire retardant).	VP: 0 mm (approx) MLT: 167°F UEL: NA LEL: NA	Zirconium, strong acids, metallic salts	Filter; none; Grav; IV [#0500, Particulates NOR (total)]
Borates, tetra, sodium salts (Pentahydrate) Na₂B₄O₇·5H₂O 12179-04-3	Borax pentahydrate, Sodium borate pentahydrate, Sodium tetraborate pentahydrate	NIOSH 1 mg/m³ OSHA† none	N.D.	Colorless or white, odorless crystals or free-flowing powder. [herbicide] [Note: Begins to lose water of hydration at 252°F.]	MW: 291.4 BP: ? Sol: 4% FL.P: NA IP: NA Sp.Gr: 1.82 Noncombustible Solid	VP: 0 mm (approx) MLT: 392°F UEL: NA LEL: NA	None reported [Note: However, see the reactivities & incompatibilities reported for the related substance Borax decahydrate above.]	Filter; none; Grav; IV [#0500, Particulates NOR (total)]
Boron oxide B₂O₃ 1303-86-2 ED7900000	Boric anhydride, Boric oxide, Boron trioxide	NIOSH 10 mg/m³ OSHA† 15 mg/m³	2000 mg/m³	Colorless, semi-transparent lumps or hard, white, odorless crystals.	MW: 69.6 BP: 3380°F Sol: 3% FL.P: NA IP: 13.50 eV Sp.Gr: 2.46 Noncombustible Solid	VP: 0 mm (approx) MLT: 842°F UEL: NA LEL: NA	Water [Note: Reacts slowly with water to form boric acid.]	Filter; none; Grav; IV [#0500, Particulates NOR (total)]

Personal protection and sanitation (See Table 3)		Recommendations for respirator selection — maximum concentration for use (MUC) (See Table 4)	Health hazards				
			Route	Symptoms (See Table 5)	First aid (See Table 6)		Target organs (See Table 5)
Skin:	N.R.	TBAL	Inh	Irrit eyes, skin, upper	Eye:	Irr immed	Eyes, skin, resp sys
Eyes:	N.R.		Ing	resp sys; derm; epis;	Skin:	Soap wash	
Wash skin:	Daily		Con	cough, dysp	Breath:	Resp support	
Remove:	N.R.				Swallow:	Medical attention	
Change:	Daily					immed	

[Borates, tetra sodium salts (Anhydrous)]

Skin:	N.R.	TBAL	Inh	Irrit eyes, skin, upper	Eye:	Irr immed	Eyes, skin, resp sys
Eyes:	N.R.		Ing	resp sys; derm; epis;	Skin:	Soap wash	
Wash skin:	Daily		Con	cough, dysp	Breath:	Resp support	
Remove:	N.R.				Swallow:	Medical attention	
Change:	Daily					immed	

[Borates, tetra sodium salts (Decahydrate)]

Skin:	N.R.	TBAL	Inh	Irrit eyes, skin, upper	Eye:	Irr immed	Eyes, skin, resp sys
Eyes:	N.R.		Ing	resp sys; derm; epis;	Skin:	Soap wash	
Wash skin:	Daily		Con	cough, dysp	Breath:	Resp support	
Remove:	N.R.				Swallow:	Medical attention	
Change:	Daily					immed	

[Borates, tetra sodium salts (Pentahydrate)]

Skin:	Prevent skin contact	NIOSH	Inh	Irrit eyes, skin, resp sys;	Eye:	Irr immed	Eyes, skin, resp sys
Eyes:	Prevent eye contact	50 mg/m³: DM*	Ing	cough; conj; skin eryt	Skin:	Water flush prompt	
Wash skin:	When contam	100 mg/m³: DMXSQ^*/SA*	Con		Breath:	Fresh air	
Remove:	When wet or contam	250 mg/m³: SA:CF*/PAPRDM^*			Swallow:	Medical attention	
Change:	N.R.	500 mg/m³: HiEF/PAPRTHiE*/SCBAF/				immed	
		SAF					
		2000 mg/m³: SAF:PD,PP					
		§: SCBAF:PD,PP/SAF:PD,PP:ASCBA					
		Escape: HiEF/SCBAE					

[Boron oxide]

Chemical name, structure/formula, CAS and RTECS Nos., and DOT ID and guide Nos.	Synonyms, trade names, and conversion factors	Exposure limits (TWA unless noted otherwise)	IDLH	Physical description	Chemical and physical properties		Incompatibilities and reactivities	Measurement method (See Table 1)
					MW, BP, SOL Fl.P, IP, Sp, Gr, flammability	VP, FRZ UEL, LEL		
Boron tribromide BBr$_3$ 10294-33-4 ED7400000 2692 157	Boron bromide, Tribromoborane 1 ppm = 10.25 mg/m^3	NIOSH C 1 ppm (10 mg/m^3) OSHA† none	N.D.	Colorless, fuming liquid with a sharp, irritating odor.	MW: 250.5 BP: 194°F Sol: Decomposes Fl.P: NA IP: 9.70 eV Sp.Gr(65°F): 2.64 Noncombustible Liquid	VP(57°F): 40 mm FRZ:-51°F UEL: NA LEL: NA	Moisture, water, heat, potassium, sodium, alcohols [Note: Attacks metals, wood & rubber. Reacts with water to form boric acid and hydrogen bromide.]	None available
Boron trifluoride BF$_3$ 7637-07-2 ED2275000 1008 125	Boron fluoride, Trifluoroborane 1 ppm = 2.77 mg/m^3	NIOSH/OSHA C 1 ppm (3 mg/m^3)	25 ppm	Colorless gas with a pungent, suffocating odor. [Note: Forms dense white fumes in moist air. Shipped as a nonliquefied compressed gas.]	MW: 67.8 BP: -148°F Sol: 106% (in cold H$_2$O) Fl.P: NA IP: 15.50 eV RGasD: 2.38 Nonflammable Gas	VP: >50 atm FRZ: -196°F UEL: NA LEL: NA	Alkali metals, calcium oxide [Note: Hydrolyzes in moist air or hot water to form boric acid, hydrogen fluoride & fluoboric acid.]	None available
Bromacil C$_9$H$_{13}$BrN$_2$O$_2$ 314-40-9 YQ9100000	5-Bromo-3-sec-butyl-6-methyluracil, 5-Bromo-6-methyl-3-(1-methylpropyl)uracil 1 ppm = 10.68 mg/m^3	NIOSH 1 ppm (10 mg/m^3) OSHA† none	N.D.	Odorless, colorless to white, crystalline solid. [herbicide] [Note: Commercially available as a wettable powder or in liquid formulations.]	MW: 261.2 BP: Sublimes Sol(77°F): 0.08% Fl.P: NA IP: ? Sp.Gr: 1.55 Noncombustible Solid, but may be dissolved in flammable liquids.	VP(212°F): 0.0008 mm MLT: 317°F (Sublimes) UEL: NA LEL: NA	Strong acids (decomposes slowly), oxidizers, heat, sparks, open flames	Filter; none; Grav; IV [#0500, Particulates NOR (total)]
Bromine Br$_2$ 7726-95-6 EF9100000 1744 154	Molecular bromine 1 ppm = 6.54 mg/m^3	NIOSH 0.1 ppm (0.7 mg/m^3) ST 0.3 ppm (2 mg/m^3) OSHA† 0.1 ppm (0.7 mg/m^3)	3 ppm	Dark reddish-brown, fuming liquid with suffocating, irritating fumes.	MW: 159.8 BP: 139°F Sol: 4% Fl.P: NA IP: 10.55 eV Sp.Gr: 3.12 Noncombustible Liquid, but accelerates the burning of combustibles.	VP: 172 mm FRZ: 19°F UEL: NA LEL: NA	Combustible organics (sawdust, wood, cotton, straw, etc.), aluminum, readily oxidizable materials, ammonia, hydrogen, acetylene, phosphorus, potassium, sodium [Note: Corrodes iron, steel, stainless steel & copper.]	Filter; Na$_2$S$_2$O$_3$; IC; IV [#6011]

Personal protection and sanitation (See Table 3)		Recommendations for respirator selection — maximum concentration for use (MUC) (See Table 4)	Health hazards				
			Route	Symptoms (See Table 5)	First aid (See Table 6)		Target organs (See Table 5)
Skin:	Prevent skin contact	TBAL	Inh	Irrit eyes, skin, resp sys;	Eye:	Irr immed	Eyes, skin, resp sys
Eyes:	Prevent eye contact		Ing	skin, eye burns; dysp,	Skin:	Water flush immed	
Wash skin:	When contam		Con	pulm edema	Breath:	Resp support	
Remove:	When wet or contam				Swallow:	Medical attention	
Change:	N.R.					immed	
Provide:	Eyewash, Quick drench						

[Boron tribromide]

Skin:	N.R.	NIOSH/OSHA	Inh	Irrit eyes, skin, nose,	Eye:	Irr immed	Eyes, skin, resp sys,
Eyes:	N.R.	10 ppm: SA*	Con	resp sys; epis; eye, skin	Skin:	Water flush immed	kidneys
Wash skin:	N.R.	25 ppm: SA:CF*/SCBAF/SAF		burns;	Breath:	Resp support	
Remove:	N.R.	§: SCBAF:PD,PP/SAF:PD,PP:ASCBA		in animals: pneu; kidney			
Change:	N.R.	Escape: GMFS/SCBAE		damage			

[Boron trifluoride]

33

Skin:	Prevent skin contact	TBAL	Inh	Irrit eyes, skin, upper	Eye:	Irr immed	Eyes, skin, resp sys,
Eyes:	Prevent eye contact		Ing	resp sys;	Skin:	Soap wash immed	thyroid
Wash skin:	When contam		Con	in animals: thyroid inj	Breath:	Resp support	
Remove:	When wet or contam				Swallow:	Medical attention	
Change:	Daily					immed	
Provide:	Eyewash, Quick drench						

[Bromacil]

Skin:	Prevent skin contact	NIOSH/OSHA	Inh	Dizz, head; lac, epis;	Eye:	Irr immed	Resp sys, eyes,
Eyes:	Prevent eye contact	2.5 ppm: SA:CF£/PAPRS⊄£	Ing	cough, feeling of	Skin:	Soap wash immed	CNS, skin
Wash skin:	When contam	3 ppm: CCRFS⊄/GMFS⊄/PAPRTS⊄£/	Con	oppression, pulm edema,	Breath:	Resp support	
Remove:	When wet or contam	SCBAF/SAF		pneu; abdom pain, diarr;	Swallow:	Medical attention	
Change:	N.R.	§: SCBAF:PD,PP/SAF:PD,PP:ASCBA		measle-like eruptions;		immed	
Provide:	Eyewash, Quick drench	Escape: GMFS⊄/SCBAE		eye, skin burns			

[Bromine]

Chemical name, structure/formula, CAS and RTECS Nos., and DOT ID and guide Nos.	Synonyms, trade names, and conversion factors	Exposure limits (TWA unless noted otherwise)	IDLH	Physical description	Chemical and physical properties		Incompatibilities and reactivities	Measurement method (See Table 1)
					MW, BP, SOL FI.P, IP, Sp, Gr, flammability	VP, FRZ UEL, LEL		
Bromine pentafluoride BrF_5 7789-30-2 EF9350000 1745 144	Bromine fluoride	NIOSH 0.1 ppm (0.7 mg/m³) OSHA† none	N.D.	Colorless to pale-yellow, fuming liquid with a pungent odor. [Note: A colorless gas above 105°F. Shipped as a compressed gas.]	MW: 174.9 BP: 105°F Sol: Reacts violently FI.P: NA IP: ? Sp.Gr: 2.48	VP: 328 mm FRZ: -77°F UEL: NA LEL: NA	Acids, halogens, arsenic, selenium, sulfur, glass, organic materials, water [Note: Reacts with all elements except inert gases, nitrogen & oxygen.]	None available
	1 ppm = 7.15 mg/m³				Noncombustible Liquid, but a very powerful oxidizer.			
Bromoform $CHBr_3$ 75-25-2 PB5600000 2515 159	Methyl tribromide, Tribromomethane	NIOSH/OSHA 0.5 ppm (5 mg/m³) [skin]	850 ppm	Colorless to yellow liquid with a chloroform-like odor. [Note: A solid below 47°F.]	MW: 252.8 BP: 301°F Sol: 0.1% FI.P: NA IP: 10.48 eV Sp.Gr: 2.89	VP: 5 mm FRZ: 47°F UEL: NA LEL: NA	Lithium, sodium, potassium, calcium, aluminum, zinc, magnesium, strong caustics, acetone [Note: Gradually decomposes, acquiring yellow color; air & light accelerate decomposition.]	Char; CS_2; GC/FID; IV [#1003, Halogenated Hydrocarbons]
	1 ppm = 10.34 mg/m³				Noncombustible Liquid			
1,3-Butadiene $CH_2=CHCH=CH_2$ 106-99-0 EI9275000 1010 116P (inhibited)	Biethylene, Bivinyl, Butadiene, Divinyl, Erythrene, Vinylethylene	NIOSH Ca See Appendix A OSHA[1910.1051] 1 ppm ST 5 ppm	Ca [2000 ppm] [10%LEL]	Colorless gas with a mild aromatic or gasoline-like odor. [Note: A liquid below 24°F. Shipped as a liquefied compressed gas.]	MW: 54.1 BP: 24°F Sol: Insoluble FI.P: NA (Gas) -105°F (Liq) IP: 9.07 eV RGasD: 1.88 Sp.Gr: 0.65 (Liquid at 21°F) Flammable Gas Class IA Flammable Liquid	VP: 2.4 atm FRZ: -164°F UEL: 12.0% LEL: 2.0%	Phenol, chlorine dioxide, copper, crotonaldehyde [Note: May contain inhibitors (such as tributylcatechol) to prevent self-polymerization. May form explosive peroxides upon exposure to air.]	Char(2); CH_2Cl_2; GC/FID; IV [#1024]
	1 ppm = 2.21 mg/m³							
n-Butane $CH_3CH_2CH_2CH_3$ 106-97-8 EJ4200000 1011 115 1075 115	normal-Butane, Butyl hydride, Diethyl, Methylethylmethane [Note: Also see specific listing for Isobutane.]	NIOSH 800 ppm (1900 mg/m³) OSHA† none	N.D.	Colorless gas with a gasoline-like or natural gas odor. [Note: Shipped as a liquefied compressed gas. A liquid below 31°F.]	MW: 58.1 BP: 31°F Sol: Slight FI.P: NA IP: 10.63 eV RGasD: 2.11 Sp.Gr: 0.6 (Liquid at 31°F) Flammable Gas Class IA Flammable Liquid	VP: 2.05 atm FRZ: -217°F UEL: 8.4% LEL: 1.6%	Strong oxidizers (e.g., nitrates & perchlorates), chlorine, fluorine, (nickel carbonyl + oxygen)	None available
	1 ppm = 2.38 mg/m³							

Personal protection and sanitation (See Table 3)	Recommendations for respirator selection — maximum concentration for use (MUC) (See Table 4)	Route	Symptoms (See Table 5)	First aid (See Table 6)	Target organs (See Table 5)
Skin: Prevent skin contact Eyes: Prevent eye contact Wash skin: When contam Remove: When wet or contam Change: N.R. Provide: Eyewash, Quick drench	TBAL	Inh Ing Con	Irrit eyes, skin, resp sys; corn nec; skin burns; cough, dysp, pulm edema; liver, kidney inj	Eye: Irr immed Skin: Water flush immed Breath: Resp support Swallow: Medical attention immed	Eyes, skin, resp sys, liver, kidneys
[Bromine pentafluoride]					
Skin: Prevent skin contact Eyes: Prevent eye contact Wash skin: When contam Remove: When wet or contam Change: N.R.	NIOSH/OSHA 12.5 ppm: SA:CF£/PAPROV£ 25 ppm: CCRFOV/GMFOV/PAPRTOV£/ SCBAF/SAF 850 ppm: SAF:PD,PP §: SCBAF:PD,PP/SAF:PD,PP:ASCBA Escape: GMFOV/SCBAE	Inh Abs Ing Con	Irrit eyes, skin, resp sys; CNS depres; liver, kidney damage	Eye: Irr immed Skin: Soap wash prompt Breath: Resp support Swallow: Medical attention immed	Eyes, skin, resp sys, CNS, liver, kidneys
[Bromoform]					
Skin: Frostbite Eyes: Frostbite Wash skin: N.R. Remove: When wet (flamm) Change: N.R. Provide: Frostbite	NIOSH ¥: SCBAF:PD,PP/SAF:PD,PP:ASCBA Escape: GMFS/SCBAE	Inh Con (liq)	Irrit eyes, nose, throat; drow, li-head; liq: frostbite; terato, repro effects; [carc]	Eye: Frostbite Skin: Frostbite Breath: Resp support	Eyes, resp sys, CNS, repro sys [hemato cancer]
[1,3-Butadiene]					
Skin: Frostbite Eyes: Frostbite Wash skin: N.R. Remove: When wet (flamm) Change: N.R. Provide: Frostbite	TBAL	Inh Con (liq)	Drow, narco, asphy; liq: frostbite	Eye: Frostbite Skin: Frostbite Breath: Resp support	CNS
[n-Butane]					

Chemical name, structure/formula, CAS and RTECS Nos., and DOT ID and guide Nos.	Synonyms, trade names, and conversion factors	Exposure limits (TWA unless otherwise noted)	IDLH	Physical description	Chemical and physical properties		Incompatibilities and reactivities	Measurement method (See Table 1)
					MW, BP, SOL Fl.P, IP, Sp, Gr, flammability	VP, FRZ UEL, LEL		
2-Butanone $CH_3COCH_2CH_3$ 78-93-3 EL6475000 1193 127 1232 127	Ethyl methyl ketone, MEK, Methyl acetone, Methyl ethyl ketone 1 ppm = 2.95 mg/m³	NIOSH 200 ppm (590 mg/m³) ST 300 ppm (885 mg/m³) OSHA† 200 ppm (590 mg/m³)	3000 ppm	Colorless liquid with a moderately sharp, fragrant, mint- or acetone-like odor.	MW: 72.1 BP: 175°F Sol: 28% Fl.P: 16°F IP: 9.54 eV Sp.Gr: 0.81 Class IB Flammable Liquid	VP: 78 mm FRZ: -123°F UEL(200°F): 11.4% LEL(200°F): 1.4%	Strong oxidizers, amines, ammonia, inorganic acids, caustics, isocyanates, pyridines	Carbon beads; CS₂; GC/FID; IV [#2500]
2-Butoxyethanol $C_4H_9OCH_2CH_2OH$ 111-76-2 KJ8575000 2369 152	Butyl Cellosolve®, Butyl oxitol, Dowanol EB, EGBE, Ektasolve EB, Ethylene glycol monobutyl ether, Jeffersol EB 1 ppm = 4.83 mg/m³	NIOSH 5 ppm (24 mg/m³) [skin] OSHA† 50 ppm (240 mg/m³) [skin]	700 ppm	Colorless liquid with a mild, ether-like odor.	MW: 118.2 BP: 339°F Sol: Miscible Fl.P: 143°F IP: 10.00 eV Sp.Gr: 0.90 Class IIIA Combustible Liquid	VP: 0.8 mm FRZ: -107°F UEL(275°F): 12.7% LEL(200°F): 1.1%	Strong oxidizers, strong caustics	Char; Methanol/ CH₂Cl₂; GC/FID; IV [#1403, Alcohols IV]
2-Butoxyethanol acetate $C_4H_9O(CH_2)_2OCOCH_3$ 112-07-2 KJ8925000	2-Butoxyethyl acetate, Butyl Cellosolve® acetate, Butyl glycol acetate, EGBEA, Ektasolve EB® acetate, Ethylene glycol monobutyl ether acetate 1 ppm = 6.55 mg/m³	NIOSH 5 ppm (33 mg/m³) OSHA none	N.D.	Colorless liquid with a pleasant, sweet, fruity odor.	MW: 160.2 BP: 378°F Sol: 1.5% Fl.P: 71°F IP: ? Sp.Gr: 0.94 Class IB Flammable Liquid	VP: 0.3 mm FRZ: -82°F UEL(275°F): 0.88% LEL(200°F): 8.54%	Oxidizers	Char; CH₂Cl₂/ Methanol; GC/FID; OSHA [#83]
n-Butyl acetate $CH_3COO[CH_2]_3CH_3$ 123-86-4 AF7350000 1123 129	Butyl acetate, n-Butyl ester of acetic acid, Butyl ethanoate 1 ppm = 4.75 mg/m³	NIOSH 150 ppm (710 mg/m³) ST 200 ppm (950 mg/m³) OSHA† 150 ppm (710 mg/m³)	1700 ppm [10%LEL]	Colorless liquid with a fruity odor.	MW: 116.2 BP: 258°F Sol: 1% Fl.P: 72°F IP: 10.00 eV Sp.Gr: 0.88 Class IB Flammable Liquid	VP: 10 mm FRZ: -107°F UEL: 7.6% LEL: 1.7%	Nitrates; strong oxidizers, alkalis & acids	Char; CS₂; GC/FID; IV [#1450, Esters I]

Personal protection and sanitation (See Table 3)		Recommendations for respirator selection — maximum concentration for use (MUC) (See Table 4)	Health hazards			
			Route	Symptoms (See Table 5)	First aid (See Table 6)	Target organs (See Table 5)
Skin:	Prevent skin contact	NIOSH/OSHA	Inh	Irrit eyes, skin, nose;	Eye: Irr immed	Eyes, skin, resp sys,
Eyes:	Prevent eye contact	3000 ppm: SA:CF$^{£}$/PAPROV$^{£}$/	Ing	head, dizz; vomit; derm	Skin: Water wash immed	CNS
Wash skin:	When contam	CCRFOV/GMFOV/SCBAF/	Con		Breath: Fresh air	
Remove:	When wet (flamm)	SAF			Swallow: Medical attention	
Change:	N.R.	§: SCBAF:PD,PP/SAF:PD,PP:ASCBA			immed	
Provide:	Eyewash	Escape: GMFOV/SCBAE				

[2-Butanone]

Skin:	Prevent skin contact	NIOSH	Inh	Irrit eyes, skin, nose,	Eye: Irr immed	Eyes, skin, resp sys,
Eyes:	Prevent eye contact	50 ppm: CCROV*/SA*	Abs	throat; hemolysis, hemog;	Skin: Soap wash prompt	CNS, hemato sys,
Wash skin:	When contam	125 ppm: SA:CF*/PAPROV*	Ing	CNS depres, head; vomit	Breath: Resp support	blood, kidneys,
Remove:	When wet or contam	250 ppm: CCRFOV/GMFOV/PAPRTOV*/	Con		Swallow: Medical attention	liver, lymphoid sys
Change:	N.R.	SCBAF/SAF			immed	
Provide:	Quick drench	700 ppm: SAF:PD,PP				
		§: SCBAF:PD,PP/SAF:PD,PP:ASCBA				
		Escape: GMFOV/SCBAE				

[2-Butoxyethanol]

Skin:	Prevent skin contact	NIOSH	Inh	Irrit eyes, skin, nose,	Eye: Irr immed	Eyes, skin, resp sys,
Eyes:	Prevent eye contact	50 ppm: CCROV*/SA*	Abs	throat; hemolysis, hemog;	Skin: Soap wash prompt	CNS, hemato sys,
Wash skin:	When contam	125 ppm: SA:CF*/PAPROV*	Ing	CNS depres, head; vomit	Breath: Resp support	blood, kidneys,
Remove:	When wet (flamm)	250 ppm: CCRFOV/GMFOV/PAPRTOV*/	Con		Swallow: Medical attention	liver, lymphoid sys
Change:	N.R.	SCBAF/SAF			immed	
		700 ppm: SAF:PD,PP				
		§: SCBAF:PD,PP/SAF:PD,PP:ASCBA				
		Escape: GMFOV/SCBAE				

[2-Butoxyethanol acetate]

Skin:	Prevent skin contact	NIOSH/OSHA	Inh	Irrit eyes, skin, upper	Eye: Irr immed	Eyes, skin, resp sys,
Eyes:	Prevent eye contact	1500 ppm: CCROV*/SA*	Ing	resp sys; head, drow,	Skin: Water flush prompt	CNS
Wash skin:	When contam	1700 ppm: SA:CF*/PAPROV*/CCRFOV/	Con	narco	Breath: Resp support	
Remove:	When wet (flamm)	GMFOV/SCBAF/SAF			Swallow: Medical attention	
Change:	N.R.	§: SCBAF:PD,PP/SAF:PD,PP:ASCBA			immed	
		Escape: GMFOV/SCBAE				

[n-Butyl acetate]

Chemical name, structure/formula, CAS and RTECS Nos., and DOT ID and guide Nos.	Synonyms, trade names, and conversion factors	Exposure limits (TWA unless noted otherwise)	IDLH	Physical description	Chemical and physical properties		Incompatibilities and reactivities	Measurement method (See Table 1)
					MW, BP, SOL Fl.P, IP, Sp, Gr, flammability	VP, FRZ UEL, LEL		
sec-Butyl acetate $CH_3COOCH(CH_3)CH_2CH_3$ 105-46-4 AF7380000 1123 129	sec-Butyl ester of acetic acid, 1-Methylpropyl acetate 1 ppm = 4.75 mg/m³	NIOSH/OSHA 200 ppm (950 mg/m³)	1700 ppm [10%LEL]	Colorless liquid with a pleasant, fruity odor.	MW: 116.2 BP: 234°F Sol: 0.8% Fl.P: 62°F IP: 9.91 eV Sp.Gr: 0.86 Class IB Flammable Liquid	VP: 10 mm FRZ: -100°F UEL: 9.8% LEL: 1.7%	Nitrates; strong oxidizers, alkalis & acids	Char; CS₂; GC/FID; IV [#1450, Esters I]
tert-Butyl acetate $CH_3COOC(CH_3)_3$ 540-88-5 AF7400000 1123 129	tert-Butyl ester of acetic acid 1 ppm = 4.75 mg/m³	NIOSH/OSHA 200 ppm (950 mg/m³)	1500 ppm [10%LEL]	Colorless liquid with a fruity odor.	MW: 116.2 BP: 208°F Sol: Insoluble Fl.P: 72°F IP: ? Sp.Gr: 0.87 Class IB Flammable Liquid	VP: ? FRZ: ? UEL: ? LEL: 1.5%	Nitrates; strong oxidizers, alkalis & acids	Char; CS₂; GC/FID; IV [#1450, Esters I]
Butyl acrylate $CH_2=CHCOOC_4H_9$ 141-32-2 UD3150000 2348 129P	n-Butyl acrylate, Butyl ester of acrylic acid, Butyl 2-propenoate 1 ppm = 5.24 mg/m³	NIOSH 10 ppm (55 mg/m³) OSHA† none	N.D.	Clear, colorless liquid with a strong, fruity odor. [Note: Highly reactive; may contain an inhibitor to prevent spontaneous polymerization.]	MW: 128.2 BP: 293°F Sol: 0.1% Fl.P: 103°F IP: ? Sp.Gr: 0.89 Class II Combustible Liquid	VP: 4 mm FRZ: -83°F UEL: 9.9% LEL: 1.5%	Strong acids & alkalis, amines, halogens, hydrogen compounds, oxidizers, heat, flame, sunlight [Note: Polymerizes readily on heating.]	None available
n-Butyl alcohol $CH_3CH_2CH_2CH_2OH$ 71-36-3 EO1400000 1120 129	1-Butanol, n-Butanol, Butyl alcohol, 1-Hydroxybutane, n-Propyl carbinol 1 ppm = 3.03 mg/m³	NIOSH C 50 ppm (150 mg/m³) [skin] OSHA† 100 ppm (300 mg/m³)	1400 ppm [10%LEL]	Colorless liquid with a strong, characteristic, mildly alcoholic odor.	MW: 74.1 BP: 243°F Sol: 9% Fl.P: 84°F IP: 10.04 eV Sp.Gr: 0.81 Class IC Flammable Liquid	VP: 6 mm FRZ: -129°F UEL: 11.2% LEL: 1.4%	Strong oxidizers, strong mineral acids, alkali metals, halogens	Char; 2-Propanol/ CS₂; GC/FID; IV [#1401, Alcohols II]

Personal protection and sanitation (See Table 3)		Recommendations for respirator selection — maximum concentration for use (MUC) (See Table 4)	Health hazards					
			Route	Symptoms (See Table 5)		First aid (See Table 6)		Target organs (See Table 5)
Skin:	Prevent skin contact	NIOSH/OSHA	Inh	Irrit eyes; head; drow;	Eye:	Irr immed	Eyes, skin, resp
Eyes:	Prevent eye contact	1700 ppm: SA:CF$^£$/PAPROV$^£$/CCRFOV/	Ing	dryness upper resp sys,	Skin:	Water flush prompt	sys, CNS
Wash skin:	When contam	GMFOV/SCBAF/SAF	Con	skin; narco	Breath:	Resp support	
Remove:	When wet (flamm)	§: SCBAF:PD,PP/SAF:PD,PP:ASCBA			Swallow:	Medical attention	
Change:	N.R.	Escape: GMFOV/SCBAE				immed	

[sec-Butyl acetate]

Skin:	Prevent skin contact	NIOSH/OSHA	Inh	Itch, inflamm eyes; irrit	Eye:	Irr immed	Resp sys, eyes,
Eyes:	Prevent eye contact	1500 ppm: SA:CF$^£$/PAPROV$^£$/CCRFOV/	Ing	upper resp tract; head;	Skin:	Water flush prompt	skin, CNS
Wash skin:	When contam	GMFOV/SCBAF/SAF	Con	narco; derm	Breath:	Resp support	
Remove:	When wet (flamm)	§: SCBAF:PD,PP/SAF:PD,PP:ASCBA			Swallow:	Medical attention	
Change:	N.R.	Escape: GMFOV/SCBAE				immed	

[tert-Butyl acetate]

Skin:	Prevent skin contact	TBAL	Inh	Irrit eyes, skin, upper	Eye:	Irr immed	Eyes, skin, resp sys
Eyes:	Prevent eye contact		Abs	resp sys; sens derm; dysp	Skin:	Soap wash immed	
Wash skin:	When contam		Ing		Breath:	Resp support	
Remove:	When wet or contam		Con		Swallow:	Medical attention	
Change:	N.R.					immed	
Provide:	Eyewash, Quick drench						

[Butyl acrylate]

Skin:	Prevent skin contact	NIOSH	Inh	Irrit eyes, nose, throat;	Eye:	Irr immed	Eyes, skin, resp sys,
Eyes:	Prevent eye contact	1250 ppm: SA:CF$^£$/PAPROV$^£$	Abs	head, verti, drow;	Skin:	Water flush prompt	CNS
Wash skin:	When contam	1400 ppm: CCRFOV/GMFOV/PAPRTOV$^£$/	Ing	corn inflamm, blurred	Breath:	Resp support	
Remove:	When wet (flamm)	SCBAF/SAF	Con	vision, lac, photo; derm;	Swallow:	Medical attention	
Change:	N.R.	§: SCBAF:PD,PP/SAF:PD,PP:ASCBA		possible auditory nerve		immed	
		Escape: GMFOV/SCBAE		damage, hearing loss;			
				CNS depres			

[n-Butyl alcohol]

Chemical name, structure/formula, CAS and RTECS Nos., and DOT ID and guide Nos.	Synonyms, trade names, and conversion factors	Exposure limits (TWA unless noted otherwise)	IDLH	Physical description	Chemical and physical properties		Incompatibilities and reactivities	Measurement method (See Table 1)
					MW, BP, SOL FI.P, IP, Sp, Gr, flammability	VP, FRZ UEL, LEL		
sec-Butyl alcohol $CH_3CH(OH)CH_2CH_3$ 78-92-2 EO1750000 1120 129	2-Butanol, Butylene hydrate, 2-Hydroxybutane, Methyl ethyl carbinol 1 ppm = 3.03 mg/m³	NIOSH 100 ppm (305 mg/m³) ST 150 ppm (455 mg/m³) OSHA† 150 ppm (450 mg/m³)	2000 ppm	Colorless liquid with a strong, pleasant odor.	MW: 74.1 BP: 211°F Sol: 16% FI.P: 75°F IP: 10.10 eV Sp.Gr: 0.81 Class IC Flammable Liquid	VP: 12 mm FRZ: -175°F UEL(212°F): 9.8% LEL(212°F): 1.7%	Strong oxidizers, organic peroxides, perchloric & permono-sulfuric acids	Char; 2-Propanol/ CS₂; GC/FID; IV [#1401, Alcohols II]
tert-Butyl alcohol $(CH_3)_3COH$ 75-65-0 EO1925000 1120 129	2-Methyl-2-propanol, Trimethyl carbinol 1 ppm = 3.03 mg/m³	NIOSH 100 ppm (300 mg/m³) ST 150 ppm (450 mg/m³) OSHA† 100 ppm (300 mg/m³)	1600 ppm·	Colorless solid or liquid (above 78°F) with a camphor-like odor. [Note: Often used in aqueous solutions.]	MW: 74.1 BP: 180°F Sol: Miscible FI.P: 52°F IP: 9.70 eV Sp.Gr: 0.79 (Solid) Combustible Solid Class IB Flammable Liquid	VP(77°F): 42 mm FRZ: 78°F UEL: 8.0% LEL: 2.4%	Strong mineral acids, strong hydrochloric acid, oxidizers	Char; 2-Butanol/ CS₂; GC/FID; IV [#1400, Alcohols I]
n-Butylamine $CH_3CH_2CH_2CH_2NH_2$ 109-73-9 EO2975000 1125 132	1-Aminobutane, Butylamine 1 ppm = 2.99 mg/m³	NIOSH/OSHA C 5 ppm (15 mg/m³) [skin]	300 ppm	Colorless liquid with a fishy, ammonia-like odor.	MW: 73.2 BP: 172°F Sol: Miscible FI.P: 10°F IP: 8.71 eV Sp.Gr: 0.74 Class IB Flammable Liquid	VP: 82 mm FRZ: -58°F UEL: 9.8% LEL: 1.7%	Strong oxidizers, strong acids [Note: May corrode some metals in presence of water.]	Si gel*; Methanol; GC/FID; IV [#2012]
tert-Butyl chromate $[(CH_3)_3CO]_2CrO_2$ 1189-85-1 GB2900000	di-tert-Butyl ester of chromic acid	NIOSH Ca 0.001 mg Cr(VI)/m³ See Appendix A See Appendix C OSHA C 0.1 mg CrO₃/m³ [skin] See Appendix C	Ca [15 mg/m³ as Cr(VI)]	Liquid. [Note: Solidifies at 32-23°F.]	MW: 230.3 BP: ? Sol: ? FI.P: ? IP: ? Sp.Gr: ?	VP: ? FRZ: 32-23°F UEL: ? LEL: ?	Reducing agents, moisture, acids, alcohols, hydrazine, combustible materials	Filter; NaOH/Na₂CO₃; IC; IV [#7604, Hexavalent Chromium]

Personal protection and sanitation (See Table 3)		Recommendations for respirator selection — maximum concentration for use (MUC) (See Table 4)	Health hazards				
			Route	Symptoms (See Table 5)	First aid (See Table 6)		Target organs (See Table 5)
Skin:	Prevent skin contact	NIOSH	Inh	Irrit eyes, skin, nose, throat; narco	Eye:	Irr immed	Eyes, skin, resp sys, CNS
Eyes:	Prevent eye contact	1000 ppm: CCROV*/SA*	Ing		Skin:	Water flush prompt	
Wash skin:	When contam	2000 ppm: SA:CF*/PAPROV*/CCRFOV/	Con		Breath:	Resp support	
Remove:	When wet (flamm)	GMFOV/SCBAF/SAF			Swallow:	Medical attention	
Change:	N.R.	§: SCBAF:PD,PP,SAF:PD,PP:ASCBA				immed	
		Escape: GMFOV/SCBAE					

[sec-Butyl alcohol]

Skin:	Prevent skin contact	NIOSH/OSHA	Inh	Irrit eyes, skin, nose, throat; drow, narco	Eye:	Irr immed	Eyes, skin, resp sys, CNS
Eyes:	Prevent eye contact	1600 ppm: SA:CFᴱ/PAPROVᴱ/CCRFOV/	Ing		Skin:	Water flush prompt	
Wash skin:	When contam	GMFOV/SCBAF/SAF	Con		Breath:	Resp support	
Remove:	When wet (flamm)	§: SCBAF:PD,PP/SAF:PD,PP:ASCBA			Swallow:	Medical attention	
Change:	N.R.	Escape: GMFOV/SCBAE				immed	

41

[tert-Butyl alcohol]

Skin:	Prevent skin contact	NIOSH/OSHA	Inh	Irrit eyes, skin, nose, throat; head; skin flush, burns	Eye:	Irr immed	Eyes, skin, resp sys
Eyes:	Prevent eye contact	50 ppm: CCRS*/SA*	Abs		Skin:	Water flush immed	
Wash skin:	When contam	125 ppm: SA:CF*/PAPRS*	Ing		Breath:	Resp support	
Remove:	When wet (flamm)	250 ppm: CCRFS/GMFS/PAPRTS*/	Con		Swallow:	Medical attention	
Change:	N.R.	SCBAF/SAF				immed	
Provide:	Eyewash, Quick drench	300 ppm: SAF:PD,PP					
		§: SCBAF:PD,PP/SAF:PD,PP:ASCBA					
		Escape: GMFS/SCBAE					

[Butylamine]

Skin:	Prevent skin contact	NIOSH	Inh	Irrit eyes, skin, resp sys; eye, skin burns; drow, musc weak; skin ulcers; lung changes; [carc]	Eye:	Irr immed	Eyes, skin, resp sys, CNS [lung cancer]
Eyes:	Prevent eye contact	¥: SCBAF:PD,PP/SAF:PD,PP:ASCBA	Abs		Skin:	Soap wash immed	
Wash skin:	When contam/Daily	Escape: GMFOVHiE/SCBAE	Ing		Breath:	Resp support	
Remove:	When wet or contam		Con		Swallow:	Medical attention	
Change:	N.R.					immed	
Provide:	Eyewash, Quick drench						

[tert-Butyl chromate]

Chemical name, structure/formula, CAS and RTECS Nos., and DOT ID and guide Nos.	Synonyms, trade names, and conversion factors	Exposure limits (TWA unless noted otherwise)	IDLH	Physical description	Chemical and physical properties		Incompatibilities and reactivities	Measurement method (See Table 1)
					MW, BP, SOL Fl.P, IP, Sp, Gr, flammability	VP, FRZ UEL, LEL		
n-Butyl glycidyl ether $C_7H_{14}O_2$ 2426-08-6 TX4200000 1993 128 (combustible liquid, n.o.s.)	BGE; 1,2-Epoxy-3-butoxypropane 1 ppm = 5.33 mg/m³	NIOSH C 5.6 ppm (30 mg/m³) [15-min] OSHA† 50 ppm (270 mg/m³)	250 ppm	Colorless liquid with an irritating odor.	MW: 130.2 BP: 327°F Sol: 2% Fl.P: 130°F IP: ? Sp.Gr: 0.91 Class II Combustible Liquid	VP(77°F): 3 mm FRZ: ? UEL: ? LEL: ?	Strong oxidizers, strong caustics	Char; CS₂; GC/FID; IV [#1616]
n-Butyl lactate $CH_3CH(OH)COOC_4H_9$ 138-22-7 OD4025000 1993 128 (combustible liquid, n.o.s.)	Butyl ester of 2-hydroxy-propanoic acid, Butyl ester of lactic acid, Butyl lactate 1 ppm = 5.98 mg/m³	NIOSH 5 ppm (25 mg/m³) OSHA† none	N.D.	Clear, colorless to white liquid with a mild, transient odor.	MW: 146.2 BP: 370°F Sol: Slight Fl.P: 160°F IP: ? Sp.Gr: 0.98 Class IIIA Combustible Liquid	VP: 0.4 mm FRZ: -45°F UEL: ? LEL: 1.15%	Strong acids & bases, strong oxidizers, heat, sparks, open flames	None available
n-Butyl mercaptan $CH_3CH_2CH_2CH_2SH$ 109-79-5 EK6300000 2347 130	Butanethiol, 1-Butanethiol, n-Butanethiol, 1-Mercaptobutane 1 ppm = 3.69 mg/m³	NIOSH C 0.5 ppm (1.8 mg/m³) [15-min] OSHA† 10 ppm (35 mg/m³)	500 ppm	Colorless liquid with a strong, garlic-, cabbage-, or skunk-like odor.	MW: 90.2 BP: 209°F Sol: 0.06% Fl.P: 35°F IP: 9.15 eV Sp.Gr: 0.83 Class IB Flammable Liquid	VP: 35 mm FRZ: -176°F UEL: ? LEL: ?	Strong oxidizers (such as dry bleaches), acids	Filter*; HCl/DCE; GC/FPD (S mode); IV [#2542, Mercaptans] [Also #2525]
o-sec-Butylphenol $CH_3CH_2CH(CH_3)C_6H_4OH$ 89-72-5 SJ8920000 2228 153 (liquid) 2229 153 (solid)	2-sec-Butylphenol, 2-(1-Methylpropyl)phenol 1 ppm = 6.14 mg/m³	NIOSH 5 ppm (30 mg/m³) [skin] OSHA† none	N.D.	Colorless liquid or solid (below 61°F).	MW: 150.2 BP: 227°F Sol: Insoluble Fl.P: 225°F IP: ? Sp.Gr: 0.89 Class IIIB Combustible Liquid Combustible Solid	VP: Low FRZ: 61°F UEL: ? LEL: ?	None reported	None available

Personal protection and sanitation (See Table 3)	Recommendations for respirator selection — maximum concentration for use (MUC) (See Table 4)	Health hazards			
		Route	Symptoms (See Table 5)	First aid (See Table 6)	Target organs (See Table 5)
Skin: Prevent skin contact Eyes: Prevent eye contact Wash skin: When contam Remove: When wet or contam Change: N.R.	NIOSH 56 ppm: CCROV*/SA* 140 ppm: SA:CF*/PAPROV* 250 ppm: CCRFOV/GMFOV/PAPRTOV*/ SCBAF/SAF §: SCBAF:PD,PP/SAF:PD,PP:ASCBA Escape: GMFOV/SCBAE	Inh Ing Con	Irrit eyes, skin, nose; sens; narco; possible hemato effects; CNS depres	Eye: Irr immed Skin: Soap wash immed Breath: Resp support Swallow: Medical attention immed	Eyes, skin, resp sys, CNS, blood
[n-Butyl glycidyl ether]					
Skin: Prevent skin contact Eyes: Prevent eye contact Wash skin: When contam Remove: When wet or contam Change: N.R. Provide: Eyewash, Quick drench	TBAL	Inh Ing Con	Irrit eyes, skin, nose, throat; drow, head, CNS depres; nau, vomit	Eye: Irr immed Skin: Soap wash immed Breath: Resp support Swallow: Medical attention immed	Eyes, skin, resp sys, CNS
[n-Butyl lactate]					
Skin: Prevent skin contact Eyes: Prevent eye contact Wash skin: When contam Remove: When wet (flamm) Change: N.R.	NIOSH 5 ppm: CCROV/SA 12.5 ppm: SA:CF/PAPROV 25 ppm: CCRFOV/GMFOV/PAPRTOV/ SCBAF/SAF 500 ppm: SA:PD,PP* §: SCBAF:PD,PP/SAF:PD,PP:ASCBA Escape: GMFOV/SCBAE	Inh Ing Con	Irrit eyes, skin; musc weak, mal, sweat, nau, vomit, head, conf; in animals: narco, inco, weak; cyan; pulm irrit; liver, kidney damage	Eye: Irr immed Skin: Soap wash prompt Breath: Resp support Swallow: Medical attention immed	Eyes, skin, resp sys, CNS, liver, kidneys
[n-Butyl mercaptan]					
Skin: Prevent skin contact Eyes: Prevent eye contact Wash skin: When contam Remove: When wet or contam Change: N.R. Provide: Eyewash, Quick drench	TBAL	Inh Abs Ing Con	Irrit eyes, skin, resp sys; skin burns	Eye: Irr immed Skin: Soap flush immed Breath: Resp support Swallow: Medical attention immed	Eyes, skin, resp sys
[o-sec-Butylphenol]					

Chemical name, structure/formula, CAS and RTECS Nos., and DOT ID and guide Nos.	Synonyms, trade names, and conversion factors	Exposure limits (TWA unless noted otherwise)	IDLH	Physical description	Chemical and physical properties		Incompatibilities and reactivities	Measurement method (See Table 1)
					MW, BP, SOL Fl.P, IP, Sp, Gr, flammability	VP, FRZ UEL, LEL		
p-tert-Butyltoluene (CH₃)₃CC₆H₄CH₃ 98-51-1 XS8400000 2667 131	4-tert-Butyltoluene, 1-Methyl-4-tert-butylbenzene 1 ppm = 6.07 mg/m³	NIOSH 10 ppm (60 mg/m³) ST 20 ppm (120 mg/m³) OSHA† 10 ppm (60 mg/m³)	100 ppm	Colorless liquid with a distinct aromatic odor, somewhat like gasoline.	MW: 148.3 BP: 379°F Sol: Insoluble Fl.P: 155°F IP: 8.28 eV Sp.Gr: 0.86 Class IIIA Combustible Liquid	VP(77°F): 0.7 mm FRZ: -62°F UEL: ? LEL: ?	Oxidizers	Char; CS₂; GC/FID; IV [#1501, Aromatic Hydro- carbons]
n-Butyronitrile CH₃CH₂CH₂CN 109-74-0 ET8750000 2411 131	Butanenitrile, Butyronitrile, 1-Cyanopropane, Propyl cyanide, n-Propyl cyanide 1 ppm = 2.83 mg/m³	NIOSH 8 ppm (22 mg/m³) OSHA none	N.D.	Colorless liquid with a sharp, suffocating odor. [Note: Forms cyanide in the body.]	MW: 69.1 BP: 244°F Sol(77°F): 3% Fl.P: 62°F IP: 11.67 eV Sp.Gr: 0.81 Class IB Flammable Liquid	VP: 14 mm FRZ: -170°F UEL: ? LEL: 1.65%	Strong oxidizers & reducing agents, strong acids & bases	Char; Benzene; GC/FID; IV [Adapt #1606]
Cadmium dust (as Cd) Cd (Metal) 7440-43-9 (Metal) EU9800000 (Metal) 2570 154 (compounds)	Cadmium metal: Cadmium Other synonyms vary depending upon the specific cadmium compound.	NIOSH* Ca See Appendix A OSHA*[1910.1027] 0.005 mg/m³ [*Note: The REL and PEL apply to all Cadmium compounds (as Cd).]	Ca [9 mg/m³ (as Cd)]	Metal: Silver-white, blue-tinged, lustrous, odorless solid.	MW: 112.4 BP: 1409°F Sol: Insoluble Fl.P: NA IP: NA Sp.Gr: 8.65 (Metal) Metal: Noncombustible Solid in bulk form, but will burn in powder form.	VP: 0 mm (approx) MLT: 610°F UEL: NA LEL: NA	Strong oxidizers; elemental sulfur, selenium & tellurium	Filter; Acid; FAAS; IV [#7048]
Cadmium fume (as Cd) CdO/Cd 1306-19-0 (CdO) EV1930000 (CdO)	CdO: Cadmium monoxide, Cadmium oxide fume Cd: Cadmium	NIOSH* Ca See Appendix A OSHA*[1910.1027] 0.005 mg/m³ [*Note: The REL and PEL apply to all Cadmium compounds (as Cd).]	Ca [9 mg/m³ (as Cd)]	Odorless, yellow-brown, finely divided partic-ulate dispersed in air.	MW: 128.4 BP: Decomposes Sol: Insoluble Fl.P: NA IP: NA Sp.Gr: 8.15 (crystalline form)/6.95 (amorphous form) Noncombustible Solid	VP: 0 mm (approx) MLT: 2599°F UEL: NA LEL: NA	Not applicable	Filter; Acid; FAAS; IV [#7048]

Personal protection and sanitation (See Table 3)		Recommendations for respirator selection — maximum concentration for use (MUC) (See Table 4)	Route	Health hazards			
				Symptoms (See Table 5)	First aid (See Table 6)		Target organs (See Table 5)
Skin:	Prevent skin contact	NIOSH/OSHA	Inh	Irrit eyes, skin; dry nose,	Eye:	Irr immed	Eyes, skin, resp sys,
Eyes:	Prevent eye contact	100 ppm: SA:CF£/PAPROV£/CCRFOV/	Ing	throat; head; low BP,	Skin:	Water flush prompt	CVS, CNS, bone
Wash skin:	When contam	GMFOV/SCBAF/SAF	Con	tacar, abnor CVS stress;	Breath:	Resp support	marrow, liver,
Remove:	When wet or contam	§: SCBAF:PD,PP/SAF:PD,PP:ASCBA		CNS, hemato depres;	Swallow:	Medical attention	kidneys
Change:	N.R.	Escape: GMFOV/SCBAE		metallic taste; liver,		immed	
				kidney inj			

[p-tert-Butyltoluene]

Skin:	Prevent skin contact	NIOSH	Inh	Irrit eyes, skin, resp	Eye:	Irr immed	Eyes, skin, resp sys,
Eyes:	Prevent eye contact	80 ppm: CCROV/SA	Abs	sys; head, dizz, weak,	Skin:	Soap wash immed	CNS, CVS
Wash skin:	When contam	200 ppm: SA:CF/PAPROV	Ing	gidd, conf, convuls;	Breath:	Resp support	
Remove:	When wet (flamm)	400 ppm: CCRFOV/GMFOV/PAPRTOV/	Con	dysp; abdom pain, nau,	Swallow:	Medical attention	
Change:	N.R.	SCBAF/SAF		vomit		immed	
Provide:	Quick drench	1000 ppm: SAF:PD,PP					
		§: SCBAF:PD,PP/SAF:PD,PP:ASCBA					
		Escape: GMFOV/SCBAE					

[n-Butryonitrile]

Skin:	N.R.	NIOSH	Inh	Pulm edema, dysp,	Eye:	Irr immed	Resp sys,
Eyes:	N.R.	¥: SCBAF:PD,PP/SAF:PD,PP:ASCBA	Ing	cough, chest tight, subs	Skin:	Soap wash	kidneys,
Wash skin:	Daily	Escape: HiEF/SCBAE		pain; head; chills, musc	Breath:	Resp support	prostate, blood
Remove:	N.R.			aches; nau, vomit, diarr;	Swallow:	Medical attention	[prostatic &
Change:	Daily			anos, emphy, prot, mild		immed	lung cancer]
				anemia; [carc]			

[Cadmium dust (as Cd)]

Skin:	N.R.	NIOSH	Inh	Pulm edema, dysp,	Breath:	Resp support	Resp sys,
Eyes:	N.R.	¥: SCBAF:PD,PP/SAF:PD,PP:ASCBA		cough, tight chest, subs			kidneys, blood
Wash skin:	Daily	Escape: HiEF/SCBAE		pain; head; chills, musc			[prostatic &
Remove:	N.R.			aches; nau, vomit, diarr;			lung cancer]
Change:	Daily			emphy, prot, anos, mild			
				anemia; [carc]			

[Cadmium fume (as Cd)]

45

Chemical name, structure/formula, CAS and RTECS Nos., and DOT ID and guide Nos.	Synonyms, trade names, and conversion factors	Exposure limits (TWA unless noted otherwise)	IDLH	Physical description	Chemical and physical properties		Incompatibilities and reactivities	Measurement method (See Table 1)
					MW, BP, SOL FI.P, IP, Sp, Gr, flammability	VP, FRZ UEL, LEL		
Calcium arsenate (as As) Ca₃(AsO₄)₂ 7778-44-1 CG0830000 1573 151	Calcium salt (2:3) of arsenic acid, Cucumber dust, Tricalcium arsenate, Tricalcium ortho-arsenate [Note: Also see specific listing for Arsenic (inorganic compounds, as As).]	NIOSH Ca C 0.002 mg/m³ [15-min] See Appendix A OSHA [1910.1018] 0.010 mg/m³	Ca [5 mg/m³ (as As)]	Colorless to white, odorless solid. [insecticide/ herbicide]	MW: 398.1 BP: Decomposes Sol(77°F): 0.01% FI.P: NA IP: NA Sp.Gr: 3.62 Noncombustible Solid	VP: 0 mm (approx) MLT: ? UEL: NA LEL: NA	None reported [Note: Produces toxic fumes of arsenic when heated to decomposition.]	Filter; Acid; HYAAS; IV [#7900, Arsenic]
Calcium carbonate CaCO₃ 1317-65-3 EV9580000	Calcium salt of carbonic acid [Note: Occurs in nature as limestone, chalk, marble, dolomite, aragonite, calcite & oyster shells.]	NIOSH 10 mg/m³ (total) 5 mg/m³ (resp) OSHA 15 mg/m³ (total) 5 mg/m³ (resp)	N.D.	White, odorless powder or colorless crystals.	MW: 100.1 BP: Decomposes Sol: 0.001% FI.P: NA IP: NA Sp.Gr: 2.7-2.95 Noncombustible Solid	VP: 0 mm (approx) MLT: 1517-2442°F (Decomposes) UEL: NA LEL: NA	Acids, alum, ammonium salts, mercury & hydrogen, fluorine, magnesium	Filter; Acid; FAAS; IV [#7020, Calcium]
Calcium cyanamide CaCN₂ 156-62-7 GS6000000 1403 138 (with >0.1% calcium carbide)	Calcium carbimide, Cyanamide, Lime nitrogen, Nitrogen lime [Note: Cyanamide is also a synonym for Hydrogen cyanamide, NH₂CN.]	NIOSH 0.5 mg/m³ OSHA† none	N.D.	Colorless, gray, or black crystals or powder. [fertilizer] [Note: Commercial grades may contain calcium carbide.]	MW: 80.1 BP: Sublimes Sol: Insoluble FI.P: NA IP: NA Sp.Gr: 2.29 Noncombustible Solid, but a fire risk if it contains calcium carbide.	VP: 0 mm (approx) MLT: 2444°F UEL: NA LEL: NA	Water [Note: May polymerize in water or alkaline solutions to dicyanamide. Decomposes in water to form acetylene & ammonia.]	Filter; none; Grav; IV [#0500, Particulates NOR (total)]
Calcium hydroxide Ca(OH)₂ 1305-62-0 EW2800000	Calcium hydrate, Caustic lime, Hydrated lime, Slaked lime	NIOSH 5 mg/m³ OSHA 15 mg/m³ (total) 5 mg/m³ (resp)	N.D.	White, odorless powder. [Note: Readily absorbs CO₂ from the air to form calcium carbonate.]	MW: 74.1 BP: Decomposes Sol(32°F): 0.2% FI.P: NA IP: NA Sp.Gr: 2.24 Noncombustible Solid	VP: 0 mm (approx) MLT: 1076°F (Decomposes) (Loses H₂O) UEL: NA LEL: NA	Maleic anhydride, phosphorus, nitroethane, nitromethane, nitroparaffins, nitropropane [Note: Attacks some metals.]	Filter; Acid; FAAS; IV [#7020, Calcium]

Personal protection and sanitation (See Table 3)	Recommendations for respirator selection — maximum concentration for use (MUC) (See Table 4)	Health hazards			
		Route	Symptoms (See Table 5)	First aid (See Table 6)	Target organs (See Table 5)
Skin: Prevent skin contact Eyes: Prevent eye contact Wash skin: When contam/Daily Remove: When wet or contam Change: Daily Provide: Eyewash, Quick drench	NIOSH ¥: SCBAF:PD,PP/SAF:PD,PP:ASCBA Escape: HiEF/SCBAE	Inh Abs Ing Con	Weak; GI dist; peri neur; skin hyperpig, palmar planter hyperkeratoses; derm; [carc]; in animals: liver damage	Eye: Irr immed Skin: Soap wash prompt Breath: Resp support Swallow: Medical attention immed	Eyes, resp sys, liver, skin, CNS, lymphatic sys [lymphatic & lung cancer]

[Calcium arsenate (as As)]

Skin: N.R. Eyes: N.R. Wash skin: N.R. Remove: N.R. Change: N.R.	TBAL	Inh Con	Irrit eyes, skin, resp sys; cough	Eye: Irr immed Skin: Soap wash Breath: Fresh air	Eyes, skin, resp sys

[Calcium carbonate]

Skin: Prevent skin contact Eyes: Prevent eye contact Wash skin: When contam Remove: When wet or contam Change: Daily Provide: Eyewash, Quick drench	TBAL	Inh Ing Con	Irrit eyes, skin, resp sys; head, verti, rapid breath, low BP, nau, vomit; skin burns, sens; cough; Antabuse-like effects	Eye: Irr immed Skin: Soap flush immed Breath: Resp support Swallow: Medical attention immed	Eyes, skin, resp sys; vasomotor sys

[Calcium cyanamide]

Skin: Prevent skin contact Eyes: Prevent eye contact Wash skin: When contam/Daily Remove: When wet or contam Change: Daily Provide: Eyewash, Quick drench	TBAL	Inh Ing Con	Irrit eyes, skin, upper resp sys; eye, skin burns; skin vesic; cough, bron, pneu	Eye: Irr immed Skin: Soap flush immed Breath: Resp support Swallow: Medical attention immed	Eyes, skin, resp sys

[Calcium hydroxide]

Chemical name, structure/formula, CAS and RTECS Nos., and DOT ID and guide Nos.	Synonyms, trade names, and conversion factors	Exposure limits (TWA unless noted otherwise)	IDLH	Physical description	Chemical and physical properties — MW, BP, SOL Fl.P, IP, Sp, Gr, flammability	VP, FRZ UEL, LEL	Incompatibilities and reactivities	Measurement method (See Table 1)
Calcium oxide CaO 1305-78-8 EW3100000 1910 157	Burned lime, Burnt lime, Lime, Pebble lime, Quick lime, Unslaked lime	NIOSH 2 mg/m^3 OSHA 5 mg/m^3	25 mg/m^3	White or gray, odorless lumps or granular powder.	MW: 56.1 BP: 5162°F Sol: Reacts Fl.P: NA IP: NA Sp.Gr: 3.34 Noncombustible Solid, but will support combustion by liberation of oxygen.	VP: 0 mm (approx) MLT: 4662°F UEL: NA LEL: NA	Water (liberates heat), fluorine, ethanol [Note: Reacts with water to form calcium hydroxide.]	Filter; Acid; FAAS; IV [#7020, Calcium]
Calcium silicate CaSiO$_3$ 1344-95-2 VV9150000	Calcium hydrosilicate, Calcium metasilicate, Calcium monosilicate, Calcium salt of silicic acid, Wollastonite (mineral)	NIOSH 10 mg/m^3 (total) 5 mg/m^3 (resp) OSHA 15 mg/m^3 (total) 5 mg/m^3 (resp)	N.D.	White or cream-colored, free-flowing powder. [Note: The commercial product is prepared from diatomaceous earth & lime.]	MW: 116.2 BP: ? Sol: 0.01% Fl.P: NA IP: NA Sp.Gr: 2.9 Noncombustible Solid	VP: 0 mm (approx) MLT: 2804°F UEL: NA LEL: NA	None reported [Note: After prolonged contact with water, solution reverts to soluble calcium salts & amorphous silica.]	Filter; Acid; FAAS; IV [#7020, Calcium]
Calcium sulfate CaSO$_4$ 7778-18-9 WS6920000	Anhydrous calcium sulfate, Anhydrous gypsum, Anhydrous sulfate of lime, Calcium salt of sulfuric acid [Note: Gypsum is the dihydrate form & Plaster of Paris is the hemihydrate form.]	NIOSH 10 mg/m^3 (total) 5 mg/m^3 (resp) OSHA 15 mg/m^3 (total) 5 mg/m^3 (resp)	N.D.	Odorless, white powder or colorless, crystalline solid. [Note: May have blue, gray, or reddish tinge.]	MW: 136.1 BP: Decomposes Sol: 0.3% Fl.P: NA IP: NA Sp.Gr: 2.96 Noncombustible Solid	VP: 0 mm (approx) MLT: 2840°F (Decomposes) UEL: NA LEL: NA	Diazomethane, aluminum,phosphorus, water [Note: Hygroscopic (i.e., absorbs moisture from the air). Reacts with water to form Gypsum & Plaster of Paris.]	Filter; none; Grav; IV [Particulates NOR: #0500 (total), #0600 (resp)]
Camphor (synthetic) C$_{10}$H$_{16}$O 76-22-2 EX1225000 2717 133	2-Camphonone, Gum camphor, Laurel camphor, Synthetic camphor	NIOSH/OSHA 2 mg/m^3	200 mg/m^3	Colorless or white crystals with a penetrating, aromatic odor.	MW: 152.3 BP: 399°F Sol: Insoluble Fl.P: 150°F IP: 8.76 eV Sp.Gr: 0.99 Combustible Solid	VP: 0.2 mm MLT: 345°F UEL: 3.5% LEL: 0.6%	Strong oxidizers (especially chromic anhydride & potassium permanganate)	Char; Methanol/ CS$_2$; GC/FID; IV [#1301, Ketones II]

Personal protection and sanitation (See Table 3)		Recommendations for respirator selection — maximum concentration for use (MUC) (See Table 4)	Route	Symptoms (See Table 5)	First aid (See Table 6)		Target organs (See Table 5)
Skin: Eyes: Wash skin: Remove: Change: Provide:	Prevent skin contact Prevent eye contact When contam/Daily When wet or contam Daily Eyewash, Quick drench	NIOSH 10 mg/m³: DM 20 mg/m³: DMXSQ/SA 25 mg/m³: SA:CF/PAPRHiE/HiEF/ SCBAF/SAF §: SCBAF:PD,PP/SAF:PD,PP:ASCBA Escape: HiEF/SCBAE	Inh Ing Con	Irrit eyes, skin, upper resp tract; ulcer, perf nasal septum; pneu; derm	Eye: Skin: Breath: Swallow:	Irr immed Water flush immed Resp support Medical attention immed	Eyes, skin, resp sys
[Calcium oxide]							
Skin: Eyes: Wash skin: Remove: Change:	N.R. N.R. N.R. N.R. N.R.	TBAL	Inh Con	Irrit eyes, skin, upper resp sys	Eye: Skin: Breath:	Irr immed Soap wash Fresh air	Eyes, skin, resp sys
[Calcium silicate]							
Skin: Eyes: Wash skin: Remove: Change:	N.R. N.R. N.R. N.R. N.R.	TBAL	Inh Con	Irrit eyes, skin, upper resp sys; conj; rhinitis, epis	Eye: Skin: Breath:	Irr immed Soap wash Fresh air	Eyes, skin, resp sys
[Calcium sulfate]							
Skin: Eyes: Wash skin: Remove: Change:	Prevent skin contact Prevent eye contact When contam When wet or contam Daily	NIOSH/OSHA 50 mg/m³: SA:CF£/PAPROVDM£ 100 mg/m³: CCRFOVHiE/GMFOVHiE/ PAPRTOVHiE£/SCBAF/SAF 200 mg/m³: SAF:PD,PP §: SCBAF:PD,PP/SAF:PD,PP:ASCBA Escape: GMFOVHiE/SCBAE	Inh Abs Ing Con	Irrit eyes, skin, muc memb; nau, vomit, diarr; head, dizz, excitement; epilep convuls	Eye: Skin: Breath: Swallow:	Irr immed Soap wash immed Resp support Medical attention immed	Eyes, skin, resp sys, CNS
[Camphor (synthetic)]							

Chemical name, structure/formula, CAS and RTECS Nos., and DOT ID and guide Nos.	Synonyms, trade names, and conversion factors	Exposure limits (TWA unless noted otherwise)	IDLH	Physical description	Chemical and physical properties		Incompatibilities and reactivities	Measurement method (See Table 1)
					MW, BP, SOL FI.P, IP, Sp, Gr, flammability	VP, FRZ UEL, LEL		
Caprolactam C₆H₁₁NO 105-60-2 CM3675000	Aminocaproic lactam, epsilon-Caprolactam, Hexahydro-2H-azepin-2-one, 2-Oxohexamethyleneimine 1 ppm = 4.63 mg/m³	NIOSH Dust: 1 mg/m³ ST 3 mg/m³ Vapor: 0.22 ppm (1 mg/m³) ST 0.66 ppm (3 mg/m³) OSHA† none	N.D.	White, crystalline solid or flakes with an unpleasant odor. [Note: Significant vapor concentrations would be expected only at elevated temperatures.]	MW: 113.2 BP: 515°F Sol: 53% FI.P: 282°F IP: ? Sp.Gr: 1.01 Combustible Solid	VP: 0.00000008 mm MLT: 156°F UEL: 8.0% LEL: 1.4%	Strong oxidizers, (acetic acid + dinitrogen trioxide)	None available
Captafol C₁₀H₉Cl₁₄NO₂S 2425-06-1 GS4900000	Captofol; Difolatan®; N-((1,1,2,2-Tetrachloro-ethyl)thio)-4-cyclohexene-1,2-dicarboximide	NIOSH Ca 0.1 mg/m³ [skin] See Appendix A OSHA† none	Ca [N.D.]	White, crystalline solid with a slight, characteristic pungent odor. [fungicide] [Note: Available commercially as a wettable powder or in liquid form.]	MW: 349.1 BP: Decomposes Sol: 0.0001% FI.P: NA IP: NA Sp.Gr: ? Noncombustible Solid, but may be dissolved in flammable liquids.	VP: 0.000008 mm MLT: 321°F (Decomposes) UEL: NA LEL: NA	Acids, acid vapors, strong oxidizers	Filter; none; Grav; IV [#0500, Particulates NOR (total)]
Captan C₉H₈Cl₃NO₂S 133-06-2 GW5075000 9188 171	Captane; N-Trichloromethylmercapto-4-cyclohexene-1,2-dicarboximide	NIOSH Ca 5 mg/m³ See Appendix A OSHA† none	Ca [N.D.]	Odorless, white, crystalline powder. [fungicide] [Note: Commercial product is a yellow powder with a pungent odor.]	MW: 300.6 BP: Decomposes Sol(77°F): 0.0003% FI.P: ? IP: NA Sp.Gr: 1.74 Combustible Solid; may be dissolved in flammable liquids.	VP: 0 mm (approx) MLT: 352°F (Decomposes) UEL: ? LEL: ?	Strong alkaline materials (e.g., hydrated lime) [Note: Corrosive to metals.]	Filter; none; Grav; IV [#0500, Particulates NOR (total)]
Carbaryl CH₃NHCOOC₁₀H₇ 63-25-2 FC5950000 2757 151	α-Naphthyl N-methyl-carbamate, 1-Naphthyl N-Methyl-carbamate, Sevin®	NIOSH/OSHA 5 mg/m³	100 mg/m³	White or gray, odorless solid. [pesticide]	MW: 201.2 BP: Decomposes Sol: 0.01% FI.P: NA IP: ? Sp.Gr: 1.23 Noncombustible Solid, but may be dissolved in flammable liquids.	VP(77°F): <0.00004 mm MLT: 293°F UEL: NA LEL: NA	Strong oxidizers, strongly alkaline pesticides	Filter; Reagent; Vis; IV [#5006]

Personal protection and sanitation (See Table 3)		Recommendations for respirator selection — maximum concentration for use (MUC) (See Table 4)	Health hazards				
			Route	Symptoms (See Table 5)		First aid (See Table 6)	Target organs (See Table 5)
Skin:	Prevent skin contact	TBAL	Inh	Irrit eyes, skin, resp	Eye:	Irr immed	Eyes, skin, resp sys,
Eyes:	Prevent eye contact		Ing	sys; epis; derm, skin	Skin:	Water wash immed	CNS, CVS, liver,
Wash skin:	When contam		Con	sens; asthma; irrity,	Breath:	Resp support	kidneys
Remove:	When wet or contam			conf, dizz, head; abdom	Swallow:	Medical attention	
Change:	Daily			cramps, diarr, nau, vomit;		immed	
				liver, kidney inj			

[Caprolactam]

Skin:	Prevent skin contact	NIOSH	Inh	Irrit eyes, skin, resp	Eye:	Irr immed	Eyes, skin, resp sys,
Eyes:	Prevent eye contact	¥: SCBAF:PD,PP/SAF:PD,PP:ASCBA	Abs	sys; derm, skin sens;	Skin:	Soap wash immed	CNS, liver, kidneys,
Wash skin:	When contam	Escape: GMFOV/SCBAE	Ing	conj; bron, wheez; diarr,	Breath:	Resp support	CVS
Remove:	When wet or contam		Con	vomit; liver, kidney inj;	Swallow:	Medical attention	[in animals:
Change:	Daily			high BP;		immed	tumors at many
Provide:	Eyewash, Quick drench			in animals: terato effects;			sites]
				[carc]			

51

[Captafol]

Skin:	Prevent skin contact	NIOSH	Inh	Irrit eyes, skin, upper	Eye:	Irr immed	Eyes, skin, resp sys,
Eyes:	Prevent eye contact	¥: SCBAF:PD,PP/SAF:PD,PP:ASCBA	Abs	resp sys; blurred vision;	Skin:	Soap wash immed	GI tract, liver,
Wash skin:	When contam/Daily	Escape: GMFOV/SCBAE	Ing	derm, skin sens; dysp;	Breath:	Resp support	kidneys
Remove:	When wet or contam		Con	diarr, vomit; [carc]	Swallow:	Medical attention	[in animals:
Change:	Daily					immed	duodenal tumors]
Provide:	Eyewash, Quick drench						

[Captan]

Skin:	Prevent skin contact	NIOSH/OSHA	Inh	Miosis, blurred vision,	Eye:	Irr immed	Resp sys, CNS,
Eyes:	Prevent eye contact	50 mg/m³: SA*	Abs	tear; rhin, salv; sweat;	Skin:	Soap wash prompt	CVS, skin,
Wash skin:	When contam	100 mg/m³: SA:CF*/SCBAF/SAF	Ing	abdom cramps, nau, vomit;	Breath:	Resp support	blood chol, repro sys
Remove:	When wet or contam	§: SCBAF:PD,PP/SAF:PD,PP:ASCBA	Con	diarr; tremor; cyan;	Swallow:	Medical attention	
Change:	Daily	Escape: GMFOVHiE/SCBAE		convuls; irrit skin;		immed	
				possible repro effects			

[Carbaryl]

Chemical name, structure/formula, CAS and RTECS Nos., and DOT ID and guide Nos.	Synonyms, trade names, and conversion factors	Exposure limits (TWA unless noted otherwise)	IDLH	Physical description	Chemical and physical properties		Incompatibilities and reactivities	Measurement method (See Table 1)
					MW, BP, SOL Fl.P, IP, Sp, Gr, flammability	VP, FRZ UEL, LEL		
Carbofuran $C_{12}H_{15}NO_3$ 1563-66-2 FB9450000 2757 151	2,3-Dihydro-2,2-dimethyl-7-benzofuranyl methyl-carbamate; Furacarb®; Furadan®	NIOSH 0.1 mg/m³ OSHA† none	N.D.	Odorless, white or grayish, crystalline solid. [insecticide] [Note: May be dissolved in a liquid carrier.]	MW: 221.3 BP: ? Sol(77°F): 0.07% Fl.P: NA IP: NA Sp.Gr: 1.18 Noncombustible Solid	VP(77°F): 0.000003 mm MLT: 304°F UEL: NA LEL: NA	Alkaline substances, acid, strong oxidizers (e.g., perchlorates, peroxides, chlorates, nitrates, permanganates)	Filter; none; Grav; IV [#0500, Particulates NOR (total)]
Carbon black C 1333-86-4 FF5800000	Acetylene black, Channel black, Furnace black, Lamp black, Thermal black	NIOSH/OSHA 3.5 mg/m³ NIOSH Ca 0.1 mg PAHs/m³ [Carbon black in presence of polycyclic aromatic hydrocarbons (PAHs)] See Appendix A See Appendix C	1750 mg/m³	Black, odorless solid.	MW: 12.0 BP: Sublimes Sol: Insoluble Fl.P: NA IP: NA Sp.Gr: 1.8-2.1 Combustible Solid that may contain flammable hydrocarbons.	VP: 0 mm (approx) MLT: Sublimes UEL: NA LEL: NA	Strong oxidizers such as chlorates, bromates & nitrates	Filter; none; Grav; IV [#5000]
Carbon dioxide CO_2 124-38-9 FF6400000 1013 120 1845 120 (dry ice) 2187 120 (liquid)	Carbonic acid gas, Dry ice [Note: Normal constituent of air (about 300 ppm).] 1 ppm = 1.80 mg/m³	NIOSH 5000 ppm (9000 mg/m³) ST 30,000 ppm (54,000 mg/m³) OSHA† 5000 ppm (9000 mg/m³)	40,000 ppm	Colorless, odorless gas. [Note: Shipped as a liquefied compressed gas. Solid form is utilized as dry ice.]	MW: 44.0 BP: Sublimes Sol(77°F): 0.2% Fl.P: NA IP: 13.77 eV RGasD: 1.53 Nonflammable Gas	VP: 56.5 atm MLT: -109°F (Sublimes) UEL: NA LEL: NA	Dusts of various metals, such as magnesium, zirconium, titanium, aluminum, chromium & manganese are ignitable and explosive when suspended in carbon dioxide. Forms carbonic acid in water.	Bag; none; GC/TCD; IV [#6603]
Carbon disulfide CS_2 75-15-0 FF6650000 1131 131	Carbon bisulfide 1 ppm = 3.11 mg/m³	NIOSH 1 ppm (3 mg/m³) ST 10 ppm (30 mg/m³) [skin] OSHA† 20 ppm C 30 ppm 100 ppm (30-min max peak)	500 ppm	Colorless to faint-yellow liquid with a sweet ether-like odor. [Note: Reagent grades are foul smelling.]	MW: 76.1 BP: 116°F Sol: 0.3% Fl.P: -22°F IP: 10.08 eV Sp.Gr: 1.26 Class IB Flammable Liquid	VP: 297 mm FRZ: -169°F UEL: 50.0% LEL: 1.3%	Strong oxidizers; chemically-active metals such as sodium, potassium & zinc; azides; rust; halogens; amines [Note: Vapors may be ignited by contact with ordinary light bulb.]	Char/ Dry tube; Toluene; GC/FPD; IV [#1600]

Personal protection and sanitation (See Table 3)		Recommendations for respirator selection — maximum concentration for use (MUC) (See Table 4)	Health hazards				
			Route	Symptoms (See Table 5)	First aid (See Table 6)	Target organs (See Table 5)

Personal protection and sanitation		Recommendations for respirator selection (MUC)	Route	Symptoms	First aid	Target organs
Skin: Prevent skin contact Eyes: Prevent eye contact Wash skin: When contam Remove: When wet or contam Change: Daily Provide: Eyewash, Quick drench		TBAL	Inh Abs Ing Con	Miosis, blurred vision; sweat, salv, abdom cramps, diarr, head, nau, vomit, weak; musc twitch, inco, convuls	Eye: Irr immed Skin: Soap flush immed Breath: Fresh air Swallow: Medical attention immed	CNS, PNS, blood chol
[Carbofuran]						
Skin: N.R. Eyes: Prevent eye contact Wash skin: Daily Remove: N.R. Change: N.R.		NIOSH/OSHA 17.5 mg/m³: DM 35 mg/m³: DMXSQ/SA 87.5 mg/m³: SA:CF/PAPRDM 175 mg/m³: HiEF/PAPRTHiE/SCBAF/SAF 1750 mg/m³: SA:PD,PP §: SCBAF:PD,PP/SAF:PD,PP:ASCBA Escape: HiEF/SCBAE	Inh Con	Cough; irrit eyes, in presence of polycyclic aromatic hydrocarbons: [carc] In presence of polycyclic aromatic hydrocarbons: NIOSH ¥: SCBAF:PD,PP/SAF:PD,PP:ASCBA Escape: HiEF/SCBAE	Eye: Irr prompt Breath: Fresh air	Resp sys, eyes [lymphatic cancer (in presence of PAHs)]
[Carbon black]						
Skin: Frostbite Eyes: Frostbite Wash skin: N.R. Remove: N.R. Change: N.R. Provide: Frostbite		NIOSH/OSHA 40,000 ppm: SA/SCBAF §: SCBAF:PD,PP/SAF:PD,PP:ASCBA Escape: SCBAE	Inh Con (liq/ sol)	Head, dizz, restless, pares; dysp; sweat, mal; incr heart rate, card output, BP; coma; asphy; convuls; frostbite (liq, dry ice)	Eye: Frostbite Skin: Frostbite Breath: Resp support	Resp sys, CVS
[Carbon dioxide]						
Skin: Prevent skin contact Eyes: Prevent eye contact Wash skin: When contam Remove: When wet (flamm) Change: N.R.		NIOSH 10 ppm: CCROV/SA 25 ppm: SA:CF/PAPROV 50 ppm: CCRFOV/GMFOV/PAPRTOV/ SCBAF/SAF 500 ppm: SA:PD,PP §: SCBAF:PD,PP/SAF:PD,PP:ASCBA Escape: GMFOV/SCBAE	Inh Abs Ing Con	Dizz, head, poor sleep, ftg, ner, anor, low-wgt; psychosis; polyneur; Parkinson-like syndrome; ocular changes; coronary heart disease; gastritis; kidney, liver inj; eye, skin burns; derm; repro effects	Eye: Irr immed Skin: Soap wash immed Breath: Resp support Swallow: Medical attention immed	CNS, PNS, CVS, eyes, kidneys, liver, skin, repro sys
[Carbon disulfide]						

53

Chemical name, structure/formula, CAS and RTECS Nos., and DOT ID and guide Nos.	Synonyms, trade names, and conversion factors	Exposure limits (TWA unless noted otherwise)	IDLH	Physical description	Chemical and physical properties		Incompatibilities and reactivities	Measurement method (See Table 1)
					MW, BP, SOL Fl.P, IP, Sp, Gr, flammability	VP, FRZ UEL, LEL		
Carbon monoxide CO 630-08-0 FG3500000 1016 119 9202 168 (cryogenic liquid)	Carbon oxide, Flue gas, Monoxide 1 ppm = 1.15 mg/m³	NIOSH 35 ppm (40 mg/m³) C 200 ppm (229 mg/m³) OSHA† 50 ppm (55 mg/m³)	1200 ppm	Colorless, odorless gas. [Note: Shipped as a nonliquefied or liquefied compressed gas.]	MW: 28.0 BP: -313°F Sol: 2% Fl.P: NA (Gas) IP: 14.01 eV RGasD: 0.97 Flammable Gas	VP: >35 atm MLT: -337°F UEL: 74% LEL: 12.5%	Strong oxidizers, bromine trifluoride, chlorine trifluoride, lithium	Bag; none; Sensor; IV [#6604]
Carbon tetrabromide CBr₄ 558-13-4 FG4725000 2516 151	Carbon bromide, Methane tetrabromide, Tetrabromomethane 1 ppm = 13.57 mg/m³	NIOSH 0.1 ppm (1.4 mg/m³) ST 0.3 ppm (4 mg/m³) OSHA† none	N.D.	Colorless to yellow-brown crystals with a slight odor.	MW: 331.7 BP: 374°F Sol: 0.02% Fl.P: NA IP: 10.31 eV Sp.Gr. 3.42 Noncombustible Solid	VP(205°F): 40 mm MLT: 194°F UEL: NA LEL: NA	Strong oxidizers, hexacyclohexyldilead, lithium	None available
Carbon tetrachloride CCl₄ 56-23-5 FG4900000 1846 151	Carbon chloride, Carbon tet, Freon® 10, Halon® 104, Tetrachloromethane 1 ppm = 6.29 mg/m³	NIOSH Ca ST 2 ppm (12.6 mg/m³) [60-min] See Appendix A OSHA† 10 ppm C 25 ppm 200 ppm (5-min max peak in any 4 hrs)	Ca [200 ppm]	Colorless liquid with a characteristic ether-like odor.	MW: 153.8 BP: 170°F Sol: 0.05% Fl.P: NA IP: 11.47 eV Sp.Gr. 1.59 Noncombustible Liquid	VP: 91 mm FRZ: -9°F UEL: NA LEL: NA	Chemically-active metals such as sodium, potassium & magnesium; fluorine; aluminum [Note: Forms highly toxic phosgene gas when exposed to flames or welding arcs.]	Char; CS₂; GC/FID; IV [#1003, Halogenated Hydrocarbons]
Carbonyl fluoride COF₂ 353-50-4 FG6125000 2417 125	Carbon difluoride oxide, Carbon fluoride oxide, Carbon oxyfluoride, Carbonyl difluoride, Fluoroformyl fluoride, Fluorophosgene 1 ppm = 2.70 mg/m³	NIOSH 2 ppm (5 mg/m³) ST 5 ppm (15 mg/m³) OSHA† none	N.D.	Colorless gas with a pungent and very irritating odor. [Note: Shipped as a liquefied compressed gas.]	MW: 66.0 BP: -118°F Sol: Reacts Fl.P: NA IP: 13.02 eV RGasD: 2.29 Nonflammable Gas	VP: 55.4 atm FRZ: -173°F UEL: NA LEL: NA	Heat, moisture, hexafluoroisopropyl-ideneamino-lithium [Note: Reacts with water to form hydrogen fluoride & carbon dioxide.]	None available

Personal protection and sanitation (See Table 3)		Recommendations for respirator selection — maximum concentration for use (MUC) (See Table 4)	Health hazards			
			Route	Symptoms (See Table 5)	First aid (See Table 6)	Target organs (See Table 5)
Skin:	Frostbite	NIOSH	Inh	Head, tachypnea, nau,	Eye: Frostbite	CVS, lungs,
Eyes:	Frostbite	350 ppm: SA	Con	weak, dizz, conf, halu;	Skin: Frostbite	blood, CNS
Wash skin:	N.R.	875 ppm: SA:CF	(liq)	cyan; depres S-T segment of	Breath: Resp support	
Remove:	When wet (flamm)	1200 ppm: GMFS†/SCBAF/SAF		electrocardiogram, angina,		
Change:	N.R.	§: SCBAF:PD,PP/SAF:PD,PP:ASCBA		syncope		
Provide:	Frostbite	Escape: GMFS†/SCBAE				

[Carbon monoxide]

Skin:	N.R.	TBAL	Inh	Irrit eyes, skin, resp	Eye: Irr immed	Eyes, skin, resp sys,
Eyes:	Prevent eye contact		Ing	sys; lac; lung, liver,	Skin: Soap wash prompt	liver, kidneys
Wash skin:	Daily		Con	kidney inj;	Breath: Resp support	
Remove:	N.R.			in animals: corn damage	Swallow: Medical attention	
Change:	Daily				immed	
Provide:	Eyewash					

[Carbon tetrabromide]

Skin:	Prevent skin contact	NIOSH	Inh	Irrit eyes, skin; CNS	Eye: Irr immed	CNS, eyes,
Eyes:	Prevent eye contact	¥: SCBAF:PD,PP/SAF:PD,PP:ASCBA	Abs	depres; nau, vomit; liver,	Skin: Soap wash immed	lungs, liver,
Wash skin:	When contam	Escape: GMFOV/SCBAE	Ing	kidney inj; drow, dizz,	Breath: Resp support	kidneys, skin
Remove:	When wet or contam		Con	inco; [carc]	Swallow: Medical attention	[in animals:
Change:	N.R.				immed	liver cancer]
Provide:	Eyewash, Quick drench					

[Carbon tetrachloride]

Skin:	Frostbite	TBAL	Inh	Irrit eyes, skin, muc	Eye: Frostbite	Eyes, skin, resp sys,
Eyes:	Frostbite		Con	memb, resp sys; eye, skin	Skin: Frostbite	bone
Wash skin:	N.R.			burns; lac; cough, pulm	Breath: Resp support	
Remove:	N.R.			edema, dysp; chronic		
Change:	N.R.			exposure: GI pain, musc		
Provide:	Frostbite			fib, skeletal fluorosis;		
				liq: frostbite		

[Carbonyl fluoride]

Chemical name, structure/formula, CAS and RTECS Nos., and DOT ID and guide Nos.	Synonyms, trade names, and conversion factors	Exposure limits (TWA unless noted otherwise)	IDLH	Physical description	Chemical and physical properties		Incompatibilities and reactivities	Measurement method (See Table 1)
					MW, BP, SOL Fl.P, IP, Sp, Gr, flammability	VP, FRZ UEL, LEL		
Catechol $C_6H_4(OH)_2$ 120-80-9 UX1050000	1,2-Benzenediol; o-Benzenediol; 1,2-Dihydroxybenzene; o-Dihydroxybenzene; 2-Hydroxyphenol; Pyrocatechol 1 ppm = 4.50 mg/m³	NIOSH 5 ppm (20 mg/m³) [skin] OSHA† none	N.D.	Colorless, crystalline solid with a faint odor. [Note: Discolors to brown in air & light.]	MW: 110.1 BP: 474°F Sol: 44% Fl.P: 261°F IP: ? Sp.Gr: 1.34 Combustible Solid	VP(244°F): 10mm MLT: 221°F UEL: ? LEL:1.4%	Strong oxidizers, nitric acid	None available
Cellulose $(C_6H_{10}O_5)_n$ 9004-34-6 FJ5691460	Hydroxycellulose, Pyrocellulose	NIOSH 10 mg/m³ (total) 5 mg/m³ (resp) OSHA 15 mg/m³ (total) 5 mg/m³ (resp)	N.D.	Odorless, white substance. [Note: The principal fiber cell wall material of vegetable tissues (wood, cotton, flax, grass, etc.).]	MW: 160,000-560,000 BP: Decomposes Sol: Insoluble Fl.P: NA IP: NA Sp.Gr: 1.27-1.61 Combustible Solid	VP: 0 mm (approx) MLT: 500-518°F (Decomposes) UEL: NA LEL: NA	Water, bromine pentafluoride, sodium nitrate, fluorine, strong oxidizers	Filter; none; Grav; IV [Particulates NOR: #0500 (total), #0600 (resp)]
Cesium hydroxide CsOH 21351-79-1 FK9800000 2682 157 2681 154 (solution)	Cesium hydrate, Cesium hydroxide dimer	NIOSH 2 mg/m³ OSHA† none	N.D.	Colorless or yellowish, crystalline solid. [Note: Hygroscopic (i.e., absorbs moisture from the air).]	MW: 149.9 BP: ? Sol(59°F): 395% Fl.P: NA IP: NA Sp.Gr: 3.68 Noncombustible Solid	VP: 0 mm (approx) MLT: 522°F UEL: NA LEL: NA	Water, acids, CO₂, metals (e.g., Al, Pb, Sn, Zn), oxygen [Note: CsOH is a strong base, causing the generation of considerable heat in contact with water or moisture.]	None available
Chlordane $C_{10}H_6Cl_8$ 57-74-9 PB9800000 2762 131	Chlordan; Chlordano; 1,2,4,5,6,7,8,8-Octachloro-3a,4,7,7a-tetrahydro-4,7-methanoindane	NIOSH Ca 0.5 mg/m³ [skin] See Appendix A OSHA 0.5 mg/m³ [skin]	Ca [100 mg/m³]	Amber-colored, viscous liquid with a pungent, chlorine-like odor. [insecticide]	MW: 409.8 BP: Decomposes Sol: 0.0001% Fl.P: NA IP: ? Sp.Gr(77°F): 1.6 Noncombustible Liquid, but may be utilized in flammable solutions.	VP: 0.00001 mm FRZ: 217-228°F UEL: NA LEL: NA	Strong oxidizers, alkaline reagents	Filter/ Chrom-102; Toluene; GC/ECD; IV [#5510]

Personal protection and sanitation (See Table 3)		Recommendations for respirator selection — maximum concentration for use (MUC) (See Table 4)	Health hazards					
			Route	Symptoms (See Table 5)		First aid (See Table 6)		Target organs (See Table 5)
Skin:	Prevent skin contact	TBAL	Inh	Irrit eyes, skin, resp	Eye:	Irr immed	Eyes, skin, resp sys,
Eyes:	Prevent eye contact		Abs	sys; skin sens, derm;	Skin:	Water wash immed	CNS, kidneys
Wash skin:	When contam		Ing	lac, burns eyes; convuls,	Breath:	Resp support	
Remove:	When wet or contam		Con	incr BP, kidney inj	Swallow:	Medical attention	
Change:	Daily					immed	
Provide:	Eyewash						

[Catechol]

Skin:	N.R.	TBAL	Inh	Irrit eyes, skin, muc	Eye:	Irr immed	Eyes, skin, resp sys
Eyes:	N.R.		Con	memb	Skin:	Soap wash	
Wash skin:	N.R.				Breath:	Fresh air	
Remove:	N.R.						
Change:	N.R.						

[Cellulose]

Skin:	Prevent skin contact	TBAL	Inh	Irrit eyes, skin, upper	Eye:	Irr immed	Eyes, skin, resp sys
Eyes:	Prevent eye contact		Ing	resp tract; eye, skin	Skin:	Water flush immed	
Wash skin:	When contam		Con	burns	Breath:	Resp support	
Remove:	When wet or contam				Swallow:	Medical attention	
Change:	Daily					immed	
Provide:	Eyewash, Quick drench						

[Cesium hydroxide]

Skin:	Prevent skin contact	NIOSH	Inh	Blurred vision; conf;	Eye:	Irr immed	CNS, eyes,
Eyes:	Prevent eye contact	¥: SCBAF:PD,PP/SAF:PD,PP:ASCBA	Abs	ataxia, delirium; cough;	Skin:	Soap wash immed	lungs, liver,
Wash skin:	When contam	Escape: GMFOVHiE/SCBAE	Ing	abdom pain, nau, vomit,	Breath:	Resp support	kidneys
Remove:	When wet or contam		Con	diarr; irrity, tremor,	Swallow:	Medical attention	[in animals:
Change:	Daily			convuls; anuria;		immed	liver cancer]
Provide:	Eyewash, Quick drench			in animals: lung, liver,			
				kidney damage; [carc]			

[Chlordane]

57

Chemical name, structure/formula, CAS and RTECS Nos., and DOT ID and guide Nos.	Synonyms, trade names, and conversion factors	Exposure limits (TWA unless noted otherwise)	IDLH	Physical description	Chemical and physical properties		Incompatibilities and reactivities	Measurement method (See Table 1)
					MW, BP, SOL FI.P, IP, Sp, Gr, flammability	VP, FRZ UEL, LEL		
Chlorinated camphene $C_{10}H_{10}Cl_8$ 8001-35-2 XW5250000 2761 151	Chlorocamphene, Octachlorocamphene, Polychlorocamphene, Toxaphene	NIOSH Ca [skin] See Appendix A OSHA† 0.5 mg/m³ [skin]	Ca [200 mg/m³]	Amber, waxy solid with a mild, piney, chlorine- and camphor-like odor. [insecticide]	MW: 413.8 BP: Decomposes Sol: 0.0003% FI.P: NA IP: ? Sp.Gr. 1.65 Noncombustible Solid, but may be dissolved in flammable liquids.	VP(77°F): 0.4 mm MLT: 149-194°F UEL: NA LEL: NA	Strong oxidizers [Note: Slightly corrosive to metals under moist conditions.]	Filter; Petroleum ether; GC/ECD; IV [#5039]
Chlorinated diphenyl oxide $C_{12}H_{10-n}Cl_nO$	Synonyms depend on the degree of chlorination of diphenyl oxide [($C_6H_5)_2)O$], ranging from monochlorodi-phenyl oxide [($C_2H_4Cl)O(C_2H_5)$] to decachlorodiphenyl oxide [($C_6Cl_5)O(C_6Cl_5)$].	NIOSH/OSHA 0.5 mg/m³	5 mg/m³	Appearance and odor vary depending upon the specific compound.	Properties vary depending upon the specific compound.		Strong oxidizers	Filter; Isooctane; GC/EConD; IV [#5025]
Chlorine Cl_2 7782-50-5 FO2100000 1017 124	Molecular chlorine	NIOSH C 0.5 ppm (1.45 mg/m³) [15-min] OSHA† C 1 ppm (3 mg/m³) 1 ppm = 2.90 mg/m³	10 ppm	Greenish-yellow gas with a pungent, irritating odor. [Note: Shipped as a liquefied compressed gas.]	MW: 70.9 BP: -29°F Sol: 0.7% FI.P: NA IP: 11.48 eV RGasD: 2.47 Nonflammable Gas, but a strong oxidizer.	VP: 6.8 atm FRZ: -150°F UEL: NA LEL: NA	Reacts explosively or forms explosive compounds with many common substances such as acetylene, ether, turpentine, ammonia, fuel gas, hydrogen & finely divided metals.	Filter; $Na_2S_2O_3$; IC; IV [#6011]
Chlorine dioxide ClO_2 10049-04-4 FO3000000	Chlorine oxide, Chlorine peroxide	NIOSH 0.1 ppm (0.3 mg/m³) ST 0.3 ppm (0.9 mg/m³) OSHA† 0.1 ppm (0.3 mg/m³) 1 ppm = 2.76 mg/m³	5 ppm	Yellow to red gas or a red-brown liquid (below 52°F) with an unpleasant odor similar to chlorine and nitric acid.	MW: 67.5 BP: 52°F Sol(77°F): 0.3% FI.P: NA (Gas) ? (Liq) IP: 10.36 eV RGasD: 2.33 Sp.Gr: 1.6 (Liquid at 32°F) Flammable Gas/Combustible Liquid	VP: >1 atm FRZ: -74°F UEL: ? LEL: ?	Organic materials, heat, phosphorus, potassium hydroxide, sulfur, mercury, carbon monoxide [Note: Unstable in light. A powerful oxidizer.]	Bub; KI; IC; OSHA [#ID202]

58

Personal protection and sanitation (See Table 3)	Recommendations for respirator selection — maximum concentration for use (MUC) (See Table 4)	Health hazards			
		Route	Symptoms (See Table 5)	First aid (See Table 6)	Target organs (See Table 5)
Skin: Prevent skin contact Eyes: Prevent eye contact Wash skin: When contam/Daily Remove: When wet or contam Change: Daily Provide: Eyewash, Quick drench	NIOSH ¥: SCBAF:PD,PP/SAF:PD,PP:ASCBA Escape: GMFOVHiE/SCBAE	Inh Abs Ing Con	Nau, conf, agitation, tremor, convuls, uncon; dry, red skin; [carc]	Eye: Irr immed Skin: Soap wash prompt Breath: Resp support Swallow: Medical attention immed	CNS, skin [in animals: liver cancer]
[Chlorinated camphene]					
Skin: Prevent skin contact Eyes: Prevent eye contact Wash skin: When contam Remove: When wet or contam Change: Daily	NIOSH/OSHA 5 mg/m³: SA/SCBAF §: SCBAF:PD,PP/SAF:PD,PP:ASCBA Escape: GMFOVAGHiE/SCBAE	Inh Ing Con	Acne-form derm, liver damage	Eye: Irr immed Skin: Soap wash prompt Breath: Resp support Swallow: Medical attention immed	Skin, liver
[Chlorinated diphenyl oxide]					
Skin: Frostbite Eyes: Frostbite Wash skin: N.R. Remove: N.R. Change: N.R. Provide: Frostbite	NIOSH 5 ppm: CCRS*/SA* 10 ppm: SA:CF*/PAPRS*/CCRFS/ GMFS/SCBAF/SAF §: SCBAF:PD,PP/SAF:PD,PP:ASCBA Escape: GMFS/SCBAE	Inh Con	Burning of eyes, nose, mouth; lac, rhin; cough, choking, subs pain; nau, vomit; head, dizz; syncope; pulm edema; pneu; hypox; derm; liq: frostbite	Eye: Frostbite Skin: Frostbite Breath: Resp support	Eyes, skin, resp sys
[Chlorine]					
Skin: Prevent skin contact (liq) Eyes: Prevent eye contact (liq) Wash skin: When contam (liq) Remove: When wet (flamm) Change: N.R. Provide: Eyewash (liq), Quick drench (liq)	NIOSH/OSHA 1 ppm: CCRS⁴/SA 2.5 ppm: SA:CF£/PAPRS£ 5 ppm: CCRFS⁴/GMFS⁴/SCBAF/SAF §: SCBAF:PD,PP/SAF:PD,PP:ASCBA Escape GMFS⁴/SCBAE	Inh Ing (liq) Con	Irrit eyes, nose, throat; cough, wheez, bron, pulm edema; chronic bron	Eye: Irr immed (liq) Skin: Soap wash immed (liq) Breath: Resp support Swallow: Medical attention immed (liq)	Eyes, resp sys
[Chlorine dioxide]					

Chemical name, structure/formula, CAS and RTECS Nos., and DOT ID and guide Nos.	Synonyms, trade names, and conversion factors	Exposure limits (TWA unless noted otherwise)	IDLH	Physical description	Chemical and physical properties		Incompatibilities and reactivities	Measurement method (See Table 1)
					MW, BP, SOL Fl.P, IP, Sp, Gr, flammability	VP, FRZ UEL, LEL		
Chlorine trifluoride CIF₃ 7790-91-2 FO2800000 1749 124	Chlorine fluoride, Chlorotrifluoride 1 ppm = 3.78 mg/m³	NIOSH/OSHA C 0.1 ppm (0.4 mg/m³)	20 ppm	Colorless gas or a greenish-yellow liquid (below 53°F) with a somewhat sweet, suffocating odor. [Note: Shipped as a liquefied compressed gas.]	MW: 92.5 BP: 53°F Sol: Reacts Fl.P: NA IP: 13.00 eV RGasD: 3.21 Sp.Gr: 1.77 (Liquid at 53°F) Nonflammable Gas Noncombustible Liquid, but contact with organic materials may result in SPONTANEOUS ignition.	VP: 1.4 atm FRZ: -105°F UEL: NA LEL: NA	Oxidizers, water, acids, combustible materials, sand, glass, metals (corrosive) [Note: Reacts with water to form chlorine & hydrofluoric acid.]	None available
Chloroacetaldehyde CICH₂CHO 107-20-0 AB2450000 2232 153	Chloroacetaldehyde (40% aqueous solution), 2-Chloroacetaldehyde, 2-Chloroethanal 1 ppm = 3.21 mg/m³	NIOSH/OSHA C 1 ppm (3 mg/m³)	45 ppm	Colorless liquid with an acrid, penetrating odor. [Note: Typically found as a 40% aqueous solution.]	MW: 78.5 BP: 186°F Sol: Miscible Fl.P: 190°F (40% soln.) IP: 10.61 eV Sp.Gr: 1.19 (40% solution) Class IIIA Combustible Liquid	VP: 100 mm FRZ: -3°F (40% soln.) UEL: ? LEL: ?	Oxidizers, acids	Si gel; Methanol; GC/ECD; IV [#2015]
α-Chloroacetophenone C₆H₅COCH₂CI 532-27-4 AM6300000 1697 153	2-Chloroacetophenone, Chloromethyl phenyl ketone, Mace®, Phenacyl chloride, Phenyl chloromethyl ketone, Tear gas 1 ppm = 6.32 mg/m³	NIOSH/OSHA 0.3 mg/m³ (0.05 ppm)	15 mg/m³	Colorless to gray crystalline solid with a sharp, irritating odor.	MW: 154.6 BP: 472°F Sol: Insoluble Fl.P: 244°F IP: 9.44 eV Sp.Gr: 1.32 Combustible Solid	VP: 0.005 mm MLT: 134°F UEL: ? LEL: ?	Water, steam, strong oxidizers [Note: Slowly corrodes metals.]	Tenax GC (2); Thermal desorp; GC/FID; II(5) [P&CAM #291]
Chloroacetyl chloride CICH₂COCI 79-04-9 AO6475000 1752 156	Chloroacetic acid chloride, Chloroacetic chloride, Monochloroacetyl chloride 1 ppm = 4.62 mg/m³	NIOSH 0.05 ppm (0.2 mg/m³) OSHA† none	N.D.	Colorless to yellowish liquid with a strong, pungent odor.	MW: 112.9 BP: 223°F Sol: Decomposes Fl.P: NA IP: 10.30 eV Sp.Gr: 1.42 Noncombustible Liquid	VP: 19 mm FRZ: -7°F UEL: NA LEL: NA	Water, alcohols, bases, metals (corrosive), amines [Note: Decomposes in water to form chloroacetic acid & hydrogen chloride gas.]	None available

Personal protection and sanitation (See Table 3)		Recommendations for respirator selection — maximum concentration for use (MUC) (See Table 4)	Health hazards			
			Route	Symptoms (See Table 5)	First aid (See Table 6)	Target organs (See Table 5)
Skin:	Prevent skin contact	NIOSH/OSHA	Inh	Eye, skin burns (liq or	Eye: Irr immed	Skin, eyes, resp sys
Eyes:	Prevent eye contact	2.5 ppm: SA:CF$^\varepsilon$	Ing	high vap conc); resp irrit;	Skin: Water flush immed	
Wash skin:	When contam (liq)	5 ppm: SCBAF/SAF	(liq)	in animals: lac, corn	Breath: Resp support	
Remove:	When wet or contam (liq)	20 ppm: SAF:PD,PP	Con	ulcer; pulm edema	Swallow: Medical attention	
Change:	N.R.	§: SCBAF:PD,PP/SAF:PD,PP:ASCBA			immed (liq)	
Provide:	Eyewash (liq), Quick drench (liq)	Escape: GMFS/SCBAE				

[Chlorine trifluoride]

Skin:	Prevent skin contact	NIOSH/OSHA	Inh	Irrit skin, eyes, muc	Eye: Irr immed	Eyes, skin, resp sys
Eyes:	Prevent eye contact	10 ppm: CCROV*/SA*	Abs	memb; skin burns; eye	Skin: Water flush immed	
Wash skin:	When contam	25 ppm: CCF*/PAPROV*	Ing	damage; pulm edema;	Breath: ssupport	
Remove:	When wet or contam	45 ppm: CCRFOV/GMFOV/PAPRTOV*/	Con	skin, resp sys sens	Swallow: Medical attention	
Change:	N.R.	SCBAF/SAF			immed	
Provide:	Eyewash, Quick drench	§: SCBAF:PD,PP/SAF:PD,PP:ASCBA				
		Escape: GMFOV/SCBAE				

[Chloroacetaldehyde]

Skin:	Prevent skin contact	NIOSH/OSHA	Inh	Irrit eyes, skin, resp sys;	Eye: Irr immed	Eyes, skin, resp sys
Eyes:	Prevent eye contact	3 mg/m^3: CCROVDM/SA	Ing	pulm edema	Skin: Soap wash immed	
Wash skin:	When contam	7.5 mg/m^3: SA:CF$^\varepsilon$/PAPROVDM$^\varepsilon$	Con		Breath: Resp support	
Remove:	When wet or contam	15 mg/m^3: CCRFOVHiE/GMFSHiE/			Swallow: Medical attention	
Change:	Daily	SCBAF/SAF			immed	
Provide:	Eyewash	§: SCBAF:PD,PP/SAF:PD,PP:ASCBA				
		Escape: GMFSHiE/SCBAE				

[α-Chloroacetophenone]

Skin:	Prevent skin contact	TBAL	Inh	Irrit eyes, skin, resp	Eye: Irr immed	Eyes, skin, resp sys
Eyes:	Prevent eye contact		Abs	sys; eye, skin burns;	Skin: Water flush immed	
Wash skin:	When contam		Ing	cough, wheez, dysp; lac	Breath: Resp support	
Remove:	When wet or contam		Con		Swallow: Medical attention	
Change:	N.R.				immed	
Provide:	Eyewash, Quick drench					

[Chloroacetyl chloride]

Chemical name, structure/formula, CAS and RTECS Nos., and DOT ID and guide Nos.	Synonyms, trade names, and conversion factors	Exposure limits (TWA unless noted otherwise)	IDLH	Physical description	Chemical and physical properties		Incompatibilities and reactivities	Measurement method (See Table 1)
					MW, BP, SOL Fl.P, IP, Sp, Gr, flammability	VP, FRZ UEL, LEL		
Chlorobenzene C_6H_5Cl 108-90-7 CZ0175000 1134 130	Benzene chloride, Chlorobenzol, MCB, Monochlorobenzene, Phenyl chloride 1 ppm = 4.61 mg/m³	NIOSH See Appendix D OSHA 75 ppm (350 mg/m³)	1000 ppm	Colorless liquid with an almond-like odor.	MW: 112.6 BP: 270°F Sol: 0.05% Fl.P: 82°F IP: 9.07 eV Sp.Gr: 1.11 Class IC Flammable Liquid	VP: 9 mm FRZ: -50°F UEL: 9.6% LEL: 1.3%	Strong oxidizers	Char; CS₂; GC/FID; IV [#1003, Halogenated Hydrocarbons]
o-Chlorobenzylidene malononitrile $ClC_6H_4CH=C(CN)_2$ 2698-41-1 OO3675000 1 ppm = 7.71 mg/m³	2-Chlorobenzalmalonitrile, CS, OCBM	NIOSH C 0.05 ppm (0.4 mg/m³) [skin] OSHA† 0.05 ppm (0.4 mg/m³)	2 mg/m³	White crystalline solid with a pepper-like odor.	MW: 188.6 BP: 590-599°F Sol: Insoluble Fl.P: ? IP: ? Sp.Gr: ? Combustible Solid	VP: 0.00003 mm MLT: 203-205°F UEL: ? LEL: ? MEC: 25 g/m³	Strong oxidizers	Filter/ Tenax GC; Reagent; HPLC/UVD; II(5) [P&CAM #304]
Chlorobromomethane CH_2BrCl 74-97-5 PA5250000 1887 160	Bromochloromethane, CB, CBM, Fluorocarbon 1011, Halon® 1011, Methyl chlorobromide 1 ppm = 5.29 mg/m³	NIOSH/OSHA 200 ppm (1050 mg/m³)	2000 ppm	Colorless to pale-yellow liquid with a chloroform-like odor. [Note: May be used as a fire extinguishing agent.]	MW: 129.4 BP: 155°F Sol: Insoluble Fl.P: NA IP: 10.77 eV Sp.Gr: 1.93 Noncombustible Liquid	VP: 115 mm FRZ: -124°F UEL: NA LEL: NA	Chemically-active metals such as calcium, powdered aluminum, zinc & magnesium	Char; CS₂; GC/FID; IV [#1003, Halogenated Hydrocarbons]
Chlorodifluoromethane $CHClF_2$ 75-45-6 PA6390000 1018 126	Difluorochloromethane, Fluorocarbon-22, Freon® 22, Genetron® 22, Monochlorodifluoromethane, Refrigerant 22 1 ppm = 3.54 mg/m³	NIOSH 1000 ppm (3500 mg/m³) ST 1250 ppm (4375 mg/m³) OSHA† none	N.D.	Colorless gas with a faint, sweetish odor. [Note: Shipped as a liquefied compressed gas.]	MW: 86.5 BP: -41°F Sol(77°F): 0.3% Fl.P: NA IP: 12.45 eV RGasD: 3.11 Nonflammable Gas	VP: 9.4 atm FRZ: -231°F UEL: NA LEL: NA	Alkalis, alkaline earth metals (e.g., powdered aluminum, sodium, potassium, zinc)	Char(2); Methylene chloride; GC/FID; IV [#1018]

Personal protection and sanitation (See Table 3)	Recommendations for respirator selection — maximum concentration for use (MUC) (See Table 4)	Health hazards			
		Route	Symptoms (See Table 5)	First aid (See Table 6)	Target organs (See Table 5)
Skin: Prevent skin contact Eyes: Prevent eye contact Wash skin: When contam Change: N.R. Remove: When wet (flamm)	OSHA 1000 ppm: SA:CF$^£$/PAPROV$^£$/CCRFOV/ GMFOV/SCBAF/SAF §: SCBAF:PD,PP/SAF:PD,PP:ASCBA Escape: GMFOV/SCBAF	Inh Ing Con	Irrit eyes, skin, nose; drow, inco; CNS depres; in animals: liver, lung, kidney inj	Eye: Irr immed Skin: Soap wash prompt Breath: Resp support Swallow: Medical attention immed	Eyes, skin, resp sys, CNS, liver

[Chlorobenzene]

Skin: Prevent skin contact Eyes: Prevent eye contact Wash skin: When contam/Daily Change: Daily Remove: When wet or contam	NIOSH/OSHA 2 mg/m^3: SA:CF$^£$/GMFSHiE/SCBAF/SAF §: SCBAF:PD,PP/SAF:PD,PP:ASCBA Escape: GMFSHiE/SCBAE	Inh Abs Ing Con	Pain, burn eyes, lac, conj; eryt eyelids, blepharospasm; irrit throat, cough, chest tight; head; eryt, vesic skin	Eye: Irr immed Skin: Soap wash immed Breath: Resp support Swallow: Medical attention immed	Eyes, skin, resp sys

[o-Chlorobenzylidene malononitrile]

Skin: Prevent skin contact Eyes: Prevent eye contact Wash skin: When contam Change: N.R. Remove: When wet or contam	NIOSH/OSHA 2000 ppm: SA:CF$^£$/PAPROV$^£$/CCRFOV/ GMFOV/SCBAF/SAF §: SCBAF:PD,PP/SAF:PD,PP:ASCBA Escape: GMFOV/SCBAE	Inh Ing Con	Irrit eyes, skin, throat; conf, dizz, CNS depres; pulm edema	Eye: Irr immed Skin: Soap wash prompt Breath: Resp support Swallow: Medical attention immed	Eyes, skin, resp sys, liver, kidneys, CNS

[Chlorobromomethane]

Skin: Frostbite Eyes: Frostbite Wash skin: N.R. Remove: N.R. Change: N.R. Provide: Frostbite	TBAL	Inh Con (liq)	Irrit resp sys; conf, drow, ringing in ears; heart palp, card arrhy; asphy; liver, kidney, spleen inj; liq: frostbite	Eye: Frostbite Skin: Frostbite Breath: Resp support	Resp sys, CVS, CNS, liver, kidneys, spleen

[Chlorodifluoromethane]

Chemical name, structure/formula, CAS and RTECS Nos., and DOT ID and guide Nos.	Synonyms, trade names, and conversion factors	Exposure limits (TWA unless noted otherwise)	IDLH	Physical description	Chemical and physical properties		Incompatibilities and reactivities	Measurement method (See Table 1)
					MW, BP, SOL Fl.P, IP, Sp, Gr, flammability	VP, FRZ UEL, LEL		
Chlorodiphenyl (42% chlorine) $C_6H_4ClC_6H_4Cl_2$ (approx) 53469-21-9 TQ1356000 2315 171	Aroclor® 1242, PCB, Polychlorinated biphenyl	NIOSH* Ca 0.001 mg/m³ See Appendix A [*Note: The NIOSH REL also applies to other PCBs.] OSHA 1 mg/m³ [skin]	Ca [5 mg/m³]	Colorless to light-colored, viscous liquid with a mild, hydrocarbon odor.	MW: 258 (approx) BP: 617-691°F Sol: Insoluble Fl.P: NA IP: ? Sp.Gr(77°F): 1.39 Nonflammable Liquid, but exposure in a fire results in the formation of a black soot containing PCBs, polychlorinated dibenzofurans & chlorinated dibenzo-p-dioxins.	VP: 0.001 mm FRZ: -2°F UEL: NA LEL: NA	Strong oxidizers	Filter/ Florisil; Hexane; GC/ECD; IV [#5503, PCBs]
Chlorodiphenyl (54% chlorine) $C_6H_3Cl_2C_6H_2Cl_3$ (approx) 11097-69-1 TQ1360000 2315 171	Aroclor® 1254, PCB, Polychlorinated biphenyl	NIOSH* Ca See Appendix A 0.001 mg/m³ [Note: The NIOSH REL also applies to other PCBs.] OSHA 0.5 mg/m³ [skin]	Ca [5 mg/m³]	Colorless to pale-yellow, viscous liquid or solid (below 50°F) with a mild, hydro-carbon odor.	MW: 326(approx) BP: 689-734°F Sol: Insoluble Fl.P: NA IP: ? Sp.Gr(77°F): 1.38 Nonflammable Liquid, but exposure in a fire results in the formation of a black soot containing PCBs, polychlorinated dibenzofurans & chlorinated dibenzo-p-dioxins.	VP: 0.00006 mm FRZ: 50°F UEL: NA LEL: NA	Strong oxidizers	Filter/ Florisil; Hexane; GC/ECD; IV [#5503, PCBs]
Chloroform $CHCl_3$ 67-66-3 FS9100000 1888 151	Methane trichloride, Trichloromethane 1 ppm = 4.88 mg/m³	NIOSH Ca See Appendix A ST 2 ppm (9.78 mg/m³) [60-min] OSHA† C 50 ppm (240 mg/m³)	Ca [500 ppm]	Colorless liquid with a pleasant odor.	MW: 119.4 BP: 143°F Sol(77°F): 0.5% Fl.P: NA IP: 11.42 eV Sp.Gr: 1.48 Noncombustible Liquid	VP: 160 mm FRZ: -82°F UEL: NA LEL: NA	Strong caustics; chemically-active metals such as aluminum or mag-nesium powder, sodium & potassium; strong oxidizers [Note: When heated to decomposition, forms phosgene gas.]	Char; CS₂; GC/FID; IV [#1003, Haloge-nated Hydro-carbons]
bis-Chloromethyl ether $(CH_2Cl)_2O$ 542-88-1 KN1575000 2249 153	BCME, bis-CME, Chloromethyl ether, Dichlorodimethyl ether, Dichloromethyl ether, Oxybis(chloromethane)	NIOSH Ca See Appendix A OSHA [1910.1008] See Appendix B	Ca [N.D.]	Colorless liquid with a suffocating odor.	MW: 115.0 BP: 223°F Sol: Reacts Fl.P: <66°F IP: ? Sp.Gr: 1.32 Class IB Flammable Liquid	VP(72°F): 30 mm FRZ: -43°F UEL: ? LEL: ?	Acids, water [Note: Reacts with water to form hydrochloric acid & formaldehyde.]	Imp; Reagent; GC/ECD; OSHA [#10]

64

Personal protection and sanitation (See Table 3)	Recommendations for respirator selection — maximum concentration for use (MUC) (See Table 4)	Health hazards			
		Route	Symptoms (See Table 5)	First aid (See Table 6)	Target organs (See Table 5)
Skin: Prevent skin contact Eyes: Prevent eye contact Wash skin: When contam Remove: When wet or contam Change: Daily Provide: Eyewash, Quick drench	NIOSH ¥: SCBAF:PD,PP/SAF:PD,PP:ASCBA Escape: GMFOVHiE/SCBAE	Inh Abs Ing Con	Irrit eyes; chloracne; liver damage; repro effects; [carc]	Eye: Irr immed Skin: Soap wash immed Breath: Resp support Swallow: Medical attention immed	Skin, eyes, liver, repro sys [in animals: tumors of the pituitary gland & liver, leukemia]

[Chlorodiphenyl (42% chlorine)]

Skin: Prevent skin contact Eyes: Prevent eye contact Wash skin: When contam Remove: When wet or contam Change: Daily Provide: Eyewash, Quick drench	NIOSH ¥: SCBAF:PD,PP/SAF:PD,PP:ASCBA Escape: GMFOVHiE/SCBAE	Inh Abs Ing Con	Irrit eyes; chloracne; liver damage; repro effects; [carc]	Eye: Irr immed Skin: Soap wash immed Breath: Resp support Swallow: Medical attention immed	Skin, eyes, liver, repro sys [in animals: tumors of the pituitary gland & liver, leukemia]

[Chlorodiphenyl (54% chlorine)]

Skin: Prevent skin contact Eyes: Prevent eye contact Wash skin: When contam Remove: When wet or contam Change: N.R. Provide: Eyewash, Quick drench	NIOSH ¥: SCBAF:PD,PP/SAF:PD,PP:ASCBA Escape: GMFOV/SCBAE	Inh Abs Ing Con	Irrit eyes, skin; dizz, mental dullness, nau, conf, head, ftg; anes; enlarged liver; [carc]	Eye: Irr immed Skin: Soap wash prompt Breath: Resp support Swallow: Medical attention immed	Liver, kidneys, heart, eyes, skin, CNS [in animals: liver & kidney cancer]

[Chloroform]

Skin: Prevent skin contact Eyes: Prevent eye contact Wash skin: When contam/Daily Remove: When wet (flamm) Change: Daily Provide: Eyewash, Quick drench	NIOSH ¥: SCBAF:PD,PP/SAF:PD,PP:ASCBA Escape: GMFOV/SCBAE	Inh Abs Ing Con	Irrit eyes, skin, muc memb, resp sys; pulm congestion, edema; corn damage, nec; decr pulm function, cough, dysp, wheez; blood-stained sputum, bronchial secretions; [carc]	Eye: Irr immed Skin: Soap wash immed Breath: Resp support Swallow: Medical attention immed	Eyes, skin, resp sys [lung cancer]

[bis-Chloromethyl ether]

Chemical name, structure/formula, CAS and RTECS Nos., and DOT ID and guide Nos.	Synonyms, trade names, and conversion factors	Exposure limits (TWA unless noted otherwise)	IDLH	Physical description	Chemical and physical properties		Incompatibilities and reactivities	Measurement method (See Table 1)
					MW, BP, SOL Fl.P, IP, Sp, Gr, flammability	VP, FRZ UEL, LEL		
Chloromethyl methyl ether CH$_3$OCH$_2$Cl 107-30-2 KN6650000 1239 131	Chlorodimethyl ether, Chloromethoxymethane, CMME, Dimethylchloroether, Methylchloromethyl ether	NIOSH Ca See Appendix A OSHA [1910.1006] See Appendix B	Ca [N.D.]	Colorless liquid with an irritating odor.	MW: 80.5 BP: 138°F Sol: Reacts Fl.P.(oc): 32°F IP: 10.25 eV Sp.Gr: 1.06 Class IB Flammable Liquid	VP(70°F): 192 mm FRZ: -154°F UEL: ? LEL: ?	Water [Note: Reacts with water to form hydrochloric acid & formaldehyde.]	Imp; Hexane; GC/ECD; II(1) [P&CAM #220]
1-Chloro-1-nitropropane CH$_3$CH$_2$CHCINO$_2$ 600-25-9 TX5075000	Korax®, Lanstan® 1 ppm = 5.06 mg/m^3	NIOSH 2 ppm (10 mg/m^3) OSHA† 20 ppm (100 mg/m^3)	100 ppm	Colorless liquid with an unpleasant odor. [fungicide]	MW: 123.6 BP: 289°F Sol: 0.5% Fl.P.(oc): 144°F IP: 9.90 eV Sp.Gr: 1.21 Class IIIA Combustible Liquid	VP(77°F): 6 mm FRZ: ? UEL: ? LEL: ?	Strong oxidizers, acids	Chrom-108; Ethyl acetate; GC/FID; II(5) [#S211]
Chloropentafluoroethane CClF$_2$CF$_3$ 76-15-3 KH7877500 1020 126	Fluorocarbon-115, Freon® 115, Genetron® 115, Halocarbon 115, Monochloropentafluoroethane 1 ppm = 6.32 mg/m^3	NIOSH 1000 ppm (6320 mg/m^3) OSHA† none	N.D.	Colorless gas with a slight, ethereal odor. [Note: Shipped as a liquefied compressed gas.]	MW: 154.5 BP: -38°F Sol(77°F): 0.006% Fl.P: NA IP: 12.96 eV RGasD: 5.55 Nonflammable Gas	VP(70°F): 7.9 atm FRZ: -223°F UEL: NA LEL: NA	Alkalis, alkaline earth metals (e.g., aluminum powder, sodium, potassium, zinc)	None available
Chloropicrin CCl$_3$NO$_2$ 76-06-2 PB6300000 1580 154 1583 154 (mixture) 2929 131 (flammable mixture)	Nitrochloroform, Nitrotrichloromethane, Trichloronitromethane 1 ppm = 6.72 mg/m^3	NIOSH/OSHA 0.1 ppm (0.7 mg/m^3)	2 ppm	Colorless to faint-yellow, oily liquid with an intensely irritating odor. [pesticide]	MW: 164.4 BP: 234°F Sol: 0.2% Fl.P: NA IP: ? Sp.Gr: 1.66 Noncombustible Liquid	VP: 18 mm FRZ: -93°F UEL: NA LEL: NA	Strong oxidizers [Note: The material may explode when heated under confinement.]	None available

Personal protection and sanitation (See Table 3)		Recommendations for respirator selection — maximum concentration for use (MUC) (See Table 4)	Health hazards					
			Route	Symptoms (See Table 5)	First aid (See Table 6)		Target organs (See Table 5)	

Personal protection and sanitation (See Table 3)		Recommendations for respirator selection — MUC (See Table 4)	Route	Symptoms (See Table 5)	First aid (See Table 6)		Target organs (See Table 5)
Skin:	Prevent skin contact	NIOSH	Inh	Irrit eyes, skin,	Eye:	Irr immed	Eyes, skin, resp sys
Eyes:	Prevent eye contact	¥: SCBAF:PD,PP/SAF:PD,PP:ASCBA	Abs	muc memb; pulm	Skin:	Soap wash immed	[in animals: skin
Wash skin:	When contam/Daily	Escape: GMFOV/SCBAE	Ing	edema, pulm congestion,	Breath:	Resp support	& lung cancer]
Remove:	When wet (flamm)		Con	pneu; skin burns, nec;	Swallow:	Medical attention	
Change:	Daily			cough, wheez, pulm		immed	
Provide:	Eyewash, Quick drench			congestion; blood			
				stained-sputum; low-wgt;			
				bronchial secretions; [carc]			

[Chloromethyl methyl ether]

Personal protection and sanitation		Recommendations for respirator selection	Route	Symptoms	First aid		Target organs
Skin:	Prevent skin contact	NIOSH	Inh	In animals: irrit eyes;	Eye:	Irr immed	Resp sys, liver,
Eyes:	Prevent eye contact	20 ppm: SA*	Ing	pulm edema; liver, kidney,	Skin:	Soap wash	kidneys, CVS, eyes
Wash skin:	When contam	50 ppm: SA:CF*/PAPROV*	Con	heart damage	Breath:	Resp support	
Remove:	When wet or contam	100 ppm: CCRFOV/GMFOV/PAPRTOV*/			Swallow:	Medical attention	
Change:	N.R.	SCBAF/SAF				immed	
		§: SCBAF:PD,PP/SAF:PD,PP:ASCBA					
		Escape: GMFOV/SCBAE					

[1-Chloro-1-nitropropane]

Personal protection and sanitation		Recommendations for respirator selection	Route	Symptoms	First aid		Target organs
Skin:	Frostbite	TBAL	Inh	Dysp; dizz, inco, narco;	Eye:	Frostbite	Skin, CNS, CVS
Eyes:	Frostbite		Con	nau, vomit; heart palp;	Skin:	Frostbite	
Wash skin:	N.R.		(liq)	card arrhy, asphy;	Breath:	Resp support	
Remove:	N.R.			liq: frostbite, derm			
Change:	N.R.						
Provide:	Frostbite						

[Chloropentafluoroethane]

Personal protection and sanitation		Recommendations for respirator selection	Route	Symptoms	First aid		Target organs
Skin:	Prevent skin contact	NIOSH/OSHA	Inh	Irrit eyes, skin, resp	Eye:	Irr immed	Eyes, skin, resp sys
Eyes:	Prevent eye contact	2 ppm: SA:CF£/PAPROV£/CCRFOV/	Ing	sys; lac; cough, pulm	Skin:	Soap wash immed	
Wash skin:	When contam	GMFOV/SCBAF/SAF	Con	edema; nau, vomit	Breath:	Resp support	
Remove:	When wet or contam	§: SCBAF:PD,PP/SAF:PD,PP:ASCBA			Swallow:	Medical attention	
Change:	N.R.	Escape: GMFOV/SCBAE				immed	
Provide:	Eyewash, Quick drench						

[Chloropicrin]

Chemical name, structure/formula, CAS and RTECS Nos., and DOT ID and guide Nos.	Synonyms, trade names, and conversion factors	Exposure limits (TWA unless noted otherwise)	IDLH	Physical description	Chemical and physical properties		Incompatibilities and reactivities	Measurement method (See Table 1)
					MW, BP, SOL FI.P, IP, Sp, Gr, flammability	VP, FRZ UEL, LEL		
ß-Chloroprene $CH_2=CCICH=CH_2$ 126-99-8 EI9625000 1991 131P (inhibited)	2-Chloro-1,3-butadiene; Chlorobutadiene; Chloroprene 1 ppm = 3.62 mg/m^3	NIOSH Ca See Appendix A C 1 ppm (3.6 mg/m^3) [15-min] OSHA† 25 ppm (90 mg/m^3) [skin]	Ca [300 ppm]	Colorless liquid with a pungent, ether-like odor.	MW: 88.5 BP: 139°F Sol: Slight FI.P: -4°F IP: 8.79 eV Sp.Gr: 0.96 Class IB Flammable Liquid	VP: 188 mm FRZ: -153°F UEL: 20.0% LEL: 4.0%	Peroxides & other oxidizers [Note: Polymerizes at room temperature unless inhibited with antioxidants.]	Char; CS$_2$; GC/FID; III [#1002]
o-Chlorostyrene $CIC_6H_4CH=CH_2$ 2039-87-4 WL4160000 	2-Chlorostyrene, ortho-Chlorostyrene, 1-Chloro-2-ethenylbenzene 1 ppm = 5.67 mg/m^3	NIOSH 50 ppm (285 mg/m^3) ST 75 ppm (428 mg/m^3) OSHA† none	N.D.	Colorless liquid.	MW: 138.6 BP: 372°F Sol: Insoluble FI.P: 138°F IP: ? Sp.Gr: 1.10 Class II Combustible Liquid	VP(77°F): 0.96 mm FRZ: -82°F UEL: ? LEL: ?	None reported	None available
o-Chlorotoluene $CIC_6H_4CH_3$ 95-49-8 XS9000000 2238 130	1-Chloro-2-methylbenzene, 2-Chloro-1-methylbenzene, 2-Chlorotoluene, o-Tolyl chloride 1 ppm = 5.18 mg/m^3	NIOSH 50 ppm (250 mg/m^3) ST 75 ppm (375 mg/m^3) OSHA† none	N.D.	Colorless liquid with an aromatic odor.	MW: 126.6 BP: 320°F Sol(77°F): 0.009% FI.P: 96°F IP: 8.83 eV Sp.Gr: 1.08 Class IC Flammable Liquid	VP(77°F): 4 mm FRZ: -31°F UEL: ? LEL: ?	Acids, alkalis, oxidizers, reducing materials, water	None available
2-Chloro-6-trichloro-methyl pyridine $CIC_5H_3NCCI_3$ 1929-82-4 US7525000	2-Chloro-6-(trichloro-methyl)pyridine; Nitrapyrin; N-serve®; 2,2,2-Tetrachloro-2-picoline	NIOSH 10 mg/m^3 (total) ST 20 mg/m^3 (total) 5 mg/m^3 (resp) OSHA 15 mg/m^3 (total) 5 mg/m^3 (resp)	N.D.	Colorless or white, crystalline solid with a mild, sweet odor.	MW: 230.9 BP: ? Sol: Insoluble FI.P: ? IP: ? Sp.Gr: ? Combustible Solid [Explosive]	VP(73°F): 0.003 mm MLT: 145°F UEL: ? LEL: ?	Aluminum, magnesium [Note: Emits oxides of nitrogen and chloride ion when heated to decomposition.]	None available

Personal protection and sanitation (See Table 3)	Recommendations for respirator selection — maximum concentration for use (MUC) (See Table 4)	Route	Health hazards Symptoms (See Table 5)	First aid (See Table 6)	Target organs (See Table 5)
Skin: Prevent skin contact Eyes: Prevent eye contact Wash skin: When contam Remove: When wet (flamm) Change: N.R. Provide: Eyewash, Quick drench	NIOSH ¥: SCBAF:PD,PP/SAF:PD,PP:ASCBA Escape: GMFOV/SCBAE	Inh Abs Ing Con	Irrit eyes, skin, resp sys; ner, irrity; derm; alopecia; repro effects; [carc]	Eye: Irr immed Skin: Soap wash immed Breath: Resp support Swallow: Medical attention immed	Eyes, skin, resp sys, repro sys [lung & skin cancer]

[ß-Chloroprene]

Skin: Prevent skin contact Eyes: Prevent eye contact Wash skin: When contam Remove: When wet or contam Change: N.R.	TBAL	Inh Ing Con	In animals: irrit eyes, skin; hema, prot, acidosis; enlarged liver, jaun	Eye: Irr immed Skin: Soap wash Breath: Resp support Swallow: Medical attention immed	Eyes, skin, liver, kidneys, CNS, PNS

[o-Chlorostyrene]

Skin: Prevent skin contact Eyes: Prevent eye contact Wash skin: When contam Remove: When wet (flamm) Change: N.R. Provide: Eyewash	TBAL	Inh Abs Ing Con	Irrit eyes, skin, muc memb; derm; drow, inco, anes; cough; liver, kidney inj	Eye: Irr immed Skin: Soap wash immed Breath: Resp support Swallow: Medical attention immed	Eyes, skin, resp sys, CNS, liver, kidneys

[o-Chlorotoluene]

Skin: Prevent skin contact Eyes: Prevent eye contact Wash skin: When contam Remove: When wet or contam Change: Daily	TBAL	Inh Abs Ing Con	No adverse effects noted in ingestion studies with animals.	Eye: Irr immed Skin: Soap wash immed Breath: Resp support Swallow: Medical attention immed	Eyes, skin

[2-Chloro-6-trichloromethyl pyridine]

Chemical name, structure/formula, CAS and RTECS Nos., and DOT ID and guide Nos.	Synonyms, trade names, and conversion factors	Exposure limits (TWA unless noted otherwise)	IDLH	Physical description	Chemical and physical properties		Incompatibilities and reactivities	Measurement method (See Table 1)
					MW, BP, SOL Fl.P, IP, Sp, Gr, flammability	VP, FRZ UEL, LEL		
Chlorpyrifos $C_9H_{11}Cl_3NO_3PS$ 2921-88-2 TF6300000 2783 55	Chlorpyrifos-ethyl; O,O-Diethyl O-3,5,6-trichloro-2-pyridyl phosphorothioate; Dursban®	NIOSH 0.2 mg/m³ ST 0.6 mg/m³ [skin] OSHA† none	N.D.	Colorless to white, crystalline solid with a mild, mercaptan-like odor. [pesticide] [Note: Commercial formulations may be combined with combustible liquids.]	MW: 350.6 BP: 320°F (Decomposes) Sol: 0.0002% Fl.P: ? IP: ? Sp.Gr: 1.40 (Liquid at 110°F) Combustible Solid	VP: 0.00002 mm MLT: 108°F UEL: ? LEL: ?	Strong acids, caustics, amines [Note: Corrosive to copper & brass.]	OVS-2; Toluene/ Acetone; GC/FPD; IV [#5600, Organo-phosporus Pesticides]
Chromic acid and chromates CrO_3 (acid) 1333-82-0 (CrO_3) GB6650000 (CrO_3) 1755 60 (acid, soln.) 1463 42 (acid, solid)	Chromic acid (CrO_3): Chromic anhydride, Chromic oxide, Chromium(VI) oxide (1:3), Chromium trioxide Synonyms of chromates (i.e., chromium(VI) compounds) such as zinc chromate vary depending upon the specific compound.	NIOSH (as Cr) Ca See Appendix A 0.001 mg/m³ See Appendix C OSHA (as CrO_3) C 0.1 mg/m³ See Appendix C	Ca [15 mg/m³ as Cr(VI)]	CrO_3: Dark-red, odorless flakes or powder. [Note: Often used in an aqueous solution (H_2CrO_4).]	MW: 100.0 BP: 482°F (Decomposes) Sol: 63% Fl.P: NA IP: NA Sp.Gr: 2.70 (CrO_3) CrO_3: Noncombustible Solid, but will accelerate the burning of combustible materials.	VP: Very low MLT: 387°F UEL: NA LEL: NA	Combustible, organic, or other readily oxidizable materials (paper, wood, sulfur, aluminum, plastics, etc.); corrosive to metals	Filter; Reagent; Vis; [#7600, Chromium, Hexavalent] [Also #7604]
Chromium(II) compounds (as Cr)	Synonyms vary depending upon the specific chromium(II) compound. [Note: Chromium(II) compounds include soluble chromous salts.]	NIOSH/OSHA 0.5 mg/m³ See Appendix C	250 mg/m³ [as Cr(II)]	Appearance and odor vary depending upon the specific chromium(II) compound.	Properties vary depending upon the specific chromium(II) compound.		Varies	Filter; Acid; FAAS; IV [#7024, Chromium]
Chromium(III) compounds (as Cr)	Synonyms vary depending upon the specific chromium(III) compound. [Note: Chromium(III) compounds include soluble chromic salts.]	NIOSH/OSHA 0.5 mg/m³ See Appendix C	25 mg/m³ [as Cr(III)]	Appearance and odor vary depending upon the specific chromium(III) compound.	Properties vary depending upon the specific chromium(III) compound.		Varies	Filter; Acid; FAAS; IV [#7024, Chromium]

Personal protection and sanitation (See Table 3)		Recommendations for respirator selection — maximum concentration for use (MUC) (See Table 4)	Health hazards				
			Route	Symptoms (See Table 5)	First aid (See Table 6)		Target organs (See Table 5)
Skin:	Prevent skin contact	TBAL	Inh	Wheez, lar spasms, salv;	Eye:	Irr immed	Resp sys, CNS,
Eyes:	Prevent eye contact		Abs	bluish lips, skin; miosis,	Skin:	Soap wash immed	PNS, plasma chol
Wash skin:	When contam		Ing	blurred vision; nau, vomit,	Breath:	Resp support	
Remove:	When wet or contam		Con	abdom cramps, diarr	Swallow:	Medical attention	
Change:	Daily					immed	

[Chlorpyrifos]

Personal protection and sanitation (See Table 3)		Recommendations for respirator selection — maximum concentration for use (MUC) (See Table 4)	Health hazards				
Skin:	Prevent skin contact	NIOSH	Inh	Irrit resp sys, nasal	Eye:	Irr immed	Blood, resp sys,
Eyes:	Prevent eye contact	¥: SCBAF:PD,PP/SAF:PD,PP:ASCBA	Ing	septum perf; liver,	Skin:	Soap flush immed	liver, kidneys,
Wash skin:	When contam	Escape: HiEF/SCBAE	Con	kidney damage; leucyt,	Breath:	Resp support	eyes, skin
Remove:	When wet or contam			leupen, monocy, eosin;	Swallow:	Medical attention	[lung cancer]
Change:	Daily			eye inj, conj; skin ulcer,		immed	
Provide:	Eyewash, Quick drench			sens derm; [carc]			

[Chromic acid and chromates]

Personal protection and sanitation (See Table 3)		Recommendations for respirator selection — maximum concentration for use (MUC) (See Table 4)	Health hazards				
Skin:	Prevent skin contact	NIOSH/OSHA	Inh	Irrit eyes; sens derm	Eye:	Irr immed	Eyes, skin
Eyes:	Prevent eye contact	2.5 mg/m³: DM*	Ing		Skin:	Water flush prompt	
Wash skin:	When contam	5 mg/m³: DMXSQ*/SA*	Con		Breath:	Resp support	
Remove:	When wet or contam	12.5 mg/m³: SA:CF*/PAPRDM*			Swallow:	Medical attention	
Change:	N.R.	25 mg/m³: HiEF/PAPRTHiE*/SCBAF/SAF				immed	
		250 mg/m³: SAF:PD,PP					
		§: SCBAF:PD,PP/SAF:PD,PP:ASCBA					
		Escape: HiEF/SCBAE					

[Chromium(II) compounds (as Cr)]

Personal protection and sanitation (See Table 3)		Recommendations for respirator selection — maximum concentration for use (MUC) (See Table 4)	Health hazards				
Skin:	Prevent skin contact	NIOSH/OSHA	Inh	Irrit eyes; sens derm	Eye:	Irr immed	Eyes, skin
Eyes:	Prevent eye contact	2.5 mg/m³: DM*	Ing		Skin:	Water flush prompt	
Wash skin:	When contam	5 mg/m³: DMXSQ*/SA*	Con		Breath:	Resp support	
Remove:	When wet or contam	12.5 mg/m³: SA:CF*/PAPRDM*			Swallow:	Medical attention	
Change:	N.R.	25 mg/m³: HiEF/PAPRTHiE*/SCBAF/SAF				immed	
		§: SCBAF:PD,PP/SAF:PD,PP:ASCBA					
		Escape: HiEF/SCBAE					

[Chromium(III) compounds (as Cr)]

Chemical name, structure/formula, CAS and RTECS Nos., and DOT ID and guide Nos.	Synonyms, trade names, and conversion factors	Exposure limits (TWA unless noted otherwise)	IDLH	Physical description	Chemical and physical properties		Incompatibilities and reactivities	Measurement method (See Table 1)
					MW, BP, SOL FI.P, IP, Sp, Gr, flammability	VP, FRZ UEL, LEL		
Chromium metal Cr 7440-47-3 GB4200000	Chrome, Chromium	NIOSH 0.5 mg/m³ See Appendix C OSHA* 1 mg/m³ See Appendix C [*Note: The PEL also applies to insoluble chromium salts.]	250 mg/m³ (as Cr)	Blue-white to steel-gray, lustrous, brittle, hard, odorless solid.	MW: 52.0 BP: 4788°F Sol: Insoluble FI.P: NA IP: NA Sp.Gr: 7.14 Noncombustible Solid in bulk form, but finely divided dust burns rapidly if heated in a flame.	VP: 0 mm (approx) MLT: 3452°F UEL: NA LEL: NA	Strong oxidizers (such as hydrogen peroxide), alkalis	Filter; Acid; FAAS; IV [#7024]
Chromyl chloride Cr(OCl)₂ 14977-61-8 GB5775000 1758 137	Chlorochromic anhydride, Chromic oxychloride, Chromium chloride oxide, Chromium dichloride dioxide, Chromium dioxide dichloride, Chromium dioxychloride, Chromium oxychloride, Dichlorodioxochromium	NIOSH Ca See Appendix A 0.001 mg Cr(VI)/m³ OSHA none	Ca [N.D.]	Deep-red liquid with a musty, burning, acrid odor. [Note: Fumes in moist air.]	MW: 154.9 BP: 243°F Sol: Reacts FI.P: NA IP: 12.60 eV Sp.Gr(77°F): 1.91 Noncombustible Liquid, but a powerful oxidizer.	VP: 20 mm FRZ: -142°F UEL: NA LEL: NA	Water, combustible substances, halides, phosphorus, turpentine [Note: Reacts violently in water; forms chromic acid, chromic chloride, hydrochloric acid & chlorine. Corrodes common metals.]	None available
Clopidol C₇H₇Cl₂NO 2971-90-6 UU7711500	Coyden®; 3,5-Dichloro-2,6-dimethyl-4-pyridinol	NIOSH 10 mg/m³ (total) ST 20 mg/m³ (total) 5 mg/m³ (resp) OSHA 15 mg/m³ (total) 5 mg/m³ (resp)	N.D.	White to light-brown, crystalline solid.	MW: 192.1 BP: ? Sol: Insoluble FI.P: NA IP: ? Sp.Gr: ? Noncombustible Solid, but dust may explode in cloud form.	VP: ? MLT: >608°F UEL: NA LEL: NA	None reported	Filter; none; Grav; IV [Particulates NOR: #0500 (total), #0600 (resp)]
Coal dust GF8281000 1361 133	Anthracite coal dust, Bituminous coal dust, Lignite coal dust	NIOSH See Appendix D OSHA† See Appendix C (Mineral Dusts)	N.D.	Dark-brown to black solid dispersed in air.	Properties vary depending upon the specific coal type. Combustible Solid; slightly explosive when exposed to flame.		None reported	Filter; none; Grav; IV [#0600, Particulates NOR (resp) [Also #7500]

Personal protection and sanitation (See Table 3)		Recommendations for respirator selection — maximum concentration for use (MUC) (See Table 4)	Health hazards				
			Route	Symptoms (See Table 5)	First aid (See Table 6)		Target organs (See Table 5)
Skin:	N.R.	NIOSH	Inh	Irrit eyes, skin; lung	Eye:	Irr immed	Eyes, skin, resp sys
Eyes:	N.R.	2.5 mg/m³: DM*	Ing	fib (histologic)	Skin:	Soap wash	
Wash skin:	N.R.	5 mg/m³: DMXSQ*/SA*	Con		Breath:	Resp support	
Remove:	N.R.	12.5 mg/m³: SA:CF*/PAPRDM*			Swallow:	Medical attention	
Change:	N.R.	25 mg/m³: HiEF/PAPRTHiE*/SCBAF/SAF				immed	
		250 mg/m³: SAF:PD,PP					
		§: SCBAF:PD,PP/SAF:PD,PP:ASCBA					
		Escape: HiEF/SCBAE					
[Chromium metal]							
Skin:	Prevent skin contact	NIOSH	Inh	Irrit eyes, skin, upper	Eye:	Irr immed	Eyes, skin, resp sys
Eyes:	Prevent eye contact	¥: SCBAF:PD,PP/SAF:PD,PP:ASCBA	Abs	resp sys; eye, skin burns	Skin:	Water flush immed	[lung cancer]
Wash skin:	When contam	Escape: GMFOV/SCBAE	Ing		Breath:	Resp support	
Remove:	When wet or contam		Con		Swallow:	Medical attention	
Change:	N.R.					immed	
Provide:	Eyewash, Quick drench						
[Chromyl chloride]							
Skin:	N.R.	TBAL	Inh	Irrit eyes, skin, nose,	Eye:	Irr immed	Eye, skin, resp sys
Eyes:	N.R.		Con	throat; cough	Skin:	Soap wash	
Wash skin:	N.R.				Breath:	Fresh air	
Remove:	N.R.						
Change:	N.R.						
[Clopidol]							
Skin:	N.R.	TBAL	Inh	Chronic bron, decr pulm	Breath:	Fresh air	Resp sys
Eyes:	N.R.			func, emphy			
Wash skin:	N.R.						
Remove:	N.R.						
Change:	N.R.						
[Coal dust]							

Chemical name, structure/formula, CAS and RTECS Nos., and DOT ID and guide Nos.	Synonyms, trade names, and conversion factors	Exposure limits (TWA unless noted otherwise)	IDLH	Physical description	Chemical and physical properties		Incompatibilities and reactivities	Measurement method (See Table 1)
					MW, BP, SOL Fl.P, IP, Sp, Gr, flammability	VP, FRZ UEL, LEL		
Coal tar pitch volatiles 65996-93-2 GF8655000	Synonyms vary depending upon the specific compound (e.g., pyrene, phenanthrene, acridine, chrysene, anthracene & benzo(a)pyrene). [Note: NIOSH considers coal tar, coal tar pitch, and creosote to be coal tar products.]	NIOSH Ca 0.1 mg/m³ (cyclohexane-extractable fraction) See Appendix A See Appendix C OSHA [1910.1002] 0.2 mg/m³ (benzene-soluble fraction) See Appendix C	Ca [80 mg/m³]	Black or dark-brown amorphous residue.	Properties vary depending upon the specific compound. Combustible Solids		Strong oxidizers	Filter; Benzene; Grav; OSHA [#58]
Cobalt metal dust & fume (as Co) Co 7440-48-4 GF8750000	Cobalt metal dust, Cobalt metal fume	NIOSH 0.05 mg/m³ OSHA† 0.1 mg/m³	20 mg/m³ (as Co)	Odorless, silver-gray to black solid.	MW: 58.9 BP: 5612°F Sol: Insoluble Fl.P: NA IP: NA Sp.Gr: 8.92 Noncombustible Solid in bulk form, but finely divided dust will burn at high temperatures.	VP: 0 mm (approx) MLT: 2719°F UEL: NA LEL: NA	Strong oxidizers, ammonium nitrate	Filter; Acid; FAAS; IV [#7027]
Cobalt carbonyl (as Co) C₈Co₂O₈ 10210-68-1 GG0300000	di-mu-Carbonylhexa-carbonyldicobalt, Cobalt octacarbonyl, Cobalt tetracarbonyl dimer, Dicobalt carbonyl, Dicobalt octacarbonyl, Octacarbonyldicobalt	NIOSH 0.1 mg/m³ OSHA† none	N.D.	Orange to dark-brown, crystalline solid. [Note: The pure substance is white.]	MW: 341.9 BP: 126°F (Decomposes) Sol: Insoluble Fl.P: NA IP: ? Sp.Gr: 1.87 Noncombustible Solid, but flammable carbon monoxide is emitted during decomposition.	VP: 0.7 mm MLT: 124°F UEL: NA LEL: NA	Air [Note: Decomposes on exposure to air or heat; stable in atmosphere of hydrogen & carbon monoxide.]	None available
Cobalt hydrocarbonyl (as Co) HCo(CO)₄ 16842-03-8 GG0900000	Hydrocobalt tetracarbonyl, Tetracarbonylhydridocobalt, Tetracarbonylhydrocobalt	NIOSH 0.1 mg/m³ OSHA† none	N.D.	Gas with an offensive odor.	MW: 172.0 BP: ? Sol: 0.05% Fl.P: NA (Gas) IP: ? RGasD: 5.93 Flammable Gas	VP: >1 atm FRZ: -15°F UEL: ? LEL: ?	Air [Note: Unstable gas that decomposes rapidly in air at room temperature to cobalt carbonyl & hydrogen.]	None available

Personal protection and sanitation (See Table 3)		Recommendations for respirator selection — maximum concentration for use (MUC) (See Table 4)	Health hazards					
			Route	Symptoms (See Table 5)	First aid (See Table 6)		Target organs (See Table 5)	

Personal protection and sanitation (See Table 3)		Recommendations for respirator selection — maximum concentration for use (MUC) (See Table 4)	Route	Symptoms (See Table 5)	First aid (See Table 6)		Target organs (See Table 5)
Skin: Eyes: Wash skin: Remove: Change:	Prevent skin contact Prevent eye contact Daily N.R. Daily	NIOSH ¥: SCBAF:PD,PP/SAF:PD,PP:ASCBA Escape: GMFOVHiE/SCBAE	Inh Con	Derm, bron, [carc]	Eye: Skin: Breath: Swallow:	Irr immed Soap wash immed Resp support Medical attention immed	Resp sys, skin, bladder, kidneys [lung, kidney & skin cancer]
[Coal tar pitch volatiles]							
Skin: Eyes: Wash skin: Remove: Change:	Prevent skin contact N.R. When contam When wet or contam Daily	NIOSH 0.25 mg/m³: DM^ 0.5 mg/m³: DMXSQ*^/DMFu*/SA* 1.25 mg/m³: SA:CF*/PAPRDM*^/ 　　　　　PAPRDMFu* 2.5 mg/m³: HiEF/SCBAF/SAF 20 mg/m³: SAF:PD,PP §: SCBAF:PD,PP/SAF:PD,PP:ASCBA Escape: HiEF/SCBAE	Inh Ing Con	Cough, dysp, wheez, decr pulm func; low-wgt; derm; diffuse nodular fib; resp hypersensitivity, asthma	Eye: Skin: Breath: Swallow:	Irr immed Soap wash Resp support Medical attention immed	Skin, resp sys
[Cobalt (dust and fume)]							
Skin: Eyes: Wash skin: Remove: Change:	Prevent skin contact Prevent eye contact When contam When wet or contam Daily	TBAL	Inh Abs Ing Con	Irrit eyes, skin, muc memb; cough, decr pulm func, wheez, dysp; in animals: liver, kidney inj; pulm edema	Eye: Skin: Breath: Swallow:	Irr immed Soap wash Resp support Medical attention immed	Eyes, skin, resp sys, blood, CNS
[Cobalt carbonyl (as Co)]							
Skin: Eyes: Wash skin: Remove: Change:	Prevent skin contact Prevent eye contact When contam When wet or contam Daily	TBAL	Inh Con	In animals: irrit resp sys; dysp, cough, decr pulm func, pulm edema	Eye: Skin: Breath:	Irr immed Soap wash Resp support	Eyes, skin, resp sys
[Cobalt hydrocarbonyl (as Co)]							

Chemical name, structure/formula, CAS and RTECS Nos., and DOT ID and guide Nos.	Synonyms, trade names, and conversion factors	Exposure limits (TWA unless noted otherwise)	IDLH	Physical description	Chemical and physical properties MW, BP, SOL FI.P, IP, Sp, Gr, flammability	VP, FRZ UEL, LEL	Incompatibilities and reactivities	Measurement method (See Table 1)
Coke oven emissions GH0346000	Synonyms vary depending upon the specific constituent.	NIOSH Ca 0.5-0.7 mg/m³ (total) (screening level) See Appendix A See Appendix C OSHA [1910.1029] 0.150 mg/m³ (benzene-soluble fraction)	Ca [N.D.]	Emissions released during the carbonization of bituminous coal for the production of coke. [Note: See Appendix C for more information.]	Properties vary depending upon the constituent.		None reported	Filter; Benzene; Grav; IV [#5023, Coal Tar Pitch Volatiles]
Copper (dusts and mists) Cu 7440-50-8 GL5325000	Copper metal dusts, Copper metal mists	NIOSH*/OSHA* 1 mg/m³ [*Note: The REL and PEL also apply to other copper compounds (as Cu) except Copper fume.]	100 mg/m³ (as Cu)	Reddish, lustrous, malleable, odorless solid.	MW: 63.5 BP: 4703°F Sol: Insoluble FI.P: NA IP: NA Sp.Gr: 8.94 Noncombustible Solid in bulk form, but powdered form may ignite.	VP: 0 mm (approx) MLT: 1981°F UEL: NA LEL: NA	Oxidizers, alkalis, sodium azide, acetylene	Filter; Acid; FAAS; IV [#7029]
Copper fume (as Cu) CuO/Cu 1317-38-0 (CuO) GL7900000 (CuO)	CuO: Black copper oxide, Copper monoxide, Copper(II) oxide, Cupric oxide Cu: Copper fume [Note: Also see specific listing for Copper (dusts and mists).]	NIOSH/OSHA 0.1 mg/m³	100 mg/m³ (as Cu)	Finely divided black particulate dispersed in air. [Note: Exposure may occur in copper & brass plants and during the welding of copper alloys.]	MW: 79.5 BP: Decomposes Sol: Insoluble FI.P: NA IP: NA Sp.Gr: 6.4 (CuO) CuO: Noncombustible Solid	VP: 0 mm (approx) MLT: 1879°F (Decomposes) UEL: NA LEL: NA [Note: See Copper (dusts and mists) for properties of Copper metal.]	CuO: Acetylene, zirconium	Filter; Acid; FAAS; IV [#7029]
Cotton dust (raw) GN2275000	Raw cotton dust	NIOSH <0.200 mg/m³ See Appendix C OSHA [Z-1-A & 1910.1043] See Appendix C	100 mg/m³	Colorless, odorless solid.	MW: ? BP: Decomposes Sol: Insoluble FI.P: NA IP: NA Sp.Gr: ? Combustible Solid	VP: 0 mm (approx) MLT: Decomposes UEL: NA LEL: NA	Strong oxidizers	Vertical elut; none; Grav; OSHA [1910.1043]

76

Personal protection and sanitation (See Table 3)	Recommendations for respirator selection — maximum concentration for use (MUC) (See Table 4)	Health hazards			
		Route	Symptoms (See Table 5)	First aid (See Table 6)	Target organs (See Table 5)
Skin: Prevent skin contact Eyes: Prevent eye contact Wash skin: Daily Remove: N.R. Change: Daily [Coke oven emissions]	NIOSH ¥: SCBAF:PD,PP/SAF:PD,PP:ASCBA Escape: GMFOVHiE/SCBAE	Inh Con	Irrit eyes, resp sys; cough, dysp, wheez; [carc]	Eye: Irr immed Breath: Resp support	Skin, resp sys, urinary sys [skin, lung, kidney & bladder cancer]
Skin: Prevent skin contact Eyes: Prevent eye contact Wash skin: When contam Remove: When wet or contam Change: Daily [Copper (dusts and mists)]	NIOSH/OSHA 5 mg/m³: DM* 10 mg/m³: DMXSQ*^/SA* 25 mg/m³: SA:CF*/PAPRDM* 50 mg/m³: HiEF/PAPRTHiE*/SCBAF/SAF 100 mg/m³: SAF:PD,PP §: SCBAF:PD,PP/SAF:PD,PP:ASCBA Escape: HiEF/SCBAE	Inh Ing Con	Irrit eyes, nose, pharynx; nasal perf; metallic taste; derm; in animals: lung, liver, kidney damage; anemia	Eye: Irr immed Skin: Soap wash prompt Breath: Resp support Swallow: Medical attention immed	Eyes, skin, resp sys, liver, kidneys (incr risk with Wilson's disease)
Skin: N.R. Eyes: N.R. Wash skin: N.R. Remove: N.R. Change: N.R. [Copper fume (as Cu)]	NIOSH/OSHA 1 mg/m³: DMFu/SA 2.5 mg/m³: SA:CF/PAPRDMFu 5 mg/m³: HiEF/SAT:CF/PAPRTHiE/ SCBAF/SAF 100 mg/m³: SAF:PD,PP §: SCBAF:PD,PP/SAF:PD,PP:ASCBA Escape: HiEF/SCBAE	Inh Con	Irrit eyes, upper resp sys; metal fume fever: chills, musc ache, nau, fever, dry throat, cough, weak, lass; metallic or sweet taste; discoloration skin, hair	Breath: Resp support	Eyes, skin, resp sys (incr risk with Wilson's disease)
Skin: N.R. Eyes: N.R. Wash skin: N.R. Remove: N.R. Change: N.R. [Cotton dust (raw)]	NIOSH 1 mg/m³: D 2 mg/m³: DXSQ/HiE/SA 5 mg/m³: SA:CF/PAPRD 10 mg/m³: HiEF/SAT:CF/PAPRTHiE/ SCBAF/SAF 100 mg/m³: SA:PD,PP §: SCBAF:PD,PP/SAF:PD,PP:ASCBA Escape: HiEF/SCBAE	Inh	Byssinosis: chest tight, cough, wheez, dysp, decr FEV; bron; mal; fever, chills, upper resp symptoms after initial exposure	Breath: Fresh air	CVS, resp sys

Chemical name, structure/formula, CAS and RTECS Nos., and DOT ID and guide Nos.	Synonyms, trade names, and conversion factors	Exposure limits (TWA unless noted otherwise)	IDLH	Physical description	Chemical and physical properties		Incompatibilities and reactivities	Measurement method (See Table 1)
					MW, BP, SOL FI.P, IP, Sp, Gr, flammability	VP, FRZ UEL, LEL		
Crag® herbicide $C_6H_3Cl_2OCH_2CH_2OSO_3Na$ 136-78-7 KK4900000	Crag® herbicide No. 1; 2-(2,4-Dichlorophenoxy)-ethyl sodium sulfate; Sesone	NIOSH 10 mg/m³ (total) 5 mg/m³ (resp) OSHA† 15 mg/m³ (total) 5 mg/m³ (resp)	500 mg/m³	Colorless to white crystalline, odorless solid. [herbicide]	MW: 309.1 BP: Decomposes Sol(77°F): 26% FI.P: NA IP: ? Sp.Gr: 1.70 Noncombustible Solid	VP: 0.1 mm MLT: 473°F (Decomposes) UEL: NA LEL: NA	Strong oxidizers, acids	Filter; Water; Vis; II(5) [#S356]
o-Cresol $CH_3C_6H_4OH$ 95-48-7 GO6300000 2076 153	ortho-Cresol, 2-Cresol, o-Cresylic acid, 1-Hydroxy-2-methylbenzene, 2-Hydroxytoluene, 2-Methyl phenol 1 ppm = 4.43 mg/m³	NIOSH 2.3 ppm (10 mg/m³) OSHA 5 ppm (22 mg/m³) [skin]	250 ppm	White crystals with a sweet, tarry odor. [Note: A liquid above 88°F.]	MW: 108.2 BP: 376°F Sol: 2% FI.P: 178°F IP: 8.93 eV Sp.Gr: 1.05 Combustible Solid Class IIIA Combustible Liquid	VP(77°F): 0.29 mm MLT: 88°F UEL: ? LEL(300°F): 1.4%	Strong oxidizers, acids	XAD-7; Methanol; GC/FID; IV [#2546, Cresols and Phenol]
m-Cresol $CH_3C_6H_4OH$ 108-39-4 GO6125000 2076 153	meta-Cresol, 3-Cresol, m-Cresylic acid, 1-Hydroxy-3-methylbenzene, 3-Hydroxytoluene, 3-Methyl phenol 1 ppm = 4.43 mg/m³	NIOSH 2.3 ppm (10 mg/m³) OSHA 5 ppm (22 mg/m³) [skin]	250 ppm	Colorless to yellowish liquid with a sweet, tarry odor. [Note: A solid below 54°F.]	MW: 108.2 BP: 397°F Sol: 2% FI.P: 187°F IP: 8.98 eV Sp.Gr: 1.03 Class IIIA Combustible Liquid	VP(77°F): 0.14 mm FRZ: 54°F UEL: ? LEL(302°F): 1.1%	Strong oxidizers, acids	XAD-7; Methanol; GC/FID; IV [#2546, Cresols and Phenol]
p-Cresol $CH_3C_6H_4OH$ 106-44-5 GO6475000 2076 153	para-Cresol, 4-Cresol, p-Cresylic acid, 1-Hydroxy-4-methylbenzene, 4-Hydroxytoluene, 4-Methyl phenol 1 ppm = 4.43 mg/m³	NIOSH 2.3 ppm (10 mg/m³) OSHA 5 ppm (22 mg/m³) [skin]	250 ppm	Crystalline solid with a sweet, tarry odor. [Note: A liquid above 95°F.]	MW: 108.2 BP: 396°F Sol: 2% FI.P: 187°F IP: 8.97 eV Sp.Gr: 1.04 Combustible Solid Class IIIA Combustible Liquid	VP(77°F): 0.11 mm MLT: 95°F UEL: ? LEL(302°F): 1.1%	Strong oxidizers, acids	XAD-7; Methanol; GC/FID; IV [#2546, Cresols and Phenol]

Personal protection and sanitation (See Table 3)		Recommendations for respirator selection — maximum concentration for use (MUC) (See Table 4)	Health hazards					
			Route	Symptoms (See Table 5)		First aid (See Table 6)		Target organs (See Table 5)

Personal protection and sanitation		Respirator selection	Route	Symptoms	First aid		Target organs
Skin:	Prevent skin contact	NIOSH	Inh	Irrit eyes, skin; liver, kidney damage; in animals: CNS effects, convuls	Eye:	Irr immed	Eyes, skin, CNS, liver, kidneys
Eyes:	Prevent eye contact	50 mg/m³: DM	Ing		Skin:	Water wash prompt	
Wash skin:	When contam	100 mg/m³: DMXSQ/SA	Con		Breath:	Resp support	
Remove:	When wet or contam	250 mg/m³: SA:CF/PAPRDM			Swallow:	Medical attention immed	
Change:	Daily	500 mg/m³: HiEF/PAPRTHiE*/SAT:CF*/ SCBAF/SAF					
		§: SCBAF:PD,PP/SAF:PD,PP:ASCBA					
		Escape: HiEF/SCBAE					
[Crag® herbicide]							
Skin:	Prevent skin contact	NIOSH	Inh	Irrit eyes, skin, muc memb; CNS effects: conf, depres, resp fail; dysp, irreg rapid resp, weak pulse; eye, skin burns; derm; lung, liver, kidney pancreas damage	Eye:	Irr immed	Eyes, skin, resp sys, CNS, liver, kidneys, pancreas, CVS
Eyes:	Prevent eye contact	23 ppm: CCROVDM/SA	Abs		Skin:	Soap wash immed	
Wash skin:	When contam	57.5 ppm: SA:CF/PAPROVDM	Ing		Breath:	Resp support	
Remove:	When wet or contam	115 ppm: CCRFOVHiE/GMFOVHiE/ PAPRTHiE*/SAT:CF*/ SCBAF/SAF	Con		Swallow:	Medical attention immed	
Change:	Daily	250 ppm: SAF:PD,PP					
Provide:	Eyewash, Quick drench	§: SCBAF:PD,PP/SAF:PD,PP:ASCBA					
		Escape: GMFOVHiE/SCBAE					
[o-Cresol]							
Skin:	Prevent skin contact	NIOSH	Inh	Irrit eyes, skin, muc memb; CNS effects: conf, depres, resp fail; dysp, irreg rapid resp, weak pulse; eye, skin burns; derm; lung, liver, kidney pancreas damage	Eye:	Irr immed	Eyes, skin, resp sys, CNS, liver, kidneys, pancreas, CVS
Eyes:	Prevent eye contact	23 ppm: CCROVDM/SA	Abs		Skin:	Soap wash immed	
Wash skin:	When contam	57.5 ppm: SA:CF/PAPROVDM	Ing		Breath:	Resp support	
Remove:	When wet or contam	115 ppm: CCRFOVHiE/GMFOVHiE/ PAPRTHiE*/SAT:CF*/ SCBAF/SAF	Con		Swallow:	Medical attention immed	
Change:	Daily	250 ppm: SAF:PD,PP					
Provide:	Eyewash, Quick drench	§: SCBAF:PD,PP/SAF:PD,PP:ASCBA					
		Escape: GMFOVHiE/SCBAE					
[m-Cresol]							
Skin:	Prevent skin contact	NIOSH	Inh	Irrit eyes, skin, muc memb; CNS effects: conf, depres, resp fail; dysp, irreg rapid resp, weak pulse; eye, skin burns; derm; lung, liver, kidney pancreas damage	Eye:	Irr immed	Eyes, skin, resp sys, CNS, liver, kidneys, pancreas, CVS
Eyes:	Prevent eye contact	23 ppm: CCROVDM/SA	Abs		Skin:	Soap wash immed	
Wash skin:	When contam	57.5 ppm: SA:CF/PAPROVDM	Ing		Breath:	Resp support	
Remove:	When wet or contam	115 ppm: CCRFOVHiE/GMFOVHiE/ PAPRTHiE*/SAT:CF*/ SCBAF/SAF	Con		Swallow:	Medical attention immed	
Change:	Daily	250 ppm: SAF:PD,PP					
Provide:	Eyewash, Quick drench	§: SCBAF:PD,PP/SAF:PD,PP:ASCBA					
		Escape: GMFOVHiE/SCBAE					
[p-Cresol]							

Chemical name, structure/formula, CAS and RTECS Nos., and DOT ID and guide Nos.	Synonyms, trade names, and conversion factors	Exposure limits (TWA unless noted otherwise)	IDLH	Physical description	Chemical and physical properties		Incompatibilities and reactivities	Measurement method (See Table 1)
					MW, BP, SOL FI.P, IP, Sp, Gr, flammability	VP, FRZ UEL, LEL		
Crotonaldehyde CH₃CH=CHCHO 4170-30-3 GP9499000 1143 131P (inhibited)	2-Butenal, ß-Methyl acrolein, Propylene aldehyde 1 ppm = 2.87 mg/m³	NIOSH 2 ppm (6 mg/m³) See Appendix C (Aldehydes) OSHA 2 ppm (6 mg/m³)	50 ppm	Water-white liquid with a suffocating odor. [Note: Turns pale-yellow on contact with air.]	MW: 70.1 BP: 219°F Sol: 18% FI.P: 45°F IP: 9.73 eV Sp.Gr: 0.87 Class IB Flammable Liquid	VP: 19 mm FRZ: -101°F UEL: 15.5% LEL: 2.1%	Caustics, ammonia, strong oxidizers, nitric acid, amines [Note: Polymerization may occur at elevated tempera-tures, such as in fire conditions.]	Bub; Reagent; PLR; IV [#3516]
Crufomate C₁₂H₁₉ClNO₃P 299-86-5 TB3850000	4-t-Butyl-2-chlorophenyl methyl methylphos-phoramidate, Dowco® 132, Ruelene®	NIOSH 5 mg/m³ ST 20 mg/m³ OSHA† none	N.D.	White, crystalline solid in pure form. [pesticide] [Note: Commercial product is a yellow oil.]	MW: 291.7 BP: Decomposes Sol: Insoluble FI.P: ? IP: ? Sp.Gr: 1.16 Combustible Solid	VP(243°F): 0.01 mm MLT: 140°F UEL: ? LEL: ?	Strongly alkaline & strongly acidic media [Note: Unstable over long periods in aqueous preparations or above 140°F.]	Filter; none; Grav; IV [#0500, Particulates NOR (total)]
Cumene C₆H₅CH(CH₃)₂ 98-82-8 GR8575000 1918 131	Cumol, Isopropyl benzene, 2-Phenyl propane 1 ppm = 4.92 mg/m³	NIOSH/OSHA 50 ppm (245 mg/m³) [skin]	900 ppm [10%LEL]	Colorless liquid with a sharp, penetrating, aromatic odor.	MW: 120.2 BP: 306°F Sol: Insoluble FI.P: 96°F IP: 8.75 eV Sp.Gr: 0.86 Class IC Flammable Liquid	VP: 8 mm FRZ: -141°F UEL: 6.5% LEL: 0.9%	Oxidizers, nitric acid, sulfuric acid [Note: Forms cumene hydroperoxide upon long exposure to air.]	Char; CS₂; GC/FID; IV [#1501, Aromatic Hydro- carbons]
Cyanamide NH₂CN 420-04-2 GS5950000	Amidocyanogen, Carbimide, CarbodIlmide, Cyanogen nitride, Hydrogen cyanamide [Note: Cyanamide is also a synonym for Calcium cyanamide.]	NIOSH 2 mg/m³ OSHA† none	N.D.	Crystalline solid.	MW: 42.1 BP: 500°F (Decomposes) Sol(59°F): 78% FI.P: 286°F IP: 10.65 eV Sp.Gr: 1.28 Combustible Solid	VP: ? MLT: 113°F UEL: ? LEL: ?	Above 104°F: Moisture, acids, or alkalis; 1,2-phenylene diamine salts [Note: Polymerization may occur on evaporation of aqueous solutions.]	Filter; none; Grav; III [#0500, Nuisance Dust (total)]

Personal protection and sanitation (See Table 3)	Recommendations for respirator selection — maximum concentration for use (MUC) (See Table 4)	Route	Symptoms (See Table 5)	First aid (See Table 6)	Target organs (See Table 5)
Skin: Prevent skin contact Eyes: Prevent eye contact Wash skin: When contam Remove: When wet (flamm) Change: N.R. Provide: Eyewash, Quick drench	NIOSH/OSHA 20 ppm: CCROV*/SA* 50 ppm: SA:CF*/PAPROV*/CCRFOV/ GMFOV/SCBAF/SAF §: SCBAF:PD,PP/SAF:PD,PP:ASCBA Escape: GMFOV/SCBAE	Inh Ing Con	Irrit eyes, resp sys; in animals: dysp, pulm edema, irrit skin	Eye: Irr immed Skin: Water flush immed Breath: Resp support Swallow: Medical attention immed	Eyes, skin, resp sys

[Crotonaldehyde]

Skin: Prevent skin contact Eyes: Prevent eye contact Wash skin: When contam Remove: When wet or contam Change: Daily	TBAL	Inh Abs Ing Con	Irrit eyes, skin, resp sys; wheez, dysp; blurred vision, lac; sweat; abdom cramps, diarr, nau, anor	Eye: Irr immed Skin: Soap wash immed Breath: Resp support Swallow: Medical attention immed	Eyes, skin, resp sys, blood chol

[Crufomate]

Skin: Prevent skin contact Eyes: Prevent eye contact Wash skin: When contam Remove: When wet (flamm) Change: N.R.	NIOSH/OSHA 500 ppm: CCROV*/SA* 900 ppm: SA:CF*/PAPROV*/CCRFOV/ GMFOV/SCBAF/SAF §: SCBAF:PD,PP/SAF:PD,PP:ASCBA Escape: GMFOV/SCBAE	Inh Abs Ing Con	Irrit eyes, skin, muc memb; derm; head, narco, coma	Eye: Irr immed Skin: Water flush prompt Breath: Resp support Swallow: Medical attention immed	Eyes, skin, resp sys, CNS

[Cumene]

Skin: Prevent skin contact Eyes: Prevent eye contact Wash skin: When contam Remove: When wet or contam Change: Daily Provide: Eyewash, Quick drench	TBAL	Inh Abs Ing Con	Irrit eyes, skin, resp sys; eye, skin burns; miosis, salv, lac, twitch; Antabuse-like effects	Eye: Irr immed Skin: Water flush immed Breath: Resp support Swallow: Medical attention immed	Eyes, skin, resp sys, CNS

[Cyanamide]

Chemical name, structure/formula, CAS and RTECS Nos., and DOT ID and guide Nos.	Synonyms, trade names, and conversion factors	Exposure limits (TWA unless noted otherwise)	IDLH	Physical description	Chemical and physical properties		Incompatibilities and reactivities	Measurement method (See Table 1)
					MW, BP, SOL FI.P, IP, Sp, Gr, flammability	VP, FRZ UEL, LEL		
Cyanogen NCCN 460-19-5 GT1925000 1026 119	Carbon nitride, Dicyan, Dicyanogen, Ethanedinitrile, Oxalonitrile 1 ppm = 2.13 mg/m³	NIOSH 10 ppm (20 mg/m³) OSHA† none	N.D.	Colorless gas with a pungent, almond-like odor. [Note: Shipped as a liquefied compressed gas. Forms cyanide in the body.]	MW: 52.0 BP: -6°F Sol: 1% FI.P: NA (Gas) IP: 13.57 eV RGasD: 1.82 Sp.Gr: 0.95 (Liquid at -6°F) Flammable Gas	VP(70°F): 5.1 atm FRZ: -18°F UEL: 32% LEL: 6.6%	Acids, water, strong oxidizers (e.g., dichlorine oxide, fluorine) [Note: Slowly hydrolyzed in water to form hydrogen cyanide, oxalic acid, or ammonia.]	None available
Cyanogen chloride CICN 506-77-4 GT2275000 1589 125 (inhibited)	Chlorcyan, Chlorine cyanide, Chlorocyanide, Chlorocyanogen 1 ppm = 2.52 mg/m³	NIOSH C 0.3 ppm (0.6 mg/m³) OSHA† none	N.D.	Colorless gas or liquid (below 55°F) with an irritating odor. [Note: Shipped as a liquefied gas. A solid below 20°F. Forms cyanide in the body.]	MW: 61.5 BP: 55°F Sol: 7% FI.P: NA IP: 12.49 eV RGasD: 2.16 Sp.Gr: 1.22 (Liquid at 32°F) Nonflammable Gas	VP: 1010 mm FRZ: 20°F UEL: NA LEL: NA	Water, acids, alkalis, ammonia, alcohols [Note: Can react very slowly with water to form hydrogen cyanide. May be stabilized to prevent polymerization.]	None available
Cyclohexane C₆H₁₂ 110-82-7 GU6300000 1145 128	Benzene hexahydride, Hexahydrobenzene, Hexamethylene, Hexanaphthene 1 ppm = 3.44 mg/m³	NIOSH/OSHA 300 ppm (1050 mg/m³)	1300 ppm [10%LEL]	Colorless liquid with a sweet, chloroform-like odor. [Note: A solid below 44°F.]	MW: 84.2 BP: 177°F Sol: Insoluble FI.P: 0°F IP: 9.88 eV Sp.Gr: 0.78 Class IB Flammable Liquid	VP: 78 mm FRZ: 44°F UEL: 8% LEL: 1.3%	Oxidizers	Char; CS₂; GC/FID; IV [#1500, Hydro-carbons]
Cyclohexanethiol C₆H₁₁SH 1569-69-3 GV7525000 3054 131	Cyclohexylmercaptan, Cyclohexylthiol 1 ppm = 4.75 mg/m³	NIOSH C 0.5 ppm (2.4 mg/m³) [15-min] OSHA none	N.D.	Colorless liquid with a strong, offensive odor.	MW: 116.2 BP: 316°F Sol: Insoluble FI.P: 110°F IP: ? Sp.Gr: 0.98 Class II Combustible Liquid	VP: 10 mm FRZ: -181°F UEL: ? LEL: ?	Oxidizers, reducing agents, strong acids, alkali metals	None available

Personal protection and sanitation (See Table 3)	Recommendations for respirator selection — maximum concentration for use (MUC) (See Table 4)	Route	Symptoms (See Table 5)	First aid (See Table 6)	Target organs (See Table 5)
Skin: Frostbite Eyes: Prevent eye contact/ Frostbite Wash skin: N.R. Remove: When wet (flamm) Change: N.R. Provide: Frostbite	TBAL	Inh Con	Irrit eyes, nose, upper resp sys; lac; cherry red lips, tachypnea, hypernea, bradycardia; head, verti, convuls; dizz, loss of appetite, low-wgt; liq: frostbite	Eye: Frostbite Skin: Frostbite Breath: Resp support	Eyes, resp sys, CNS, CVS

[Cyanogen]

Skin: Prevent skin contact (liq) Eyes: Prevent eye contact (liq) Wash skin: When contam (liq) Remove: When wet or contam (liq) Change: N.R. Provide: Eyewash (liq), Quick drench (liq)	TBAL	Inh Abs (liq) Con (liq)	Irrit eyes, upper resp sys; cough, delayed pulm edema; weak, head, gidd, dizz, conf, nau, vomit; irreg heartbeat; irrit skin (liq)	Eye: Irr immed Skin: Water wash immed (liq) Breath: Resp support Swallow: Medical attention immed	Eyes, skin, resp sys, CNS, CVS

[Cyanogen chloride]

Skin: Prevent skin contact Eyes: Prevent eye contact Wash skin: When contam Remove: When wet (flamm) Change: N.R.	NIOSH/OSHA 1300 ppm: SA:CF$^\varepsilon$/PAPROV$^\varepsilon$/CCRFOV/ GMFOV/SCBAF/SAF §: SCBAF:PD,PP/SAF:PD,PP:ASCBA Escape: GMFOV/SCBAE	Inh Ing Con	Irrit eyes, skin, resp sys; drow; derm; narco, coma	Eye: Irr immed Skin: Water flush prompt Breath: Resp support Swallow: Medical attention immed	Eyes, skin, resp sys, CNS

[Cyclohexane]

Skin: Prevent skin contact Eyes: Prevent eye contact Wash skin: When contam Remove: When wet or contam Change: N.R. Provide: Eyewash, Quick drench	NIOSH 5 ppm: CCROV/SA 12.5 ppm: SA:CF/PAPROV 25 ppm: CCRFOV/GMFOV/PAPRTOV/ SCBAF/SAF §: SCBAF:PD,PP/SAF:PD,PP:ASCBA Escape: GMFOV/SCBAE	Inh Abs Ing Con	Irrit eyes, skin, resp sys; head, dizz, weak, nau, vomit, convuls; cough, wheez, laryngitis, dysp	Eye: Irr immed Skin: Soap flush immed Breath: Resp support Swallow: Medical attention immed	Eyes, skin, resp sys, CNS

[Cyclohexanethiol]

Chemical name, structure/formula, CAS and RTECS Nos., and DOT ID and guide Nos.	Synonyms, trade names, and conversion factors	Exposure limits (TWA unless noted otherwise)	IDLH	Physical description	Chemical and physical properties		Incompatibilities and reactivities	Measurement method (See Table 1)
					MW, BP, SOL Fl.P, IP, Sp, Gr, flammability	VP, FRZ UEL, LEL		
Cyclohexanol C₆H₁₁OH 108-93-0 GV7875000 1993 128 (combustible liquid, n.o.s.)	Anol, Cyclohexyl alcohol, Hexahydrophenol, Hexalin, Hydralin, Hydroxycyclohexane 1 ppm = 4.10 mg/m³	NIOSH 50 ppm (200 mg/m³) [skin] OSHA† 50 ppm (200 mg/m³)	400 ppm	Sticky solid or colorless to light-yellow liquid (above 77°F) with a camphor-like odor.	MW: 100.2 BP: 322°F Sol: 4% Fl.P: 154°F IP: 10.00 eV Sp.Gr. 0.96 Class IIIA Combustible Liquid	VP: 1 mm MLT: 77°F UEL: ? LEL: ?	Strong oxidizers (such as hydrogen peroxide & nitric acid)	Char; 2-Propanol/ CS₂; GC/FID; IV [#1402, Alcohols III]
Cyclohexanone C₆H₁₀O 108-94-1 GW1050000 1915 127	Anone, Cyclohexyl ketone, Pimelic ketone 1 ppm = 4.02 mg/m³	NIOSH 25 ppm (100 mg/m³) [skin] OSHA† 50 ppm (200 mg/m³)	700 ppm	Water-white to pale-yellow liquid with a peppermint- or acetone-like odor.	MW: 98.2 BP: 312°F Sol: 15% Fl.P: 146°F IP: 9.14 eV Sp.Gr. 0.95 Class IIIA Combustible Liquid	VP: 5 mm FRZ: -49°F UEL: 9.4% LEL(212°F): 1.1%	Oxidizers, nitric acid	Char; CS₂; GC/FID; IV [#1300, Ketones I]
Cyclohexene C₆H₁₀ 110-83-8 GW2500000 2256 130	Benzene tetrahydride, Tetrahydrobenzene 1 ppm = 3.36 mg/m³	NIOSH/OSHA 300 ppm (1015 mg/m³)	2000 ppm	Colorless liquid with a sweet odor.	MW: 82.2 BP: 181°F Sol: Insoluble Fl.P: 11°F IP: 8.95 eV Sp.Gr. 0.81 Class IB Flammable Liquid	VP: 67 mm FRZ: -154°F UEL: ? LEL: ?	Strong oxidizers [Note: Forms explosive peroxides with oxygen upon storage.]	Char; CS₂; GC/FID; IV [#1500, Hydro-carbons]
Cyclohexylamine C₆H₁₁NH₂ 108-91-8 GX0700000 2357 132	Aminocyclohexane, Aminohexahydrobenzene, Hexahydroaniline, Hexahydrobenzenamine 1 ppm = 4.06 mg/m³	NIOSH 10 ppm (40 mg/m³) OSHA† none	N.D.	Colorless or yellow liquid with a strong, fishy, amine-like odor.	MW: 99.2 BP: 274°F Sol: Miscible Fl.P: 88°F IP: 8.37 eV Sp.Gr. 0.87 Class IC Flammable Liquid	VP: 11 mm FRZ: 0°F UEL: 9.4% LEL: 1.5%	Oxidizers, organic compounds, acid anhydrides, acid chlorides, acids, lead [Note: Corrosive to copper, aluminum, zinc & galvanized steel.]	Si gel; H₂SO₄; GC/FID; II [#221]

Personal protection and sanitation (See Table 3)		Recommendations for respirator selection — maximum concentration for use (MUC) (See Table 4)	Health hazards			
			Route	Symptoms (See Table 5)	First aid (See Table 6)	Target organs (See Table 5)
Skin:	Prevent skin contact	NIOSH/OSHA	Inh	Irrit eyes, skin, nose,	Eye: Irr immed	Eyes, skin, resp sys
Eyes:	Prevent eye contact	400 ppm: CCROV*/PAPROV*/GMFOV/	Abs	throat; skin; narco	Skin: Water wash prompt	
Wash skin:	When contam	SA*/SCBAF	Ing		Breath: Resp support	
Remove:	When wet or contam	§: SCBAF:PD,PP/SAF:PD,PP:ASCBA	Con		Swallow: Medical attention	
Change:	Daily	Escape: GMFOV/SCBAE			immed	

[Cyclohexanol]

Skin:	Prevent skin contact	NIOSH	Inh	Irrit eyes, skin, muc memb;	Eye: Irr immed	Eyes, skin, resp sys,
Eyes:	Prevent eye contact	625 ppm: SA:CF£/PAPROV£	Abs	head; narco, coma; derm;	Skin: Water flush prompt	CNS, liver, kidneys
Wash skin:	When contam	700 ppm: CCRFOV/GMFOV/PAPRTOV£/	Ing	in animals: liver, kidney	Breath: Resp support	
Remove:	When wet or contam	SCBAF/SAF	Con	damage	Swallow: Medical attention	
Change:	N.R.	§: SCBAF:PD,PP/SAF:PD,PP:ASCBA			immed	
		Escape: GMFOV/SCBAE				

[Cyclohexanone]

Skin:	Prevent skin contact	NIOSH/OSHA	Inh	Irrit eyes, skin, resp	Eye: Irr immed	Eyes, skin, resp sys,
Eyes:	Prevent eye contact	2000 ppm: SA:CF£/PAPROV£/CCRFOV/	Ing	sys; drow	Skin: Soap wash prompt	CNS
Wash skin:	When contam	GMFOV/SCBAF/SAF	Con		Breath: Resp support	
Remove:	When wet (flamm)	§: SCBAF:PD,PP/SAF:PD,PP:ASCBA			Swallow: Medical attention	
Change:	N.R.	Escape: GMFOV/SCBAE			immed	

[Cyclohexene]

Skin:	Prevent skin contact	TBAL	Inh	Irrit eyes, skin, muc	Eye: Irr immed	Eyes, skin, resp sys,
Eyes:	Prevent eye contact		Abs	memb, resp sys; eye, skin	Skin: Water flush immed	CNS
Wash skin:	When contam		Ing	burns; skin sens; cough,	Breath: Resp support	
Remove:	When wet (flamm)		Con	pulm edema; drow, li-head,	Swallow: Medical attention	
Change:	N.R.			dizz; diarr, nau, vomit	immed	
Provide:	Eyewash, Quick drench					

[Cyclohexylamine]

Chemical name, structure/formula, CAS and RTECS Nos., and DOT ID and guide Nos.	Synonyms, trade names, and conversion factors	Exposure limits (TWA unless noted otherwise)	IDLH	Physical description	Chemical and physical properties		Incompatibilities and reactivities	Measurement method (See Table 1)
					MW, BP, SOL Fl.P, IP, Sp, Gr, flammability	VP, FRZ UEL, LEL		
Cyclonite $C_3H_6N_6O_6$ 121-82-4 XY9450000	Cyclotrimethylenetrini- tramine; Hexahydro-1,3,5-trinitro- s-triazine; RDX; Trimethylenetrinitramine; 1,3,5-Trinitro-1,3,5- triazacyclohexane	NIOSH 1.5 mg/m³ ST 3 mg/m³ [skin] OSHA† none	N.D.	White, crystalline powder. [Note: A powerful high explosive.]	MW: 222.2 BP: ? Sol: Insoluble Fl.P: Explodes IP: ?	VP(230°F): 0.0004 mm MLT: 401°F UEL: ? LEL: ?	Strong oxidizers, combustible materials, heat [Note: Detonates on contact with mercury fulminate.]	Filter; none; Grav; IV [#0500, Particulates NOR (total)]
					Sp.Gr. 1.82 Combustible Solid [EXPLOSIVE!]			
Cyclopentadiene C_5H_6 542-92-7 GY1000000	1,3-Cyclopentadiene	NIOSH/OSHA 75 ppm (200 mg/m³)	750 ppm	Colorless liquid with an irritating, terpene-like odor.	MW: 66.1 BP: 107°F Sol: Insoluble Fl.P(oc): 77°F IP: 8.56 eV	VP: 400 mm FRZ:-121°F UEL: ? LEL: ?	Strong oxidizers, fuming nitric acid, sulfuric acid [Note: Polymerizes to dicyclopentadiene upon standing.]	Chrom-104*; Ethyl acetate; GC/FID; IV [#2523]
	1 ppm = 2.70 mg/m³				Sp.Gr. 0.80 Class IC Flammable Liquid			
Cyclopentane C_5H_{10} 287-92-3 GY2390000 1146 128	Pentamethylene	NIOSH 600 ppm (1720 mg/m³) OSHA† none	N.D.	Colorless liquid with a mild, sweet odor.	MW: 70.2 BP: 121°F Sol: Insoluble Fl.P: -35°F IP: 10.52 eV	VP(88°F): 400 mm FRZ:-137°F UEL:8.7% LEL:1.1%	Strong oxidizers (e.g., chlorine, bromine, fluorine)	None available
	1 ppm = 2.87 mg/m³				Sp.Gr. 0.75 Class IB Flammable Liquid			
Cyhexatin $(C_6H_{11})_3SnOH$ 13121-70-5 WH8750000	TCHH, Tricyclohexylhydroxy- stannane, Tricyclohexylhydroxytin, Tricyclohexylstannium hydroxide, Tricyclohexyltin hydroxide	NIOSH 5 mg/m³ [25 mg/m³ (as Sn)] OSHA† 0.32 mg/m³ [0.1 mg/m³ (as Sn)]	80 mg/m³ [(as Sn)]	Colorless to white, nearly odorless, crystalline powder. [insecticide]	MW: 385.2 BP: 442°F (Decomposes) Sol: Insoluble Fl.P: NA IP: NA	VP: 0 mm (approx) MLT: 383°F UEL: NA LEL: NA	Strong oxidizers, ultraviolet light	Filter/ XAD-2; CH₃COOH/ CH₃CN; HPLC/ GFAAS; IV [#5504, Organotin]
					Sp.Gr: ?			

Personal protection and sanitation (See Table 3)		Recommendations for respirator selection — maximum concentration for use (MUC) (See Table 4)	Health hazards				
			Route	Symptoms (See Table 5)	First aid (See Table 6)		Target organs (See Table 5)
Skin:	Prevent skin contact	TBAL	Inh	Irrit eyes, skin; head,	Eye:	Irr immed	Eyes, skin, CNS
Eyes:	Prevent eye contact		Abs	irrity, ftg, weak, tremor,	Skin:	Soap flush immed	
Wash skin:	When contam/Daily		Ing	nau, dizz, vomit, insom,	Breath:	Resp support	
Remove:	When wet or contam		Con	convuls	Swallow:	Medical attention	
Change:	Daily					immed	
Provide:	Eyewash, Quick drench						

[Cyclonite]

Personal protection and sanitation (See Table 3)		Recommendations for respirator selection — maximum concentration for use (MUC) (See Table 4)	Health hazards				
Skin:	Prevent skin contact	NIOSH/OSHA	Inh	Irrit eyes, nose	Eye:	Irr immed	Eyes, resp sys
Eyes:	Prevent eye contact	750 ppm: CCROV/GMFOV/PAPROV/SA/	Ing		Skin:	Soap wash prompt	
Wash skin:	When contam	SCBAF	Con		Breath:	Resp support	
Remove:	When wet (flamm)	§: SCBAF:PD,PP/SAF:PD,PP:ASCBA			Swallow:	Medical attention	
Change:	N.R.	Escape: GMFOV/SCBAE				immed	

[Cyclopentadiene]

Personal protection and sanitation (See Table 3)		Recommendations for respirator selection — maximum concentration for use (MUC) (See Table 4)	Health hazards				
Skin:	Prevent skin contact	TBAL	Inh	Irrit eyes, skin, nose,	Eye:	Irr immed	Eyes, skin, resp sys,
Eyes:	Prevent eye contact		Ing	throat; li-head, dizz,	Skin:	Soap wash	CNS
Wash skin:	Daily		Con	euph, inco, nau, vomit,	Breath:	Resp support	
Remove:	When wet (flamm)			stupor; dry, cracking skin	Swallow:	Medical attention	
Change:	N.R.					immed	

[Cyclopentane]

Personal protection and sanitation (See Table 3)		Recommendations for respirator selection — maximum concentration for use (MUC) (See Table 4)	Health hazards				
Skin:	Prevent skin contact	OSHA	Inh	Irrit eyes, skin, resp	Eye:	Irr immed	Eyes, skin, resp sys,
Eyes:	N.R.	3.2 mg/m³: CCROVDM/SA	Abs	sys; head, verti; sore	Skin:	Soap wash immed	liver, kidneys
Wash skin:	When contam	8 mg/m³: SA:CF/PAPROVDM	Ing	throat, cough; abdom pain,	Breath:	Resp support	
Remove:	When wet or contam	16 mg/m³: CCRFOVHiE/GMFOVHiE/	Con	vomit; skin burns, pruritus;	Swallow:	Medical attention	
Change:	Daily	PAPRTOVHiE/SAT:CF/		in animals: liver, kidney		immed	
		SCBAF/SAF		damage			
		80 mg/m³: SAF:PD,PP					
		§: SCBAF:PD,PP/SAF:PD,PP:ASCBA					
		Escape: GMFOVHiE/SCBAE					

[Cyhexatin]

Chemical name, structure/formula, CAS and RTECS Nos., and DOT ID and guide Nos.	Synonyms, trade names, and conversion factors	Exposure limits (TWA unless noted otherwise)	IDLH	Physical description	Chemical and physical properties		Incompatibilities and reactivities	Measurement method (See Table 1)
					MW, BP, SOL Fl.P, IP, Sp, Gr, flammability	VP, FRZ UEL, LEL		
2,4-D $Cl_2C_6H_3OCH_2COOH$ 94-75-7 AG6825000 2765 152	Dichlorophenoxyacetic acid; 2,4-Dichlorophenoxyacetic acid	NIOSH/OSHA 10 mg/m³	100 mg/m³	White to yellow, crystalline, odorless powder. [herbicide]	MW: 221.0 BP: Decomposes Sol: 0.05% Fl.P: NA IP: ? Sp.Gr: 1.57 Noncombustible Solid, but may be dissolved in flammable liquids.	VP(320°F): 0.4 mm MLT: 280°F UEL: NA LEL: NA	Strong oxidizers	Filter; Methanol; HPLC/UVD; IV [#5001]
DDT $(C_6H_4Cl)_2CHCCl_3$ 50-29-3 KJ3325000 2761 151	p,p'-DDT; Dichlorodiphenyltrichloro-ethane; 1,1,1-Trichloro-2,2-bis(p-chlorophenyl)ethane	NIOSH Ca See Appendix A 0.5 mg/m³ OSHA 1 mg/m³ [skin]	Ca [500 mg/m³]	Colorless crystals or off-white powder with a slight, aromatic odor. [pesticide]	MW: 354.5 BP: 230°F (Decomposes) Sol: Insoluble Fl.P: 162-171°F IP: ? Sp.Gr: 0.99 Combustible Solid	VP: 0.0000002 mm MLT: 227°F UEL: ? LEL: ?	Strong oxidizers, alkalis	Filter; Isooctane; GC/ECD; II(3) [#S274]
Decaborane $B_{10}H_{14}$ 17702-41-9 HD1400000 1868 134	Decaboron tetradecahydride	NIOSH 0.3 mg/m³ (0.05 ppm) ST 0.9 mg/m³ (0.15 ppm) [skin] OSHA† 0.3 mg/m³ (0.05 ppm) [skin] 1 ppm = 5.00 mg/m³	15 mg/m³	Colorless to white crystalline solid with an intense, bitter, chocolate-like odor.	MW: 122.2 BP: 415°F Sol: Slight Fl.P: 176°F IP: 9.88 eV Sp.Gr: 0.94 Combustible Solid	VP: 0.2 mm MLT: 211°F UEL: ? LEL: ?	Oxidizers, water, halogenated com-pounds (especially carbon tetrachloride) [Note: May ignite SPONTANEOUSLY on exposure to air. Decomposes slowly in hot water.]	None available
1-Decanethiol $CH_3(CH_2)_9SH$ 143-10-2 1 ppm = 7.13 mg/m³	Decylmercaptan, n-Decylmercaptan, 1-Mercaptodecane	NIOSH C 0.5 ppm (3.6 mg/m³) [15-min] OSHA none	N.D.	Colorless liquid with a strong odor.	MW: 174.4 BP: 465°F Sol: Insoluble Fl.P: 209°F IP: ? Sp.Gr: 0.84 Class IIIB Combustible Liquid	VP: ? FRZ: -15°F UEL: ? LEL: ?	Oxidizers, strong acids & bases, alkali metals, nitric acid	None available

Personal protection and sanitation (See Table 3)		Recommendations for respirator selection — maximum concentration for use (MUC) (See Table 4)	Route	Symptoms (See Table 5)	First aid (See Table 6)		Target organs (See Table 5)
Skin:	Prevent skin contact	NIOSH/OSHA	Inh	Weak, stupor,	Eye:	Irr immed	Skin, CNS, liver,
Eyes:	Prevent eye contact	100 mg/m³: CCROVDMFu/GMFOVHiE/	Abs	hyporeflexia, musc twitch;	Skin:	Soap wash prompt	kidneys
Wash skin:	When contam	PAPROVDMFu/SA/SCBAF	Ing	convuls; derm;	Breath:	Resp support	
Remove:	When wet or contam	§ : SCBAF:PD,PP/SAF:PD,PP:ASCBA	Con	in animals: liver, kidney inj	Swallow:	Medical attention	
Change:	Daily	Escape: GMFOVHiE/SCBAE				immed	

[2,4-D]

Skin:	Prevent skin contact	NIOSH	Inh	Irrit eyes, skin; pares	Eye:	Irr immed	Eyes, skin, CNS,
Eyes:	Prevent eye contact	¥: SCBAF:PD,PP/SAF:PD,PP:ASCBA	Abs	tongue, lips, face; tremor;	Skin:	Soap wash prompt	kidneys, liver, PNS
Wash skin:	When contam	Escape: GMFOVHiE/SCBAE	Ing	appre, dizz, conf, mal,	Breath:	Resp support	[in animals:
Remove:	When wet or contam		Con	head, ftg; convuls; paresis	Swallow:	Medical attention	liver, lung &
Change:	Daily			hands; vomit; [carc]		immed	lymphatic tumors]
Provide:	Eyewash, Quick drench						

[DDT]

Skin:	Prevent skin contact	NIOSH/OSHA	Inh	Dizz, head, nau, li-head,	Eye:	Irr immed	CNS, liver, kidneys
Eyes:	Prevent eye contact	3 mg/m³: SA	Abs	drow; inco, local musc	Skin:	Soap wash immed	
Wash skin:	When contam/Daily	7.5 mg/m³: SA:CF	Ing	spasm, tremor, convuls;	Breath:	Resp support	
Remove:	When wet or contam	15 mg/m³: SAT:CF/SCBAF/SAF	Con	ftg;	Swallow:	Medical attention	
Change:	Daily	§ : SCBAF:PD,PP/SAF:PD,PP:ASCBA		in animals: dysp; weak;		immed	
Provide:	Eyewash, Quick drench	Escape: GMFOVHiE/SCBAE		liver, kidney damage			

[Decaborane]

Skin:	Prevent skin contact	NIOSH	Inh	Irrit eyes, skin, resp	Eye:	Irr immed	Eyes, skin, resp sys,
Eyes:	Prevent eye contact	5 ppm: CCROV/SA	Abs	sys; conf, dizz, head,	Skin:	Soap wash	CNS
Wash skin:	When contam	12.5 ppm: SA:CF/PAPROV	Ing	drow, nau, vomit, weak,	Breath:	Resp support	
Remove:	When wet or contam	25 ppm: CCRFOV/GMFOV/PAPRTOV/	Con	convuls	Swallow:	Medical attention	
Change:	N.R.	SCBAF/SAF				immed	
		§ : SCBAF:PD,PP/SAF:PD,PP:ASCBA					
		Escape: GMFOV/SCBAE					

[1-Decanethiol]

Chemical name, structure/formula, CAS and RTECS Nos., and DOT ID and guide Nos.	Synonyms, trade names, and conversion factors	Exposure limits (TWA unless noted otherwise)	IDLH	Physical description	Chemical and physical properties		Incompatibilities and reactivities	Measurement method (See Table 1)
					MW, BP, SOL FI.P, IP, Sp, Gr, flammability	VP, FRZ UEL, LEL		
Demeton $(C_2H_5O)_2PSOC_2H_4SC_2H_5$ 8065-48-3 TF3150000	O-O-Diethyl-O(and S)-2-(ethylthio)ethyl phosphorothioate mixture; Systox®	NIOSH/OSHA 0.1 mg/m³ [skin]	10 mg/m³	Amber, oily liquid with a sulfur-like odor. [insecticide]	MW: 258.3 BP: Decomposes Sol: 0.01% Fl.P: 113°F IP: ? Sp.Gr: 1.12 Class II Combustible Liquid	VP: 0.0003 mm FRZ: <-13°F UEL: ? LEL: ?	Strong oxidizers, alkalis, water	Filter/ XAD-2; Toluene; GC/FPD; IV [#5514]
Diacetone alcohol $CH_3COCH_2C(CH_3)_2OH$ 123-42-2 SA9100000 1148 129	Diacetone, 4-Hydroxy-4-methyl-2-pentanone, 2-Methyl-2-pentanol-4-one 1 ppm = 4.75 mg/m³	NIOSH/OSHA 50 ppm (240 mg/m³)	1800 ppm [10%LEL]	Colorless liquid with a faint, minty odor.	MW: 116.2 BP: 334°F Sol: Miscible Fl.P: 125°F IP: ? Sp.Gr: 0.94 Class II Combustible Liquid	VP: 1 mm FRZ: -47°F UEL: 6.9% LEL: 1.8%	Strong oxidizers, strong alkalis	Char; 2-Propanol/ CS₂; GC/FID; IV [#1402, Alcohols III]
2,4-Diaminoanisole (and its salts) $(NH_2)_2C_6H_3OCH_3$ 615-05-4 BZ8580500	1,3-Diamino-4-methoxy-benzene; 4-Methoxy-1,3-benzene-diamine; 4-Methoxy-m-phenylene-diamine Synonyms of salts vary depending upon the specific compound.	NIOSH Ca Minimize occupational exposure (especially skin exposures) See Appendix A OSHA none	Ca [N.D.]	Colorless solid (needles). [Note: The primary use (including its salts such as 2,4-diaminoanisole sulfate) is a component of hair & fur dye formu-lations.]	MW: 138.2 BP: ? Sol: ? Fl.P: ? IP: ? Sp.Gr: ? Combustible Solid	VP: ? MLT: 153°F UEL: ? LEL: ?	Strong oxidizers	None available
o-Dianisidine $(NH_2C_6H_3OCH_3)_2$ 119-90-4 DD0875000	Dianisidine; 3,3'-Dianisidine; 3,3'-Dimethoxybenzidine	NIOSH Ca See Appendix A See Appendix C OSHA See Appendix C	Ca [N.D.]	Colorless crystals that turn a violet color on standing. [Note: Used as a basis for many dyes.]	MW: 244.3 BP: ? Sol: Insoluble Fl.P: 403°F IP: ? Sp.Gr: ? Combustible Solid	VP: ? MLT: 279°F UEL: ? LEL: ?	Oxidizers	Filter; Water; HPLC/UVD; IV [#5013, Dyes]

Personal protection and sanitation (See Table 3)		Recommendations for respirator selection — maximum concentration for use (MUC) (See Table 4)	Health hazards				
			Route	Symptoms (See Table 5)	First aid (See Table 6)		Target organs (See Table 5)
Skin:	Prevent skin contact	NIOSH/OSHA	Inh	Irrit eyes, skin; miosis,	Eye:	Irr immed	Eyes, skin, resp sys,
Eyes:	Prevent eye contact	1 mg/m³: SA	Abs	ache eyes, rhin, head;	Skin:	Soap wash immed	CVS, CNS, blood chol
Wash skin:	When contam	2.5 mg/m³: SA:CF	Ing	chest tight, wheez, lar	Breath:	Resp support	
Remove:	When wet or contam	5 mg/m³: SAT:CF/SCBAF/SAF	Con	spasm, salv, cyan; anor,	Swallow:	Medical attention	
Change:	Daily	10 mg/m³: SA:PD,PP		nau, vomit, abdom cramps,		immed	
Provide:	Eyewash, Quick drench	§: SCBAF:PD,PP/SAF:PD,PP:ASCBA		diarr; local sweat; musc			
		Escape: GMFOVHiE/SCBAE		fasc, weak, para; gidd, conf,			
				ataxia; convuls, coma; low			
				BP; card irreg			
[Demeton]							
Skin:	Prevent skin contact	NIOSH/OSHA	Inh	Irrit eyes, skin, nose,	Eye:	Irr immed	Eyes, skin, resp
Eyes:	Prevent eye contact	1250 ppm: SA:CF£/PAPROV£	Ing	throat; corn damage;	Skin:	Water flush prompt	sys, CNS, liver
Wash skin:	When contam	1800 ppm: CCRFOV/GMFOV/PAPRTOV£/ Con		in animals: narco,	Breath:	Resp support	
Remove:	When wet or contam	SCBAF/SAF		liver damage	Swallow:	Medical attention	
Change:	N.R.	§: SCBAF:PD,PP/SAF:PD,PP:ASCBA				immed	
		Escape: GMFOV/SCBAE					
[Diacetone alcohol]							
Skin:	Prevent skin contact	NIOSH	Inh	In animals: irrit skin;	Eye:	Irr immed	Skin, thyroid, liver,
Eyes:	Prevent eye contact	¥: SCBAF:PD,PP/SAF:PD,PP:ASCBA	Abs	thyroid, liver changes;	Skin:	Soap wash immed	repro sys
Wash skin:	When contam/Daily	Escape: GMFOVHiE/SCBAE	Ing	terato effects; [carc]	Breath:	Resp support	[in animals:
Remove:	When wet or contam		Con		Swallow:	Medical attention	thyroid, liver,
Change:	Daily					immed	skin & lymphatic
Provide:	Eyewash, Quick drench						sys tumors]
[2,4-Diaminoanisole (and its salts)]							
Skin:	Prevent skin contact	NIOSH	Inh	Irrit skin;	Eye:	Irr immed	Skin, kidneys, liver,
Eyes:	Prevent eye contact	¥: SCBAF:PD,PP/SAF:PD,PP:ASCBA	Abs	in animals: kidney, liver	Skin:	Soap wash immed	thyroid, spleen
Wash skin:	When contam/Daily	Escape: GMFOVHiE/SCBAE	Ing	damage; thyroid, spleen	Breath:	Resp support	[in animals
Remove:	When wet or contam		Con	changes; [carc]	Swallow:	Medical attention	bladder, liver,
Change:	Daily					immed	stomach & mammary
Provide:	Eyewash, Quick drench						gland tumors]
[o-Dianisidine]							

Chemical name, structure/formula, CAS and RTECS Nos., and DOT ID and guide Nos.	Synonyms, trade names, and conversion factors	Exposure limits (TWA unless noted otherwise)	IDLH	Physical description	Chemical and physical properties		Incompatibilities and reactivities	Measurement method (See Table 1)
					MW, BP, SOL FI.P, IP, Sp, Gr, flammability	VP, FRZ UEL, LEL		
Diazinon® C₁₂H₂₁N₂O₃PS 333-41-5 TF3325000 2783 152	Basudin®; Diazide®; O,O-Diethyl-O-2-isopropyl-4-methyl-6-pyrimidinyl-phosphorothioate; Spectracide®	NIOSH 0.1 mg/m³ [skin] OSHA† none	N.D.	Colorless liquid with a faint ester-like odor. [insecticide] [Note: Technical grade is pale to dark brown.]	MW: 304.4 BP: Decomposes Sol: 0.004% FI.P: 180°F IP: ? Sp.Gr. 1.12 Class IIIA Combustible Liquid	VP: 0.0001 mm FRZ: ? UEL: ? LEL: ?	Strong acids & alkalis, copper-containing compounds [Note: Hydrolyzes slowly in water & dilute acid.]	OVS-2; Toluene/Acetone; GC/FPD; IV [#5600, Organo-phosphorus Pesticides]
Diazomethane CH₂N₂ 334-88-3 PA7000000	Azimethylene, Azomethylene, Diazirine 1 ppm = 1.72 mg/m³	NIOSH/OSHA 0.2 ppm (0.4 mg/m³)	2 ppm	Yellow gas with a musty odor. [Note: Shipped as a liquefied compressed gas.]	MW: 42.1 BP: -9°F Sol: Reacts FI.P: NA (Gas) IP: 9.00 eV RGasD: 1.45 Flammable Gas [EXPLOSIVE!]	VP: >1 atm FRZ: -229°F UEL: ? LEL: ?	Alkali metals, water, drying agents such as calcium arsenate [Note: May explode violently on heating, exposure to sunlight, or contact with rough edges such as ground glass.]	XAD-2*; CS₂; GC/FID; IV [#2515]
Diborane B₂H₆ 19287-45-7 HQ9275000 1911 119	Boroethane, Boron hydride, Diboron hexahydride 1 ppm = 1.13 mg/m³	NIOSH/OSHA 0.1 ppm (0.1 mg/m³)	15 ppm	Colorless gas with a repulsive, sweet odor. [Note: Usually shipped in pressurized cylinders diluted with hydrogen, argon, nitrogen, or helium.]	MW: 27.7 BP: -135°F Sol: Reacts FI.P: NA (Gas) IP: 11.38 eV RGasD: 0.97 Flammable Gas	VP(62°F): 39.5 atm FRZ: -265°F UEL: 88% LEL: 0.8%	Water, halogenated compounds, aluminum, lithium, oxidized surfaces, acids [Note: Will ignite spontaneously in moist air at room temperature. Reacts with water to form hydrogen & boric acid.]	Filter/Char*; H₂O₂; PES; IV [#6006]
1,2-Dibromo-3-chloro-propane CH₂BrCHBrCH₂Cl 96-12-8 TX8750000 2872 159	1-Chloro-2,3-dibromo-propane; DBCP; Dibromochloropropane 1 ppm = 9.67 mg/m³	NIOSH Ca See Appendix A OSHA [1910.1044] 0.001 ppm	Ca [N.D.]	Dense yellow or amber liquid with a pungent odor at high concentra-tions. [pesticide] [Note: A solid below 43°F.]	MW: 236.4 BP: 384°F Sol: 0.1% FI.P(oc): 170°F IP: ? Sp.Gr. 2.05 Class IIIA Combustible Liquid	VP: 0.8 mm FRZ: 43°F UEL: ? LEL: ?	Chemically-active metals such as aluminum, magnesium & tin alloys [Note: Corrosive to metals.]	None available

Personal protection and sanitation (See Table 3)		Recommendations for respirator selection — maximum concentration for use (MUC) (See Table 4)	Route	Symptoms (See Table 5)	First aid (See Table 6)		Target organs (See Table 5)
Skin: Eyes: Wash skin: Remove: Change: Provide:	Prevent skin contact Prevent eye contact When contam When wet or contam Daily Eyewash, Quick drench	TBAL	Inh Abs Ing Con	Irrit eyes; miosis, blurred vision; dizz, conf, weak, convuls; dysp; salv, abdom cramps, nau, vomit	Eye: Skin: Breath: Swallow:	Irr immed Soap wash immed Resp support Medical attention immed	Eyes, resp sys, CNS, CVS, blood chol

[Diazinon®]

Skin: Eyes: Wash skin: Remove: Change: Provide:	Frostbite Frostbite N.R. When wet (flamm) N.R. Frostbite	NIOSH/OSHA 2 ppm: SA*/SCBAF §: SCBAF:PD,PP/SAF:PD,PP:ASCBA Escape: GMFOV/SCBAF	Inh Con (liq)	Irrit eyes; cough, short breath; head, ftg; flush skin, fever; chest pain, pulm edema, pneuitis; asthma; liq: frostbite	Eye: Skin: Breath:	Frostbite Frostbite Resp support	Eyes, resp sys

93

[Diazomethane]

Skin: Eyes: Wash skin: Remove: Change:	N.R. N.R. N.R. N.R. N.R.	NIOSH/OSHA 1 ppm: SA 2.5 ppm: SA:CF 5 ppm: SAT:CF/SCBAF/SAF 15 ppm: SA:PD,PP §: SCBAF:PD,PP/SAF:PD,PP:ASCBA Escape: GMFS/SCBAE	Inh	Chest tight, precordial pain, short breath, non-productive cough, nau; head, li-head, verti, chills, fever, ftg, weak, tremor, musc fasc; in animals: liver, kidney damage; pulm edema; hemorr	Breath:	Resp support	Resp sys, CNS, liver, kidneys

[Diborane]

Skin: Eyes: Wash skin: Remove: Change: Provide:	Prevent skin contact Prevent eye contact When contam/Daily When wet or contam Daily Eyewash, Quick drench	NIOSH ¥: SCBAF:PD,PP/SAF:PD,PP:ASCBA Escape: GMFOVHiE/SCBAE	Inh Abs Ing Con	Irrit eyes, skin, nose, throat; drow; nau, vomit; pulm edema; liver, kidney inj; sterility; [carc]	Eye: Skin: Breath: Swallow:	Irr immed Soap wash immed Resp support Medical attention immed	Eyes, skin, resp sys, CNS, liver, kidneys, spleen, repro sys, digestive sys [in animals: cancer of the nasal cavity, tongue, pharynx, lungs, stomach, adrenal & mammary glands]

[1,2-Dibromo-3-chloropropane]

Chemical name, structure/formula, CAS and RTECS Nos., and DOT ID and guide Nos.	Synonyms, trade names, and conversion factors	Exposure limits (TWA unless noted otherwise)	IDLH	Physical description	Chemical and physical properties		Incompatibilities and reactivities	Measurement method (See Table 1)
					MW, BP, SOL Fl.P, IP, Sp, Gr, flammability	VP, FRZ UEL, LEL		
2-N-Dibutylaminoethanol ($C_4H_9)_2NCH_2CH_2OH$ 102-81-8 KK3850000 2873 153	Dibutylaminoethanol; 2-Dibutylaminoethanol; 2-Di-N-butylaminoethanol; 2-Di-N-butylaminoethyl alcohol; N,N-Dibutylethanolamine 1 ppm = 7.09 mg/m³	NIOSH 2 ppm (14 mg/m³) [skin] OSHA† none	N.D.	Colorless liquid with a faint, amine-like odor.	MW: 173.3 BP: 446°F Sol: 0.4% Fl.P: 195°F IP: ? Sp.Gr: 0.86 Class IIIA Combustible Liquid	VP: 0.1 mm FRZ: ? UEL: ? LEL: ?	Oxidizers	Si gel; Methanol/ Water; GC/FID; IV [#2007, Amino-ethanol Compounds]
Dibutyl phosphate ($C_4H_9O)_2(OH)PO$ 107-66-4 TB9605000	Dibutyl acid o-phosphate, di-n-Butyl hydrogen phosphate, Dibutyl phosphoric acid 1 ppm = 8.60 mg/m³	NIOSH 1 ppm (5 mg/m³) ST 2 ppm (10 mg/m³) OSHA† 1 ppm (5 mg/m³)	30 ppm	Pale amber, odorless liquid.	MW: 210.2 BP: 212°F (Decomposes) Sol: Insoluble Fl.P: ? IP: ? Sp.Gr: 1.06 Combustible Liquid	VP: 1 mm (approx) FRZ: ? UEL: ? LEL: ?	Strong oxidizers	Filter; CH₃CN; GC/FPD; IV [#5017]
Dibutylphthalate $C_6H_4(COOC_4H_9)_2$ 84-74-2 TI0875000	DBP; Dibutyl 1,2-benzene-dicarboxylate; Di-n-butyl phthalate	NIOSH/OSHA 5 mg/m³	4000 mg/m³	Colorless to faint yellow, oily liquid with a slight, aromatic odor.	MW: 278.3 BP: 644°F Sol(77°F): 0.001% Fl.P: 315°F IP: ? Sp.Gr: 1.05 Class IIIB Combustible Liquid	VP: 0.00007 mm FRZ: -31°F UEL: ? LEL(456°F): 0.5%	Nitrates; strong oxidizers, alkalis & acids; liquid chlorine	Filter; CS₂; GC/FID; IV [#5020]
Dichloroacetylene ClC≡CCl 7572-29-4 AP1080000	DCA, Dichloroethyne [Note: DCA is a possible decomposition product of trichloroethylene or trichloroethane.] 1 ppm = 3.88 mg/m³	NIOSH Ca See Appendix A C 0.1 ppm (0.4 mg/m³) OSHA† none	Ca [N.D.]	Volatile oil with a disagreeable, sweetish odor. [Note: A gas above 90°F. DCA is not produced commercially.]	MW: 94.9 BP: 90°F (Explodes) Sol: ? Fl.P: ? IP: ? Sp.Gr: 1.26 Combustible Liquid	VP: ? FRZ: -58 to -87°F UEL: ? LEL: ?	Oxidizers, heat, shock	None available

Personal protection and sanitation (See Table 3)	Recommendations for respirator selection — maximum concentration for use (MUC) (See Table 4)	Route	Symptoms (See Table 5)	First aid (See Table 6)	Target organs (See Table 5)
Skin: Prevent skin contact Eyes: Prevent eye contact Wash skin: When contam Remove: When wet or contam Change: N.R. Provide: Eyewash, Quick drench	TBAL	Inh Abs Ing Con	In animals: irrit eyes, skin, nose, derm; skin, corn nec; low-wgt	Eye: Irr immed Skin: Soap flush immed Breath: Resp support Swallow: Medical attention immed	Eyes, skin, resp sys

[2-N-Dibutylaminoethanol]

Personal protection and sanitation	Recommendations for respirator selection	Route	Symptoms	First aid	Target organs
Skin: Prevent skin contact Eyes: Prevent eye contact Wash skin: When contam Remove: When wet or contam Change: N.R. Provide: Quick drench	NIOSH/OSHA 10 ppm: SA 25 ppm: SA:CF 30 ppm: SAT:CF/SCBAF/SAF §: SCBAF:PD,PP/SAF:PD,PP:ASCBA Escape: GMFOVHiE/SCBAE	Inh Ing Con	Irrit eyes, skin, resp sys; head	Eye: Irr immed Skin: Soap wash prompt Breath: Resp support Swallow: Medical attention immed	Eyes, skin, resp sys

[Dibutyl phosphate]

Personal protection and sanitation	Recommendations for respirator selection	Route	Symptoms	First aid	Target organs
Skin: N.R. Eyes: Prevent eye contact Wash skin: N.R. Remove: N.R. Change: N.R.	NIOSH/OSHA 50 mg/m³: DMF 125 mg/m³: SA:CF£/PAPRDM£ 250 mg/m³: HiEF/SCBAF/SAF 4000 mg/m³: SAF:PD,PP §: SCBAF:PD,PP/SAF:PD,PP:ASCBA Escape: HiEF/SCBAE	Inh Ing Con	Irrit eyes, upper resp sys, stomach	Eye: Irr immed Skin: Wash regularly Breath: Resp support Swallow: Medical attention immed	Eyes, resp sys, GI tract

[Dibutyl phthalate]

Personal protection and sanitation	Recommendations for respirator selection	Route	Symptoms	First aid	Target organs
Skin: Prevent skin contact Eyes: Prevent eye contact Wash skin: When contam Remove: When wet (flamm) Change: N.R. Provide: Eyewash, Quick drench	NIOSH ¥: SCBAF:PD,PP/SAF:PD,PP:ASCBA Escape: GMFOV/SCBAE	Inh Abs Ing Con	Head, loss of appetite, nau, vomit, intense jaw pain; cranial nerve palsy; in animals: kidney, liver, brain inj; low-wgt; [carc]	Eye: Irr immed Skin: Soap flush immed Breath: Resp support Swallow: Medical attention immed	CNS [in animals: kidney tumors]

[Dichloroacetylene]

Chemical name, structure/formula, CAS and RTECS Nos., and DOT ID and guide Nos.	Synonyms, trade names, and conversion factors	Exposure limits (TWA unless noted otherwise)	IDLH	Physical description	Chemical and physical properties		Incompatibilities and reactivities	Measurement method (See Table 1)
					MW, BP, SOL Fl.P, IP, Sp, Gr, flammability	VP, FRZ UEL, LEL		
o-Dichlorobenzene $C_6H_4Cl_2$ 95-50-1 CZ4500000 1591 152	o-DCB; 1,2-Dichlorobenzene; ortho-Dichlorobenzene; o-Dichlorobenzol 1 ppm = 6.01 mg/m³	NIOSH/OSHA C 50 ppm (300 mg/m³)	200 ppm	Colorless to pale-yellow liquid with a pleasant, aromatic odor. [herbicide]	MW: 147.0 BP: 357°F Sol: 0.01% Fl.P: 151°F IP: 9.06 eV Sp.Gr. 1.30 Class IIIA Combustible Liquid	VP: 1 mm FRZ: 1°F UEL: 9.2% LEL: 2.2%	Strong oxidizers, aluminum, chlorides, acids, acid fumes	Char; CS₂; GC/FID; IV [#1003, Halogenated Hydrocarbons]
p-Dichlorobenzene $C_6H_4Cl_2$ 106-46-7 CZ4550000 1592 152	p-DCB; 1,4-Dichlorobenzene; para-Dichlorobenzene; Dichloricide 1 ppm = 6.01 mg/m³	NIOSH Ca See Appendix A OSHA† 75 ppm (450 mg/m³)	Ca [150 ppm]	Colorless or white crystalline solid with a mothball-like odor. [insecticide]	MW: 147.0 BP: 345°F Sol: 0.008% Fl.P: 150°F IP: 8.98 eV Sp.Gr. 1.25 Combustible Solid, but may take some effort to ignite.	VP: 1.3 mm MLT: 128°F UEL: ? LEL: 2.5%	Strong oxidizers (such as chlorine or permanganate)	Char; CS₂; GC/FID; IV [#1003, Halogenated Hydrocarbons]
3,3'-Dichlorobenzidine (and its salts) $NH_2ClC_6H_3C_6H_3ClNH_2$ 91-94-1 DD0525000 1591 152	4,4'-Diamino-3,3'-dichloro-biphenyl; Dichlorobenzidine base; o,o'-Dichlorobenzidine; 3,3'-Dichlorobiphenyl-4,4'-diamine; 3,3'-Dichloro-4,4'-biphenyl-diamine; 3,3'-Dichloro-4,4'-diamino-biphenyl	NIOSH Ca See Appendix A OSHA [1910.1007] See Appendix B	Ca [N.D.]	Gray to purple, crystalline solid.	MW: 253.1 BP: 788°F Sol(59°F): 0.07% Fl.P: ? IP: ? Sp.Gr. ?	VP: ? MLT: 271°F UEL: ? LEL: ?	None reported	Filter/ Si gel; Reagent; HPLC/UVD; IV [#5509]
Dichlorodifluoromethane CCl_2F_2 75-71-8 PA8200000 1028 126	Difluorodichloromethane, Fluorocarbon 12, Freon® 12, Genetron® 12, Halon® 122, Propellant 12, Refrigerant 12 1 ppm = 4.95 mg/m³	NIOSH/OSHA 1000 ppm (4950 mg/m³)	15,000 ppm	Colorless gas with an ether-like odor at extremely high concentrations. [Note: Shipped as a liquefied compressed gas.]	MW: 120.9 BP: -22°F Sol(77°F): 0.03% Fl.P: NA IP: 11.75 eV RGasD: 4.2 Nonflammable Gas	VP: 5.7 atm FRZ: -252°F UEL: NA LEL: NA	Chemically-active metals such as sodium, potassium, calcium, powdered aluminum, zinc & magnesium	Char(2); CH₂Cl₂; GC/FID; IV [#1018]

Personal protection and sanitation (See Table 3)		Recommendations for respirator selection — maximum concentration for use (MUC) (See Table 4)	Health hazards				
			Route	Symptoms (See Table 5)	First aid (See Table 6)		Target organs (See Table 5)
Skin:	Prevent skin contact	NIOSH/OSHA	Inh	Irrit eyes, nose; liver,	Eye:	Irr immed	Eyes, skin, resp sys,
Eyes:	Prevent eye contact	200 ppm: CCRFOV/PAPROV£/SCBAF/SAF	Abs	kidney damage; skin	Skin:	Soap wash prompt	liver, kidneys
Wash skin:	When contam	§: SCBAF:PD,PP/SAF:PD,PP:ASCBA	Ing	blisters	Breath:	Resp support	
Remove:	When wet or contam	Escape: GMFOV/SCBAE	Con		Swallow:	Medical attention	
Change:	N.R.					immed	

[o-Dichlorobenzene]

Skin:	Prevent skin contact	NIOSH	Inh	Eye irrit, swell periorb;	Eye:	Irr immed	Liver, resp sys,
Eyes:	Prevent eye contact	¥: SCBAF:PD,PP/SAF:PD,PP:ASCBA	Abs	profuse rhinitis; head,	Skin:	Soap wash	eyes, kidneys,
Wash skin:	When contam/Daily	Escape: GMFOV/SCBAE	Ing	anor, nau, vomit; low-wgt,	Breath:	Resp support	skin
Remove:	When wet or contam		Con	jaun, cirr;	Swallow:	Medical attention	[in animals:
Change:	Daily			in animals: liver, kidney		immed	liver & kidney
Provide:	Eyewash, Quick drench			inj; [carc]			cancer]

[p-Dichlorobenzene]

Skin:	Prevent skin contact	NIOSH	Inh	Skin sens, derm; head, dizz;	Eye:	Irr immed	Bladder, liver,
Eyes:	Prevent eye contact	¥: SCBAF:PD,PP/SAF:PD,PP:ASCBA	Abs	caustic burns; frequent	Skin:	Soap wash immed	lung, skin, GI
Wash skin:	When contam/Daily	Escape: HiEF/SCBAE	Ing	urination, dysuria; hema;	Breath:	Resp support	tract
Remove:	When wet or contam		Con	GI upset; upper resp	Swallow:	Medical attention	[in animals:
Change:	Daily			infection; [carc]		immed	liver & bladder
Provide:	Eyewash, Quick drench						cancer]

[3,3'-Dichlorobenzidine (and its salts)]

Skin:	Frostbite	NIOSH/OSHA	Inh	Dizz, tremor, asphy,	Eye:	Frostbite	CVS, PNS
Eyes:	Frostbite	10,000 ppm: SA	Con	uncon, card arrhy, card	Skin:	Frostbite	
Wash skin:	N.R.	15,000 ppm: SA:CF/SCBAF/SAF	(liq)	arrest; liq: frostbite	Breath:	Resp support	
Remove:	N.R.	§: SCBAF:PD,PP/SAF:PD,PP:ASCBA					
Change:	N.R.	Escape: GMFOV/SCBAE					
Provide:	Frostbite						

[Dichlorodifluoromethane]

Chemical name, structure/formula, CAS and RTECS Nos., and DOT ID and guide Nos.	Synonyms, trade names, and conversion factors	Exposure limits (TWA unless noted otherwise)	IDLH	Physical description	Chemical and physical properties		Incompatibilities and reactivities	Measurement method (See Table 1)
					MW, BP, SOL FI.P, IP, Sp, Gr, flammability	VP, FRZ UEL, LEL		
1,3-Dichloro-5,5-dimethylhydantoin $C_5H_6Cl_2N_2O_2$ 118-52-5 MU0700000	Dactin, DDH, Halane	NIOSH 0.2 mg/m³ ST 0.4 mg/m³ OSHA† 0.2 mg/m³	5 mg/m³	White powder with a chlorine-like odor.	MW: 197.0 BP: ? Sol: 0.2% FI.P: 346°F IP: ? Sp.Gr: 1.5 Combustible Solid	VP: ? MLT: 270°F UEL: ? LEL: ?	Water, strong acids, easily oxidized materials such as ammonia salts & sulfides	None available
1,1-Dichloroethane $CHCl_2CH_3$ 75-34-3 KI0175000 2362 130	Asymmetrical dichloroethane; Ethylidene chloride; 1,1-Ethylidene dichloride 1 ppm = 4.05 mg/m³	NIOSH 100 ppm (400 mg/m³) See Appendix C (Chloroethanes) OSHA 100 ppm (400 mg/m³)	3000 ppm	Colorless, oily liquid with a chloroform-like odor.	MW: 99.0 BP: 135°F Sol: 0.6% FI.P: 2°F IP: 11.06 eV Sp.Gr: 1.18 Class IB Flammable Liquid	VP: 182 mm FRZ: -143°F UEL:11.4% LEL: 5.4%	Strong oxidizers, strong caustics	Char; CS_2; GC/FID; IV [#1003, Halogenated Hydrocarbons]
1,2-Dichloroethylene ClCH=CHCl 540-59-0 KV9360000 1150 132P	Acetylene dichloride, cis-Acetylene dichloride, trans-Acetylene dichloride, sym-Dichloroethylene 1 ppm = 3.97 mg/m³	NIOSH/OSHA 200 ppm (790 mg/m³)	1000 ppm	Colorless liquid (usually a mixture of the cis & trans isomers) with a slightly acrid, chloroform-like odor.	MW: 97.0 BP: 118-140°F Sol: 0.4% FI.P: 36-39°F IP: 9.65 eV Sp.Gr(77°F): 1.27 Class IB Flammable Liquid	VP: 180-265 mm FRZ: -57 to -115°F UEL: 12.8% LEL: 5.6%	Strong oxidizers, strong alkalis, potassium hydroxide, copper [Note: Usually contains inhibitors to prevent polymerization.]	Char; CS_2; GC/FID; IV [#1003, Halogenated Hydrocarbons]
Dichloroethyl ether $(ClCH_2CH_2)_2O$ 111-44-4 KN0875000 1916 152	bis(2-Chloroethyl)ether; 2,2'-Dichlorodiethyl ether; 2,2'-Dichloroethyl ether 1 ppm = 5.85 mg/m³	NIOSH Ca See Appendix A 5 ppm (30 mg/m³) ST 10 ppm (60 mg/m³) [skin] OSHA† C 15 ppm (90 mg/m³) [skin]	Ca [100 ppm]	Colorless liquid with a chlorinated solvent-like odor.	MW: 143.0 BP: 352°F Sol:1% FI.P: 131°F IP: ? Sp.Gr: 1.22 Class II Combustible Liquid	VP: 0.7 mm FRZ: -58°F UEL: ? LEL: 2.7%	Strong oxidizers [Note: Decomposes in presence of moisture to form hydrochloric acid.]	Char; CS_2; GC/FID; IV [#1004]

Personal protection and sanitation (See Table 3)		Recommendations for respirator selection — maximum concentration for use (MUC) (See Table 4)	Health hazards			
			Route	Symptoms (See Table 5)	First aid (See Table 6)	Target organs (See Table 5)
Skin:	Prevent skin contact	NIOSH/OSHA	Inh	Irrit eyes, muc memb,	Eye: Irr immed	Eyes, resp sys
Eyes:	Prevent eye contact	2 mg/m³: SA	Ing	resp sys	Skin: Soap wash prompt	
Wash skin:	When contam	5 mg/m³: SA:CF/SCBAF/SAF	Con		Breath: Resp support	
Remove:	When wet or contam	§: SCBAF:PD,PP/SAF:PD,PP:ASCBA			Swallow: Medical attention	
Change:	Daily	Escape: GMFSHiE/SCBAE			immed	
Provide:	Eyewash					

[1,3-Dichloro-5,5-dimethylhydantoin]

Skin:	Prevent skin contact	NIOSH/OSHA	Inh	Irrit skin; CNS depres;	Eye: Irr immed	Skin, liver,
Eyes:	Prevent eye contact	1000 ppm: SA	Ing	liver, kidney, lung	Skin: Soap flush prompt	kidneys, lungs,
Wash skin:	When contam	2500 ppm: SA:CF	Con	damage	Breath: Resp support	CNS
Remove:	When wet (flamm)	3000 ppm: SCBAF/SAF			Swallow: Medical attention	
Change:	N.R.	§: SCBAF:PD,PP/SAF:PD,PP:ASCBA			immed	
		Escape: GMFOV/SCBAE				

[1,1-Dichloroethane]

Skin:	Prevent skin contact	NIOSH/OSHA	Inh	Irrit eyes, resp sys; CNS	Eye: Irr immed	Eyes, resp sys, CNS
Eyes:	Prevent eye contact	1000 ppm: SA:CF£/PAPROV£/CCRFOV/	Ing	depres	Skin: Soap wash prompt	
Wash skin:	When contam	GMFOV/SCBAF/SAF	Con		Breath: Resp support	
Remove:	When wet (flamm)	§: SCBAF:PD,PP/SAF:PD,PP:ASCBA			Swallow: Medical attention	
Change:	N.R.	Escape: GMFOV/SCBAE			immed	

[1,2-Dichloroethylene]

Skin:	Prevent skin contact	NIOSH	Inh	Irrit nose, throat, resp	Eye: Irr immed	Eyes, resp sys,
Eyes:	Prevent eye contact	¥: SCBAF:PD,PP/SAF:PD,PP:ASCBA	Abs	sys; lac; cough; nau, vomit;	Skin: Soap wash	liver
Wash skin:	When contam	Escape: GMFOV/SCBAE	Ing	in animals: pulm edema;	Breath: Resp support	[in animals:
Remove:	When wet or contam		Con	liver damage; [carc]	Swallow: Medical attention	liver tumors]
Change:	N.R.				immed	
Provide:	Eyewash, Quick drench					

[Dichloroethyl ether]

99

Chemical name, structure/formula, CAS and RTECS Nos., and DOT ID and guide Nos.	Synonyms, trade names, and conversion factors	Exposure limits (TWA unless noted otherwise)	IDLH	Physical description	Chemical and physical properties		Incompatibilities and reactivities	Measurement method (See Table 1)
					MW, BP, SOL Fl.P, IP, Sp, Gr, flammability	VP, FRZ UEL, LEL		
Dichloromonofluoro-methane CHCl₂F 75-43-4 PA8400000 1029 126	Dichlorofluoromethane, Fluorodichloromethane, Freon® 21, Genetron® 21, Halon® 112, Refrigerant 21 1 ppm = 4.21 mg/m³	NIOSH 10 ppm (40 mg/m³) OSHA† 1000 ppm (4200 mg/m³)	5000 ppm	Colorless gas with a slight, ether-like odor. [Note: A liquid below 48°F. Shipped as a liquefied compressed gas.]	MW: 102.9 BP: 48°F Sol(86°F): 0.7% Fl.P: NA IP: 12.39 eV RGasD: 3.57 Nonflammable Gas	VP(70°F): 1.6 atm FRZ: -211°F UEL: NA LEL: NA	Chemically-active metals such as sodium, potassium, calcium, powdered aluminum, zinc & magnesium; acid; acid fumes	Char(2); CS₂; GC/FID; IV [#2516]
1,1-Dichloro-1-nitro-ethane CH₃CCl₂NO₂ 594-72-9 KI1050000 2650 153	Dichloronitroethane 1 ppm = 5.89 mg/m³	NIOSH/OSHA 2 ppm (10 mg/m³) OSHA† C 10 ppm (60 mg/m³)	25 ppm	Colorless liquid with an unpleasant odor. [fumigant]	MW: 143.9 BP: 255°F Sol: 0.3% Fl.P: 136°F IP: ? Sp.Gr: 1.43 Class II Combustible Liquid	VP: 15mm FRZ: ? UEL: ? LEL: ?	Strong oxidizers [Note: Corrosive to iron in presence of moisture.]	Char(pet); CS₂; GC/FID; IV [#1601]
1,3-Dichloropropene ClHC=CHCH₂Cl 542-75-6 UC8310000 2047 132	3-Chloroallyl chloride; DCP; 1,3-Dichloro-1-propene; 1,3-Dichloropropylene; Telone® 1 ppm = 4.54 mg/m³	NIOSH Ca 1 ppm (5 mg/m³) [skin] See Appendix A OSHA† none	Ca [N.D.]	Colorless to straw-colored liquid with a sharp, sweet, irritating, chloroform-like odor. [insecticide] [Note: Exists as mixture of cis- & trans-isomers.]	MW: 111.0 BP: 226°F Sol: 0.2% Fl.P: 77°F IP: ? Sp.Gr: 1.21 Class IC Flammable Liquid	VP: 28 mm FRZ: -119°F UEL: 14.5% LEL: 5.3%	Aluminum, magnesium, halogens, oxidizers [Note: Epichlorohydrin may be added as a stabilizer.]	None available
2,2-Dichloropropionic acid CH₃CCl₂COOH 75-99-0 UF0690000 1760 154	Dalapon; 2,2-Dichloropropanoic acid; α,α-Dichloropropionic acid 1 ppm = 5.85 mg/m³	NIOSH 1 ppm (6 mg/m³) OSHA† none	N.D.	Colorless liquid with an acrid odor. [herbicide] [Note: A white to tan powder below 46°F. The sodium salt, a white powder, is often used.]	MW: 143.0 BP: 374°F Sol: 50% Fl.P: NA IP: ? Sp.Gr: 1.40 Noncombustible Liquid	VP: ? FRZ: 46°F UEL: NA LEL: NA	Metals [Note: Very corrosive to aluminum & copper alloys. Reacts slowly in water to form hydrochloric & pyruvic acids.]	None available

Personal protection and sanitation (See Table 3)		Recommendations for respirator selection — maximum concentration for use (MUC) (See Table 4)	Health hazards				
			Route	Symptoms (See Table 5)	First aid (See Table 6)		Target organs (See Table 5)
Skin:	Frostbite	NIOSH	Inh	Asphy, card arrhy,	Eye:	Frostbite	Resp sys, CVS
Eyes:	Frostbite	100 ppm: SA	Con	card arrest;	Skin:	Frostbite	
Wash skin:	N.R.	250 ppm: SA:CF	(liq)	liq: frostbite	Breath	Resp support	
Remove:	N.R.	500 ppm: SCBAF/SAF					
Change:	N.R.	5000 ppm: SA:PD,PP					
Provide:	Frostbite	§: SCBAF:PD,PP/SAF:PD,PP:ASCBA					
		Escape: GMFOV/SCBAE					

[Dichloromonofluoromethane]

Skin:	Prevent skin contact	NIOSH	Inh	In animals: irrit eyes,	Eye:	Irr immed	Eyes, skin, resp sys,
Eyes:	Prevent eye contact	20 ppm: SA	Ing	skin; liver, heart, kidney	Skin:	Soap wash immed	liver, kidneys, CVS
Wash skin:	When contam	25 ppm: SA:CF/SCBAF/SAF	Con	damage; pulm edema, hemorr	Breath:	Resp support	
Remove:	When wet or contam	§: SCBAF:PD,PP/SAF:PD,PP:ASCBA			Swallow:	Medical attention	
Change:	N.R.	Escape: GMFOV/SCBAE				immed	

[1,1-Dichloro-1-nitroethane]

Skin:	Prevent skin contact	NIOSH	Inh	Irrit eyes, skin, resp	Eye:	Irr immed	Eyes, skin, resp sys,
Eyes:	Prevent eye contact	¥: SCBAF:PD,PP/SAF:PD,PP:ASCBA	Abs	sys; eye, skin burns; lac;	Skin:	Soap flush immed	CNS, liver, kidneys
Wash skin:	When contam	Escape: GMFOV/SCBAE	Ing	head, dizz;	Breath:	Resp support	[in animals:
Remove:	When wet (flamm)		Con	in animals: liver, kidney	Swallow:	Medical attention	cancer of the
Change:	N.R.			damage; [carc]		immed	bladder, liver,
Provide:	Eyewash, Quick drench						lung & forestomach]

[1,3-Dichloropropene]

Skin:	Prevent skin contact	TBAL	Inh	Irrit eyes, skin, upper	Eye:	Irr immed	Eyes, skin, resp sys,
Eyes:	Prevent eye contact		Ing	resp sys; eye, skin burns;	Skin:	Water flush immed	GI tract, CNS
Wash skin:	When contam		Con	lass, loss of appetite,	Breath:	Resp support	
Remove:	When wet or contam			diarr, vomit, slowing of	Swallow:	Medical attention	
Change:	N.R.			pulse; CNS depres		immed	
Provide:	Eyewash, Quick drench						

[2,2-Dichloropropionic acid]

Chemical name, structure/formula, CAS and RTECS Nos., and DOT ID and guide Nos.	Synonyms, trade names, and conversion factors	Exposure limits (TWA unless noted otherwise)	IDLH	Physical description	Chemical and physical properties		Incompatibilities and reactivities	Measurement method (See Table 1)
					MW, BP, SOL Fl.P, IP, Sp, Gr, flammability	VP, FRZ UEL, LEL		
Dichlorotetrafluoro-ethane CClF$_2$CClF$_2$ 76-14-2 KI1101000 1958 126	1,2-Dichlorotetra-fluoroethane; Freon® 114; Genetron® 114; Halon® 242; Refrigerant 114 1 ppm = 6.99 mg/m³	NIOSH/OSHA 1000 ppm (7000 mg/m³)	15,000 ppm	Colorless gas with a faint, ether-like odor at high concentrations. [Note: A liquid below 38°F. Shipped as a liquefied compressed gas.]	MW: 170.9 BP: 38°F Sol: 0.01% Fl.P: NA IP: 12.20 eV RGasD: 5.93 Nonflammable Gas	VP(70°F): 1.9 atm FRZ: -137°F UEL: NA LEL: NA	Chemically-active metals such as sodium, potassium, calcium, powdered aluminum, zinc & magnesium; acids; acid fumes	Char(2); CH$_2$Cl$_2$; GC/FID; IV [#1018]
Dichlorvos (CH$_3$O)$_2$P(O)OCH=CCl$_2$ 62-73-7 TC0350000 2783 152	DDVP; 2,2-Dichlorovinyl dimethyl phosphate 1 ppm = 9.04 mg/m³	NIOSH/OSHA 1 mg/m³ [skin]	100 mg/m³	Colorless to amber liquid with a mild, chemical odor. [Note: Insecticide that may be absorbed on a dry carrier.]	MW: 221.0 BP: Decomposes Sol: 0.5% Fl.P: >175°F IP: ? Sp.Gr(77°F): 1.42 Class III Combustible Liquid	VP: 0.01 mm FRZ: ? UEL: ? LEL: ?	Strong acids, strong alkalis [Note: Corrosive to iron & mild steel.]	XAD-2; Toluene; GC/FPD; II(5) [P&CAM #295]
Dicrotophos C$_8$H$_{16}$NO$_5$P 141-66-2 TC3850000	Bidrin®, Carbicron®, 2-Dimethyl cis-2-dimethyl-carbamoyl-1-methylvinyl-phosphate 1 ppm = 9.70 mg/m³	NIOSH 0.25 mg/m³ [skin] OSHA† none	N.D.	Yellow-brown liquid with a mild, ester odor. [insecticide]	MW: 237.2 BP: 752°F Sol: Miscible Fl.P: >200°F IP: ? Sp.Gr(59°F): 1.22 Class IIIB Combustible Liquid	VP: 0.0001 mm FRZ: ? UEL: ? LEL: ?	Metals [Note: Corrosive to cast iron, mild steel, brass & stainless steel.]	OVS-2; Toluene/ Acetone; GC/FPD; IV [#5600, Organo-phosphorus Pesticides]
Dicyclopentadiene C$_{10}$H$_{12}$ 77-73-6 PC1050000 2048 129	Bicyclopentadiene; DCPD; 1,3-Dicyclopentadiene dimer; 3a,4,7,7a-Tetrahydro-4,7-methanoindene [Note: Exists in two stereoisomeric forms.] 1 ppm = 5.41 mg/m³	NIOSH 5 ppm (30 mg/m³) OSHA† none	N.D.	Colorless, crystal-line solid with a disagreeable, camphor-like odor. [Note: A liquid above 90°F.]	MW: 132.2 BP: 342°F Sol: 0.02% Fl.P(oc): 90°F IP: ? Sp.Gr: 0.98 (Liquid at 95°F) Class IC Flammable Liquid Combustible Solid	VP: 1.4 mm FRZ: 90°F UEL: 6.3% LEL: 0.8%	Oxidizers [Note: Depolymerizes at boiling point and forms two molecules of cyclopentadiene. Must be inhibited and maintained under an inert atmosphere to prevent polymerization.]	None available

Personal protection and sanitation (See Table 3)		Recommendations for respirator selection — maximum concentration for use (MUC) (See Table 4)	Health hazards					
			Route	Symptoms (See Table 5)	First aid (See Table 6)		Target organs (See Table 5)	
Skin:	Frostbite	NIOSH/OSHA	Inh	Irrit resp sys; asphy;	Eye:	Frostbite	Resp sys, CVS	
Eyes:	Frostbite	10,000 ppm: SA	Con	card arrhy, card arrest;	Skin:	Frostbite		
Wash skin:	N.R.	15,000 ppm: SA:CF/SCBAF/SAF	(liq)	liq: frostbite	Breath:	Resp support		
Remove:	N.R.	§ SCBAF:PD,PP/SAF:PD,PP:ASCBA						
Change:	N.R.	Escape: GMFOV/SCBAE						
Provide:	Frostbite							

[Dichlorotetrafluoroethane]

Personal protection and sanitation (See Table 3)		Recommendations for respirator selection — maximum concentration for use (MUC) (See Table 4)	Health hazards					
Skin:	Prevent skin contact	NIOSH/OSHA	Inh	Irrit eyes, skin; miosis,	Eye:	Irr immed	Resp sys, CVS,	
Eyes:	Prevent eye contact	10 mg/m³: SA	Abs	ache eyes; rhin; head;	Skin:	Soap wash immed	CNS, eyes, skin,	
Wash skin:	When contam	25 mg/m³: SA:CF	Ing	chest tight, wheez, lar	Breath:	Resp support	blood chol	
Remove:	When wet or contam	50 mg/m³: SAT.CF/SCBAF/SAF	Con	spasm, salv; cyan; anor,	Swallow:	Medical attention		
Change:	N.R.	100 mg/m³: SA:PD,PP		nau, vomit, diarr; sweat;		immed		
		§ SCBAF:PD,PP/SAF:PD,PP:ASCBA		musc fasc, para, gidd,				
		Escape: GMFOVHiE/SCBAE		ataxia; convuls; low BP,				
				card irreg				

[Dichlorvos]

Personal protection and sanitation (See Table 3)		Recommendations for respirator selection — maximum concentration for use (MUC) (See Table 4)	Health hazards					
Skin:	Prevent skin contact	TBAL	Inh	Head, nau, dizz, anxiety,	Eye:	Irr immed	CNS, blood chol	
Eyes:	Prevent eye contact		Abs	restless, musc twitch,	Skin:	Water wash immed		
Wash skin:	When contam		Ing	weak, tremor, inco, vomit,	Breath:	Resp support		
Remove:	When wet or contam		Con	abdom cramps, diarr; salv,	Swallow:	Medical attention		
Change:	Daily			sweat, lac, rhinitis; anor,		immed		
Provide:	Quick drench			mal				

[Dicrotophos]

Personal protection and sanitation (See Table 3)		Recommendations for respirator selection — maximum concentration for use (MUC) (See Table 4)	Health hazards					
Skin:	Prevent skin contact	TBAL	Inh	Irrit eyes, skin, nose,	Eye:	Irr immed	Eyes, skin, resp sys,	
Eyes:	Prevent eye contact		Ing	throat; inco, head; sneez,	Skin:	Soap flush immed	CNS, kidneys	
Wash skin:	When contam		Con	cough; skin blisters;	Breath:	Resp support		
Remove:	When wet or contam			in animals: kidney, lung	Swallow:	Medical attention		
Change:	Daily			damage		immed		
Provide:	Eyewash, Quick drench							

[Dicyclopentadiene]

Chemical name, structure/formula, CAS and RTECS Nos., and DOT ID and guide Nos.	Synonyms, trade names, and conversion factors	Exposure limits (TWA unless noted otherwise)	IDLH	Physical description	Chemical and physical properties		Incompatibilities and reactivities	Measurement method (See Table 1)
					MW, BP, SOL FI.P, IP, Sp, Gr, flammability	VP, FRZ UEL, LEL		
Dicyclopentadienyl iron $(C_5H_5)_2Fe$ 102-54-5 LK0700000	bis(Cyclopentadienyl)iron, Ferrocene, Iron dicyclopentadienyl	NIOSH 10 mg/m^3 (total) 5 mg/m^3 (resp) OSHA† 15 mg/m^3 (total) 5 mg/m^3 (resp)	N.D.	Orange, crystalline solid with a camphor-like odor.	MW: 186.1 BP: 480°F Sol: Insoluble FI.P: ? IP: 6.88 eV Sp.Gr: ? Combustible Solid	VP: ? MLT: 343°F UEL: ? LEL: ?	Ammonium perchlorate, tetranitromethane, mercury(II) nitrate	Filter; H$_2$SO$_4$/H$_2$O$_2$/ HCl; ICP; OSHA [#ID125G, Iron Oxide Fume]
Dieldrin $C_{12}H_8Cl_6O$ 60-57-1 IO1750000 2761 151	HEOD; 1,2,3,4,10,10-Hexachloro-6,7-epoxy-1,4,4a,5,6,7,8,8a-octahydro-1,4-endo,exo-5,8-dimethanonaphthalene	NIOSH Ca See Appendix A 0.25 mg/m^3 [skin] OSHA 0.25 mg/m^3 [skin]	Ca [50 mg/m^3]	Colorless to light-tan crystals with a mild, chemical odor. [insecticide]	MW: 380.9 BP: Decomposes Sol: 0.02% FI.P: NA IP: ? Sp.Gr: 1.75 Noncombustible Solid	VP(77°F): 8 x 10^{-7} mm MLT: 349°F UEL: NA LEL: NA	Strong oxidizers, active metals such as sodium, strong acids, phenols	Filter; Isooctane; GC/ECD; II(3) [#S283]
Diesel exhaust	Synonyms vary depending upon the specific diesel exhaust component.	NIOSH Ca See Appendix A OSHA none	Ca [N.D.]	Appearance and odor vary depending upon the specific diesel exhaust component.	Properties vary depending upon the specific diesel exhaust component.		Varies	Filter; none; EGA/TOA; IV [#5040, Elemental Carbon]
Diethanolamine (HOCH$_2$CH$_2$)$_2$NH 111-42-2 KL2975000 1 ppm = 4.30 mg/m^3	DEA; Di(2-hydroxyethyl)amine; 2,2'-Dihydroxydiethylamine; Diolamine; bis(2-Hydroxyethyl)amine; 2,2'-Iminodiethanol	NIOSH 3 ppm (15 mg/m^3) OSHA† none	N.D.	Colorless crystals or a syrupy, white liquid (above 82°F) with a mild, ammonia-like odor.	MW: 105.2 BP: 516°F (Decomposes) Sol: 95% FI.P: 279°F IP: ? Sp.Gr: 1.10 Class IIIB Combustible Liquid Combustible Solid	VP: <0.01 mm MLT: 82°F UEL: 9.8% LEL: 1.6%	Oxidizers, strong acids, acid anhydrides, halides [Note: Reacts with CO$_2$ in the air. Hygroscopic (i.e., absorbs moisture from the air). Corrosive to copper, zinc & galvanized iron.]	Imp; Reagent; IC; IV [#3509, Amino-ethanol Compounds II]

Personal protection and sanitation (See Table 3)		Recommendations for respirator selection — maximum concentration for use (MUC) (See Table 4)	Health hazards			
			Route	Symptoms (See Table 5)	First aid (See Table 6)	Target organs (See Table 5)
Skin: Eyes: Wash skin: Remove: Change:	N.R. N.R. N.R. N.R. Daily	TBAL	Inh Ing Con	Possible irrit eyes, skin, resp sys; in animals: liver, RBC, testicular changes	Eye: Skin: Breath: Swallow:	Irr immed Soap wash Resp support Medical attention immed	Eyes, skin, resp sys, liver, blood, repro sys
[Dicyclopentadienyl iron]						
Skin: Eyes: Wash skin: Remove: Change: Provide:	Prevent skin contact Prevent eye contact When contam/Daily When wet or contam Daily Eyewash, Quick drench	NIOSH ¥: SCBAF:PD,PP/SAF:PD,PP:ASCBA Escape: GMFOVHiE/SCBAE	Inh Abs Ing Con	Head, dizz; nau, vomit, mal, sweat; myoclonic limb jerks; clonic, tonic convuls; coma; [carc]; in animals: liver, kidney damage	Eye: Skin: Breath: Swallow:	Irr immed Soap wash immed Resp support Medical attention immed	CNS, liver, kidneys, skin [in animals: lung, liver, thyroid & adrenal gland tumors]
[Dieldrin]						
Skin: Eyes: Wash skin: Remove: Change:	N.R. N.R. N.R. N.R. N.R.	NIOSH ¥: SCBAF:PD,PP/SAF:PD,PP:ASCBA Escape: GMFOVHiE/SCBAE	Inh Con	Eye irrit, pulm func changes; [carc]	Breath;	Resp support	Eyes, resp sys [in animals: lung tumors]
[Diesel exhaust]						
Skin: Eyes: Wash skin: Remove: Change: Provide:	Prevent skin contact Prevent eye contact When contam When wet or contam Daily Eyewash, Quick drench	TBAL	Inh Ing Con	Irrit eyes, skin, nose, throat; eye burns, corn nec; skin burns; lac, cough, sneez	Eye: Skin: Breath: Swallow:	Irr immed Water flush immed Resp support Medical attention immed	Eyes, skin, resp sys
[Diethanolamine]						

105

Chemical name, structure/formula, CAS and RTECS Nos., and DOT ID and guide Nos.	Synonyms, trade names, and conversion factors	Exposure limits (TWA unless noted otherwise)	IDLH	Physical description	Chemical and physical properties MW, BP, SOL Fl.P, IP, Sp, Gr, flammability	VP, FRZ UEL, LEL	Incompatibilities and reactivities	Measurement method (See Table 1)
Diethylamine $(C_2H_5)_2NH$ 109-89-7 HZ8750000 1154 132	Diethamine; N,N-Diethylamine; N-Ethylethanamine 1 ppm = 2.99 mg/m³	NIOSH 10 ppm (30 mg/m³) ST 25 ppm (75 mg/m³) OSHA† 25 ppm (75 mg/m³)	200 ppm	Colorless liquid with a fishy, ammonia-like odor.	MW: 73.1 BP: 132°F Sol: Miscible Fl.P: -15°F IP: 8.01 eV Sp.Gr: 0.71 Class IB Flammable Liquid	VP: 192 mm FRZ: -58°F UEL: 10.1% LEL: 1.8%	Strong oxidizers, strong acids, cellulose nitrate	Si gel; H₂SO₄/ Methanol; GC/FID; IV [#2010]
2-Diethylaminoethanol $(C_2H_5)_2NCH_2CH_2OH$ 100-37-8 KK5075000 2686 132	Diethylaminoethanol; 2-Diethylaminoethyl alcohol; N,N-Diethylethanolamine; Diethyl-(2-hydroxyethyl)-amine; 2-Hydroxytriethylamine 1 ppm = 4.79 mg/m³	NIOSH/OSHA 10 ppm (50 mg/m³) [skin]	100 ppm	Colorless liquid with a nauseating, ammonia-like odor.	MW: 117.2 BP: 325°F Sol: Miscible Fl.P: 126°F IP: ? Sp.Gr: 0.89 Class II Combustible Liquid	VP: 1 mm FRZ: -94°F UEL: ? LEL: ?	Strong oxidizers, strong acids	Si gel; Methanol/ Water; GC/FID; IV [#2007, Amino-ethanol Compounds I]
Diethylenetriamine $(NH_2CH_2CH_2)_2NH$ 111-40-0 IE1225000 2079 154	N-(2-Aminoethyl)1,2-ethanediamine; bis(2-Aminoethyl)amine; DETA; 2,2'-Diaminodiethylamine 1 ppm = 4.22 mg/m³	NIOSH 1 ppm (4 mg/m³) [skin] OSHA† none	N.D.	Colorless to yellow liquid with a strong, ammonia-like odor. [Note: Hygroscopic (i.e., absorbs moisture from the air).]	MW: 103.2 BP: 405°F Sol: Miscible Fl.P: 208°F IP: ? Sp.Gr: 0.96 Class IIIB Combustible Liquid	VP: 0.4 mm FRZ: -38°F UEL: 6.7% LEL: 2%	Oxidizers, strong acids, cellulose nitrate [Note: May form explosive complexes with silver, cobalt, or chromium compounds. Corrosive to aluminum, copper, brass & zinc.]	XAD-2*; DMF; HPLC/UVD; IV [#2540]
Diethyl ketone $CH_3CH_2COCH_2CH_3$ 96-22-0 SA8050000 1156 127	DEK, Dimethylacetone, Ethyl ketone, Metacetone, 3-Pentanone, Propione 1 ppm = 3.53 mg/m³	NIOSH 200 ppm (705 mg/m³) OSHA† none	N.D.	Colorless liquid with an acetone-like odor.	MW: 86.2 BP: 215°F Sol: 5% Fl.P(oc): 55°F IP: 9.32 eV Sp.Gr: 0.81 Class IB Flammable Liquid	VP(77°F): 35 mm FRZ: -44°F UEL: 6.4% LEL: 1.6%	Strong oxidizers, alkalis, mineral acids, (hydrogen peroxide + nitric acid)	None available

Personal protection and sanitation (See Table 3)		Recommendations for respirator selection — maximum concentration for use (MUC) (See Table 4)	Health hazards					
			Route	Symptoms (See Table 5)		First aid (See Table 6)		Target organs (See Table 5)
Skin:	Prevent skin contact	NIOSH	Inh	Irrit eyes, skin, resp sys;	Eye:	Irr immed	Eyes, skin, resp sys,
Eyes:	Prevent eye contact	200 ppm: SA:CF£/PAPRS£/CCRFS/	Abs	in animals: myocardial	Skin:	Water flush immed	CVS
Wash skin:	When contam	GMFS/SCBAF/SAF	Ing	degeneration	Breath:	Resp support	
Remove:	When wet (flamm)	§: SCBAF:PD,PP/SAF:PD,PP:ASCBA	Con		Swallow:	Medical attention	
Change:	N.R.	Escape: GMFS/SCBAE				immed	
Provide:	Eyewash (>0.5%), Quick drench (liq)						

[Diethylamine]

Skin:	Prevent skin contact	NIOSH/OSHA	Inh	Irrit eyes, skin, resp sys;	Eye:	Irr immed	Eyes, skin, resp sys
Eyes:	Prevent eye contact	100 ppm: CCROV*/GMFOV/PAPROV*/	Abs	nau, vomit	Skin:	Water flush immed	
Wash skin:	When contam	SA*/SCBAF	Ing		Breath:	Resp support	
Remove:	When wet or contam	§: SCBAF:PD,PP/SAF:PD,PP:ASCBA	Con		Swallow:	Medical attention	
Change:	N.R.	Escape: GMFOV/SCBAE				immed	
Provide:	Eyewash (>5%), Quick drench						

[2-Diethylaminoethanol]

Skin:	Prevent skin contact	TBAL	Inh	Irrit eyes, skin, muc memb,	Eye:	Irr immed	Eyes, skin, resp sys
Eyes:	Prevent eye contact		Abs	upper resp sys; derm, skin	Skin:	Water flush immed	
Wash skin:	When contam		Ing	sens; eye, skin nec; cough,	Breath:	Resp support	
Remove:	When wet or contam		Con	dysp, pulm sens	Swallow:	Medical attention	
Change:	N.R.					immed	
Provide:	Eyewash, Quick drench						

[Diethylenetriamine]

Skin:	N.R.	TBAL	Inh	Irrit eyes, skin, muc memb,	Eye:	Irr immed	Eyes, skin, resp sys
Eyes:	Prevent eye contact		Ing	resp sys; cough, sneez	Skin:	Soap wash	
Wash skin:	Daily		Con		Breath:	Resp support	
Remove:	When wet (flamm)				Swallow:	Medical attention	
Change:	N.R.					immed	

[Diethyl ketone]

Chemical name, structure/formula, CAS and RTECS Nos., and DOT ID and guide Nos.	Synonyms, trade names, and conversion factors	Exposure limits (TWA unless noted otherwise)	IDLH	Physical description	Chemical and physical properties		Incompatibilities and reactivities	Measurement method (See Table 1)
					MW, BP, SOL Fl.P, IP, Sp, Gr, flammability	VP, FRZ UEL, LEL		
Diethyl phthalate $C_6H_4(COOC_2H_5)_2$ 84-66-2 TI1050000	DEP, Diethyl ester of phthalic acid, Ethyl phthalate	NIOSH 5 mg/m³ OSHA† none	N.D.	Colorless to water-white, oily liquid with a very slight, aromatic odor. [pesticide]	MW: 222.3 BP: 563°F Sol(77°F): 0.1% Fl.P(oc): 322°F IP: ? Sp.Gr: 1.12 Class IIIB Combustible Liquid; however, ignition is difficult.	VP(77°F): 0.002 mm FRZ:-41°F UEL: ? LEL(368°F): 0.7%	Strong oxidizers, strong acids, nitric acid, permanganates, water	OVS-Tenax; Toluene; GC/FID; OSHA [#104]
Difluorodibromomethane CBr_2F_2 75-61-6 PA7525000 1941 159	Dibromodifluoromethane, Freon® 12B2, Halon® 1202 1 ppm = 8.58 mg/m³	NIOSH/OSHA 100 ppm (860 mg/m³)	2000 ppm	Colorless, heavy liquid or gas (above 76°F) with a characteristic odor.	MW: 209.8 BP: 76°F Sol: Insoluble Fl.P: NA IP: 11.07 eV Sp.Gr(59°F): 2.29 Noncombustible Liquid Nonflammable Gas	VP: 620 mm FRZ:-231°F UEL: NA LEL: NA	Chemically-active metals such as sodium, potassium, calcium, powdered aluminum, zinc & magnesium	Char(2); 2-Propanol; GC/FID; IV [#1012]
Diglycidyl ether $C_6H_{10}O_3$ 2238-07-5 KN2350000	DGE; Diallyl ether dioxide; Di(2,3-epoxypropyl) ether; 2-Epoxypropyl ether; bis(2,3-Epoxypropyl) ether 1 ppm = 5.33 mg/m³	NIOSH Ca See Appendix A 0.1 ppm (0.5 mg/m³) OSHA† C 0.5 ppm (2.8 mg/m³)	Ca [10 ppm]	Colorless liquid with a strong, irritating odor.	MW: 130.2 BP: 500°F Sol: ? Fl.P: 147°F IP: ? Sp.Gr: 1.12 Class IIIA Combustible Liquid	VP(77°F): 0.09 mm FRZ: ? UEL: ? LEL: ?	Strong oxidizers	None available
Diisobutyl ketone $[(CH_3)_2CHCH_2]_2CO$ 108-83-8 MJ5775000 1157 127	DIBK; sym-Diisopropyl acetone; 2,6-Dimethyl-4-heptanone; Isovalerone; Valerone 1 ppm = 5.82 mg/m³	NIOSH 25 ppm (150 mg/m³) OSHA† 50 ppm (290 mg/m³)	500 ppm	Colorless liquid with a mild, sweet odor.	MW: 142.3 BP: 334°F Sol: 0.05% Fl.P: 120°F IP: 9.04 eV Sp.Gr: 0.81 Class II Combustible Liquid	VP: 2 mm FRZ: -43°F UEL(200°F): 7.1% LEL(200°F): 0.8%	Strong oxidizers	Char; CS₂; GC/FID; IV [#1300, Ketones I]

Personal protection and sanitation (See Table 3)		Recommendations for respirator selection — maximum concentration for use (MUC) (See Table 4)	Health hazards				
			Route	Symptoms (See Table 5)	First aid (See Table 6)		Target organs (See Table 5)
Skin: Eyes: Wash skin: Remove: Change:	N.R. N.R. N.R. N.R. N.R.	TBAL	Inh Ing Con	Irrit eyes, skin, nose, throat; head, dizz, nau; lac; possible polyneur, vestibular dysfunc; pain, numb, weak, spasms in arms & legs; in animals: repro effects	Eye: Skin: Breath: Swallow:	Irr immed Wash regularly Resp support Medical attention immed	Eyes, skin, resp sys, CNS, PNS, repro sys

[Diethyl phthalate]

Skin: Eyes: Wash skin: Remove: Change:	Prevent skin contact Prevent eye contact N.R. When wet or contam N.R.	NIOSH/OSHA 1000 ppm: SA 2000 ppm: SA:CF/SCBAF/SAF §: SCBAF:PD,PP/SAF:PD,PP:ASCBA Escape: GMFOV/SCBAE	Inh Ing Con	In animals: irrit resp sys; CNS symptoms; liver damage	Eye: Skin: Breath: Swallow:	Irr immed Water flush immed Resp support Medical attention immed	Resp sys, CNS, liver

[Difluorodibromomethane]

Skin: Eyes: Wash skin: Remove: Change: Provide:	Prevent skin contact Prevent eye contact When contam/Daily When wet or contam Daily Eyewash, Quick drench	NIOSH ¥: SCBAF:PD,PP/SAF:PD,PP:ASCBA Escape: GMFOV/SCBAE	Inh Abs Ing Con	Irrit eyes, skin, resp sys; skin burns; in animals: hemato sys, lung, liver, kidney damage; repro effects; [carc]	Eye: Skin: Breath: Swallow:	Irr immed Soap wash immed Resp support Medical attention immed	Eyes, skin, resp sys, repro sys [in animals: skin tumors]

[Diglycidyl ether]

Skin: Eyes: Wash skin: Remove: Change:	Prevent skin contact N.R. When contam When wet or contam N.R.	NIOSH 500 ppm: SA:CF£/PAPROV£/CCRFOV/ GMFOV/SCBAF/SAF §: SCBAF:PD,PP/SAF:PD,PP:ASCBA Escape: GMFOV/SCBAE	Inh Ing Con	Irrit eyes, skin, nose, throat; head, dizz; derm; liver, kidney damage	Eye: Skin: Breath: Swallow:	Irr immed Soap wash prompt Resp support Medical attention immed	Eyes, skin, resp sys, CNS, liver, kidneys

[Diisobutyl ketone]

Chemical name, structure/formula, CAS and RTECS Nos., and DOT ID and guide Nos.	Synonyms, trade names, and conversion factors	Exposure limits (TWA unless noted otherwise)	IDLH	Physical description	Chemical and physical properties		Incompatibilities and reactivities	Measurement method (See Table 1)
					MW, BP, SOL Fl.P, IP, Sp, Gr, flammability	VP, FRZ UEL, LEL		
Diisopropylamine [(CH$_3$)$_2$CH]$_2$NH 108-18-9 IM4025000 1158 132	**DIPA,** N-(1-Methylethyl)-2-propanamine 1 ppm = 4.14 mg/m^3	NIOSH/OSHA 5 ppm (20 mg/m^3) [skin]	200 ppm	Colorless liquid with an ammonia- or fish-like odor.	MW: 101.2 BP: 183°F Sol: Miscible Fl.P: 20°F IP: 7.73 eV Sp.Gr. 0.72 Class IB Flammable Liquid	VP: 70 mm FRZ: -141°F UEL:7.1% LEL:1.1%	Strong oxidizers, strong acids	Imp; KOH; GC/FID; II(4) [#S141]
Dimethyl acetamide CH$_3$CON(CH$_3$)$_2$ 127-19-5 AB7700000	N,N-Dimethyl acetamide; DMAC 1 ppm = 3.56 mg/m^3	NIOSH/OSHA 10 ppm (35 mg/m^3) [skin]	300 ppm	Colorless liquid with a weak, ammonia- or fish-like odor.	MW: 87.1 BP: 329°F Sol: Miscible Fl.P(oc): 158°F IP: 8.81 eV Sp.Gr: 0.94 Class IIIA Combustible Liquid	VP: 2 mm FRZ: -4°F UEL(320°F): 11.5% LEL(212°F): 1.8%	Carbon tetrachloride, other halogenated compounds when in contact with iron, oxidizers	Si gel; Methanol; GC/FID; IV [#2004]
Dimethylamine (CH$_3$)$_2$NH 124-40-3 IP8750000 1032 118 (anhydrous) 1160 129 (solution)	Dimethylamine (anhydrous), N-Methylmethanamine 1 ppm = 1.85 mg/m^3	NIOSH/OSHA 10 ppm (18 mg/m^3)	500 ppm	Colorless gas with an ammonia- or fish-like odor. [Note: A liquid below 44°F. Shipped as a liquefied compressed gas.]	MW: 45.1 BP: 44°F Sol(140°F): 24% Fl.P: NA (Gas) 20°F (Liq) IP: 8.24 eV RGasD:1.56 Sp.Gr: 0.67 (Liquid at 44°F) Flammable Gas/Class IA Flammable Liquid	VP: 1.7 atm FRZ: -134°F UEL:14.4% LEL:2.8%	Strong oxidizers, chlorine, mercury, acraldehyde, fluorides, maleic anhydride, aluminum, brass, copper, zinc	Si gel; H$_2$SO$_4$/Methanol; GC/FID; IV [#2010]
4-Dimethylamino-azobenzene C$_6$H$_5$NNC$_6$H$_4$N(CH$_3$)$_2$ 60-11-7 BX7350000	Butter yellow; DAB; p-Dimethylaminoazobenzene; N,N-Dimethyl-4-aminoazo-benzene; Methyl yellow	NIOSH Ca See Appendix A OSHA[1910.1015] See Appendix B	Ca [N.D.]	Yellow, leaf-shaped crystals.	MW: 225.3 BP: Sublimes Sol:0.001% Fl.P: ? IP: ? Sp.Gr: ?	VP: 0.0000003 mm (est.) MLT: 237°F UEL: ? LEL: ?	None reported	G-chrom P; 2-Propanol; GC/FID; II(4) [P&CAM #284]

110

Personal protection and sanitation (See Table 3)		Recommendations for respirator selection — maximum concentration for use (MUC) (See Table 4)	Health hazards				
			Route	Symptoms (See Table 5)	First aid (See Table 6)		Target organs (See Table 5)
Skin:	Prevent skin contact	NIOSH/OSHA	Ing	Irrit eyes, skin, resp sys;	Eye:	Irr immed	Eyes, skin, resp sys
Eyes:	Prevent eye contact (>5%)	125 ppm: SA:CF£/PAPROV£	Abs	nau, vomit; head; vis dist	Skin:	Water wash immed	
Wash skin:	When contam	200 ppm: CCRFOV/GMFOV/PAPRTOV£/	Ing		Breath:	Resp support	
Remove:	When wet (flamm)	SCBAF/SAF	Con		Swallow:	Medical attention	
Change:	N.R.	§: SCBAF:PD,PP/SAF:PD,PP:ASCBA				immed	
Provide:	Eyewash (>5%)	Escape: GMFOV/SCBAE					

[Diisopropylamine]

Skin:	Prevent skin contact	NIOSH/OSHA	Inh	Irrit skin; jaun, liver	Eye:	Irr immed	Skin, liver, CNS
Eyes:	Prevent eye contact	100 ppm: SA	Abs	damage; depres, leth,	Skin:	Water flush immed	
Wash skin:	When contam	250 ppm: SA:CF	Ing	halu, delusions	Breath:	Resp support	
Remove:	When wet or contam	300 ppm: SCBAF/SAF	Con		Swallow:	Medical attention	
Change:	N.R.	§: SCBAF:PD,PP/SAF:PD,PP:ASCBA				immed	
Provide:	Quick drench	Escape: GMFOV/SCBAE					

[Dimethyl acetamide]

Skin:	Prevent skin contact (liq)/	NIOSH/OSHA	Inh	Irrit nose, throat;	Eye:	Irr immed (liq)/	Eyes, skin, resp sys
	Frostbite	250 ppm: SA:CF£	Con	sneez, cough, dysp;		Frostbite	
Eyes:	Prevent eye contact (liq)/	500 ppm: SCBAF/SAF	(liq)	pulm edema; conj; derm;	Skin:	Water flush immed	
	Frostbite	§: SCBAF:PD,PP/SAF:PD,PP:ASCBA		liq: frostbite		(liq)/Frostbite	
Wash skin:	When contam (liq)	Escape: GMFS/SCBAE			Breath:	Resp support	
Remove:	When wet (flamm)						
Change:	N.R.						
Provide:	Eyewash (liq), Quick drench (liq),						
	Frostbite						

[Dimethylamine]

Skin:	Prevent skin contact	NIOSH	Inh	Enlarged liver; liver,	Eye:	Irr immed	Skin, resp sys,
Eyes:	Prevent eye contact	¥: SCBAF:PD,PP/SAF:PD,PP:ASCBA	Abs	kidney dysfunc; contact	Skin:	Soap wash immed	liver, kidneys,
Wash skin:	When contam/Daily	Escape: HiEF/SCBAE	Ing	derm; cough, wheez, dysp;	Breath:	Resp support	bladder
Remove:	When wet or contam		Con	bloody sputum; bronchial	Swallow:	Medical attention	[in animals:
Change:	Daily			secretions; frequent		immed	liver & bladder
Provide:	Eyewash, Quick drench			urination, hema, dysuria;			tumors]
				[carc]			

[4-Dimethylaminoazobenzene]

111

Chemical name, structure/formula, CAS and RTECS Nos., and DOT ID and guide Nos.	Synonyms, trade names, and conversion factors	Exposure limits (TWA unless noted otherwise)	IDLH	Physical description	Chemical and physical properties		Incompatibilities and reactivities	Measurement method (See Table 1)
					MW, BP, SOL Fl.P, IP, Sp, Gr, flammability	VP, FRZ UEL, LEL		
bis(2-(Dimethylamino)-ethyl)ether $C_8H_{20}N_2O$ 3033-62-3 KR9460000	NIAX® A99; NIAX® Catalyst A1; 2,2'-Oxybis(N,N-dimethyl ethylamine) [(CH$_3$)$_2$NCH$_2$CH$_2$OCH$_2$CH$_2$N(CH$_3$)$_2$] [Note: A component (5%) of NIAX® Catalyst ESN, along with dimethylaminopropio-nitrile (95%).]	NIOSH/OSHA See Appendix C (Niax® Catalyst ESN)	N.D.	Liquid.	MW: 160.3 BP: 372°F Sol: ? Fl.P: ? Sp.Gr: ?	VP: ? FRZ: ? UEL: ? LEL: ? IP: ?	None reported	None available
Dimethylamino-propionitrile (CH$_3$)$_2$NCH$_2$CH$_2$CN 1738-25-6 UG1575000	3-(Dimethylamino)-propionitrile; N,N-Dimethylamino-3-propionitrile [Note: A component (95%) of NIAX® Catalyst ESN, along with bis(2-(dimethylamino)-ethyl) ether (5%).]	NIOSH/OSHA See Appendix C (Niax® Catalyst ESN)	N.D.	Colorless liquid.	MW: 98.2 BP: 342°F Sol: Miscible Fl.P: 147°F IP: ? Sp.Gr(86°F): 0.86 Class IIIA Combustible Liquid	VP(135°F): 10mm FRZ: -48°F UEL: ? LEL: ?	Oxidizers [Note: Emits toxic oxides of nitrogen and cyanide fumes when heated to decomposition.]	None available
N,N-Dimethylaniline $C_6H_5N(CH_3)_2$ 121-69-7 BX4725000 2253 153	N,N-Dimethylbenzeneamine; N,N-Dimethylphenylamine [Note: Also known as Dimethylaniline which is a correct synonym for Xylidine.] 1 ppm = 4.96 mg/m³	NIOSH 5 ppm (25 mg/m³) ST 10 ppm (50 mg/m³) [skin] OSHA† 5 ppm (25 mg/m³) [skin]	100 ppm	Pale-yellow, oily liquid with an amine-like odor. [Note: A solid below 36°F.]	MW: 121.2 BP: 378°F Sol: 2% Fl.P: 142°F IP: 7.14 eV Sp.Gr: 0.96 Class IIIA Combustible Liquid	VP: 1 mm FRZ: 36°F UEL: ? LEL: ?	Strong oxidizers, strong acids, benzoyl peroxide	Si gel; Ethanol; GC/FID; IV [#2002, Aromatic Amines]
Dimethyl carbamoyl chloride (CH$_3$)$_2$NCOCl 79-44-7 FD4200000 2262 156	Chloroformic acid dimethylamide; Dimethylcarbamic chloride; N,N-Dimethylcarbamoyl chloride; DMCC	NIOSH Ca See Appendix A OSHA none	Ca [N.D.]	Clear, colorless liquid.	MW: 107.6 BP: 329°F Sol: Reacts Fl.P: 155°F IP: ? Sp.Gr: 1.17 Class IIIA Combustible Liquid	VP: ? FRZ: -27°F UEL: ? LEL: ?	Acids, water [Note: Rapidly hydrolyzes in water to dimethylamine, carbon dioxide, and hydrogen chloride.]	None available

Personal protection and sanitation (See Table 3)		Recommendations for respirator selection — maximum concentration for use (MUC) (See Table 4)	Health hazards					
			Route	Symptoms (See Table 5)	First aid (See Table 6)		Target organs (See Table 5)	

Skin: Eyes: Wash skin: Remove: Change: Provide:	Prevent skin contact Prevent eye contact When contam When wet or contam N.R. Eyewash, Quick drench	NIOSH ¥: SCBAF:PD,PP/SAF:PD,PP:ASCBA Escape: GMFOV/SCBAE	Inh Abs Ing Con	Possible urinary dysfunc; neurological disorders; in animals: irrit eyes, skin	Eye: Skin: Breath: Swallow:	Irr immed Water flush immed Resp support Medical attention immed	Eyes, skin, urinary tract, PNS

[bis(2-(Dimethylamino)ethyl)ether]

Skin: Eyes: Wash skin: Remove: Change: Provide:	Prevent skin contact Prevent eye contact When contam When wet or contam N.R. Eyewash, Quick drench	NIOSH ¥: SCBAF:PD,PP/SAF:PD,PP:ASCBA Escape: GMFOV/SCBAE	Inh Abs Ing Con	Irrit eyes, skin; urinary dysfunc; neurological disorders; pins & needles in hands & feet; musc weak, lass, nau, vomit; decr nerve conduction in lower legs	Eye: Skin: Breath: Swallow:	Irr immed Water flush immed Resp support Medical attention immed	Eyes, skin, urinary tract, PNS

[Dimethylaminopropionitrile]

Skin: Eyes: Wash skin: Remove: Change: Provide:	Prevent skin contact Prevent eye contact When contam When wet or contam N.R. Quick drench	NIOSH/OSHA 50 ppm: SA 100 ppm: SA:CF/SCBAF/SAF §: SCBAF:PD,PP/SAF:PD,PP:ASCBA Escape: GMFOV/SCBAE	Inh Abs Ing Con	Anoxia symptoms: cyan, weak, dizz, ataxia; methemo	Eye: Skin: Breath: Swallow:	Irr immed Soap wash immed Resp support Medical attention immed	Blood, kidneys, liver, CVS

[N,N-Dimethylaniline]

Skin: Eyes: Wash skin: Remove: Change: Provide:	Prevent skin contact Prevent eye contact When contam When wet or contam N.R. Eyewash, Quick drench	NIOSH ¥: SCBAF:PD,PP/SAF:PD,PP:ASCBA Escape: GMFOV/SCBAE	Inh Abs Ing Con	Irrit eyes, skin, nose, throat, resp sys; eye, skin burns; cough, wheez, laryngitis, dysp; head, nau, vomit; liver inj; [carc]	Eye: Skin: Breath: Swallow:	Irr immed Water flush immed Resp support Medical attention immed	Eyes, skin, resp sys, liver [in animals: nasal cancer]

[Dimethyl carbamoyl chloride]

Chemical name, structure/formula, CAS and RTECS Nos., and DOT ID and guide Nos.	Synonyms, trade names, and conversion factors	Exposure limits (TWA unless noted otherwise)	IDLH	Physical description	Chemical and physical properties — MW, BP, SOL, Fl.P, IP, Sp, Gr, flammability	VP, FRZ, UEL, LEL	Incompatibilities and reactivities	Measurement method (See Table 1)
Dimethyl-1,2-dibromo-2,2-dichlorethyl phosphate $(CH_3O)_2P(O)OCHBrCBrCl_2$ 300-76-5 TB9450000	Dibrom®; 1,2-Dibromo-2,2-dichloro-ethyl dimethyl phosphate; Naled	NIOSH 3 mg/m³ [skin] OSHA† 3 mg/m³	200 mg/m³	Colorless to white solid or straw-colored liquid (above 80°F) with a slightly pungent odor. [insecticide]	MW: 380.8 BP: Decomposes Sol: Insoluble Fl.P: NA IP: ? Sp.Gr(77°F): 1.96 Noncombustible Solid	VP: 0.0002 mm MLT: 80°F UEL: NA LEL: NA	Strong oxidizers, acids, sunlight, water [Note: Corrosive to metals. Hydrolyzed in presence of water.]	None available
Dimethylformamide $HCON(CH_3)_2$ 68-12-2 LQ2100000 2265 129	Dimethyl formamide; N,N-Dimethylformamide; DMF 1 ppm = 2.99 mg/m³	NIOSH/OSHA 10 ppm (30 mg/m³) [skin]	500 ppm	Colorless to pale-yellow liquid with a faint, amine-like odor.	MW: 73.1 BP: 307°F Sol: Miscible Fl.P: 136°F IP: 9.12 eV Sp.Gr: 0.95 Class II Combustible Liquid	VP: 3 mm FRZ: -78°F UEL: 15.2% LEL(212°F): 2.2%	Carbon tetrachloride; other halogenated compounds when in contact with iron; strong oxidizers; alkyl aluminums; inorganic nitrates	Si gel; Methanol; GC/FID; IV [#2004]
1,1-Dimethylhydrazine $(CH_3)_2NNH_2$ 57-14-7 MV2450000 1163 131	Dimazine, DMH, UDMH, Unsymmetrical dimethyl-hydrazine 1 ppm = 2.46 mg/m³	NIOSH Ca See Appendix A C 0.06 ppm (0.15 mg/m³) [2-hr] OSHA 0.5 ppm (1 mg/m³) [skin]	Ca [15 ppm]	Colorless liquid with an ammonia- or fish-like odor.	MW: 60.1 BP: 147°F Sol: Miscible Fl.P: 5°F IP: 8.05 eV Sp.Gr: 0.79 Class IB Flammable Liquid	VP: 103 mm FRZ: -72°F UEL: 95% LEL: 2%	Oxidizers, halogens, metallic mercury, fuming nitric acid, hydrogen peroxide [Note: May ignite SPONTANEOUSLY in contact with oxidizers.]	Bub; Pho-acid; Vis; IV [#3515]
Dimethylphthalate $C_6H_4(COOCH_3)_2$ 131-11-3 TI1575000 9188 171	Dimethyl ester of 1,2-benzenedicarboxylic acid; DMP	NIOSH/OSHA 5 mg/m³	2000 mg/m³	Colorless, oily liquid with a slight, aromatic odor. [Note: A solid below 42°F.]	MW: 194.2 BP: 543°F Sol: 0.4% Fl.P: 295°F IP: 9.64 eV Sp.Gr: 1.19 Class IIIB Combustible Liquid; however, ignition is difficult.	VP: 0.01 mm FRZ: 42°F UEL: ? LEL(358°F): 0.9%	Nitrates; strong oxidizers, alkalis & acids	OVS-Tenax; Toluene; GC/FID; OSHA [#104]

114

Personal protection and sanitation (See Table 3)		Recommendations for respirator selection — maximum concentration for use (MUC) (See Table 4)	Health hazards			
			Route	Symptoms (See Table 5)	First aid (See Table 6)	Target organs (See Table 5)
Skin:	Prevent skin contact	NIOSH/OSHA	Inh	Irrit eyes, skin; miosis,	Eye: Irr immed	Eyes, skin, resp sys,
Eyes:	Prevent eye contact	30 mg/m³: DMFu/HiE/SA	Abs	lac; head; chest tight,	Skin: Soap wash immed	CNS, CVS, blood chol
Wash skin:	When contam	75 mg/m³: SA:CF/PAPRDMFu	Ing	wheez, lar spasm; salv;	Breath: Resp support	
Remove:	When wet or contam	150 mg/m³: HiEF/SAT:CF/PAPRTHiE/	Con	cyan; anor, nau, vomit,	Swallow: Medical attention	
Change:	Daily	SCBAF/SAF		abdom cramp, diarr; weak,	immed	
Provide:	Eyewash	200 mg/m³: SA:PD,PP		twitch, para; gidd, ataxia,		
		§: SCBAF:PD,PP/SAF:PD,PP:ASCBA		convuls; low BP; card		
		Escape: HiEF/SCBAE		irreg		

[Dimethyl-1,2-dibromo-2,2-dichloroethyl phosphate]

Skin:	Prevent skin contact	NIOSH	Inh	Irrit eyes, skin, resp sys;	Eye: Irr immed	Eyes, skin, resp sys,
Eyes:	Prevent eye contact	100 ppm: SA*	Abs	nau, vomit, colic; liver	Skin: Water flush prompt	liver, kidneys, CVS
Wash skin:	When contam	250 ppm: SA:CF*	Ing	damage, enlarged liver;	Breath: Resp support	
Remove:	When wet or contam	500 ppm: SAT:CF*/SCBAF/SAF	Con	high BP; face flush; derm;	Swallow: Medical attention	
Change:	N.R.	§: SCBAF:PD,PP/SAF:PD,PP:ASCBA		in animals: kidney, heart	immed	
		Escape: GMFOV/SCBAE		damage		

[Dimethylformamide]

Skin:	Prevent skin contact	NIOSH	Inh	Irrit eyes, skin; choking,	Eye: Irr immed	CNS, liver, GI
Eyes:	Prevent eye contact	¥: SCBAF:PD,PP/SAF:PD,PP:ASCBA	Abs	chest pain, dysp; leth;	Skin: Water flush immed	tract, blood,
Wash skin:	When contam	Escape: GMFS/SCBAE	Ing	nau; anoxia; convuls; liver	Breath: Resp support	resp sys, eyes,
Remove:	When wet (flamm)		Con	inj; [carc]	Swallow: Medical attention	skin
Change:	N.R.				immed	[in animals:
Provide:	Eyewash, Quick drench					tumors of the
						lungs, liver,
						blood vessels &
						intestines]

[1,1-Dimethylhydrazine]

Skin:	N.R.	NIOSH/OSHA	Inh	Irrit eyes, upper resp sys;	Eye: Irr prompt	Eyes, resp sys, GI
Eyes:	Prevent eye contact	50 mg/m³: DMF	Ing	stomach pain	Skin: Wash regularly	tract
Wash skin:	N.R.	125 mg/m³: SA:CF£/PAPRDM£	Con		Breath: Resp support	
Remove:	N.R.	250 mg/m³: HiEF/SCBAF/SAF			Swallow: Medical attention	
Change:	N.R.	2000 mg/m³: SAF:PD,PP			immed	
		§: SCBAF:PD,PP/SAF:PD,PP:ASCBA				
		Escape: HiEF/SCBAE				

[Dimethylphthalate]

Chemical name, structure/formula, CAS and RTECS Nos., and DOT ID and guide Nos.	Synonyms, trade names, and conversion factors	Exposure limits (TWA unless noted otherwise)	IDLH	Physical description	Chemical and physical properties		Incompatibilities and reactivities	Measurement method (See Table 1)
					MW, BP, SOL Fl.P, IP, Sp, Gr, flammability	VP, FRZ UEL, LEL		
Dimethyl sulfate $(CH_3)_2SO_4$ 77-78-1 WS8225000 1595 156	Dimethyl ester of sulfuric acid, Dimethylsulfate, Methyl sulfate 1 ppm = 5.16 mg/m³	NIOSH Ca See Appendix A 0.1 ppm (0.5 mg/m³) [skin] OSHA† 1 ppm (5 mg/m³) [skin]	Ca [7 ppm]	Colorless, oily liquid with a faint, onion-like odor.	MW: 126.1 BP: 370°F (Decomposes) Sol(64°F): 3% Fl.P: 182°F IP: ? Sp.Gr: 1.33 Class IIIA Combustible Liquid	VP: 0.1 mm FRZ: -25°F UEL: ? LEL: ?	Strong oxidizers, ammonia solutions [Note: Decomposes in water to sulfuric acid; corrosive to metals.]	Porapak-P; Diethyl ether; GC/EConD; IV [#2524]
Dinitolmide $(NO_2)_2C_6H_2(CH_3)CONH_2$ 148-01-6 XS4200000	3,5-Dinitro-o-toluamide; 2-Methyl-3,5-dinitro-benzamide; Zoalene	NIOSH 5 mg/m³ OSHA† none	N.D.	Yellowish, crystalline solid.	MW: 225.2 BP: ? Sol: Slight Fl.P: NA IP: ? Sp.Gr: ? Noncombustible Solid	VP: ? MLT: 351°F UEL: NA LEL: NA	None reported	Filter; none; Grav; IV [#0500, Particulates NOR (total)]
o-Dinitrobenzene $C_6H_4(NO_2)_2$ 528-29-0 CZ7450000 1597 152	ortho-Dinitrobenzene; 1,2-Dinitrobenzene	NIOSH/OSHA 1 mg/m³ [skin]	50 mg/m³	Pale white or yellow, crystalline solid.	MW: 168.1 BP: 606°F Sol: 0.05% Fl.P: 302°F IP: 10.71 eV Sp.Gr: 1.57 Combustible Solid	VP: ? MLT: 244°F UEL: ? LEL: ?	Strong oxidizers, caustics, metals such as tin & zinc [Note: Prolonged exposure to fire and heat may result in an explosion due to SPONTANEOUS decomposition.]	Filter/Bub; Methanol; HPLC/UVD; II(4) [#S214]
m-Dinitrobenzene $C_6H_4(NO_2)_2$ 99-65-0 CZ7350000 1597 152	meta-Dinitrobenzene; 1,3-Dinitrobenzene	NIOSH/OSHA 1 mg/m³ [skin]	50 mg/m³	Pale white or yellow, crystalline solid.	MW: 168.1 BP: 572°F Sol: 0.02% Fl.P: 302°F IP: 10.43 eV Sp.Gr: 1.58 Combustible Solid	VP: ? MLT: 192°F UEL: ? LEL: ?	Strong oxidizers, caustics, metals such as tin & zinc [Note: Prolonged exposure to fire and heat may result in an explosion due to SPONTANEOUS decomposition.]	Filter/Bub; Methanol; HPLC/UVD; II(4) [#S214]

Personal protection and sanitation (See Table 3)		Recommendations for respirator selection — maximum concentration for use (MUC) (See Table 4)	Health hazards			
			Route	Symptoms (See Table 5)	First aid (See Table 6)	Target organs (See Table 5)
Skin:	Prevent skin contact	NIOSH	Inh	Irrit eyes, nose; head;	Eye: Irr immed	Eyes, skin, resp sys,
Eyes:	Prevent eye contact	¥: SCBAF:PD,PP/SAF:PD,PP:ASCBA	Abs	gidd; conj; photo; periorb	Skin: Water flush immed	liver, kidneys,
Wash skin:	When contam	Escape: GMFS/SCBAE	Ing	edema; dysphonia, aphonia,	Breath: Resp support	CNS
Remove:	When wet or contam		Con	dysphagia, productive	Swallow: Medical attention	[in animals:
Change:	N.R.			cough; chest pain; dysp,	immed	nasal & lung cancer]
Provide:	Eyewash, Quick drench			cyan; vomit, diarr; dysuria;		
				analgesia; fever; album,		
				hema; eye, skin burns;		
				delirium; [carc]		
[Dimethyl sulfate]						
Skin:	Prevent skin contact	TBAL	Inh	Contact eczema;	Eye: Irr immed	Skin, liver, blood
Eyes:	Prevent eye contact		Ing	in animals: methemo, liver	Skin: Soap wash immed	
Wash skin:	When contam		Con	changes	Breath: Resp support	
Remove:	When wet or contam				Swallow: Medical attention	
Change:	Daily				immed	
[Dinitolmide]						
Skin:	Prevent skin contact	NIOSH/OSHA	Inh	Anoxia, cyan; vis dist,	Eye: Irr immed	Eyes, skin, blood,
Eyes:	Prevent eye contact	5 mg/m³: DM	Abs	central scotomas; bad	Skin: Soap wash immed	liver, CVS, CNS
Wash skin:	When contam	10 mg/m³: DMXSQ/HiE/SA	Ing	taste, burning mouth, dry	Breath: Resp support	
Remove:	When wet or contam	25 mg/m³: SA:CF/PAPRDM	Con	throat, thirst; yellowing	Swallow: Medical attention	
Change:	Daily	50 mg/m³: HiEF/SAT:CF/PAPRTHiE/		hair, eyes, skin; anemia;	immed	
Provide:	Quick drench	SCBAF/SAF		liver damage		
		§: SCBAF:PD,PP/SAF:PD,PP:ASCBA				
		Escape: HiEF/SCBAE				
[o-Dinitrobenzene]						
Skin:	Prevent skin contact	NIOSH/OSHA	Inh	Anoxia, cyan; vis dist,	Eye: Irr immed	Eyes, skin, blood,
Eyes:	Prevent eye contact	5 mg/m³: DM	Abs	central scotomas; bad	Skin: Soap wash immed	liver, CVS, CNS
Wash skin:	When contam	10 mg/m³: DMXSQ/HiE/SA	Ing	taste, burning mouth, dry	Breath: Resp support	
Remove:	When wet or contam	25 mg/m³: SA:CF/PAPRDM	Con	throat, thirst; yellowing	Swallow: Medical attention	
Change:	Daily	50 mg/m³: HiEF/SAT:CF/PAPRTHiE/		hair, eyes, skin; anemia;	immed	
Provide:	Quick drench	SCBAF/SAF		liver damage		
		§: SCBAF:PD,PP/SAF:PD,PP:ASCBA				
		Escape: HiEF/SCBAE				
[m-Dinitrobenzene]						

117

Chemical name, structure/formula, CAS and RTECS Nos., and DOT ID and guide Nos.	Synonyms, trade names, and conversion factors	Exposure limits (TWA unless noted otherwise)	IDLH	Physical description	Chemical and physical properties		Incompatibilities and reactivities	Measurement method (See Table 1)
					MW, BP, SOL Fl.P, IP, Sp, Gr, flammability	VP, FRZ UEL, LEL		
p-Dinitrobenzene $C_6H_4(NO_2)_2$ 100-25-4 CZ7525000 1597 152	para-Dinitrobenzene; 1,4-Dinitrobenzene	NIOSH/OSHA 1 mg/m³ [skin]	50 mg/m³	Pale white or yellow, crystalline solid.	MW: 168.1 BP: 570°F Sol: 0.01% Fl.P: ? IP: 10.50 eV Sp.Gr: 1.63 Combustible Solid	VP: ? MLT: 343°F UEL: ? LEL: ?	Strong oxidizers, caustics, metals such as tin & zinc [Note: Prolonged exposure to fire and heat may result in an explosion due to SPONTANEOUS decomposition.]	Filter/Bub; Methanol; HPLC/UVD; II(4) [#S214]
Dinitro-o-cresol $CH_3C_6H_2OH(NO_2)_2$ 534-52-1 GO9625000 1598 153	4,6-Dinitro-o-cresol; 3,5-Dinitro-2-hydroxy-toluene; 4,6-Dinitro-2-methyl phenol; DNC; DNOC	NIOSH/OSHA 0.2 mg/m³ [skin]	5 mg/m³	Yellow, odorless solid. [insecticide]	MW: 198.1 BP: 594°F Sol: 0.01% Fl.P: NA IP: ? Sp.Gr: 1.1 (estimated) Noncombustible Solid	VP: 0.00005 mm MLT: 190°F UEL: NA LEL: NA MEC: 30 g/m³	Strong oxidizers	Filter/Bub; 2-Propanol; HPLC/UVD; II(5) [#S166]
Dinitrotoluene $C_6H_3CH_3(NO_2)_2$ 25321-14-6 XT1300000 1600 152 (molten) 2038 152 (solid)	Dinitrotoluol, DNT, Methyldinitrobenzene	NIOSH Ca See Appendix A 1.5 mg/m³ [skin] OSHA 1.5 mg/m³ [skin]	Ca [50 mg/m³]	Orange-yellow crystalline solid with a character-istic odor. [Note: Often shipped molten.]	MW: 182.2 BP: 572°F Sol: Insoluble Fl.P: 404°F IP: ? Sp.Gr: 1.32 Combustible Solid, but difficult to ignite.	VP: 1 mm MLT: 158°F UEL: ? LEL: ?	Strong oxidizers, caustics, metals such as tin & zinc [Note: Commercial grades will decompose at 482°F, with self-sustaining decomposition at 536°F.]	Filter/ Tenax; GC/TEA-EAP; OSHA [#44]
Di-sec octyl phthalate $C_{24}H_{38}O_4$ 117-81-7 TI0350000	DEHP, Di(2-Ethylhexyl)phthalate, DOP, bis-(2-Ethylhexyl)-phthalate, Octyl phthalate [$C_6H_4(COOCH_2CH(C_2H_5)C_4H_9)_2$]	NIOSH Ca See Appendix A 5 mg/m³ ST 10 mg/m³ OSHA† 5 mg/m³	Ca [5000 mg/m³]	Colorless, oily liquid with a slight odor.	MW: 390.5 BP: 727°F Sol(75°F): 0.00003% Fl.P(oc): 420°F IP: ? Sp.Gr: 0.99 Class IIIB Combustible Liquid	VP: <0.01 mm FRZ: -58°F UEL: ? LEL(474°F): 0.3%	Nitrates; strong oxidizers, acids & alkalis	Filter; CS₂; GC/FID; IV [#5020, di(2-Ethyl-hexyl) Phthalate]

Personal protection and sanitation (See Table 3)	Recommendations for respirator selection — maximum concentration for use (MUC) (See Table 4)	Route	Symptoms (See Table 5)	First aid (See Table 6)	Target organs (See Table 5)
Skin: Prevent skin contact Eyes: Prevent eye contact Wash skin: When contam Remove: When wet or contam Change: Daily Provide: Quick drench	NIOSH/OSHA 5 mg/m³: DM 10 mg/m³: DMXSQ/HiE/SA 25 mg/m³: SA:CF/PAPRDM 50 mg/m³: HiEF/SAT:CF/PAPRTHiE/ SCBAF/SAF §: SCBAF:PD,PP/SAF:PD,PP:ASCBA Escape: HiEF/SCBAE	Inh Abs Ing Con	Anoxia, cyan; vis dist, central scotomas; bad taste, burning mouth, dry throat, thirst; yellowing hair, eyes, skin; anemia; liver damage	Eye: Irr immed Skin: Soap wash immed Breath: Resp support Swallow: Medical attention immed	Eyes, skin, blood, liver, CVS, CNS

[p-Dinitrobenzene]

Skin: Prevent skin contact Eyes: Prevent eye contact Wash skin: When contam/Daily Remove: When wet or contam Change: Daily	NIOSH/OSHA 2 mg/m³: DMF 5 mg/m³: HiEF/SA:CF£/PAPRDM£/ SCBAF/SAF §: SCBAF:PD,PP/SAF:PD,PP:ASCBA Escape: HiEF/SCBAE	Inh Abs Ing Con	Sense of well being; head, fever, lass, profuse sweat, excess thirst, tacar, hyperpnea, cough, short breath, coma	Eye: Irr immed Skin: Soap wash immed Breath: Resp support Swallow: Medical attention immed	CVS, endocrine sys

[Dinitro-o-cresol]

Skin: Prevent skin contact Eyes: Prevent eye contact Wash skin: When contam/Daily Remove: When wet or contam Change: Daily Provide: Quick drench	NIOSH ¥: SCBAF:PD,PP/SAF:PD,PP:ASCBA Escape: GMFOVHiE/SCBAE	Inh Abs Ing Con	Anoxia, cyan; anemia, jaun; repro effects; [carc]	Eye: Irr immed Skin: Soap wash immed Breath: Resp support Swallow: Medical attention immed	Blood, liver, CVS, repro sys [in animals: liver, skin & kidney tumors]

[Dinitrotoluene]

Skin: N.R. Eyes: N.R. Wash skin: N.R. Remove: N.R. Change: N.R.	NIOSH ¥: SCBAF:PD,PP/SAF:PD,PP:ASCBA Escape: HiEF/SCBAE	Inh Ing Con	Irrit eyes, muc memb; in animals: liver damage; terato effects; [carc]	Eye: Irr immed Breath: Resp support Swallow: Medical attention immed	Eyes, resp sys, CNS, liver, repro sys, GI tract [in animals: liver tumors]

[Di-sec octyl phthalate]

Chemical name, structure/formula, CAS and RTECS Nos., and DOT ID and guide Nos.	Synonyms, trade names, and conversion factors	Exposure limits (TWA unless noted otherwise)	IDLH	Physical description	Chemical and physical properties		Incompatibilities and reactivities	Measurement method (See Table 1)
					MW, BP, SOL Fl.P, IP, Sp, Gr, flammability	VP, FRZ UEL, LEL		
Dioxane $C_4H_8O_2$ 123-91-1 JG8225000 1165 127	Diethylene dioxide; Diethylene ether; Dioxan; p-Dioxane; 1,4-Dioxane 1 ppm = 3.60 mg/m³	NIOSH Ca See Appendix A C 1 ppm (3.6 mg/m³) [30-min] OSHA† 100 ppm (360 mg/m³) [skin]	Ca [500 ppm]	Colorless liquid or solid (below 53°F) with a mild, ether-like odor.	MW: 88.1 BP: 214°F Sol: Miscible Fl.P: 55°F IP: 9.13 eV Sp.Gr: 1.03 Class IB Flammable Liquid	VP: 29 mm FRZ: 53°F UEL: 22% LEL: 2.0%	Strong oxidizers, decaborane, triethynyl aluminum	Char; CS₂; GC/FID; IV [#1602]
Dioxathion $C_4H_6O_2[SPS(OC_2H_5)_2]_2$ 78-34-2 TE3350000	Delnav®; p-Dioxane-2,3-diyl ethyl phosphorodithioate; Dioxane phosphate; 2,3-p-Dioxanethiol S,S-bis-(O,O-diethyl phosphoro-dithioate); Navadel®	NIOSH 0.2 mg/m³ [skin] OSHA† none	N.D.	Viscous, brown, tan, or dark-amber liquid. [insecticide] [Note: Technical product is a mixture of cis- & trans-isomers.]	MW: 456.6 BP: ? Sol: Insoluble Fl.P: NA IP: ? Sp.Gr(79°F): 1.26 Noncombustible Liquid	VP: ? FRZ: -4°F UEL: NA LEL: NA	Alkalis, iron or tin surfaces, heat	None available
Diphenyl $C_6H_5C_6H_5$ 92-52-4 DU8050000	Biphenyl, Phenyl benzene 1 ppm = 6.31 mg/m³	NIOSH/OSHA 1 mg/m³ (0.2 ppm)	100 mg/m³	Colorless to pale-yellow solid with a pleasant, characteristic odor. [fungicide]	MW: 154.2 BP: 489°F Sol: Insoluble Fl.P: 235°F IP: 7.95 eV Sp.Gr: 1.04 Combustible Solid	VP: 0.005 mm MLT: 156°F UEL(311°F): 5.8% LEL(232°F): 0.6%	Oxidizers	Tenax GC; CCI₄; GC/FID; IV [#2530, Biphenyl]
Diphenylamine $(C_6H_5)_2NH$ 122-39-4 JJ7800000	Anilinobenzene, DPA, Phenylaniline, N-Phenylaniline, N-Phenylbenzenamine [Note: The carcinogen 4-Aminodiphenyl may be present as an impurity in the commercial product.]	NIOSH 10 mg/m³ OSHA† none	N.D.	Colorless, tan, amber, or brown crystalline solid with a pleasant, floral odor. [fungicide]	MW: 169.2 BP: 576°F Sol: 0.03% Fl.P: 307°F IP: 7.40 eV Sp.Gr: 1.16 Combustible Solid; explosive if a cloud of dust is exposed to a source of ignition.	VP(227°F): 1mm MLT: 127°F UEL: ? LEL: ?	Oxidizers, hexachloro-melamine, trichloro-melamine	Filter*(2); Methanol; HPLC/UV; OSHA [#78]

Personal protection and sanitation (See Table 3)		Recommendations for respirator selection — maximum concentration for use (MUC) (See Table 4)	Health hazards				
			Route	Symptoms (See Table 5)	First aid (See Table 6)		Target organs (See Table 5)
Skin: Eyes: Wash skin: Remove: Change: Provide:	Prevent skin contact Prevent eye contact When contam When wet (flamm) N.R. Eyewash, Quick drench	NIOSH ¥: SCBAF:PD,PP/SAF:PD,PP:ASCBA Escape: GMFOV/SCBAE	Inh Abs Ing Con	Irrit eyes, skin, nose, throat; drow, head; nau, vomit; liver damage; kidney failure; [carc]	Eye: Skin: Breath: Swallow:	Irr immed Water wash prompt Resp support Medical attention immed	Eyes, skin, resp sys, liver, kidneys [in animals: lung, liver & nasal cavity tumors]
[Dioxane]							
Skin: Eyes: Wash skin: Remove: Change: Provide:	Prevent skin contact Prevent eye contact When contam When wet or contam N.R. Eyewash, Quick drench	TBAL	Inh Abs Ing Con	Irrit eyes, skin; head, gidd, verti, weak; rhin, chest tight; miosis; nau, vomit, abdom cramps, diarr, salv; musc fasc; conf, drow	Eye: Skin: Breath: Swallow:	Irr immed Soap flush immed Resp support Medical attention immed	Eyes, skin, resp sys, CNS, CVS, blood chol
[Dioxathion]							
Skin: Eyes: Wash skin: Remove: Change: Provide:	Prevent skin contact Prevent eye contact When contam When wet or contam Daily Eyewash (molt), Quick drench (molt)	NIOSH/OSHA 10 mg/m³: CCROVDM/SA 25 mg/m³: SA:CF*/PAPROVDM* 50 mg/m³: CCRFOVHiE/GMFOVHiE/ PAPRTOVHiE*/SCBAF/SAF 100 mg/m³: SAF:PD,PP §: SCBAF:PD,PP/SAF:PD,PP:ASCBA Escape: GMFOVHiE/SCBAE	Inh Abs Ing Con	Irrit eyes, throat; head, nau, ftg, numb limbs; liver damage	Eye: Skin: Breath: Swallow:	Irr immed Soap wash prompt Resp support Medical attention immed	Eyes, resp sys, liver, CNS
[Diphenyl]							
Skin: Eyes: Wash skin: Remove: Change:	Prevent skin contact Prevent eye contact Daily When wet or contam Daily	TBAL	Inh Abs Ing Con	Irrit eyes, skin, muc memb; eczema; tacar, hypertension; cough, sneez; methemo; incr BP, heart rate; prot, hema, bladder inj; in animals: terato effects	Eye: Skin: Breath: Swallow:	Irr immed Soap wash prompt Resp support Medical attention immed	Eyes, skin, resp sys, CVS, blood, bladder, repro sys
[Diphenylamine]							

Chemical name, structure/formula, CAS and RTECS Nos., and DOT ID and guide Nos.	Synonyms, trade names, and conversion factors	Exposure limits (TWA unless noted otherwise)	IDLH	Physical description	Chemical and physical properties		Incompatibilities and reactivities	Measurement method (See Table 1)
					MW, BP, SOL FI.P, IP, Sp, Gr, flammability	VP, FRZ UEL, LEL		
Dipropylene glycol methyl ether $CH_3OC_3H_6OC_3H_6OH$ 34590-94-8 JM1575000	Dipropylene glycol monomethyl ether, Dowanol® 50B	NIOSH 100 ppm (600 mg/m³) ST 150 ppm (900 mg/m³) [skin] OSHA† 100 ppm (600 mg/m³) [skin]	600 ppm	Colorless liquid with a mild, ether-like odor.	MW: 148.2 BP: 408°F Sol: Miscible FI.P: 180°F IP: ? Sp.Gr: 0.95 Class IIIA Combustible Liquid	VP: 0.5 mm FRZ:-112°F UEL: 3.0% LEL(392°F): 1.1%	Strong oxidizers	Char; CS₂; GC/FID; II(2) [#S69]
	1 ppm = 6.06 mg/m³							
Dipropyl ketone $(CH_3CH_2CH_2)_2CO$ 123-19-3 MJ5600000 2710 127	Butyrone, DPK, 4-Heptanone, Heptan-4-one, Propyl ketone	NIOSH 50 ppm (235 mg/m³) OSHA† none	N.D.	Colorless liquid with a pleasant odor.	MW: 114.2 BP: 291°F Sol: Insoluble FI.P: 120°F IP: 9.10 eV Sp.Gr: 0.82 Class II Combustible Liquid	VP: 5 mm FRZ: -27°F UEL: ? LEL: ?	Oxidizers	Char; CS₂; GC/FID; OSHA [Adapt #7]
	1 ppm = 4.67 mg/m³							
Diquat (Diquat dibromide) $C_{12}H_{12}N_2Br_2$ 85-00-7 JM5690000 2781 151 (solid) 2782 131 (liquid)	Diquat dibromide; 1,1'-Ethylene-2,2'-bipyridyllium dibromide [Note: Diquat is a cation ($C_{12}H_{12}N_2^{++}$, 1,1'-Ethylene-2,2-bipyridyl-lium ion). Various diquat salts are commercially available.]	NIOSH 0.5 mg/m³ OSHA† none	N.D.	Dibromide salt: Yellow crystals. [herbicide] [Note: Commercial product may be found in a liquid concentrate or a solution.]	MW: 344.1 BP: Decomposes Sol: 70% FI.P: ? IP: ? Sp.Gr: 1.22-1.27 Combustible Solid, but does not readily ignite and burns with difficulty.	VP: <0.00001 mm MLT: 635°F UEL: ? LEL: ?	Alkalis, UV light, basic solutions [Note: Concentrated diquat solutions corrode aluminum.]	None available
Disulfiram $[(C_2H_5)_2NCS]_2S_2$ 97-77-8 JO1225000	Antabuse®, bis(Diethylthiocarbamoyl) disulfide, Ro-Sulfiram®, TETD, Tetraethylthiuram disulfide	NIOSH 2 mg/m³ [Precautions should be taken to avoid concurrent exposure to ethylene dibromide.] OSHA† none	N.D.	White, yellowish, or light-gray powder with a slight odor. [fungicide]	MW: 296.6 BP: ? Sol: 0.02% FI.P: NA IP: ? Sp.Gr: 1.30 Noncombustible Solid	VP: ? MLT: 158°F UEL: NA LEL: NA	None reported	None available

Personal protection and sanitation (See Table 3)		Recommendations for respirator selection — maximum concentration for use (MUC) (See Table 4)	Health hazards					
			Route	Symptoms (See Table 5)	First aid (See Table 6)		Target organs (See Table 5)
Skin:	N.R.	NIOSH/OSHA	Inh	Irrit eyes, nose, throat;	Eye:	Irr immed	Eyes, resp sys,
Eyes:	N.R.	600 ppm: SA/SCBAF	Abs	weak, li-head, head	Skin:	Water wash prompt	CNS
Wash skin:	N.R.	§: SCBAF:PD,PP/SAF:PD,PP:ASCBA	Ing		Breath:	Resp support	
Remove:	N.R.	Escape: GMFOVHiE/SCBAE	Con		Swallow:	Medical attention	
Change:	N.R.					immed	

[Dipropylene glycol methyl ether]

Skin:	Prevent skin contact	TBAL	Inh	Irrit eyes, skin; CNS	Eye:	Irr immed	Eyes, skin, CNS,
Eyes:	Prevent eye contact		Ing	depres, dizz, som, decr	Skin:	Soap wash	liver
Wash skin:	Daily		Con	breath;	Breath:	Resp support	
Remove:	When wet or contam			in animals: liver inj; narco	Swallow:	Medical attention	
Change:	N.R.					immed	

123

[Dipropyl ketone]

Skin:	Prevent skin contact	TBAL	Inh	Irrit eyes, skin, muc memb,	Eye:	Irr immed	Eyes, skin, resp sys,
Eyes:	Prevent eye contact		Abs	resp sys; rhin, epis; skin	Skin:	Water flush immed	kidneys, liver, CNS
Wash skin:	When contam		Ing	burns; nau, vomit, diarr,	Breath:	Resp support	
Remove:	When wet or contam		Con	mal; kidney, liver inj;	Swallow:	Medical attention	
Change:	Daily			cough, chest pain, dysp,		immed	
Provide:	Quick drench			pulm edema; tremor, convuls;			
				delayed healing of wounds			

[Diquat (Diquat bromide)]

Skin:	Prevent skin contact	TBAL	Inh	Irrit eyes, skin, resp sys;	Eye:	Irr immed	Eyes, skin, resp sys,
Eyes:	Prevent eye contact		Ing	sens derm; lass, ftg,	Skin:	Soap wash immed	CNS, PNS, liver
Wash skin:	When contam		Con	tremor, restless, head,	Breath:	Resp support	
Remove:	When wet or contam			dizz; metallic taste;	Swallow:	Medical attention	
Change:	Daily			peri neur; liver damage		immed	

[Disulfiram]

Chemical name, structure/formula, CAS and RTECS Nos., and DOT ID and guide Nos.	Synonyms, trade names, and conversion factors	Exposure limits (TWA unless noted otherwise)	IDLH	Physical description	Chemical and physical properties		Incompatibilities and reactivities	Measurement method (See Table 1)
					MW, BP, SOL Fl.P, IP, Sp, Gr, flammability	VP, FRZ UEL, LEL		
Disulfoton $C_8H_{19}O_2PS_3$ 298-04-4 TD9275000 2783 152	O,O-Diethyl S-2-(ethylthio)-ethyl phosphorodithioate; Di-Syston®; Thiodemeton [(C₂H₅O)₂P(S)S(CH₂)₂SC₂H₅]	NIOSH 0.1 mg/m³ [skin] OSHA† none	N.D.	Oily, colorless to yellow liquid with a characteristic, sulfur odor. [insecticide] [Note: Technical product is a brown liquid.]	MW: 274.4 BP: ? Sol(73°F): 0.003% Fl.P: >180°F IP: ? Sp.Gr. 1.14 Combustible Liquid, but will not ignite easily.	VP: 0.0002 mm FRZ: >-13°F UEL: ? LEL: ?	Alkalis	OVS-2; Toluene/ Acetone; GC/FPD; IV [#5600, Organo-phosphorus Pesticides]
2,6-Di-tert-butyl-p-cresol [C(CH₃)₃]₂CH₃C₆H₂OH 128-37-0 GO7875000	BHT; Butylated hydroxytoluene; Dibutylated hydroxytoluene; 4-Methyl-2,6-di-tert-butyl phenol	NIOSH 10 mg/m³ OSHA† none	N.D.	White to pale-yellow, crystalline solid with a slight, phenolic odor. [food preservative]	MW: 220.4 BP: 509°F Sol: 0.00004% Fl.P: 261°F IP: ? Sp.Gr. 1.05 Class IIIB Combustible Liquid	VP: 0.01 mm MLT: 158°F UEL: ? LEL: ?	Oxidizers	Si gel; Methanol/ CS₂; GC/FID; II(1) [P&CAM #226]
Diuron C₆H₃Cl₂NHCON(CH₃)₂ 330-54-1 YS8925000	3-(3,4-Dichlorophenyl)-1,1-dimethylurea; Direx®; Karmex®	NIOSH 10 mg/m³ OSHA† none	N.D.	White, odorless, crystalline solid. [herbicide]	MW: 233.1 BP: 356°F (Decomposes) Sol: 0.004% Fl.P: NA IP: ? Sp.Gr. ? Noncombustible Solid	VP: 0.000000002 mm MLT: 316°F UEL: NA LEL: NA	Strong acids	Filter; none; Grav; IV [#0500, Particulates NOR (total)]
Divinyl benzene C₆H₄(HC=CH₂)₂ 1321-74-0 (mixed isomers) CZ9370000 2049 130	Diethyl benzene, DVB, Vinylstyrene [Note: Commercial product contains all 3 isomers, but m-isomer predominates. Usually contains an inhibitor to prevent polymerization.] 1 ppm = 5.33 mg/m³	NIOSH 10 ppm (50 mg/m³) OSHA† none	N.D.	Pale, straw-colored liquid.	MW: 130.2 BP: 392°F Sol: 0.005% Fl.P(oc): 169°F IP: ? Sp.Gr. 0.93 Class IIIA Combustible Liquid	VP: 0.7 mm FRZ: -88°F UEL: 6.2% LEL:1.1%	None reported	Char*; Toluene; GC/FID; OSHA [#89]

Personal protection and sanitation (See Table 3)		Recommendations for respirator selection — maximum concentration for use (MUC) (See Table 4)	Health hazards				
			Route	Symptoms (See Table 5)	First aid (See Table 6)		Target organs (See Table 5)
Skin:	Prevent skin contact	TBAL	Inh	Irrit eyes, skin; nau,	Eye:	Irr immed	Eyes, skin, resp sys,
Eyes:	Prevent eye contact		Abs	vomit, abdom cramps, diarr,	Skin:	Soap flush immed	CNS, CVS, blood chol
Wash skin:	When contam		Ing	salv; head, gidd, verti,	Breath:	Resp support	
Remove:	When wet or contam		Con	weak; rhin, chest tight;	Swallow:	Medical attention	
Change:	Daily			blurred vision, miosis;		immed	
Provide:	Eyewash, Quick drench			card irreg; musc fasc;			
				dysp; eye, skin burns			
[Disulfoton]							
Skin:	Prevent skin contact	TBAL	Inh	Irrit eyes, skin;	Eye:	Irr immed	Eyes, skin
Eyes:	Prevent eye contact		Ing	in animals: decr growth	Skin:	Soap wash	
Wash skin:	When contam		Con	rate, incr liver weight	Breath:	Fresh air	
Remove:	When wet or contam				Swallow:	Medical attention	
Change:	Daily					immed	
[2,6-Di-tert-butyl-p-cresol]							
Skin:	Prevent skin contact	TBAL	Inh	Irrit eyes, skin, nose,	Eye:	Irr immed	Eyes, skin, resp sys,
Eyes:	Prevent eye contact		Ing	throat;	Skin:	Water flush immed	blood
Wash skin:	Daily		Con	in animals: anemia, methemo	Breath:	Resp support	
Remove:	N.R.				Swallow:	Medical attention	
Change:	Daily					immed	
[Diuron]							
Skin:	Prevent skin contact	TBAL	Inh	Irrit eyes, skin, resp	Eye:	Irr immed	Eyes, skin, resp sys,
Eyes:	Prevent eye contact		Ing	sys; skin burns;	Skin:	Soap flush immed	CNS
Wash skin:	When contam		Con	in animals: CNS depres	Breath:	Resp support	
Remove:	When wet or contam				Swallow:	Medical attention	
Change:	N.R.					immed	
Provide:	Eyewash, Quick drench						
[Divinyl benzene]							

Chemical name, structure/formula, CAS and RTECS Nos., and DOT ID and guide Nos.	Synonyms, trade names, and conversion factors	Exposure limits (TWA unless noted otherwise)	IDLH	Physical description	Chemical and physical properties		Incompatibilities and reactivities	Measurement method (See Table 1)
					MW, BP, SOL Fl.P, IP, Sp, Gr, flammability	VP, FRZ UEL, LEL		
1-Dodecanethiol $CH_3(CH_2)_{11}SH$ 112-55-0 JR3155000 1228 131	Dodecyl mercaptan, 1-Dodecyl mercaptan, n-Dodecyl mercaptan, Lauryl mercaptan, n-Lauryl mercaptan, 1-Mercaptododecane 1 ppm = 8.28 mg/m³	NIOSH C 0.5 ppm (4.1 mg/m³) [15-min] OSHA none	N.D.	Colorless, water-white, or pale-yellow, oily liquid with a mild, skunk-like odor. [Note: A solid below 15°F.]	MW: 202.4 BP: 441-478°F Sol: Insoluble Fl.P(oc): 190°F IP: ? Sp.Gr: 0.85 Class IIIA Combustible Liquid	VP(77°F): 3 mm FRZ: 15°F UEL: ? LEL: ?	Strong oxidizers & acids, strong bases, reducing agents, alkali metals, water, steam	None available
Emery Al_2O_3 1302-74-5 (corundum) GN0231000 (corundum)	Aluminum oxide, Aluminum trioxide, Corundum, Impure corundum, Natural aluminum oxide [Note: Emery is an impure variety of Al_2O_3 which may contain small impurities of iron, magnesium & silica. Corundum is natural Al_2O_3.]	NIOSH See Appendix D OSHA† 15mg/m³ (total) 5 mg/m³ (resp)	N.D.	Odorless, white, crystalline powder.	See α-Alumina for physical & chemical properties.			Filter; none; Grav; IV [Particulates NOR: #0500 (total), #0600 (resp)]
Endosulfan $C_9H_6Cl_6O_3S$ 115-29-7 RB9275000 2761 151	Benzoepin; Endosulphan; 6,7,8,9,10-Hexachloro-1,5,5a,6,9,9a-hexahydro-6,9-methano-2,4,3-benzo-dioxathiepin-3-oxide; Thiodan®	NIOSH 0.1 mg/m³ [skin] OSHA† none	N.D.	Brown crystals with a slight, sulfur dioxide odor. [insecticide] [Note: Technical product is a tan, waxy, isomer mixture.]	MW: 406.9 BP: Decomposes Sol: 0.00001% Fl.P: NA IP: ? Sp.Gr: 1.74 Noncombustible Solid, but may be dissolved in flammable liquids.	VP(77°F): 0.00001 mm MLT: 223°F UEL: NA LEL: NA	Alkalis, acids, water [Note: Corrosive to iron. Hydrolyzes slowly on contact with water or decomposes in presence of alkalis and acids to form sulfur dioxide.]	None available
Endrin $C_{12}H_8Cl_6O$ 72-20-8 IO1575000 2761 151	1,2,3,4,10,10-Hexachloro-6,7-epoxy-1,4,4a,5,6,7,8,8a-octahydro-1,4-endo,endo-5,8-dimethanonaphthalene; Hexadrin®	NIOSH/OSHA 0.1 mg/m³ [skin]	2 mg/m³	Colorless to tan, crystalline solid with a mild, chemical odor. [insecticide]	MW: 380.9 BP: Decomposes Sol: Insoluble Fl.P: NA IP: ? Sp.Gr: 1.70 Noncombustible Solid, but may be dissolved in flammable liquids.	VP: Low MLT: 392°F (Decomposes) UEL: NA LEL: NA	Strong oxidizers, strong acids, parathion [Note: May emit hydrogen chloride & phosgene when heated or burned.]	Filter/ Chrom-102; Toluene; GC/ECD; IV [#5519]

Personal protection and sanitation (See Table 3)		Recommendations for respirator selection — maximum concentration for use (MUC) (See Table 4)	Health hazards				
			Route	Symptoms (See Table 5)	First aid (See Table 6)		Target organs (See Table 5)
Skin:	Prevent skin contact	NIOSH	Inh	Irrit eyes, skin, resp sys;	Eye:	Irr immed	Eyes, skin, resp sys,
Eyes:	Prevent eye contact	5 ppm: CCROV/SA	Ing	cough; dizz, dysp, weak,	Skin:	Soap wash immed	CNS, blood
Wash skin:	When contam	12.5 ppm: SA:CF/PAPROV	Con	conf, cyan; abdom pain,	Breath:	Resp support	
Remove:	When wet or contam	25 ppm: CCRFOV/GMFOV/PAPRTOV/		nau; skin sens	Swallow:	Medical attention	
Change:	N.R.	SCBAF/SAF				immed	
Provide:	Eyewash	§: SCBAF:PD,PP/SAF:PD,PP:ASCBA					
		Escape: GMFOV/SCBAE					

[1-Dodecanethiol]

Personal protection and sanitation (See Table 3)		Recommendations for respirator selection — maximum concentration for use (MUC) (See Table 4)	Health hazards				
Skin:	N.R.	TBAL	Inh	Irrit eyes, skin, resp sys	Eye:	Irr immed	Eyes, skin, resp sys
Eyes:	N.R.		Ing		Breath:	Fresh air	
Wash skin:	N.R.		Con		Swallow:	Medical attention	
Remove:	N.R.					immed	
Change:	N.R.						

[Emery]

127

Personal protection and sanitation (See Table 3)		Recommendations for respirator selection — maximum concentration for use (MUC) (See Table 4)	Health hazards				
Skin:	Prevent skin contact	TBAL	Inh	Irrit skin; nau, conf,	Eye:	Irr immed	Skin, CNS, liver,
Eyes:	Prevent eye contact		Abs	agitation, flushing, dry	Skin:	Soap flush immed	kidneys, repro sys
Wash skin:	When contam		Ing	mouth, tremor, convuls,	Breath:	Resp support	
Remove:	When wet or contam		Con	head;	Swallow:	Medical attention	
Change:	Daily			in animals: kidney, liver		immed	
Provide:	Eyewash, Quick drench			inj; decr testis weight			

[Endosulfan]

Personal protection and sanitation (See Table 3)		Recommendations for respirator selection — maximum concentration for use (MUC) (See Table 4)	Health hazards				
Skin:	Prevent skin contact	NIOSH/OSHA	Inh	Epilep convuls; stupor,	Eye:	Irr immed	CNS, liver
Eyes:	Prevent eye contact	1 mg/m³: CCROVDMFu/SA	Abs	head, dizz; abdom	Skin:	Soap wash immed	
Wash skin:	When contam	2 mg/m³: SA:CF/PAPROVDMFu/	Ing	discomfort, nau, vomit;	Breath:	Resp support	
Remove:	When wet or contam	CCRFOVHiE/GMFOVHiE/	Con	insom; aggressiveness,	Swallow:	Medical attention	
Change:	Daily	SCBAF/SAF		conf; leth, weak; anor;		immed	
Provide:	Eyewash, Quick drench	§: SCBAF:PD,PP/SAF:PD,PP:ASCBA		in animals: liver damage			
		Escape: GMFOVHiE/SCBAE					

[Endrin]

Chemical name, structure/formula, CAS and RTECS Nos., and DOT ID and guide Nos.	Synonyms, trade names, and conversion factors	Exposure limits (TWA unless noted otherwise)	IDLH	Physical description	Chemical and physical properties		Incompatibilities and reactivities	Measurement method (See Table 1)
					MW, BP, SOL FI.P, IP, Sp, Gr, flammability	VP, FRZ UEL, LEL		
Enflurane CHF$_2$OCF$_2$CHClF 13838-16-9 KN6800000 1 ppm = 7.55 mg/m^3	2-Chloro-1-(difluoro-methoxy)-1,1,2-trifluoro-ethane; 2-Chloro-1,1,2-trifluoro-ethyl difluoromethyl ether; Ethrane®	NIOSH* C 2 ppm (15.1 mg/m^3) [60-min] [*Note: REL for exposure to waste anesthetic gas.] OSHA none	N.D.	Clear, colorless liquid with a mild, sweet odor. [inhalation anesthetic]	MW: 184.5 BP: 134°F Sol: Low FI.P: NA IP: ? Sp.Gr(77°F): 1.52 Noncombustible Liquid	VP: 175mm FRZ: ? UEL: NA LEL: NA	None reported	Anasorb; CS$_2$; GC/FID; OSHA [#103]
Epichlorohydrin C$_3$H$_5$OCl 106-89-8 TX4900000 2023 131P	1-Chloro-2,3-epoxypropane; 2-Chloropropylene oxide; γ-Chloropropylene oxide	NIOSH Ca See Appendix A OSHA† 5 ppm (19 mg/m^3) [skin]	Ca [75 ppm]	Colorless liquid with a slightly irritating, chloroform-like odor.	MW: 92.5 BP: 242°F Sol: 7% FI.P: 93°F IP: 10.60 eV Sp.Gr: 1.18 Class IC Flammable Liquid	VP: 13 mm FRZ: -54°F UEL: 21.0% LEL: 3.8%	Strong oxidizers, strong acids, certain salts, caustics, zinc, aluminum, water [Note: May polymerize in presence of strong acids and bases, particularly when hot.]	Char; CS$_2$; GC/FID; IV [#1010]
EPN C$_{14}$H$_{14}$O$_4$NSP 2104-64-5 TB1925000	Ethyl p-nitrophenyl benzenethionophosphonate, O-Ethyl O-(4-nitrophenyl) phenylphosphonothioate [C$_2$H$_5$O(C$_6$H$_5$)P(S)OC$_6$H$_4$NO$_2$]	NIOSH/OSHA 0.5 mg/m^3 [skin]	5 mg/m^3	Yellow solid with an aromatic odor. [pesticide] [Note: A brown liquid above 97°F.]	MW: 323.3 BP: ? Sol: Insoluble FI.P: NA IP: ? Sp.Gr(77°F): 1.27 Noncombustible Solid	VP(212°F): 0.0003 mm MLT: 97°F UEL: NA LEL: NA	Strong oxidizers	Filter; Isooctane; GC/FPD; IV [#5012]
Ethanolamine NH$_2$CH$_2$CH$_2$OH 141-43-5 KJ5775000 2491 153	2-Aminoethanol, ß-Aminoethyl alcohol, Ethylolamine, 2-Hydroxyethylamine, Monoethanolamine 1 ppm = 2.50 mg/m^3	NIOSH 3 ppm (8 mg/m^3) ST 6 ppm (15 mg/m^3) OSHA† 3 ppm (6 mg/m^3)	30 ppm	Colorless, viscous liquid or solid (below 51°F) with an unpleasant, ammonia-like odor.	MW: 61.1 BP: 339°F Sol: Miscible FI.P: 186°F IP: 8.96 eV Sp.Gr: 1.02 Class IIIA Combustible Liquid	VP: 0.4 mm FRZ: 51°F UEL: 23.5% LEL(284°F): 3.0%	Strong oxidizers, strong acids, iron [Note: May attack copper, brass, and rubber.]	Si gel; Methanol/ Water; GC/FID; IV [#2007, Amino-ethanol Compounds]

Personal protection and sanitation (See Table 3)		Recommendations for respirator selection — maximum concentration for use (MUC) (See Table 4)	Health hazards				
			Route	Symptoms (See Table 5)	First aid (See Table 6)		Target organs (See Table 5)
Skin:	N.R.	TBAL	Inh	Irrit eyes; CNS depres,	Eye:	Irr immed	Eyes, CNS
Eyes:	Prevent eye contact		Ing	analgesia, anes, sez,	Skin:	Soap wash	
Wash skin:	N.R.		Con	resp depres	Breath:	Resp support	
Remove:	N.R.				Swallow:	Medical attention	
Change:	N.R.					immed	

[Enflurane]

Skin:	Prevent skin contact	NIOSH	Inh	Irrit eyes, skin with deep	Eye:	Irr immed	Eyes, skin, resp sys,
Eyes:	Prevent eye contact	¥: SCBAF:PD,PP/SAF:PD,PP:ASCBA	Abs	pain; nau, vomit; abdom	Skin:	Soap wash immed	kidneys, liver,
Wash skin:	When contam	Escape: GMFOVAG/SCBAE	Ing	pain; resp distress, cough;	Breath:	Resp support	repro sys
Remove:	When wet (flamm)		Con	cyan; repro effects; [carc]	Swallow:	Medical attention	[in animals:
Change:	N.R.					immed	nasal cancer]
Provide:	Eyewash, Quick drench						

129

[Epichlorohydrin]

Skin:	Prevent skin contact	NIOSH/OSHA	Inh	Irrit eyes, skin; miosis,	Eye:	Irr immed	Eyes, skin, resp sys,
Eyes:	Prevent eye contact	5 mg/m³: SA/SCBAF	Abs	lac; rhin; head; chest	Skin:	Soap wash immed	CVS, CNS, blood chol
Wash skin:	When contam	§: SCBAF:PD,PP/SAF:PD,PP:ASCBA	Ing	tight, wheez, lar spasm;	Breath:	Resp support	
Remove:	When wet or contam	Escape: GMFOVHiE/SCBAE	Con	salv; cyan; anor, nau,	Swallow:	Medical attention	
Change:	Daily			abdom cramps, diarr; para,		immed	
Provide:	Eyewash, Quick drench			convuls; low BP, card irreg			

[EPN]

Skin:	Prevent skin contact	NIOSH/OSHA	Inh	Irrit eyes, skin, resp	Eye:	Irr immed	Eyes, skin, resp sys,
Eyes:	Prevent eye contact	30 ppm: CCRS*/GMFS/PAPRS*/SA*/	Ing	sys; leth	Skin:	Water flush prompt	CNS
Wash skin:	When contam	SCBAF	Con		Breath:	Resp support	
Remove:	When wet or contam	§: SCBAF:PD,PP/SAF:PD,PP:ASCBA			Swallow:	Medical attention	
Change:	Daily	Escape: GMFS/SCBAE				immed	
Provide:	Eyewash						

[Ethanolamine]

Chemical name, structure/formula, CAS and RTECS Nos., and DOT ID and guide Nos.	Synonyms, trade names, and conversion factors	Exposure limits (TWA unless noted otherwise)	IDLH	Physical description	Chemical and physical properties		Incompatibilities and reactivities	Measurement method (See Table 1)
					MW, BP, SOL FI.P, IP, Sp, Gr, flammability	VP, FRZ UEL, LEL		
Ethion [(C$_2$H$_5$O)$_2$P(S)S]$_2$CH$_2$ 563-12-2 TE4550000 2783 152	O,O,O',O'-Tetraethyl S,S'-methylene di(phosphoro-dithioate)	NIOSH 0.4 mg/m^3 [skin] OSHA† none	N.D.	Colorless to amber-colored, odorless liquid. [insecticide] [Note: A solid below 10°F. The technical product has a very disagreeable odor.]	MW: 384.5 BP: >302°F (Decomposes) Sol: 0.0001% FI.P: 349°F IP: ? Sp.Gr: 1.22 Class IIIB Combustible Liquid	VP: 0.0000015 mm FRZ: 10°F UEL: ? LEL: ?	Acids, alkalis	OVS-2; Toluene/ Acetone; GC/FPD; IV [#5600, Organo-phosphorus Pesticides
2-Ethoxyethanol C$_2$H$_5$OCH$_2$CH$_2$OH 110-80-5 KK8050000 1171 127	Cellosolve®, EGEE, Ethylene glycol monoethyl ether 1 ppm = 3.69 mg/m^3	NIOSH 0.5 ppm (1.8 mg/m^3) [skin] OSHA 200 ppm (740 mg/m^3) [skin]	500 ppm	Colorless liquid with a sweet, pleasant, ether-like odor.	MW: 90.1 BP: 275°F Sol: Miscible FI.P: 110°F IP: ? Sp.Gr: 0.93 Class II Combustible Liquid	VP: 4 mm FRZ: -130°F UEL(200°F): 15.6% LEL(200°F): 1.7%	Strong oxidizers	Char; Methanol/ CH$_2$Cl$_2$; GC/FID; IV [#1403, Alcohols IV]
2-Ethoxyethyl acetate CH$_3$COOCH$_2$CH$_2$OC$_2$H$_5$ 111-15-9 KK8225000 1172 129	Cellosolve® acetate, EGEEA, Ethylene glycol monoethyl ether acetate, Glycol monoethyl ether acetate 1 ppm = 5.41 mg/m^3	NIOSH 0.5 ppm (2.7 mg/m^3) [skin] OSHA 100 ppm (540 mg/m^3) [skin]	500 ppm	Colorless liquid with a mild odor.	MW: 132.2 BP: 313°F Sol: 23% FI.P: 124°F IP: ? Sp.Gr: 0.98 Class II Combustible Liquid	VP: 2 mm FRZ: -79°F UEL: ? LEL:1.7%	Nitrates; strong oxidizers, alkalis & acids	Char; CS$_2$; GC/FID; IV [#1450, Esters I]
Ethyl acetate CH$_3$COOC$_2$H$_5$ 141-78-6 AH5425000 1173 129	Acetic ester, Acetic ether, Ethyl ester of acetic acid, Ethyl ethanoate 1 ppm = 3.60 mg/m^3	NIOSH/OSHA 400 ppm (1400 mg/m^3)	2000 ppm [10%LEL]	Colorless liquid with an ether-like, fruity odor.	MW: 88.1 BP: 171°F Sol(77°F): 10% FI.P: 24°F IP: 10.01 eV Sp.Gr: 0.90 Class IB Flammable Liquid	VP: 73 mm FRZ: -117°F UEL:11.5% LEL: 2.0%	Nitrates; strong oxidizers, alkalis & acids	Char; CS$_2$; GC/FID; IV [#1457]

Personal protection and sanitation (See Table 3)		Recommendations for respirator selection — maximum concentration for use (MUC) (See Table 4)	Health hazards				
			Route	Symptoms (See Table 5)	First aid (See Table 6)		Target organs (See Table 5)
Skin:	Prevent skin contact	TBAL	Inh	Irrit eyes, skin; nau,	Eye:	Irr immed	Eyes, skin, resp sys,
Eyes:	Prevent eye contact		Abs	vomit, abdom cramps, diarr,	Skin:	Soap wash immed	CNS, CVS, blood chol
Wash skin:	When contam		Ing	salv; head, gidd, verti,	Breath:	Resp support	
Remove:	When wet or contam		Con	weak; rhin, chest tight;	Swallow:	Medical attention	
Change:	Daily			blurred vision, miosis;		immed	
Provide:	Eyewash, Quick drench			card irreg; musc fasc; dysp			

[Ethion]

Personal protection and sanitation		Recommendations for respirator selection	Route	Symptoms	First aid		Target organs
Skin:	Prevent skin contact	NIOSH	Inh	In animals: irrit eyes,	Eye:	Irr immed	Eyes, resp sys,
Eyes:	Prevent eye contact	5 ppm: SA*	Abs	resp sys; blood changes;	Skin:	Water flush prompt	blood, kidneys,
Wash skin:	When contam	12.5 ppm: SA:CF*	Ing	liver, kidney, lung damage;	Breath:	Resp support	liver, repro sys,
Remove:	When wet or contam	25 ppm: SCBAF/SAF	Con	repro, terato effects	Swallow:	Medical attention	hemato sys
Change:	N.R.	500 ppm: SA:PD,PP*				immed	
		§ : SCBAF:PD,PP/SAF:PD,PP:ASCBA					
		Escape: GMFOV/SCBAE					

[2-Ethoxyethanol]

131

Personal protection and sanitation		Recommendations for respirator selection	Route	Symptoms	First aid		Target organs
Skin:	Prevent skin contact	NIOSH	Inh	Irrit eyes, nose; vomit;	Eye:	Irr immed	Eyes, resp sys,
Eyes:	Prevent eye contact	5 ppm: CCROV*/SA*	Abs	kidney damage; para;	Skin:	Water flush prompt	GI tract, repro sys,
Wash skin:	When contam	12.5 ppm: SA:CF*/PAPROV*	Ing	in animals: repro,	Breath:	Resp support	hemato sys
Remove:	When wet or contam	25 ppm: CCROV/GMFOV/PAPRTOV*/	Con	terato effects	Swallow:	Medical attention	
Change:	N.R.	SCBAF/SAF				immed	
		500 ppm: SA:PD,PP*					
		§ : SCBAF:PD,PP/SAF:PD,PP:ASCBA					
		Escape: GMFOV/SCBAE					

[2-Ethoxyethyl acetate]

Personal protection and sanitation		Recommendations for respirator selection	Route	Symptoms	First aid		Target organs
Skin:	Prevent skin contact	NIOSH/OSHA	Inh	Irrit eyes, skin, nose,	Eye:	Irr immed	Eyes, skin, resp sys
Eyes:	Prevent eye contact	2000 ppm: SA:CFᴱ/PAPROVᴱ/CCRFOV/	Ing	throat; narco; derm	Skin:	Water flush prompt	
Wash skin:	When contam	GMFOV/SCBAF/SAF	Con		Breath:	Resp support	
Remove:	When wet (flamm)	§ : SCBAF:PD,PP/SAF:PD,PP:ASCBA			Swallow:	Medical attention	
Change:	N.R.	Escape: GMFOV/SCBAE				immed	

[Ethyl acetate]

Chemical name, structure/formula, CAS and RTECS Nos., and DOT ID and guide Nos.	Synonyms, trade names, and conversion factors	Exposure limits (TWA unless noted otherwise)	IDLH	Physical description	MW, BP, SOL Fl.P, IP, Sp, Gr, flammability	VP, FRZ UEL, LEL	Incompatibilities and reactivities	Measurement method (See Table 1)
Ethyl acrylate $CH_2=CHCOOC_2H_5$ 140-88-5 AT0700000 1917 129P (inhibited)	Ethyl acrylate (inhibited), Ethyl ester of acrylic acid, Ethyl propenoate 1 ppm = 4.09 mg/m³	NIOSH Ca See Appendix A OSHA† 25 ppm (100 mg/m³) [skin]	Ca [300 ppm]	Colorless liquid with an acrid odor.	MW: 100.1 BP: 211°F Sol: 2% Fl.P: 48°F IP: 10.30 eV Sp.Gr. 0.92 Class IB Flammable Liquid	VP: 29 mm FRZ: -96°F UEL: 14% LEL: 1.4%	Oxidizers, peroxides, polymerizers, strong alkalis, moisture, chlorosulfonic acid [Note: Polymerizes readily unless an inhibitor such as hydroquinone is added.]	Char; CS₂; GC/FID; IV [#1450, Esters I]
Ethyl alcohol CH_3CH_2OH 64-17-5 KQ6300000 1170 127	Alcohol, Cologne spirit, Ethanol, EtOH, Grain alcohol 1 ppm = 1.89 mg/m³	NIOSH/OSHA 1000 ppm (1900 mg/m³)	3300 ppm [10%LEL]	Clear, colorless liquid with a weak, ethereal, vinous odor.	MW: 46.1 BP: 173°F Sol: Miscible Fl.P: 55°F IP: 10.47 eV Sp.Gr. 0.79 Class IB Flammable Liquid	VP: 44 mm FRZ: -173°F UEL: 19% LEL: 3.3%	Strong oxidizers, potassium dioxide, bromine pentafluoride, acetyl bromide, acetyl chloride, platinum, sodium	Char; 2-Butanol/ CS₂; GC/FID; IV [#1400, Alcohols I]
Ethylamine $CH_3CH_2NH_2$ 75-04-7 KH2100000 1036 118	Aminoethane, Ethylamine (anhydrous), Monoethylamine 1 ppm = 1.85 mg/m³	NIOSH/OSHA 10 ppm (18 mg/m³)	600 ppm	Colorless gas or water-white liquid (below 62°F) with an ammonia-like odor. [Note: Shipped as a liquefied compressed gas.]	MW: 45.1 BP: 62°F Sol: Miscible Fl.P: 1°F IP: 8.86 eV RGasD: 1.61 Sp.Gr. 0.69 (Liquid) Flammable Gas Class IA Flammable Liquid	VP: 874 mm FRZ: -114°F UEL: 14.0% LEL: 3.5%	Strong acids; strong oxidizers; copper, tin & zinc in presence of moisture; cellulose nitrate; chlorine; hypochlorites	Si gel; H₂SO₄; GC/FID; II(3) [#S144]
Ethyl benzene $CH_3CH_2C_6H_5$ 100-41-4 DA0700000 1175 129	Ethylbenzol, Phenylethane 1 ppm = 4.34 mg/m³	NIOSH 100 ppm (435 mg/m³) ST 125 ppm (545 mg/m³) OSHA† 100 ppm (435 mg/m³)	800 ppm [10%LEL]	Colorless liquid with an aromatic odor.	MW: 106.2 BP: 277°F Sol: 0.01% Fl.P: 55°F IP: 8.76 eV Sp.Gr. 0.87 Class IB Flammable Liquid	VP: 7 mm FRZ: -139°F UEL: 6.7% LEL: 0.8%	Strong oxidizers	Char; CS₂; GC/FID; IV [#1501, Aromatic Hydro-carbons]

	Personal protection and sanitation (See Table 3)	Recommendations for respirator selection — maximum concentration for use (MUC) (See Table 4)		Health hazards			
			Route	Symptoms (See Table 5)	First aid (See Table 6)		Target organs (See Table 5)

	Personal protection and sanitation	Respirator selection	Route	Symptoms	First aid	Target organs
Skin: Prevent skin contact Eyes: Prevent eye contact Wash skin: When contam Remove: When wet (flamm) Change: N.R. Provide: Eyewash, Quick drench	NIOSH ¥: SCBAF:PD,PP/SAF:PD,PP:ASCBA Escape: GMFOV/SCBAE	Inh Abs Ing Con	Irrit eyes, skin, resp sys; [carc]	Eye: Irr immed Skin: Water flush immed Breath: Resp support Swallow: Medical attention immed	Eyes, skin, resp sys [in animals: tumors of the forestomach]	
[Ethyl acrylate]						
Skin: Prevent skin contact Eyes: Prevent eye contact Wash skin: When contam Remove: When wet (flamm) Change: N.R.	NIOSH/OSHA 3300 ppm: SA/SCBAF §: SCBAF:PD,PP/SAF:PD,PP:ASCBA Escape: SCBAE	Inh Ing Con	Irrit eyes, skin, nose; head, drow, ftg, narco; cough; liver damage; anemia; repro, terato effects	Eye: Irr immed Skin: Water flush prompt Breath: Fresh air Swallow: Medical attention immed	Eyes, skin, resp sys, CNS, liver, blood, repro sys	
[Ethyl alcohol]						
Skin: Prevent skin contact (liq) Eyes: Prevent eye contact (liq) Wash skin: When contam (liq) Remove: When wet or contam (liq) Change: N.R. Provide: Eyewash (liq), Quick drench (liq)	NIOSH/OSHA 250 ppm: SA:CF£/PAPRS£ 500 ppm: CCRFS/GMFS/SCBAF/SAF 600 ppm: SAF:PD,PP §: SCBAF:PD,PP/SAF:PD,PP:ASCBA Escape: GMFS/SCBAE	Inh Abs (liq) Ing (liq) Con (liq)	Irrit eyes, skin, resp sys; skin burns, derm	Eye: Irr immed (liq) Skin: Water flush immed (liq) Breath: Resp support Swallow: Medical attention immed (liq)	Eyes, skin, resp sys	
[Ethylamine]						
Skin: Prevent skin contact Eyes: Prevent eye contact Wash skin: When contam Remove: When wet (flamm) Change: N.R.	NIOSH/OSHA 800 ppm: CCROV*/GMFOV/PAPROV*/SA*/SCBAF §: SCBAF:PD,PP/SAF:PD,PP:ASCBA Escape: GMFOV/SCBAE	Inh Ing Con	Irrit eyes, skin, muc memb; head; derm; narco, coma	Eye: Irr immed Skin: Water flush prompt Breath: Resp support Swallow: Medical attention immed	Eyes, skin, resp sys, CNS	
[Ethyl benzene]						

Chemical name, structure/formula, CAS and RTECS Nos., and DOT ID and guide Nos.	Synonyms, trade names, and conversion factors	Exposure limits (TWA unless noted otherwise)	IDLH	Physical description	Chemical and physical properties		Incompatibilities and reactivities	Measurement method (See Table 1)
					MW, BP, SOL Fl.P, IP, Sp, Gr, flammability	VP, FRZ UEL, LEL		
Ethyl bromide CH₃CH₂Br 74-96-4 KH6475000 1891 131	Bromoethane, Monobromoethane 1 ppm = 4.46 mg/m³	NIOSH See Appendix D OSHA† 200 ppm (890 mg/m³)	2000 ppm	Colorless to yellow liquid with an ether-like odor. [Note: A gas above 101°F.]	MW: 109.0 BP: 101°F Sol: 0.9% Fl.P: <4°F IP: 10.29 eV Sp.Gr. 1.46 Class IB Flammable Liquid	VP: 375 mm FRZ: -182°F UEL: 8.0% LEL: 6.8%	Chemically-active metals such as sodium, potassium, calcium, powdered aluminum, zinc & magnesium	Char; 2-Propanol; GC/FID; IV [#1011]
Ethyl butyl ketone CH₃CH₂CO[CH₂]₃CH₃ 106-35-4 MJ5250000 1224 127	Butyl ethyl ketone, 3-Heptanone 1 ppm = 4.67 mg/m³	NIOSH/OSHA 50 ppm (230 mg/m³)	1000 ppm	Colorless liquid with a powerful, fruity odor.	MW: 114.2 BP: 298°F Sol: 1% Fl.P(oc): 115°F IP: 9.02 eV Sp.Gr. 0.82 Class II Combustible Liquid	VP: 4 mm FRZ: -38°F UEL: ? LEL: ?	Oxidizers, acetaldehyde, perchloric acid	Char; Methanol/ CS₂; GC/FID; IV [#1301, Ketones II]
Ethyl chloride CH₃CH₂Cl 75-00-3 KH7525000 1037 115	Chloroethane, Hydrochloric ether, Monochloroethane, Muriatic ether 1 ppm = 2.64 mg/m³	NIOSH Handle with caution in the workplace. See Appendix C (Chloroethanes) OSHA 1000 ppm (2600 mg/m³)	3800 ppm [10%LEL]	Colorless gas or liquid (below 54°F) with a pungent, ether-like odor. [Note: Shipped as a liquefied compressed gas.]	MW: 64.5 BP: 54°F Sol: 0.6% Fl.P: NA (Gas) -58°F (Liq) IP: 10.97 eV RGasD: 2.23 Sp.Gr: 0.92 (Liquid at 32°F) Flammable Gas Class IA Flammable Liquid	VP: 1000 mm FRZ: -218°F UEL: 15.4% LEL: 3.8%	Chemically-active metals such as sodium, potassium, calcium, powdered aluminum, zinc & magnesium; oxidizers; water or steam [Note: Reacts with water to form hydrochloric acid.]	Char(2); CS₂; GC/FID; IV [#2519]
Ethylene chlorohydrin CH₂ClCH₂OH 107-07-3 KK0875000 1135 131	2-Chloroethanol, 2-Chloroethyl alcohol, Ethylene chlorhydrin 1 ppm = 3.29 mg/m³	NIOSH C 1 ppm (3 mg/m³) [skin] OSHA† 5 ppm (16 mg/m³) [skin]	7 ppm	Colorless liquid with a faint, ether-like odor.	MW: 80.5 BP: 262°F Sol: Miscible Fl.P: 140°F IP: 10.90 eV Sp.Gr. 1.20 Class IIIA Combustible Liquid	VP: 5 mm FRZ: -90°F UEL: 15.9% LEL: 4.9%	Strong oxidizers, strong caustics, water or steam	Char(pet); 2-Propanol/ CS₂; GC/FID; IV [#2513]

Personal protection and sanitation (See Table 3)	Recommendations for respirator selection — maximum concentration for use (MUC) (See Table 4)	Health hazards			
		Route	Symptoms (See Table 5)	First aid (See Table 6)	Target organs (See Table 5)

Personal protection and sanitation	Recommendations for respirator selection (MUC)	Route	Symptoms	First aid	Target organs
Skin: Prevent skin contact Eyes: Prevent eye contact Wash skin: When contam Remove: When wet (flamm) Change: N.R.	OSHA 2000 ppm: SA/SCBAF §: SCBAF:PD,PP/SAF:PD,PP:ASCBA Escape: GMFOV/SCBAE	Inh Ing Con	Irrit eyes, skin, resp sys; CNS depres; pulm edema; liver, kidney disease; card arrhy, card arrest	Eye: Irr immed Skin: Soap flush prompt Breath: Resp support Swallow: Medical attention immed	Eyes, skin, resp sys, liver, kidneys, CVS, CNS

[Ethyl bromide]

| Skin: Prevent skin contact
Eyes: Prevent eye contact
Wash skin: When contam
Remove: When wet or contam
Change: N.R. | NIOSH/OSHA
500 ppm: CCROV*/SA*
1000 ppm: SA:CF*/PAPROV*/CCRFOV/ GMFOV/SCBAF/SAF
§: SCBAF:PD,PP/SAF:PD,PP:ASCBA
Escape: GMFOV/SCBAE | Inh
Ing
Con | Irrit eyes, skin, muc memb; head, narco, coma; derm | Eye: Irr immed
Skin: Water flush
Breath: Resp support
Swallow: Medical attention immed | Eyes, skin, resp sys, CNS |

[Ethyl butyl ketone]

| Skin: Prevent skin contact (liq)
Eyes: Prevent eye contact (liq)
Wash skin: N.R.
Remove: When wet (flamm)
Change: N.R. | OSHA
3800 ppm: SA*/SCBAF
§: SCBAF:PD,PP/SAF:PD,PP:ASCBA
Escape: GMFOV/SCBAE | Inh
Abs (liq)
Ing (liq)
Con | Inco, inebri; abdom cramps; card arrhy, card arrest; liver, kidney damage | Eye: Irr immed (liq)
Skin: Water flush prompt (liq)
Breath: Resp support
Swallow: Medical attention immed (liq) | Liver, kidneys, resp sys, CVS, CNS |

[Ethyl chloride]

| Skin: Prevent skin contact
Eyes: Prevent eye contact
Wash skin: When contam
Remove: When wet or contam
Change: N.R.
Provide: Eyewash, Quick drench | NIOSH
7 ppm: SA*/SCBAF
§: SCBAF:PD,PP/SAF:PD,PP:ASCBA
Escape: GMFOV/SCBAE | Inh
Abs
Ing
Con | Irrit muc memb; nau, vomit, verti, inco; numb; vis dist; head; thirst; delirium; low BP; collapse, shock, coma; liver, kidney damage | Eye: Irr immed
Skin: Water flush immed
Breath: Resp support
Swallow: Medical attention immed | Resp sys, liver, kidneys, CNS, CVS, eyes |

[Ethylene chlorohydrin]

Chemical name, structure/formula, CAS and RTECS Nos., and DOT ID and guide Nos.	Synonyms, trade names, and conversion factors	Exposure limits (TWA unless noted otherwise)	IDLH	Physical description	Chemical and physical properties		Incompatibilities and reactivities	Measurement method (See Table 1)
					MW, BP, SOL Fl.P, IP, Sp, Gr, flammability	VP, FRZ UEL, LEL		
Ethylenediamine $NH_2CH_2CH_2NH_2$ 107-15-3 KH8575000 1604 132	1,2-Diaminoethane; 1,2-Ethanediamine; Ethylenediamine (anhydrous) 1 ppm = 2.46 mg/m³	NIOSH/OSHA 10 ppm (25 mg/m³)	1000 ppm	Colorless, viscous liquid with an ammonia-like odor. [fungicide] [Note: A solid below 47°F.]	MW: 60.1 BP: 241°F Sol: Miscible Fl.P: 93°F IP: 8.60 eV Sp.Gr: 0.91 Class IC Flammable Liquid	VP: 11 mm FRZ: 47°F UEL(212°F): 12% LEL(212°F): 2.5%	Strong acids & oxidizers, carbon tetrachloride & other chlorinated organic compounds, carbon disulfide [Note: Corrosive to metals.]	XAD-2*; DMF; HPLC/UVD; IV [#2540]
Ethylene dibromide $BrCH_2CH_2Br$ 106-93-4 KH9275000 1605 154	1,2-Dibromoethane; Ethylene bromide; Glycol dibromide 1 ppm = 7.69 mg/m³	NIOSH Ca See Appendix A 0.045 ppm C 0.13 ppm [15-min] OSHA 20 ppm C 30 ppm 50 ppm [5-min max peak]	Ca [100 ppm]	Colorless liquid or solid (below 50°F) with a sweet odor. [fumigant]	MW: 187.9 BP: 268°F Sol: 0.4% Fl.P: NA IP: 9.45 eV Sp.Gr: 2.17 Noncombustible Liquid	VP: 12 mm FRZ: 50°F UEL: NA LEL: NA	Chemically-active metals such as sodium, potassium, calcium, hot aluminum & magnesium; liquid ammonia; strong oxidizers	Char; Benzene/ Methanol; GC/ECD; IV [#1008]
Ethylene dichloride $ClCH_2CH_2Cl$ 107-06-2 KI0525000 1184 129	1,2-Dichloroethane; Ethylene chloride; Glycol dichloride 1 ppm = 4.05 mg/m³	NIOSH Ca See Appendix A, C (Chloroethanes) 1 ppm (4 mg/m³) ST 2 ppm (8 mg/m³) OSHA† 50 ppm C 100 ppm 200 ppm (5-min max peak in any 3 hrs)	Ca [50 ppm]	Colorless liquid with a pleasant, chloroform-like odor. [Note: Decomposes slowly, becomes acidic & darkens in color.]	MW: 99.0 BP: 182°F Sol: 0.9% Fl.P: 56°F IP: 11.05 eV Sp.Gr: 1.24 Class IB Flammable Liquid	VP: 64 mm FRZ: -32°F UEL: 16% LEL: 6.2%	Strong oxidizers & caustics; chemically-active metals such as magnesium or aluminum powder, sodium & potassium; liquid ammonia [Note: Decomposes to vinyl chloride & HCl above 1112°F.]	Char; CS₂; GC/FID; IV [#1003, Halogenated Hydrocarbons]
Ethylene glycol $HOCH_2CH_2OH$ 107-21-1 KW2975000	1,2-Dihydroxyethane; 1,2-Ethanediol; Glycol; Glycol alcohol; Monoethylene glycol	NIOSH See Appendix D OSHA† none	N.D.	Clear, colorless, syrupy, odorless liquid. [antifreeze] [Note: A solid below 9°F.]	MW: 62.1 BP: 388°F Sol: Miscible Fl.P: 232°F IP: ? Sp.Gr: 1.11 Class IIIB Combustible Liquid	VP: 0.06 mm FRZ: 9°F UEL: 15.3% LEL: 3.2%	Strong oxidizers, chromium trioxide, potassium permanganate, sodium peroxide [Note: Hygroscopic (i.e., absorbs moisture from the air).]	OVS-7; Methanol; GC/FID; IV [#5523]

Personal protection and sanitation (See Table 3)		Recommendations for respirator selection — maximum concentration for use (MUC) (See Table 4)	Health hazards			
			Route	Symptoms (See Table 5)	First aid (See Table 6)	Target organs (See Table 5)
Skin:	Prevent skin contact	NIOSH/OSHA	Inh	Irrit nose, resp sys;	Eye: Irr immed	Skin, resp sys,
Eyes:	Prevent eye contact	250 ppm: SA:CF$^\varepsilon$/PAPRS$^\varepsilon$	Abs	sens derm; asthma; liver,	Skin: Water flush immed	liver, kidneys
Wash skin:	When contam/Daily	500 ppm: CCRFS/GMFS/PAPRTS$^\varepsilon$/	Ing	kidney damage	Breath: Resp support	
Remove:	When wet (flamm)	SCBAF/SAF	Con		Swallow: Medical attention	
Change:	Daily	1000 ppm: SAF:PD,PP			immed	
Provide:	Eyewash (>5%), Quick drench	§: SCBAF:PD,PP/SAF:PD,PP:ASCBA				
		Escape: GMFS/SCBAE				

[Ethylenediamine]

Skin:	Prevent skin contact	NIOSH	Inh	Irrit eyes, skin, resp sys;	Eye: Irr immed	Eyes, skin, resp sys,
Eyes:	Prevent eye contact	¥: SCBAF:PD,PP/SAF:PD,PP:ASCBA	Abs	derm with vesic; liver,	Skin: Soap wash immed	liver, kidneys,
Wash skin:	When contam	Escape: GMFOV/SCBAE	Ing	heart, spleen, kidney	Breath: Resp support	repro sys
Remove:	When wet or contam		Con	damage; repro effects;	Swallow: Medical attention	[in animals:
Change:	N.R.			[carc]	immed	skin & lung
Provide:	Eyewash, Quick drench					tumors]

[Ethylene dibromide]

137

Skin:	Prevent skin contact	NIOSH	Inh	Irrit eyes, corn opac;	Eye: Irr immed	Eyes, skin, kidneys,
Eyes:	Prevent eye contact	¥: SCBAF:PD,PP/SAF:PD,PP:ASCBA	Abs	CNS depres; nau, vomit;	Skin: Soap wash prompt	liver, CNS, CVS
Wash skin:	When contam	Escape: GMFOV/SCBAE	Ing	derm; liver, kidney,	Breath: Resp support	[in animals:
Remove:	When wet (flamm)		Con	CVS damage; [carc]	Swallow: Medical attention	forestomach,
Change:	N.R.				immed	mammary gland &
Provide:	Eyewash, Quick drench					circulatory sys
						cancer]

[Ethylene dichloride]

Skin:	Prevent skin contact	TBAL	Inh	Irrit eyes, skin, nose,	Eye: Irr immed	Eyes, skin, resp sys,
Eyes:	Prevent eye contact		Ing	throat; nau, vomit, abdom	Skin: Water wash immed	CNS
Wash skin:	When contam		Con	pain, weak; dizz, stupor,	Breath: Resp support	
Remove:	When wet or contam			convuls, CNS depres; skin	Swallow: Medical attention	
Change:	Daily			sens	immed	

[Ethylene glycol]

Chemical name, structure/formula, CAS and RTECS Nos., and DOT ID and guide Nos.	Synonyms, trade names, and conversion factors	Exposure limits (TWA unless noted otherwise)	IDLH	Physical description	Chemical and physical properties		Incompatibilities and reactivities	Measurement method (See Table 1)
					MW, BP, SOL Fl.P, IP, Sp, Gr, flammability	VP, FRZ UEL, LEL		
Ethylene glycol dinitrate $O_2NOCH_2CH_2ONO_2$ 628-96-6 KW5600000 1185 131P (inhibited)	EGDN; 1,2-Ethanediol dinitrate; Ethylene dinitrate; Ethylene nitrate; Glycol dinitrate; Nitroglycol 1 ppm = 6.22 mg/m³	NIOSH ST 0.1 mg/m³ [skin] OSHA† C 0.2 ppm (1 mg/m³) [skin]	75 mg/m³	Colorless to yellow, oily, odorless liquid. [Note: An explosive ingredient (60-80%) in dynamite along with nitroglycerine (40-20%).]	MW: 152.1 BP: 387°F Sol: Insoluble Fl.P: 419°F IP: ? Sp. Gr. 1.49 Explosive Liquid	VP: 0.05 mm FRZ: -8°F UEL: ? LEL: ?	Acids, alkalis	Tenax GC; Ethanol; GC/ECD; IV [#2507]
Ethyleneimine C_2H_5N 151-56-4 KX5075000 Ethylimine 1185 131P (inhibited)	Aminoethylene, Azirane, Aziridine, Dimethyleneimine, Dimethylenimine, Ethylenimine, 1 ppm = 1.76 mg/m³	NIOSH Ca See Appendix A OSHA [1910.1012] See Appendix B	Ca [100 ppm]	Colorless liquid with an ammonia-like odor. [Note: Usually contains inhibitors to prevent polymerization.]	MW: 43.1 BP: 133°F Sol: Miscible Fl.P: 12°F IP: 9.20 eV Sp.Gr. 0.83 Class IB Flammable Liquid	VP: 160 mm FRZ: -97°F UEL: 54.8% LEL: 3.3%	Polymerizes explosively in presence of acids [Note: Explosive silver derivatives may be formed with silver alloys (e.g., silver solder).]	Bub; CHCl₃; HPLC/UVD; IV [#3514]
Ethylene oxide C_2H_4O 75-21-8 KX2450000 1040 119	Dimethylene oxide; 1,2-Epoxyethane; Oxirane 1 ppm = 1.80 mg/m³	NIOSH Ca See Appendix A <0.1 ppm (<0.18 mg/m³) C 5 ppm (9 mg/m³) [10-min/day] OSHA [1910.1047] 1 ppm 5 ppm [15-min Excursion]	Ca [800 ppm]	Colorless gas or liquid (below 51°F) with an ether-like odor.	MW: 44.1 BP: 51°F Sol: Miscible Fl.P: NA (Gas) -20°F (Liq) IP: 10.56 eV RGasD: 1.49 Sp.Gr: 0.82 (Liquid at 50°F) Flammable Gas Class IA Flammable Liquid	VP: 1.46 atm FRZ: -171°F UEL: 100% LEL: 3.0%	Strong acids, alkalis & oxidizers; chlorides of iron, aluminum & tin; oxides of iron & aluminum; water	Char(pet)*; DMF; GC/ECD; IV [#1614]
Ethylene thiourea $C_3H_6N_2S$ 96-45-7 NI9625000	1,3-Ethylene-2-thiourea; N,N-Ethylenethiourea; ETU; 2-Imidazolidine-2-thione	NIOSH Ca See Appendix A Use encapsulated form. OSHA none	Ca [N.D.]	White to pale-green, crystalline solid with a faint, amine odor. [Note: Used as an accelerator in the curing of poly-chloroprene & other elastomers.]	MW: 102.2 BP: 446-595°F Sol(86°F): 2% Fl.P: 486°F IP: 8.15 eV Sp.Gr: ? Combustible Solid	VP: 16 mm MLT: 392°F UEL: ? LEL: ?	Acrolein	Filter; Water; Vis; IV [#5011]

Personal protection and sanitation (See Table 3)		Recommendations for respirator selection — maximum concentration for use (MUC) (See Table 4)	Health hazards			
			Route	Symptoms (See Table 5)	First aid (See Table 6)	Target organs (See Table 5)
Skin:	Prevent skin contact	NIOSH	Inh	Throb head; dizz; nau,	Eye: Irr immed	Skin, CVS, blood
Eyes:	Prevent eye contact	1 mg/m³: SA*	Abs	vomit, abdom pain;	Skin: Soap wash immed	liver, kidneys
Wash skin:	When contam	2.5 mg/m³: SA:CF*	Ing	hypotension, flush, palp,	Breath: Resp support	
Remove:	When wet (flamm)	5 mg/m³: SAT:CF*/SCBAF/SAF	Con	angina; methemo; delirium,	Swallow: Medical attention	
Change:	Daily	75 mg/m³: SAF:PD,PP		CNS depres; irrit skin;	immed	
Provide:	Quick drench	§: SCBAF:PD,PP/SAF:PD,PP:ASCBA		in animals: anemia;		
		Escape: GMFOVHiE/SCBAE		liver, kidney damage		
[Ethylene glycol dinitrate]						
Skin:	Prevent skin contact	NIOSH	Inh	Irrit eyes, skin, nose,	Eye: Irr immed	Eyes, skin,
Eyes:	Prevent eye contact	¥: SCBAF:PD,PP/SAF:PD,PP:ASCBA	Abs	throat; nau, vomit; head,	Skin: Soap wash immed	resp sys, liver,
Wash skin:	When contam/Daily	Escape: GMFOV/SCBAE	Ing	dizz; pulm edema; liver,	Breath: Resp support	kidneys
Remove:	When wet or contam		Con	kidney damage; eye burns;	Swallow: Medical attention	[in animals:
Change:	Daily			skin sens; [carc]	immed	lung & liver
Provide:	Eyewash, Quick drench					tumors]
[Ethyleneimine]						
Skin:	Prevent skin contact (liq)	NIOSH	Inh	Irrit eyes, skin, nose,	Eye: Irr immed	Eyes, skin, resp sys,
Eyes:	Prevent eye contact (liq)	5 ppm: GMFS†/SCBAF/SAF	Ing	throat; peculiar taste;	Skin: Water flush immed	liver, CNS, blood,
Wash skin:	When contam (liq)	§: SCBAF:PD,PP/SAF:PD,PP:ASCBA	(liq)	head; nau, vomit, diarr;	Breath: Resp support	kidneys, repro sys
Remove:	When wet (flamm)	Escape: GMFS†/SCBAE	Con	dysp, cyan, pulm edema;	Swallow: Medical attention	[peritoneal cancer,
Change:	N.R.			drow, inco; EKG abnor; eye,	immed (liq)	leukemia]
Provide:	Quick drench (liq)			skin burns (liq or high		
				vap conc); liq: frostbite;		
				repro effects; [carc];		
				in animals: convuls;		
				liver, kidney damage		
[Ethylene oxide]						
Skin:	Prevent skin contact	NIOSH	Inh	Irrit eyes;	Eye: Irr immed	Eyes, skin, thyroid,
Eyes:	Prevent eye contact	¥: SCBAF:PD,PP/SAF:PD,PP:ASCBA	Ing	in animals: thickening of	Skin: Soap wash immed	repro sys
Wash skin:	When contam/Daily	Escape: GMFOVHiE/SCBAE	Con	the skin; goiter; terato	Breath: Resp support	[in animals: liver,
Remove:	When wet or contam			effects; [carc]	Swallow: Medical attention	thyroid & lymphatic
Change:	Daily				immed	sys tumors]
[Ethylene thiourea]						

139

Chemical name, structure/formula, CAS and RTECS Nos., and DOT ID and guide Nos.	Synonyms, trade names, and conversion factors	Exposure limits (TWA unless noted otherwise)	IDLH	Physical description	Chemical and physical properties		Incompatibilities and reactivities	Measurement method (See Table 1)
					MW, BP, SOL Fl.P, IP, Sp, Gr, flammability	VP, FRZ UEL, LEL		
Ethyl ether $C_2H_5OC_2H_5$ 60-29-7 KI5775000 1155 127	Diethyl ether, Diethyl oxide, Ether, Ethyl oxide, Solvent ether 1 ppm = 3.03 mg/m³	NIOSH See Appendix D OSHA† 400 ppm (1200 mg/m³)	1900 ppm [10%LEL]	Colorless liquid with a pungent, sweetish odor. [Note: A gas above 94°F.]	MW: 74.1 BP: 94°F Sol: 8% Fl.P: -49°F IP: 9.53 eV Sp.Gr: 0.71 Class IA Flammable Liquid	VP: 440 mm FRZ: -177°F UEL: 36.0% LEL: 1.9%	Strong oxidizers, halogens, sulfur, sulfur compounds [Note: Tends to form explosive peroxides under influence of air and light.]	Char; Ethyl acetate; GC/FID; IV [#1610]
Ethyl formate CH₃CH₂OCHO 109-94-4 LQ8400000 1190 129	Ethyl ester of formic acid, Ethyl methanoate 1 ppm = 3.03 mg/m³	NIOSH/OSHA 100 ppm (300 mg/m³)	1500 ppm	Colorless liquid with a fruity odor.	MW: 74.1 BP: 130°F Sol(64°F): 9% Fl.P: -4°F IP: 10.61 eV Sp.Gr: 0.92 Class IB Flammable Liquid	VP: 200 mm FRZ: -113°F UEL: 16.0% LEL: 2.8%	Nitrates; strong oxidizers, alkalis & acids [Note: Decomposes slowly in water to form ethyl alcohol and formic acid.]	Char; CS₂; GC/FID; IV [#1452]
Ethylidene norbornene C_9H_{12} 16219-75-3 RB9450000	ENB, 5-Ethylidenebicyclo(2.2.1)-hept-2-ene, 5-Ethylidene-2-norbornene [Note: Due to its reactivity, ENB may be stabilized with tert-butyl catechol.] 1 ppm = 4.92 mg/m³	NIOSH C 5 ppm (25 mg/m³) OSHA† none	N.D.	Colorless to white liquid with a turpentine-like odor.	MW: 120.2 BP: 298°F Sol: ? Fl.P(oc): 101°F IP: ? Sp.Gr: 0.90 Class II Combustible Liquid	VP: 4 mm FRZ: -112°F UEL: ? LEL: ?	Oxygen [Note: ENB should be stored in a nitrogen atmosphere since it reacts with oxygen.]	None available
Ethyl mercaptan CH₃CH₂SH 75-08-1 K19625000 2363 130	Ethanethiol, Ethyl sulfhydrate, Mercaptoethane 1 ppm = 2.54 mg/m³	NIOSH C 0.5 ppm (1.3 mg/m³) [15-min] OSHA† C 10 ppm (25 mg/m³)	500 ppm	Colorless liquid with a strong, skunk-like odor. [Note: A gas above 95°F.]	MW: 62.1 BP: 95°F Sol: 0.7% Fl.P: -55°F IP: 9.29 eV Sp.Gr: 0.84 Class IA Flammable Liquid	VP: 442 mm FRZ: -228°F UEL: 18.0% LEL: 2.8%	Strong oxidizers [Note: Reacts violently with calcium hypochlorite.]	Filter*; HCl/DCE; GC/FPD; IV [#2542]

Personal protection and sanitation (See Table 3)		Recommendations for respirator selection — maximum concentration for use (MUC) (See Table 4)	Health hazards					
			Route	Symptoms (See Table 5)		First aid (See Table 6)		Target organs (See Table 5)
Skin:	Prevent skin contact	OSHA	Inh	Irrit eyes, skin, upper	Eye:	Irr immed	Eyes, skin, resp sys,
Eyes:	Prevent eye contact	1900 ppm: CCROV*/GMFOV/PAPROV*/	Ing	resp sys; dizz, drow, head,	Skin:	Water wash prompt	CNS
Wash skin:	N.R.	SA*/SCBAF	Con	excited, narco; nau, vomit	Breath:	Resp support	
Remove:	When wet (flamm)	§: SCBAF:PD,PP/SAF:PD,PP:ASCBA			Swallow:	Medical attention	
Change:	N.R.	Escape: GMFOV/SCBAE				immed	

[Ethyl ether]

Skin:	Prevent skin contact	NIOSH/OSHA	Inh	Irrit eyes, upper resp	Eye:	Irr immed	Eyes, resp sys,
Eyes:	Prevent eye contact	1500 ppm: SA:CF^E/PAPROV^E/CCRFOV/	Ing	sys;	Skin:	Water flush immed	CNS
Wash skin:	When contam	GMFOV/SCBAF/SAF	Con	in animals: narco	Breath:	Resp support	
Remove:	When wet (flamm)	§: SCBAF:PD,PP/SAF:PD,PP:ASCBA			Swallow:	Medical attention	
Change:	N.R.	Escape: GMFOV/SCBAE				immed	

[Ethyl formate]

Skin:	Prevent skin contact	TBAL	Inh	Irrit eyes, skin, nose,	Eye:	Irr immed	Eyes, skin, resp sys,
Eyes:	Prevent eye contact		Abs	throat; head; cough, dysp;	Skin:	Soap wash immed	CNS, liver, kidneys,
Wash skin:	Daily		Ing	nau, vomit; olfactory,	Breath:	Resp support	urogenital sys, bone
Remove:	When wet or contam		Con	taste changes; chemical	Swallow:	Medical attention	marrow
Change:	N.R.			pneu (aspir liq);		immed	
				in animals: liver, kidney,			
				urogenital inj; bone marrow			
				effects			

[Ethylidene norbornene]

Skin:	Prevent skin contact	NIOSH	Inh	Irrit muc memb; head, nau;	Eye:	Irr immed	Eyes, resp sys,
Eyes:	Prevent eye contact	5 ppm: CCROV/SA	Ing	in animals: inco, weak;	Skin:	Soap wash immed	liver, kidneys,
Wash skin:	When contam	12.5 ppm: SA:CF/PAPROV	Con	liver, kidney damage;	Breath:	Resp support	blood
Remove:	When wet (flamm)	25 ppm: CCRFOV/GMFOV/SAT:CF/		damage; cyan; narco	Swallow:	Medical attention	
Change:	N.R.	PAPRTOV/SCBAF/SAF				immed	
		500 ppm: SA:PD,PP					
		§: SCBAF:PD,PP/SAF:PD,PP:ASCBA					
		Escape: GMFOV/SCBAE					

[Ethyl mercaptan]

Chemical name, structure/formula, CAS and RTECS Nos., and DOT ID and guide Nos.	Synonyms, trade names, and conversion factors	Exposure limits (TWA unless noted otherwise)	IDLH	Physical description	Chemical and physical properties		Incompatibilities and reactivities	Measurement method (See Table 1)
					MW, BP, SOL Fl.P, IP, Sp, Gr, flammability	VP, FRZ UEL, LEL		
N-Ethylmorpholine $C_4H_8ONCH_2CH_3$ 100-74-3 QE4025000	4-Ethylmorpholine	NIOSH 5 ppm (23 mg/m³) [skin] OSHA† 20 ppm (94 mg/m³) [skin] 1 ppm = 4.71 mg/m³	100 ppm	Colorless liquid with an ammonia-like odor.	MW: 115.2 BP: 281°F Sol: Miscible Fl.P(oc): 90°F IP: ? Sp.Gr: 0.90 Class IC Flammable Liquid	VP: 6 mm FRZ: -81°F UEL: ? LEL: ?	Strong acids, strong oxidizers	Si gel; H₂SO₄ GC/FID; II(3) [#S146]
Ethyl silicate $(C_2H_5)_4SiO_4$ 78-10-4 VV9450000 1292 132	Ethyl orthosilicate, Ethyl silicate (condensed), Tetraethoxysilane, Tetraethyl orthosilicate, Tetraethyl silicate	NIOSH 10 ppm (85 mg/m³) OSHA† 100 ppm (850 mg/m³) 1 ppm = 8.52 mg/m³	700 ppm	Colorless liquid with a sharp, alcohol-like odor.	MW: 208.3 BP: 336°F Sol: Reacts Fl.P: 99°F IP: 9.77 eV Sp.Gr: 0.93 Class IC Flammable Liquid	VP: 1 mm FRZ: -117°F UEL: ? LEL: ?	Strong oxidizers, water [Note: Reacts with water to form a silicone adhesive (a milky-white mass).]	XAD-2; CS₂; GC/FID; II(3) [#S264]
Fenamiphos $C_{13}H_{22}NO_3PS$ 22224-92-6 TB3675000	Ethyl 3-methyl-4-(methyl-thio)phenyl-(1-methyl-ethyl)phosphoramidate, Nemacur®, Phenamiphos	NIOSH 0.1 mg/m³ [skin] OSHA† none	N.D.	Off-white to tan, waxy solid. [insecticide] [Note: Found commercially as a granular ingredi-ent (5-15%) or in an emulsifiable concentrate (400 g/l).]	MW: 303.4 BP: ? Sol: 0.03% Fl.P: ? IP: ? Sp.Gr: 1.14	VP: 0.00005 mm MLT: 121°F UEL: ? LEL: ?	None reported [Note: May hydrolyze under alkaline conditions.]	OVS-2; Toluene/ Acetone; GC/FID; IV [#5600, Organo-phosphorus Pesticides]
Fensulfothion $C_{11}H_{17}O_4PS_2$ 115-90-2 TF3850000	Dasanit®; O,O-Diethyl O-(p-methyl-sulfinyl)phenyl)-phosphorothioate; Terracur P® [(C₂H₅O)₂P(S)OC₆H₄S(O)CH₃]	NIOSH 0.1 mg/m³ OSHA† none	N.D.	Brown liquid or yellow oil. [pesticide]	MW: 308.4 BP: ? Sol(77°F): 0.2% Fl.P: ? IP: ? Sp.Gr: 1.20 Combustible Liquid	VP: ? FRZ: ? UEL: ? LEL: ?	Alkalis	None available

Personal protection and sanitation (See Table 3)		Recommendations for respirator selection — maximum concentration for use (MUC) (See Table 4)	Health hazards				
			Route	Symptoms (See Table 5)	First aid (See Table 6)	Target organs (See Table 5)	

Skin:	Prevent skin contact	NIOSH	Inh	Irrit eyes, nose, throat;	Eye:	Irr immed	Eyes, resp sys
Eyes:	Prevent eye contact	50 ppm: CCROV*/SA*	Abs	vis dist: corn edema,	Skin:	Water flush prompt	
Wash skin:	When contam	100 ppm: SA:CF*/PAPROV*/CCRFOV/	Ing	blue-gray vision, colored	Breath:	Resp support	
Remove:	When wet (flamm)	GMFOV/SCBAF/SAF	Con	haloes	Swallow:	Medical attention	
Change:	N.R.	§: SCBAF:PD,PP/SAF:PD,PP:ASCBA				immed	
Provide:	Eyewash (>15%), Quick drench	Escape: GMFOV/SCBAE					

[N-Ethylmorpholine]

Skin:	Prevent skin contact	NIOSH	Inh	Irrit eyes, nose;	Eye:	Irr immed	Eyes, resp sys, Eyes:
Eyes:	Prevent eye contact	100 ppm: SA*	Ing	in animals: lac; dysp,	Skin:	Soap wash prompt	liver, kidneys,
Wash skin:	When contam	250 ppm: SA:CF*	Con	pulm edema; tremor, narco;	Breath:	Resp support	blood, skin
Remove:	When wet (flamm)	500 ppm: SCBAF/SAF		liver, kidney damage;	Swallow:	Medical attention	
Change:	N.R.	700 ppm: SAF:PD,PP		anemia		immed	
		§: SCBAF:PD,PP/SAF:PD,PP:ASCBA					
		Escape: GMFOV/SCBAE					

[Ethyl silicate]

Skin:	Prevent skin contact	TBAL	Inh	Nau, vomit, abdom cramps,	Eye:	Irr immed	Resp sys, CNS, CVS,
Eyes:	Prevent eye contact		Abs	diarr, salv; head, gidd,	Skin:	Soap flush immed	blood chol
Wash skin:	When contam/Daily		Ing	verti, weak; rhin, chest	Breath:	Resp support	
Remove:	When wet or contam		Con	tight; blurred vision,	Swallow:	Medical attention	
Change:	Daily			miosis; card irreg; musc		immed	
Provide:	Quick drench			fasc; dysp			

[Fenamiphos]

Skin:	Prevent skin contact	TBAL	Inh	Irrit skin; nau, vomit,	Eye:	Irr immed	Skin, resp sys, CNS,
Eyes:	Prevent eye contact		Abs	abdom cramps, diarr, salv;	Skin:	Soap flush immed	CVS, blood chol
Wash skin:	When contam		Ing	head, gidd, verti, weak;	Breath:	Resp support	
Remove:	When wet or contam		Con	rhin, chest tight; blurred	Swallow:	Medical attention	
Change:	N.R.			vision, miosis; card		immed	
Provide:	Eyewash, Quick drench			irreg; musc fasc; dysp			

[Fensulfothion]

143

Chemical name, structure/formula, CAS and RTECS Nos., and DOT ID and guide Nos.	Synonyms, trade names, and conversion factors	Exposure limits (TWA unless noted otherwise)	IDLH	Physical description	Chemical and physical properties		Incompatibilities and reactivities	Measurement method (See Table 1)
					MW, BP, SOL FI.P, IP, Sp, Gr, flammability	VP, FRZ UEL, LEL		
Fenthion C₁₀H₁₅O₃PS 55-38-9 TF9625000	Baytex®; Entex®; O,O-Dimethyl O-3-methyl-4-methylthiophenyl phosphorothioate [(CH₃O)₂P(S)OC₆H₃(CH₃)SCH₃]	NIOSH See Appendix D OSHA† none	N.D.	Colorless to brown liquid with a slight, garlic-like odor. [insecticide]	MW: 278.3 BP: ? Sol: 0.006% FI.P: NA IP: ? Sp.Gr: 1.25 Noncombustible Liquid	VP: 0.00003 mm FRZ: 43°F UEL: NA LEL: NA	Oxidizers	None available
Ferbam [(CH₃)₂NCS₂]₃Fe 14484-64-1 NO8750000	tris(Dimethyldithio-carbamato)iron, Ferric dimethyl dithio-carbamate	NIOSH 10 mg/m³ OSHA† 15 mg/m³	800 mg/m³	Dark brown to black, odorless solid. [fungicide]	MW: 416.5 BP: Decomposes Sol: 0.01% FI.P: ? IP: 7.72 eV Sp.Gr: ? Combustible Solid	VP: 0 mm (approx) MLT: >356°F (Decomposes) UEL: ? LEL: ? MEC: 55 g/m³	Strong oxidizers, moisture	Filter; none; Grav; IV [#0500, Particulates, NOR (total)]
Ferrovanadium dust FeV 12604-58-9 LK2900000	Ferrovanadium	NIOSH* 1 mg/m³ ST 3 mg/m³ [*Note: The REL also applies to Vanadium metal and Vanadium carbide.] OSHA† 1 mg/m³	500 mg/m³	Dark, odorless particulate dispersed in air. [Note: Ferro-vanadium metal is an alloy usually contain-ing 50-80% vanadium.]	MW: 106.8 BP: ? Sol: Insoluble FI.P: NA IP: NA Sp.Gr: ? Metal: Noncombustible Solid, but dust may be an explosion hazard.	VP: 0 mm (approx) MLT: 2696-2768°F UEL: NA LEL: NA MEC: 1.3 g/m³	Strong oxidizers	Filter; Acid; FAAS; OSHA [#ID121, #ID125G]
Fibrous glass dust LK3651000	Fiber glas®, Fiberglass, Glass fibers, Glass wool [Note: Usually produced from borosilicate & low alkali silicate glasses.]	NIOSH 3 fibers/cm³ (fibers ≤ 3.5 µm in diameter & ≥10 µm in length) 5 mg/m³ (total) OSHA 15 mg/m³ (total) 5 mg/m³ (resp)	N.D.	Typically, glass filaments >3 µm in diameter or glass "wool" with diameters down to 0.05 µm & >1 µm in length.	MW: NA BP: NA Sol: Insoluble FI.P: NA IP: NA Sp.Gr: 2.5 Noncombustible Fibers	VP: 0 mm (approx) MLT: ? UEL: NA LEL: NA	None reported	Filter; none; PCM; IV [#7400, Asbestos and Other Fibers]

144

	Personal protection and sanitation (See Table 3)	Recommendations for respirator selection — maximum concentration for use (MUC) (See Table 4)	Route	Symptoms (See Table 5)	First aid (See Table 6)	Target organs (See Table 5)
Skin: Eyes: Wash skin: Remove: Change:	Prevent skin contact Prevent eye contact When contam When wet or contam Daily	TBAL	Inh Abs Ing Con	Nau, vomit, abdom cramps, diarr, salv; head, gidd, vert, weak; rhin, chest tight; blurred vision, miosis; card irregularities; musc fasc; dysp	Eye: Skin: Breath: Swallow:	Irr immed Soap flush immed Resp support Medical attention immed	Resp sys, CNS, CVS, plasma chol

[Fenthion]

Skin: Eyes: Wash skin: Remove: Change:	Prevent skin contact Prevent eye contact When contam When wet or contam Daily	NIOSH 50 mg/m^3: D 100 mg/m^3: DXSQ*/HiE*/SA* 250 mg/m^3: SA:CF*/PAPRD* 500 mg/m^3: HiEF/SAT:CF*/PAPRTHiE*/SCBAF/SAF 800 mg/m^3: SAF:PD,PP §: SCBAF:PD,PP/SAF:PD,PP:ASCBA Escape: HiEF/SCBAE	Inh Ing Con	Irrit eyes, resp tract; derm; GI dist	Eye: Skin: Breath: Swallow:	Irr immed Soap wash prompt Resp support Medical attention immed	Eyes, skin, resp sys, GI tract

[Ferbam]

145

Skin: Eyes: Wash skin: Remove: Change:	N.R. N.R. N.R. N.R. N.R.	NIOSH/OSHA 5 mg/m^3: DM* 10 mg/m^3: DMXSQ*/SA* 25 mg/m^3: SA:CF*/PAPRDM* 50 mg/m^3: HiEF/SAT:CF*/PAPRTHiE*/SCBAF/SAF 500 mg/m^3: SAF:PD,PP §: SCBAF:PD,PP/SAF:PD,PP:ASCBA Escape: HiEF/SCBAE	Inh Con	Irrit eyes, resp sys; in animals: bron, pneuitis	Eye: Breath:	Irr immed Resp support	Eyes, resp sys

[Ferrovanadium dust]

Skin: Eyes: Wash skin: Remove: Change:	Prevent skin contact Prevent eye contact Daily N.R. Daily	NIOSH 5X REL: D 10X REL: DXSQ/HiE/SA 25X REL: SA:CF/PAPRD 50X REL: HiEF/PAPRTHiE/SCBAF/SAF 1000X REL: SAF:PD,PP §: SCBAF:PD,PP/SAF:PD,PP:ASCBA Escape: HiEF/SCBAE	Inh Con	Irrit eyes, skin, nose, throat; dysp	Eye: Breath:	Irr immed Fresh air	Eyes, skin, resp sys

[Fibrous glass dust]

146

Chemical name, structure/formula, CAS and RTECS Nos., and DOT ID and guide Nos.	Synonyms, trade names, and conversion factors	Exposure limits (TWA unless noted otherwise)	IDLH	Physical description	Chemical and physical properties		Incompatibilities and reactivities	Measurement method (See Table 1)
					MW, BP, SOL Fl.P, IP, Sp, Gr, flammability	VP, FRZ UEL, LEL		
Fluorine F₂ 7782-41-4 LM6475000 9192 167 (cryogenic liquid) 1045 124 (compressed)	Fluorine-19 1 ppm = 1.55 mg/m³	NIOSH/OSHA 0.1 ppm (0.2 mg/m³)	25 ppm	Pale-yellow to greenish gas with a pungent, irritating odor.	MW: 38.0 BP: -307°F Sol: Reacts Fl.P: NA IP: 15.70 eV RGasD: 1.31 Nonflammable Gas, but an extremely strong oxidizer.	VP: >1 atm FRZ: -363°F UEL: NA LEL: NA	Water, nitric acid, oxidizers, organic compounds [Note: Reacts violently with all combustible materials, except the metal containers in which it is shipped. Reacts with H₂O to form hydrofluoric acid.]	None available
Fluorotrichloromethane CCl₃F 75-69-4 PB6125000 1 ppm = 5.62 mg/m³	Freon® 11, Monofluorotrichloromethane, Refrigerant 11, Trichlorofluoromethane, Trichloromonofluoromethane	NIOSH C 1000 ppm (5600 mg/m³) OSHA† 1000 ppm (5600 mg/m³)	2000 ppm	Colorless to water-white, nearly odorless liquid or gas (above 75°F).	MW: 137.4 BP: 75°F Sol(75°F): 0.1% Fl.P: NA IP: 11.77 eV Sp.Gr: 1.47 (Liquid at 75°F) RGasD: 4.74 Noncombustible Liquid Nonflammable Gas	VP: 690 mm FRZ: -168°F UEL: NA LEL: NA	Chemically-active metals such as sodium, potassium, calcium, powdered aluminum, zinc, magnesium & lithium shavings; granular barium	Char; CS₂; GC/FID; IV [#1006, Trichloro-fluoro-methane]
Fluoroxene CF₃CH₂OCH=CH₂ 406-90-6 KO4250000 1 ppm = 5.16 mg/m³	2,2,2-Trifluoroethoxy-ethene; 2,2,2-Trifluoroethyl vinyl ether	NIOSH* C 2 ppm (10.3 mg/m³) [60-min] [*Note: REL for exposure to waste anesthetic gas.] OSHA none	N.D.	Liquid. [inhalation anesthetic] [Note: A gas above 109°F.]	MW: 126.1 BP: 109°F Sol: ? Fl.P: ? IP: ? Sp.Gr: 1.14 Combustible Liquid [potentially EXPLOSIVE!].	VP: 286 mm FRZ: ? UEL: ? LEL: ?	None reported	None available
Fonofos C₁₀H₁₅OPS₂ 944-22-9 TA5950000 1 ppm = 10.07 mg/m³	Dyfonate®, Dyphonate, O-Ethyl-S-phenyl ethyl-phosphorothioate, Fonophos	NIOSH 0.1 mg/m³ [skin] OSHA† none	N.D.	Light-yellow liquid with an aromatic odor. [insecticide]	MW: 246.3 BP: ? Sol: 0.001% Fl.P: >201°F IP: ? Sp.Gr: 1.15 Class IIIB Combustible Liquid	VP(77°F): 0.0002 mm FRZ: ? UEL: ? LEL: ?	None reported	OVS-2; Toluene/Acetone; GC/FPD; IV [#5600, Organo-phosphorus Pesticides]

Personal protection and sanitation (See Table 3)		Recommendations for respirator selection — maximum concentration for use (MUC) (See Table 4)	Health hazards				
			Route	Symptoms (See Table 5)	First aid (See Table 6)		Target organs (See Table 5)
Skin:	Prevent skin contact (liq)	NIOSH/OSHA	Inh	Irrit eyes, nose, resp sys;	Eye:	Irr immed	Eyes, skin, resp sys,
Eyes:	Prevent eye contact	1 ppm: SA*	Con	lar spasm, bron spasm;	Skin:	Water flush immed	liver, kidneys
Wash skin:	When contam (liq)	2.5 ppm: SA:CF*		pulm edema; eye, skin burns;	Breath:	Resp support	
Remove:	When wet or contam (liq)	5 ppm: SCBAF/SAF		in animals: liver, kidney			
Change:	N.R.	25 ppm: SAF:PD,PP		damage			
Provide:	Eyewash (liq), Quick drench (liq)	§: SCBAF:PD,PP/SAF:PD,PP:ASCBA					
		Escape: GMFS⁴/SCBAE					

[Fluorine]

Skin:	Prevent skin contact	NIOSH/OSHA	Inh	Inco, tremor; derm; card	Eye:	Irr immed	Skin, resp sys, CVS
Eyes:	Prevent eye contact	2000 ppm: SA/SCBAF	Ing	arrhy, card arrest; asphy;	Skin:	Water flush immed	
Wash skin:	N.R.	§: SCBAF:PD,PP/SAF:PD,PP:ASCBA	Con	liq: frostbite	Breath:	Resp support	
Remove:	When wet or contam	Escape: GMFOV/SCBAE			Swallow:	Medical attention	
Change:	N.R.					immed	
Provide:	Eyewash, Quick drench						

147

[Fluorotrichloromethane]

Skin:	N.R.	TBAL	Inh	Irrit eyes; CNS depres,	Eye:	Irr immed	Eyes, CNS
Eyes:	Prevent eye contact		Ing	analgesia, anes, sez,	Skin:	Soap wash	
Wash skin:	N.R.		Con	resp depres	Breath:	Resp support	
Remove:	N.R.				Swallow:	Medical attention	
Change:	N.R.					immed	

[Fluroxene]

Skin:	Prevent skin contact	TBAL	Inh	Nau, vomit, abdom cramps,	Eye:	Irr immed	Resp sys, CNS, CVS,
Eyes:	Prevent eye contact		Abs	diarr, salv; head, gidd,	Skin:	Soap flush immed	blood chol
Wash skin:	When contam		Ing	verti, weak; rhin, chest	Breath:	Resp support	
Remove:	When wet or contam		Con	tight; blurred vision,	Swallow:	Medical attention	
Change:	Daily			miosis; card irreg; musc		immed	
Provide:	Eyewash, Quick drench			fasc; dysp			

[Fonofos]

Chemical name, structure/formula, CAS and RTECS Nos., and DOT ID and guide Nos.	Synonyms, trade names, and conversion factors	Exposure limits (TWA unless noted otherwise)	IDLH	Physical description	Chemical and physical properties		Incompatibilities and reactivities	Measurement method (See Table 1)
					MW, BP, SOL Fl.P, IP, Sp, Gr, flammability	VP, FRZ UEL, LEL		
Formaldehyde HCHO 50-00-0 LP8925000	Methanal, Methyl aldehyde, Methylene oxide	NIOSH Ca See Appendix A 0.016 ppm C 0.1 ppm [15-min] OSHA [1910.1048] 0.75 ppm ST 2 ppm 1 ppm = 1.23 mg/m³	Ca [20 ppm]	Nearly colorless gas with a pungent, suffocating odor. [Note: Often used in an aqueous solution (see specific listing for Formalin).]	MW: 30.0 BP: -6°F Sol: Miscible Fl.P: NA (Gas) IP: 10.88 eV RGasD: 1.04 Flammable Gas	VP: >1 atm FRZ: -134°F UEL: 73% LEL: 7.0%	Strong oxidizers, alkalis & acids; phenols; urea [Note: Pure formaldehyde has a tendency to polymerize. Reacts with HCl to form bis-chloromethyl ether.]	Filter/Imp(2); none; Vis; IV [#3500] [Also #2541]
Formalin (as formaldehyde) 1198 132 2209 132	Formaldehyde solution [Note: Formalin is an aqueous solution that is 37% formaldehyde by weight; inhibited solutions contain 6-12% methyl alcohol. Also see specific listings for Formaldehyde and Methyl alcohol.]	NIOSH Ca See Appendix A 0.016 ppm C 0.1 ppm [15-min] OSHA [1910.1048] 0.75 ppm ST 2 ppm	Ca [20 ppm]	Colorless liquid with a pungent odor.	MW: Varies BP: 214°F Sol: Miscible Fl.P: 185°F IP: ? Sp.Gr: 1.08 Class IIIA Combustible Liquid	VP: 1 mm FRZ: ? UEL: 73% LEL: 7%	Strong oxidizers, alkalis & acids; phenols; urea; oxides; isocyanates; caustics; anhydrides	Filter/Imp(2); none; Vis; IV [#3500] [Also #2541]
Formamide HCONH₂ 75-12-7 LQ0525000	Carbamaldehyde, Methanamide	NIOSH 10 ppm (15 mg/m³) [skin] OSHA† none 1 ppm = 1.85 mg/m³	N.D.	Colorless, oily liquid. [Note: A solid below 37°F.]	MW: 45.1 BP: 411°F (Decomposes) Sol: Miscible Fl.P(oc): 310°F IP: 10.20 eV Sp.Gr: 1.13 Class IIIB Combustible Liquid	VP(86°F): 0.1 mm FRZ: 37°F UEL: ? LEL: ?	Oxidizers, iodine, pyridine, sulfur trioxide, copper, brass, lead [Note: Hygroscopic (i.e., absorbs moisture from the air).]	None available
Formic acid HCOOH 64-18-6 LQ4900000 1779 153	Formic acid (85-95% in aqueous solution); Hydrogen carboxylic acid; Methanoic acid	NIOSH/OSHA 5 ppm (9 mg/m³)	30 ppm	Colorless liquid with a pungent, penetrating odor. [Note: Often used in an aqueous solution.]	MW: 46.0 BP: 224°F (90% soln.) Sol: Miscible Fl.P(oc): 122°F (90% soln.) IP: 11.05 eV Sp.Gr: 1.22 (90% solution) Class II Combustible Liquid (90% solution)	VP: 35 mm FRZ: 20°F (90% soln.) UEL: 57% (90% soln.) LEL: 18% (90% soln.)	Strong oxidizers, strong caustics, concentrated sulfuric acid [Note: Corrosive to metals.]	Si gel*; Water; IC; IV [#2011]

| | | | | | | | | 1 ppm = 1.88 mg/m³ |

Personal protection and sanitation (See Table 3)		Recommendations for respirator selection — maximum concentration for use (MUC) (See Table 4)	Health hazards				
			Route	Symptoms (See Table 5)	First aid (See Table 6)		Target organs (See Table 5)
Skin:	N.R.	NIOSH	Inh	Irrit eyes, nose, throat,	Eye:	Irr immed	Eyes, resp sys
Eyes:	Prevent eye contact	¥: SCBAF:PD,PP/SAF:PD,PP:ASCBA	Con	resp sys; lac; cough;	Breath:	Resp support	[nasal cancer]
Wash skin:	N.R.	Escape: GMFS/SCBAE		bron spasm; [carc]			
Remove:	N.R.						
Change:	N.R.						
[Formaldehyde]							
Skin:	Prevent skin contact	NIOSH	Inh	Irrit eyes, nose, throat,	Eye:	Irr immed	Eyes, skin, resp sys
Eyes:	Prevent eye contact	¥: SCBAF:PD,PP/SAF:PD,PP:ASCBA	Ing	resp sys; lac; cough;	Skin:	Water flush prompt	[nasal cancer]
Wash skin:	When contam	Escape: GMFS/SCBAE	Con	bron spasm; derm; [carc]	Breath:	Resp support	
Remove:	When wet or contam				Swallow:	Medical attention	
Change:	N.R.					immed	
Provide:	Eyewash, Quick drench						
[Formalin (as formaldehyde)]							
Skin:	N.R.	TBAL	Inh	Irrit eyes, skin, muc memb;	Eye:	Irr immed	Eyes, skin, resp sys,
Eyes:	Prevent eye contact		Ing	drow, ftg; nau, acidosis;	Skin:	Water wash	CNS, repro sys
Wash skin:	N.R.		Con	skin eruptions;	Breath:	Resp support	
Remove:	N.R.			in animals: repro effects	Swallow:	Medical attention	
Change:	N.R.					immed	
[Formamide]							
Skin:	Prevent skin contact	NIOSH/OSHA	Inh	Irrit eyes, skin, throat;	Eye:	Irr immed	Eyes, skin, resp sys
Eyes:	Prevent eye contact	30 ppm: SA*/SCBAF	Ing	skin burns, derm; lac;	Skin:	Water flush immed	
Wash skin:	When contam	§: SCBAF:PD,PP/SAF:PD,PP:ASCBA	Con	rhin; cough, dysp; nau	Breath:	Resp support	
Remove:	When wet or contam	Escape: GMFOVHiE/SCBAE			Swallow:	Medical attention	
Change:	N.R.					immed	
Provide:	Eyewash, Quick drench						
[Formic acid]							

Chemical name, structure/formula, CAS and RTECS Nos., and DOT ID and guide Nos.	Synonyms, trade names, and conversion factors	Exposure limits (TWA unless noted otherwise)	IDLH	Physical description	Chemical and physical properties		Incompatibilities and reactivities	Measurement method (See Table 1)
					MW, BP, SOL FI.P, IP, Sp, Gr, flammability	VP, FRZ UEL, LEL		
Furfural $C_5H_4O_2$ 98-01-1 LT7000000	Fural, 2-Furancarboxaldehyde, Furfuraldehyde, 2-Furfuraldehyde	NIOSH See Appendix D OSHA† 5 ppm (20 mg/m³) [skin]	100 ppm	Colorless to amber liquid with an almond-like odor. [Note: Darkens in light and air.]	MW: 96.1 BP: 323°F Sol: 8% FI.P: 140°F IP: 9.21 eV	VP: 2 mm FRZ: -34°F UEL: 19.3% LEL: 2.1%	Strong acids, oxidizers, strong alkalis [Note: May polymerize on contact with strong acids or strong alkalis.]	XAD-2*; Toluene; GC/FID; IV [#2529]
1199 132P	1 ppm = 3.93 mg/m³				Sp.Gr. 1.16 Class IIIA Combustible Liquid			
Furfuryl alcohol $C_5H_6O_2$ 98-00-0 LU9100000	2-Furylmethanol, 2-Hydroxymethylfuran	NIOSH 10 ppm (40 mg/m³) ST 15 ppm (60 mg/m³) [skin] OSHA† 50 ppm (200 mg/m³)	75 ppm	Colorless to amber liquid with a faint, burning odor. [Note: Darkens on exposure to light.]	MW: 98.1 BP: 338°F Sol: Miscible FI.P: 149°F IP: ?	VP(77°F): 0.6 mm FRZ: 6°F UEL: 16.3% LEL: 1.8%	Strong oxidizers & acids [Note: Contact with organic acids may lead to polymerization.]	Porapak-Q; Acetone; GC/FID; IV [#2505]
2874 153	1 ppm = 4.01 mg/m³				Sp.Gr. 1.13 Class IIIA Combustible Liquid			
Gasoline 8006-61-9 LX3300000	Motor fuel, Motor spirits, Natural gasoline, Petrol [Note: A complex mixture of volatile hydrocarbons (paraffins, cycloparaffins & aromatics).]	NIOSH Ca See Appendix A OSHA† none	Ca [N.D.]	Clear liquid with a characteristic odor.	MW: 72 (approx) BP: 102°F Sol: Insoluble FI.P: -45°F IP: ?	VP: 38-300 mm FRZ: ? UEL: 7.6% LEL: 1.4%	Strong oxidizers such as peroxides, nitric acid & perchlorates	None available
1203 128	1 ppm = 2.95 mg/m³ (approx)				Class IB Flammable Liquid			
Germanium tetrahydride GeH_4 7782-65-2 LY4900000	Germane, Germanium hydride, Germanomethane, Monogermane [Note: Used chiefly for the production of high purity germanium for use in semiconductors.]	NIOSH 0.2 ppm (0.6 mg/m³) OSHA† none	N.D.	Colorless gas with a pungent odor. [Note: Shipped as a compressed gas.]	MW: 76.6 BP: -127°F Sol: Insoluble FI.P: NA (Gas) IP: 11.34 eV	VP: >1 atm FRZ: -267°F UEL: ? LEL: ?	Bromine	None available
2192 119	1 ppm = 3.13 mg/m³				RGasD: 2.65 Flammable Gas (may ignite SPONTANEOUSLY in air).			

Personal protection and sanitation (See Table 3)		Recommendations for respirator selection — maximum concentration for use (MUC) (See Table 4)	Health hazards			
			Route	Symptoms (See Table 5)	First aid (See Table 6)	Target organs (See Table 5)
Skin:	Prevent skin contact	OSHA	Inh	Irrit eyes, skin, upper	Eye:	Irr immed	Eyes, skin, resp sys
Eyes:	Prevent eye contact	50 ppm: CCROV*/SA*	Abs	resp sys; head; derm	Skin:	Water flush prompt	
Wash skin:	When contam	100 ppm: SA:CF*/CCRFOV/PAPROV*/	Ing		Breath:	Resp support	
Remove:	When wet or contam	GMFOV/SCBAF/SAF	Con		Swallow:	Medical attention	
Change:	N.R.	§: SCBAF:PD,PP/SAF:PD,PP:ASCBA				immed	
		Escape: GMFOV/SCBAE					

[Furfural]

Skin:	Prevent skin contact	NIOSH/OSHA	Inh	Irrit eyes, muc memb; dizz;	Eye:	Irr immed	Eyes, skin, resp sys
Eyes:	Prevent eye contact	75 ppm: CCROV*/GMFOV/PAPROV*/	Abs	nau, diarr; diuresis; resp,	Skin:	Water flush immed	CNS
Wash skin:	When contam	SA*/SCBAF	Ing	body temperature depres;	Breath:	Resp support	
Remove:	When wet or contam	§: SCBAF:PD,PP/SAF:PD,PP:ASCBA	Con	vomit; derm	Swallow:	Medical attention	
Change:	N.R.	Escape: GMFOV/SCBAE				immed	
Provide:	Quick drench						

151

[Furfuryl alcohol]

Skin:	Prevent skin contact	NIOSH	Inh	Irrit eyes, skin, muc memb;	Eye:	Irr immed	Eyes, skin, resp sys,
Eyes:	Prevent eye contact	¥: SCBAF:PD,PP/SAF:PD,PP:ASCBA	Abs	derm; head, ftg, blurred	Skin:	Soap flush immed	CNS, liver, kidneys
Wash skin:	When contam	Escape: GMFOV/SCBAE	Ing	vision, dizz, slurred	Breath:	Resp support	[in animals:
Remove:	When wet (flamm)		Con	speech, conf, convuls;	Swallow:	Medical attention	liver & kidney
Change:	N.R.			chemical pneu (aspir);		immed	cancer]
Provide:	Eyewash, Quick drench			possible liver, kidney			
				damage; [carc]			

[Gasoline]

Skin:	N.R.	TBAL	Inh	Mal, head, gidd, fainting;	Breath:	Resp support	CNS, kidneys, blood
Eyes:	N.R.			dysp; nau, vomit; kidney			
Wash skin:	N.R.			inj; hemolytic effects			
Remove:	N.R.						
Change:	N.R.						

[Germanium tetrahydride]

Chemical name, structure/formula, CAS and RTECS Nos., and DOT ID and guide Nos.	Synonyms, trade names, and conversion factors	Exposure limits (TWA unless noted otherwise)	IDLH	Physical description	Chemical and physical properties		Incompatibilities and reactivities	Measurement method (See Table 1)
					MW, BP, SOL Fl.P, IP, Sp, Gr, flammability	VP, FRZ UEL, LEL		
Glutaraldehyde OCH(CH₂)₃CHO 111-30-8 MA2450000	Glutaric dialdehyde; 1,5-Pentanedial 1 ppm = 4.09 mg/m³	NIOSH C 0.2 ppm (0.8 mg/m³) See Appendix C (Aldehydes) OSHA† none	N.D.	Colorless liquid with a pungent odor.	MW: 100.1 BP: 212°F Sol: Miscible Fl.P: NA IP: ? Sp.Gr: 1.10 Noncombustible Liquid	VP: 17 mm FRZ: 7°F UEL: NA LEL: NA	Strong oxidizers, strong bases [Note: Alkaline solutions of glutaraldehyde (i.e., activated glutaraldehyde) react with alcohol, ketones, amines, hydrazines & proteins.]	Sil gel*; Acetonitrile; HPLC/UV; IV [#2532]
Glycerin (mist) HOCH₂CH(OH)CH₂OH 56-81-5 MA8050000	Glycerin (anhydrous); Glycerol; Glycyl alcohol; 1,2,3-Propanetriol; Trihydroxypropane	NIOSH See Appendix D OSHA† 15 mg/m³ (total) 5 mg/m³ (resp)	N.D.	Clear, colorless, odorless, syrupy liquid or solid (below 64°F). [Note: The solid form melts above 64°F but the liquid form freezes at a much lower temperature.]	MW: 92.1 BP: 554°F (Decomposes) Sol: Miscible Fl.P: 320°F IP: ? Sp.Gr: 1.26 Class IIIB Combustible Liquid	VP(122°F): 0.003 mm MLT: 64°F UEL: ? LEL: ?	Strong oxidizers (e.g., chromium trioxide, potassium chlorate, potassium perman- ganate) [Note: Hygroscopic (i.e., absorbs moisture from the air).]	Filter; none; Grav; IV [Particulates NOR: #0500 (total), #0600 (resp)]
Glycidol C₃H₆O₂ 556-52-5 UB4375000	2,3-Epoxy-1-propanol; Epoxypropyl alcohol; Glycide; Hydroxymethyl ethylene oxide; 2-Hydroxymethyl oxiran; 3-Hydroxypropylene oxide 1 ppm = 3.03 mg/m³	NIOSH 25 ppm (75 mg/m³) OSHA† 50 ppm (150 mg/m³)	150 ppm	Colorless liquid.	MW: 74.1 BP: 320°F (Decomposes) Sol: Miscible Fl.P: 162°F IP: ? Sp.Gr: 1.12 Class IIIA Combustible Liquid	VP(77°F): 0.9 mm FRZ: -49°F UEL: ? LEL: ?	Strong oxidizers, nitrates	Char; THF; GC/FID; IV [#1608]
Glycolonitrile HOCH₂CN 107-16-4 AM0350000	Cyanomethanol; Formaldehyde cyanohydrin; Glycolic nitrile; Glyconitrile; Hydroxyacetonitrile 1 ppm = 2.34 mg/m³	NIOSH C 2 ppm (5 mg/m³) [15-min] OSHA none	N.D.	Colorless, odorless, oily liquid. [Note: Forms cyanide in the body.]	MW: 57.1 BP: 361°F (Decomposes) Sol: Soluble Fl.P: ? IP: ? Sp.Gr(66°F): 1.10 Combustible Liquid	VP(145°F): 1 mm FRZ: <-98°F UEL: ? LEL: ?	Traces of alkalis (promote violent polymerization)	None available

Personal protection and sanitation (See Table 3)		Recommendations for respirator selection — maximum concentration for use (MUC) (See Table 4)	Health hazards				
			Route	Symptoms (See Table 5)	First aid (See Table 6)		Target organs (See Table 5)
Skin:	Prevent skin contact	TBAL	Inh	Irrit eyes, skin, resp sys;	Eye:	Irr immed	Eyes, skin, resp sys
Eyes:	Prevent eye contact		Abs	derm, sens skin; cough,	Skin:	Water flush immed	
Wash skin:	When contam		Ing	asthma; nau, vomit	Breath:	Resp support	
Remove:	When wet or contam		Con		Swallow:	Medical attention immed	
Change:	N.R.						
Provide:	Eyewash, Quick drench						

[Glutaraldehyde]

Personal protection and sanitation		MUC					
Skin:	N.R.	TBAL	Inh	Irrit eyes, skin, resp sys;	Eye:	Irr immed	Eyes, skin, resp sys,
Eyes:	N.R.		Con	head, nau, vomit; kidney inj	Skin:	Water wash	kidneys
Wash skin:	N.R.				Breath:	Fresh air	
Remove:	N.R.						
Change:	N.R.						

[Glycerin (mist)]

Personal protection and sanitation		MUC					
Skin:	Prevent skin contact	NIOSH	Inh	Irrit eyes, skin, nose,	Eye:	Irr immed	Eyes, resp sys,
Eyes:	Prevent eye contact	150 ppm: SA*/SCBAF	Ing	throat; narco	Skin:	Water wash prompt	CNS
Wash skin:	When contam	§: SCBAF:PD,PP/SAF:PD,PP:ASCBA	Con		Breath:	Resp support	
Remove:	When wet or contam	Escape: GMFOV/SCBAE			Swallow:	Medical attention immed	
Change:	N.R.						

[Glycidol]

Personal protection and sanitation		MUC					
Skin:	Prevent skin contact	NIOSH	Inh	Irrit eyes, skin, resp sys;	Eye:	Irr immed	Eyes, skin, resp sys,
Eyes:	Prevent eye contact	20 ppm: SA	Abs	head, dizz, weak, gidd,	Skin:	Water wash immed	CNS, CVS
Wash skin:	When contam	50 ppm: SA:CF	Ing	conf, convuls; dysp; abdom	Breath:	Resp support	
Remove:	When wet or contam	100 ppm: SCBAF/SAF	Con	pain, nau, vomit	Swallow:	Medical attention immed	
Change:	Daily	250 ppm: SAF:PD,PP					
Provide:	Eyewash, Quick drench	§: SCBAF:PD,PP/SAF:PD,PP:ASCBA					
		Escape: GMFOV/SCBAE					

[Glycolonitrile]

Chemical name, structure/formula, CAS and RTECS Nos., and DOT ID and guide Nos.	Synonyms, trade names, and conversion factors	Exposure limits (TWA unless noted otherwise)	IDLH	Physical description	Chemical and physical properties		Incompatibilities and reactivities	Measurement method (See Table 1)
					MW, BP, SOL FI.P, IP, Sp, Gr, flammability	VP, FRZ UEL, LEL		
Grain dust (oat, wheat, barley) MD7900000	None [Note: Grain dust consists of 60-75% organic materials (cereal grains) & 25-40% inorganic materials (soil), and includes fertilizers, pesticides & microorganisms.]	NIOSH 4 mg/m³ OSHA 10 mg/m³	N.D.	Mixture of grain and all the other substances associated with its cultivation & harvesting.	Properties depend upon the specific component of the grain dust.		None reported	Filter; none; Grav; IV [#0500, Particulates NOR (total)]
Graphite (natural) C 7782-42-5 MD9659600	Black lead, Mineral carbon, Plumbago, Silver graphite, Stove black [Note: Also see specific listing for Graphite (synthetic).]	NIOSH 2.5 mg/m³ (resp) OSHA† 15 mppcf	1250 mg/m³	Steel gray to black, greasy feeling, odorless solid.	MW: 12.0 BP: Sublimes Sol: Insoluble FI.P: NA IP: NA Sp.Gr: 2.0-2.25 Combustible Solid	VP: 0 mm (approx) MLT: 6602°F (Sublimes) UEL: NA LEL: NA	Very strong oxidizers such as fluorine, chlorine trifluoride & potassium peroxide	Filter; none; Grav; IV [Particulates NOR: #0500 (total), #0600 (resp)]
Graphite (synthetic) C 7440-44-0 FF5250100 1362 133 (carbon, activated)	Activated carbon [Note: Also see specific listing for Graphite (natural).]	NIOSH See Appendix D OSHA† 15 mg/m³ (total) 5 mg/m³ (resp)	N.D.	Steel gray to black, greasy feeling, odorless solid.	MW: 12.0 BP: Sublimes Sol: Insoluble FI.P: NA IP: NA Sp.Gr: 1.5-1.8 Combustible Solid	VP: 0 mm (approx) MLT: 6602°F (Sublimes) UEL: NA LEL: NA	Very strong oxidizers such as fluorine, chlorine trifluoride & potassium peroxide	Filter; none; Grav; IV [Particulates NOR: #0500 (total), #0600 (resp)]
Gypsum CaSO₄•2H₂O 13397-24-5 MG2360000	Calcium(II) sulfate dihydrate, Gypsum stone, Hydrated calcium sulfate, Mineral white [Note: Gypsum is the dihydrate form of calcium sulfate; Plaster of Paris is the hemihydrate form.]	NIOSH 10 mg/m³ (total) 5 mg/m³ (resp) OSHA 15 mg/m³ (total) 5 mg/m³ (resp)	N.D.	White or nearly white, odorless, crystalline solid.	MW: 172.2 BP: ? Sol(77°F): 0.2% FI.P: NA IP: NA Sp.Gr: 2.32 Noncombustible Solid	VP: 0 mm (approx) MLT: 262-325°F (Loses H₂O) UEL: NA LEL: NA	Aluminum (at high temperatures), diazomethane	Filter; none; Grav; IV [Particulates NOR: #0500 (total), #0600 (resp)]

Personal protection and sanitation (See Table 3)	Recommendations for respirator selection — maximum concentration for use (MUC) (See Table 4)	Health hazards			
		Route	Symptoms (See Table 5)	First aid (See Table 6)	Target organs (See Table 5)
Skin: N.R. Eyes: N.R. Wash skin: N.R. Remove: N.R. Change: Daily	TBAL	Inh Con	Irrit eyes, skin, upper resp sys; cough, dysp, wheez, asthma, bron, chronic obstructive pulm disease; conj, derm, rhinitis, grain fever	Eye: Irr immed Breath: Fresh air	Eyes, skin, resp sys

[Grain dust (oat, wheat, barley)]

Personal protection and sanitation (See Table 3)	Recommendations for respirator selection — maximum concentration for use (MUC) (See Table 4)	Health hazards			
Skin: N.R. Eyes: N.R. Wash skin: N.R. Remove: N.R. Change: N.R.	NIOSH 12.5 mg/m^3: D 25 mg/m^3: DXSQ/SA 62.5 mg/m^3: PAPRD/SA:CF 125 mg/m^3: HiEF/PAPRTHiE/SAT:CF/ SCBAF/SAF 1250 mg/m^3: SAF:PD,PP §: SCBAF:PD,PP/SAF:PD,PP:ASCBA Escape: HiEF/SCBAE	Inh Con	Cough, dysp, black sputum, decr pulm func, lung fib	Eye: Irr immed Breath: Fresh air	Resp sys, CVS

[Graphite (natural)]

Skin: N.R. Eyes: N.R. Wash skin: N.R. Remove: N.R. Change: N.R.	TBAL	Inh Con	Cough, dysp, black sputum, decr pulm func, lung fib	Eye: Irr immed Breath: Fresh air	Resp sys, CVS

[Graphite (synthetic)]

Skin: N.R. Eyes: N.R. Wash skin: N.R. Remove: N.R. Change: N.R.	TBAL	Inh Con	Irrit eyes, skin, muc memb; upper resp sys; cough, sneez, rhin	Eye: Irr immed Breath: Fresh air	Eyes, skin, resp sys

[Gypsum]

Chemical name, structure/formula, CAS and RTECS Nos., and DOT ID and guide Nos.	Synonyms, trade names, and conversion factors	Exposure limits (TWA unless noted otherwise)	IDLH	Physical description	Chemical and physical properties		Incompatibilities and reactivities	Measurement method (See Table 1)
					MW, BP, SOL Fl.P, IP, Sp, Gr, flammability	VP, FRZ UEL, LEL		
Hafnium Hf 7440-58-6 MG4600000 1326 170 (powder, wet) 2545 135 (powder, dry)	Celtium, Elemental hafnium, Hafnium metal	NIOSH*/OSHA* 0.5 mg/m³ [*Note: The REL and PEL also apply to other hafnium compounds (as Hf).]	50 mg/m³ (as Hf)	Highly lustrous, ductile, grayish solid.	MW: 178.5 BP: 8316°F Sol: Insoluble Fl.P: NA IP: NA Sp.Gr. 13.31 Explosive in powder form (either dry or with <25% water); finely divided powder can be ignited by static electricity or even SPONTANEOUSLY.	VP: 0 mm (approx) MLT: 4041°F UEL: NA LEL: NA	Strong oxidizers, chlorine	Filter; Acid; PES; II(5) [#S194]
Halothane CF₃CHBrCl 151-67-7 KH6550000	1-Bromo-1-chloro-2,2,2-trifluoroethane; 2-Bromo-2-chloro-1,1,1-trifluoroethane; 1,1,1-Trifluoro-2-bromo-2-chloroethane; 2,2,2-Trifluoro-1-bromo-1-chloroethane 1 ppm = 8.07 mg/m³	NIOSH* C 2 ppm (16.2 mg/m³) [60-min] [*Note: REL for exposure to waste anesthetic gas.] OSHA none	N.D.	Clear, colorless liquid with a sweetish, pleasant odor. [inhalation anesthetic] [Note: May be stabilized with 0.01% thymol.]	MW: 197.4 BP: 122°F Sol: 0.3% Fl.P: NA IP: ? Sp.Gr. 1.87 Noncombustible Liquid	VP: 243 mm FRZ: -180°F UEL: NA LEL: NA	May attack rubber & some plastics; sensitive to light.	Char(2); CS₂; GC/FID; OSHA [#29]
Heptachlor C₁₀H₅Cl₇ 76-44-8 PC0700000 2761 151 (organochlorine pesticide, solid)	1,4,5,6,7,8,8-Heptachloro-3a,4,7,7a-tetrahydro-4,7-methanoindene	NIOSH Ca See Appendix A 0.5 mg/m³ [skin] OSHA 0.5 mg/m³ [skin]	Ca [35 mg/m³]	White to light tan crystals with a camphor-like odor. [insecticide]	MW: 373.4 BP: 293°F (Decomposes) Sol: 0.0006% Fl.P: NA IP: ? Sp.Gr. 1.66 Noncombustible Solid, but may be dissolved in flammable liquids.	VP(77°F): 0.0003 mm MLT: 203°F UEL: NA LEL: NA	Iron, rust	Chrom-102; Toluene; GC/ECD; II(5) [#S287]
n-Heptane CH₃[CH₂]₅CH₃ 142-82-5 MI7700000 1206 128	Heptane, normal-Heptane 1 ppm = 4.10 mg/m³	NIOSH 85 ppm (350 mg/m³) C 440 ppm (1800 mg/m³) [15-min] OSHA† 500 ppm (2000 mg/m³)	750 ppm	Colorless liquid with a gasoline-like odor.	MW: 100.2 BP: 209°F Sol: 0.0003% Fl.P: 25°F IP: 9.90 eV Sp.Gr. 0.68 Class IB Flammable Liquid	VP(72°F): 40 mm FRZ: -131°F UEL: 6.7% LEL: 1.05%	Strong oxidizers	Char; CS₂; GC/FID; IV [#1500; Hydro-carbons]

Personal protection and sanitation (See Table 3)		Recommendations for respirator selection — maximum concentration for use (MUC) (See Table 4)	Health hazards			
			Route	Symptoms (See Table 5)	First aid (See Table 6)	Target organs (See Table 5)
Skin: Eyes: Wash skin: Remove: Change: Provide:	Prevent skin contact Prevent eye contact When contam/Daily When wet or contam Daily Eyewash, Quick drench	NIOSH/OSHA 2.5 mg/m³: DM 5 mg/m³: DMXSQ/SA 12.5 mg/m³: SA:CF*/PAPRDM* 25 mg/m³: HiEF/SAT:CF*/PAPRTHiE*/ SCBAF/SAF 50 mg/m³: SAF:PD,PP §: SCBAF:PD,PP/SAF:PD,PP:ASCBA Escape: HiEF/SCBAE	Inh Ing Con	In animals: irrit eyes, skin, muc memb; liver damage	Eye: Skin: Breath: Swallow:	Irr immed Soap wash prompt Resp support Medical attention immed	Eyes, skin, muc memb, liver
[Hafnium]						
Skin: Eyes: Wash skin: Remove: Change: Provide:	Prevent skin contact Prevent eye contact When contam When wet or contam N.R. Eyewash	TBAL	Inh Abs Ing Con	Irrit eyes, skin, resp sys; conf, drow, dizz, nau, analgesia, anes; card arrhy; liver, kidney damage; decr audio-visual performance; in animals: repro effects	Eye: Skin: Breath: Swallow:	Irr immed Soap wash prompt Resp support Medical attention immed	Eyes, skin, resp sys, CVS, CNS, liver, kidneys, repro sys
[Halothane]						
Skin: Eyes: Wash skin: Remove: Change: Provide:	Prevent skin contact Prevent eye contact When contam/Daily When wet or contam Daily Eyewash, Quick drench	NIOSH ¥: SCBAF:PD,PP/SAF:PD,PP:ASCBA Escape: GMFOVHiE/SCBAE	Inh Abs Ing Con	In animals: tremor, convuls; liver damage; [carc]	Eye: Skin: Breath: Swallow:	Irr immed Soap wash immed Resp support Medical attention immed	CNS, liver [in animals: liver cancer]
[Heptachlor]						
Skin: Eyes: Wash skin: Remove: Change:	Prevent skin contact Prevent eye contact When contam When wet (flamm) N.R.	NIOSH 750 ppm: CCROV/GMFOV/PAPROV/ SA/SCBAF §: SCBAF:PD,PP/SAF:PD,PP:ASCBA Escape: GMFOV/SCBAE	Inh Ing Con	Li-head, gidd, stupor, verti, inco; loss of appetite, nau; derm; chemical pneu (aspir liq); uncon	Eye: Skin: Breath: Swallow:	Irr immed Soap wash prompt Resp support Medical attention immed	Skin, resp sys, CNS
[n-Heptane]						

Chemical name, structure/formula, CAS and RTECS Nos., and DOT ID and guide Nos.	Synonyms, trade names, and conversion factors	Exposure limits (TWA unless noted otherwise)	IDLH	Physical description	Chemical and physical properties		Incompatibilities and reactivities	Measurement method (See Table 1)
					MW, BP, SOL Fl.P, IP, Sp, Gr, flammability	VP, FRZ UEL, LEL		
1-Heptanethiol CH₃[CH₂]₆SH 1639-09-4 MJ1400000 1228 131	Heptyl mercaptan, n-Heptyl mercaptan 1 ppm = 5.41 mg/m³	NIOSH C 0.5 ppm (2.7 mg/m³) [15-min] OSHA none	N.D.	Colorless liquid with a strong odor.	MW: 132.3 BP: 351°F Sol: Insoluble Fl.P: 115°F IP: ? Sp.Gr: 0.84 Class II Combustible Liquid	VP: ? FRZ: -46°F UEL: ? LEL: ?	Oxidizers, reducing agents, strong acids & bases, alkali metals	None available
Hexachlorobutadiene Cl₂C=CClCCl=CCl₂ 87-68-3 EJ0700000 2279 151	HCBD; Hexachloro-1,3-butadiene; 1,3-Hexachlorobutadiene; Perchlorobutadiene 1 ppm = 10.66 mg/m³	NIOSH Ca See Appendix A 0.02 ppm (0.24 mg/m³) [skin] OSHA† none	Ca [N.D.]	Clear, colorless liquid with a mild, turpentine-like odor.	MW: 260.7 BP: 419°F Sol: Insoluble Fl.P: ? IP: ? Sp.Gr: 1.55 Combustible Liquid	VP: 0.2 mm FRZ: -6°F UEL: ? LEL: ?	Oxidizers	XAD-2; Hexane; GC/ECD; IV [#2543]
Hexachlorocyclo-pentadiene C₅Cl₆ 77-47-4 GY1225000 2646 151	HCCPD; Hexachloro-1,3-cyclo-pentadiene; 1,2,3,4,5,5-Hexachloro-1,3-cyclopentadiene; Perchlorocyclopentadiene 1 ppm = 11.16 mg/m³	NIOSH 0.01 ppm (0.1 mg/m³) OSHA† none	N.D.	Pale-yellow to amber-colored liquid with a pungent, unpleasant odor. [Note: A solid below 16°F.]	MW: 272.8 BP: 462°F Sol(77°F): 0.0002% (Reacts) Fl.P: NA IP: ? Sp.Gr: 1.71 Noncombustible Liquid	VP(77°F): 0.08 mm FRZ: 16°F UEL: NA LEL: NA	Water, light [Note: Reacts slowly with water to form hydrochloric acid; will corrode iron & most metals in presence of moisture. Explosive hydrogen gas may collect in enclosed spaces in the presence of moisture.]	Porapak(2); Hexane; GC/ECD; IV [#2518]
Hexachloroethane Cl₃CCCl₃ 67-72-1 KI4025000 9037 151	Carbon hexachloride, Ethane hexachloride, Perchloroethane 1 ppm = 9.68 mg/m³	NIOSH Ca See Appendix A See Appendix C (Chloroethanes) 1 ppm (10 mg/m³) [skin] OSHA 1 ppm (10 mg/m³) [skin]	Ca [300 ppm]	Colorless crystals with a camphor-like odor.	MW: 236.7 BP: Sublimes Sol(72°F): 0.005% Fl.P: NA IP: 11.22 eV Sp.Gr: 2.09 Noncombustible Solid	VP: 0.2 mm MLT: 368°F (Sublimes) UEL: NA LEL: NA	Alkalis; metals such as zinc, cadmium, aluminum, hot iron & mercury	Char; CS₂; GC/FID; IV [#1003, Halogenated Hydrocarbons]

158

Personal protection and sanitation (See Table 3)	Recommendations for respirator selection — maximum concentration for use (MUC) (See Table 4)	Health hazards			
		Route	Symptoms (See Table 5)	First aid (See Table 6)	Target organs (See Table 5)
Skin: Prevent skin contact Eyes: Prevent eye contact Wash skin: When contam Remove: When wet or contam Change: N.R.	NIOSH 5 ppm: CCROV/SA 12.5 ppm: SA:CF/PAPROV 25 ppm: CCRFOV/GMFOV/PAPRTOV/ SCBAF/SAF §: SCBAF:PD,PP/SAF:PD,PP:ASCBA Escape: GMFOV/SCBAE	Inh Ing Con	Irrit eyes, skin, nose, throat; weak, cyan, incr respiration, nau, drow, head, vomit	Eye: Irr immed Skin: Soap wash Breath: Resp support Swallow: Medical attention immed	Eyes, skin, resp sys, CNS, blood

[1-Heptanethiol]

| Skin: Prevent skin contact
Eyes: Prevent eye contact
Wash skin: When contam
Remove: When wet or contam
Change: N.R.
Provide: Eyewash, Quick drench | NIOSH
¥: SCBAF:PD,PP/SAF:PD,PP:ASCBA
Escape: GMFOV/SCBAE | Inh
Abs
Ing
Con | In animals: irrit eyes, skin, resp sys; kidney damage; [carc] | Eye: Irr immed
Skin: Soap wash immed
Breath: Resp support
Swallow: Medical attention immed | Eyes, skin, resp sys, kidneys
[in animals: kidney tumors] |

159

[Hexachlorobutadiene]

| Skin: Prevent skin contact
Eyes: Prevent eye contact
Wash skin: When contam
Remove: When wet or contam
Change: N.R.
Provide: Eyewash, Quick drench | TBAL | Inh
Abs
Ing
Con | Irrit eyes, skin, resp sys; eye, skin burns; lac; sneez, cough, dysp, salv, pulm edema; nau, vomit, diarr; in animals: liver, kidney inj | Eye: Irr immed
Skin: Soap flush immed
Breath: Resp support
Swallow: Medical attention immed | Eyes, skin, resp sys, liver, kidneys |

[Hexachlorocyclopentadiene]

| Skin: Prevent skin contact
Eyes: Prevent eye contact
Wash skin: When contam/Daily
Remove: When wet or contam
Change: Daily
Provide: Eyewash, Quick drench | NIOSH
¥: SCBAF:PD,PP/SAF:PD,PP:ASCBA
Escape: GMFOV/SCBAE | Inh
Abs
Ing
Con | Irrit eyes, skin, muc memb; in animals: kidney damage; [carc] | Eye: Irr immed
Skin: Soap wash immed
Breath: Resp support
Swallow: Medical attention immed | Eyes, skin, resp sys, kidneys
[in animals: liver cancer] |

[Hexachloroethane]

Chemical name, structure/formula, CAS and RTECS Nos., and DOT ID and guide Nos.	Synonyms, trade names, and conversion factors	Exposure limits (TWA unless noted otherwise)	IDLH	Physical description	Chemical and physical properties		Incompatibilities and reactivities	Measurement method (See Table 1)
					MW, BP, SOL Fl.P, IP, Sp, Gr, flammability	VP, FRZ UEL, LEL		
Hexachloronaphthalene $C_{10}H_2Cl_6$ 1335-87-1 QJ7350000	Halowax® 1014	NIOSH/OSHA 0.2 mg/m³ [skin]	2 mg/m³	White to light-yellow solid with an aromatic odor.	MW: 334.9 BP: 650-730°F Sol: Insoluble Fl.P: NA IP: ? Sp.Gr: 1.78 Noncombustible Solid	VP: <1 mm MLT: 279°F UEL: NA LEL: NA	Strong oxidizers	Filter; Hexane; GC/ECD; II(2) [#S100]
1-Hexadecanethiol $CH_3[CH_2]_{15}SH$ 2917-26-2 1228 131 (liquid)	Cetyl mercaptan, Hexadecanethiol-1, n-Hexadecanethiol, Hexadecyl mercaptan	NIOSH C 0.5 ppm (5.3 mg/m³) [15-min] OSHA none 1 ppm = 10.59 mg/m³	N.D.	Colorless liquid or solid (below 64-68°F) with a strong odor.	MW: 258.5 BP: ? Sol: Insoluble Fl.P: 215°F IP: ? Sp.Gr: 0.85 Class IIIB Combustible Liquid	VP: 0.1 mm FRZ: 64-68°F UEL: ? LEL: ?	Oxidizers, strong acids & bases, alkali metals, reducing agents	None available
Hexafluoroacetone $(CF_3)_2CO$ 684-16-2 UC2450000 2420 125	Hexafluoro-2-propanone; 1,1,1,3,3,3-Hexafluoro-2-propanone; HFA; Perfluoroacetone	NIOSH 0.1 ppm (0.7 mg/m³) [skin] OSHA† none 1 ppm = 6.79 mg/m³	N.D.	Colorless gas with a musty odor. [Note: Shipped as a liquefied compressed gas.]	MW: 166.0 BP: -18°F Sol: Reacts Fl.P: NA IP: 11.81 eV RGasD: 5.76 Nonflammable Gas, but highly reactive with water & other substances, releasing heat.	VP: 5.8 atm FRZ: -188°F UEL: NA LEL: NA	Water, acids [Note: Hygroscopic (i.e., absorbs moisture from the air); reacts with moisture to form a highly acidic sesquihydrate.]	None available
Hexamethylene diisocyanate $OCN[CH_2]_6NCO$ 822-06-0 MO1740000 2281 156	1,6-Diisocyanatohexane; HDI; Hexamethylene-1,6-diisocyanate; 1,6-Hexamethylene diisocyanate; HMDI	NIOSH 0.005 ppm (35 µg/m³) C 0.020 ppm (140 µg/m³) [10-min] OSHA none 1 ppm = 6.88 mg/m³	N.D.	Clear, colorless to slightly yellow liquid with a sharp, pungent odor.	MW: 168.2 BP: 415°F Sol: Low (Reacts) Fl.P: 284°F IP: ? Sp.Gr(77°F): 1.04 Class IIIB Combustible Liquid	VP(77°F): 0.5 mm FRZ: -89°F UEL: ? LEL: ?	Water, alcohols, strong bases, amines, carboxylic acids, organotin catalysts [Note: Reacts slowly with water to form carbon dioxide. Avoid heating above 392°F (polymerizes).]	Imp; Reagent; HPLC/UVD; IV [#5522, Isocy-anates]

Personal protection and sanitation (See Table 3)	Recommendations for respirator selection — maximum concentration for use (MUC) (See Table 4)	Route	Symptoms (See Table 5)	First aid (See Table 6)	Target organs (See Table 5)
Skin: Prevent skin contact Eyes: Prevent eye contact Wash skin: When contam/Daily Remove: When wet or contam Change: Daily	NIOSH/OSHA 2 mg/m³: SA*/SCBAF §: SCBAF:PD,PP/SAF:PD,PP:ASCBA Escape: GMFOV/SCBAE	Inh Abs Ing Con	Acne-form derm, nau, conf, jaun, coma	Eye: Irr immed Skin: Soap wash prompt Breath: Resp support Swallow: Medical attention immed	Skin, liver

[Hexachloronaphthalene]

Skin: Prevent skin contact Eyes: Prevent eye contact Wash skin: When contam Remove: When wet or contam Change: Daily	NIOSH 5 ppm: CCROV/SA 12.5 ppm: SA:CF/PAPROV 25 ppm: CCRFOV/GMFOV/PAPRTOV/ SCBAF/SAF §: SCBAF:PD,PP/SAF:PD,PP:ASCBA Escape: GMFOV/SCBAE	Inh Abs Ing Con	Irrit eyes, resp sys; head, dizz, weak, cyan, nau, convuls	Eye: Irr immed Skin: Soap wash immed Breath: Resp support Swallow: Medical attention immed	Eyes, skin, resp sys, CNS, blood

161

[1-Hexadecanethiol]

Skin: Prevent skin contact/ Frostbite Eyes: Prevent eye contact/ Frostbite Wash skin: N.R. Remove: N.R. Change: N.R. Provide: Frostbite	TBAL	Inh Abs Con	Irrit eyes, skin, muc memb, resp sys; pulm edema; liq: frostbite; in animals: terato, repro effects, kidney inj	Eye: Frostbite Skin: Frostbite Breath: Resp support	Eyes, skin, resp sys, kidneys, repro sys

[Hexafluoroacetone]

Skin: Prevent skin contact Eyes: Prevent eye contact Wash skin: When contam Remove: When wet or contam Change: N.R. Provide: Eyewash, Quick drench	NIOSH 0.05 ppm: SA* 0.125 ppm: SA:CF* 0.25 ppm: SCBAF/SAF 1 ppm: SAF:PD,PP §: SCBAF:PD,PP/SAF:PD,PP:ASCBA Escape: GMFOV/SCBAE	Inh Ing Con	Irrit eyes, skin, resp sys; cough, dysp, bron, wneez, pulm edema, asthma; corn damage, skin blisters	Eye: Irr immed Skin: Soap flush immed Breath: Resp support Swallow: Medical attention immed	Eyes, skin, resp sys

[Hexamethylene diisocyanate]

Chemical name, structure/formula, CAS and RTECS Nos., and DOT ID and guide Nos.	Synonyms, trade names, and conversion factors	Exposure limits (TWA unless noted otherwise)	IDLH	Physical description	Chemical and physical properties		Incompatibilities and reactivities	Measurement method (See Table 1)
					MW, BP, SOL Fl.P, IP, Sp, Gr, flammability	VP, FRZ UEL, LEL		
Hexamethyl phosphoramide [(CH$_3$)$_2$N]$_3$PO 680-31-9 TD0875000	Hexamethylphosphoric triamide, Hexamethylphosphoro-triamide, HMPA, Tris(dimethylamino)-phosphine oxide	NIOSH Ca See Appendix A OSHA none	Ca [N.D.]	Clear, colorless liquid with an aromatic or mild, amine-like odor. [Note: A solid below 43°F.]	MW: 179.2 BP: 451°F Sol: Miscible Fl.P: 222°F IP: ? Sp.Gr: 1.03 Class IIIB Combustible Liquid	VP: 0.03 mm FRZ: 43°F UEL: ? LEL: ?	Oxidizers, strong acids, chemically-active metals (e.g., potassium, sodium, magnesium, zinc)	None available
n-Hexane CH$_3$[CH$_2$]$_4$CH$_3$ 110-54-3 MN9275000 1208 128	Hexane, Hexyl hydride, normal-Hexane 1 ppm = 3.53 mg/m^3	NIOSH 50 ppm (180 mg/m^3) OSHA† 500 ppm (1800 mg/m^3)	1100 ppm [10%LEL]	Colorless liquid with a gasoline-like odor.	MW: 86.2 BP: 156°F Sol: 0.002% Fl.P: -7°F IP: 10.18 eV Sp.Gr: 0.66 Class IB Flammable Liquid	VP: 124 mm FRZ: -219°F UEL: 7.5% LEL: 1.1%	Strong oxidizers	Char; CS$_2$; GC/FID; IV [#1500, Hydro-carbons]
Hexane isomers (excluding n-Hexane) C$_6$H$_{14}$ 1208 128	Diethylmethylmethane; Dllsopropyl; 2,2-Dimethylbutane; 2,3-Dimethylbutane; Isohexane; 2-Methylpentane; 3-Methylpentane; [Note: Also see specific listing for n-Hexane.] 1 ppm = 3.53 mg/m^3	NIOSH 100 ppm (350 mg/m^3) C 510 ppm (1800 mg/m^3) [15-min] OSHA† none	N.D.	Clear liquids with mild, gasoline-like odors. [Note: Includes all the isomers of hexane except n-hexane.]	MW: 86.2 BP: 122-145°F Sol: Insoluble Fl.P: -54 to 19°F IP: ? Sp.Gr: 0.65-0.66 Class IB Flammable Liquids	VP: ? FRZ: -245 to -148°F UEL: ? LEL: ?	Strong oxidizers	None available
n-Hexanethiol CH$_3$[CH$_2$]$_5$SH 111-31-9 MO4550000	1-Hexanethiol, Hexyl mercaptan, n-Hexyl mercaptan, n-Hexylthiol 1 ppm = 4.83 mg/m^3	NIOSH C 0.5 ppm (2.7 mg/m^3) [15-min] OSHA none	N.D.	Colorless liquid with an unpleasant odor.	MW: 118.2 BP: 304°F Sol: Insoluble Fl.P: 68°F IP: ? Sp.Gr: 0.84 Class IB Flammable Liquid	VP: ? FRZ: -113°F UEL: ? LEL: ?	Oxidizers, reducing agents, strong acids & bases, alkali metals	None available

	Personal protection and sanitation (See Table 3)	Recommendations for respirator selection — maximum concentration for use (MUC) (See Table 4)	Health hazards			
			Route	Symptoms (See Table 5)	First aid (See Table 6)	Target organs (See Table 5)
Skin:	Prevent skin contact	NIOSH	Inh	Irrit eyes, skin, resp sys;	Eye: Irr immed	Eyes, skin, resp sys,
Eyes:	Prevent eye contact	¥: SCBAF:PD,PP/SAF:PD,PP:ASCBA	Abs	dysp; abdom pain; [carc]	Skin: Water flush immed	CNS, GI tract
Wash skin:	When contam	Escape: GMFOV/SCBAE	Ing		Breath: Resp support	[in animals: cancer
Remove:	When wet or contam		Con		Swallow: Medical attention	of the nasal
Change:	N.R.				immed	cavity]
Provide:	Eyewash, Quick drench					

[Hexamethyl phosphoramide]

Skin:	Prevent skin contact	NIOSH	Inh	Irrit eyes, nose; li-head;	Eye: Irr immed	Eyes, skin, resp sys,
Eyes:	Prevent eye contact	500 ppm: SA*	Ing	nau, head; peri neur: numb	Skin: Soap wash immed	CNS, PNS
Wash skin:	When contam	1100 ppm: SA:CF*/SCBAF/SAF	Con	extremities, musc weak;	Breath: Resp support	
Remove:	When wet (flamm)	§: SCBAF:PD,PP/SAF:PD,PP:ASCBA		derm; gidd; chemical pneu	Swallow: Medical attention	
Change:	N.R.	Escape: GMFOV/SCBAE		(aspir liq)	immed	

[n-Hexane]

163

Skin:	Prevent skin contact	NIOSH	Inh	Irrit eyes, skin, resp sys;	Eye: Irr immed	Eyes, skin, resp sys,
Eyes:	Prevent eye contact	1000 ppm: SA*	Ing	head, gidd, dizz, li-head;	Skin: Soap wash immed	CNS
Wash skin:	When contam	2500 ppm: SA:CF*	Con	nau; chemical pneu (aspir	Breath: Resp support	
Remove:	When wet (flamm)	5000 ppm: SAT:CF*/SCBAF/SAF		liq); derm	Swallow: Medical attention	
Change:	N.R.	§: SCBAF:PD,PP/SAF:PD,PP:ASCBA			immed	
		Escape: GMFOV/SCBAE				

[Hexane isomers (excluding n-Hexane)]

Skin:	Prevent skin contact	NIOSH	Inh	Irrit eyes, skin, nose,	Eye: Irr immed	Eyes, skin, resp sys,
Eyes:	Prevent eye contact	5 ppm: CCROV/SA	Ing	throat; weak, cyan, incr	Skin: Soap wash immed	CNS, blood
Wash skin:	When contam	12.5 ppm: SA:CF/PAPROV	Con	respiration, nau, drow,	Breath: Resp support	
Remove:	When wet (flamm)	25 ppm: CCRFOV/GMFOV/PAPRTOV/		head, vomit	Swallow: Medical attention	
Change:	N.R.	SCBAF/SAF			immed	
		§: SCBAF:PD,PP/SAF:PD,PP:ASCBA				
		Escape: GMFOV/SCBAE				

[n-Hexanethiol]

Chemical name, structure/formula, CAS and RTECS Nos., and DOT ID and guide Nos.	Synonyms, trade names, and conversion factors	Exposure limits (TWA unless noted otherwise)	IDLH	Physical description	Chemical and physical properties		Incompatibilities and reactivities	Measurement method (See Table 1)
					MW, BP, SOL Fl.P, IP, Sp, Gr, flammability	VP, FRZ UEL, LEL		
2-Hexanone $CH_3CO[CH_2]_3CH_3$ 591-78-6 MP1400000 1 ppm = 4.10 mg/m³	Butyl methyl ketone, MBK, Methyl butyl ketone, Methyl n-butyl ketone	NIOSH 1 ppm (4 mg/m³) OSHA† 100 ppm (410 mg/m³)	1600 ppm	Colorless liquid with an acetone-like odor.	MW: 100.2 BP: 262°F Sol: 2% Fl.P: 77°F IP: 9.34 eV Sp.Gr: 0.81 Class IC Flammable Liquid	VP: 11 mm FRZ: -71°F UEL: 8% LEL: ?	Strong oxidizers	Char; CS₂; GC/FID; IV [#1300, Ketones I]
Hexone $CH_3COCH_2CH(CH_3)_2$ 108-10-1 SA9275000 1245 127 1 ppm = 4.10 mg/m³	Isobutyl methyl ketone, Methyl isobutyl ketone, 4-Methyl 2-pentanone, MIBK	NIOSH 50 ppm (205 mg/m³) ST 75 ppm (300 mg/m³) OSHA† 100 ppm (410 mg/m³)	500 ppm	Colorless liquid with a pleasant odor.	MW: 100.2 BP: 242°F Sol: 2% Fl.P: 64°F IP: 9.30 eV Sp.Gr: 0.80 Class IB Flammable Liquid	VP: 16 mm FRZ: -120°F UEL(200°F): 8.0% LEL(200°F): 1.2%	Strong oxidizers, potassium tert-butoxide	Char; CS₂; GC/FID; IV [#1300, Ketones I]
sec-Hexyl acetate $C_8H_{16}O_2$ 108-84-9 SA7525000 1233 129 1 ppm = 5.90 mg/m³	1,3-Dimethylbutyl acetate; Methylisoamyl acetate [CH₃COOCH(CH₃)CH₂CH(CH₃)₂]	NIOSH/OSHA 50 ppm (300 mg/m³)	500 ppm	Colorless liquid with a mild, pleasant, fruity odor.	MW: 144.2 BP: 297°F Sol: 0.08% Fl.P: 113°F IP: ? Sp.Gr: 0.86 Class II Combustible Liquid	VP: 3 mm FRZ: -83°F UEL: ? LEL: ?	Nitrates; strong oxidizers, alkalis & acids	Char; CS₂; GC/FID; IV [#1450, Esters I]
Hexylene glycol $(CH_3)_2COHCH_2CHOHCH_3$ 107-41-5 SA0810000 1 ppm = 4.83 mg/m³	2,4-Dihydroxy-2-methyl-pentane; 2-Methyl-2,4-pentanediol; 4-Methyl-2,4-pentanediol; 2-Methylpentane-2,4-diol	NIOSH C 25 ppm (125 mg/m³) OSHA† none	N.D.	Colorless liquid with a mild, sweetish odor.	MW: 118.2 BP: 388°F Sol: Miscible Fl.P: 209°F IP: ? Sp.Gr: 0.92 Class IIIB Combustible Liquid	VP: 0.05 mm FRZ: -58°F (Sets to glass) UEL(est): 7.4% LEL(calc): 1.3%	Strong oxidizers, strong acids [Note: Hygroscopic (i.e., absorbs moisture from the air).]	None available

Personal protection and sanitation (See Table 3)		Recommendations for respirator selection — maximum concentration for use (MUC) (See Table 4)	Health hazards				
			Route	Symptoms (See Table 5)	First aid (See Table 6)		Target organs (See Table 5)
Skin: Eyes: Wash skin: Remove: Change:	Prevent skin contact Prevent eye contact When contam When wet (flamm) N.R.	NIOSH 10 ppm: SA 25 ppm: SA:CF 50 ppm: SAT:CF/SCBAF/SAF 1600 ppm: SAF:PD,PP §: SCBAF:PD,PP/SAF:PD,PP:ASCBA Escape: GMFOV/SCBAE	Inh Abs Ing Con	Irrit eyes, nose; peri neur: weak, pares; derm; head, drow	Eye: Skin: Breath: Swallow:	Irr immed Soap wash immed Resp support Medical attention immed	Eyes, skin, resp sys, CNS, PNS
[2-Hexanone]							
Skin: Eyes: Wash skin: Remove: Change:	Prevent skin contact Prevent eye contact When contam When wet (flamm) N.R.	NIOSH 500 ppm: CCROV*/GMFOV/PAPROV*/ SA*/SCBAF §: SCBAF:PD,PP/SAF:PD,PP:ASCBA Escape: GMFOV/SCBAE	Inh Ing Con	Irrit eyes, skin, muc memb; head, narco, coma; derm; in animals: liver, kidney damage	Eye: Skin: Breath: Swallow:	Irr immed Water flush prompt Resp support Medical attention immed	Eyes, skin, resp sys CNS, liver, kidneys
[Hexone]							
Skin: Eyes: Wash skin: Remove: Change:	Prevent skin contact Prevent eye contact When contam When wet or contam N.R.	NIOSH/OSHA 500 ppm: CCROV*/GMFOV/PAPROV*/ SA*/SCBAF §: SCBAF:PD,PP/SAF:PD,PP:ASCBA Escape: GMFOV/SCBAE	Inh Ing Con	Irrit eyes, skin, nose, throat; head; in animals: narco	Eye: Skin: Breath: Swallow:	Irr immed Water flush prompt Resp support Medical attention immed	Eyes, skin, resp sys, CNS
[sec-Hexyl acetate]							
Skin: Eyes: Wash skin: Remove: Change: Provide:	Prevent skin contact Prevent eye contact When contam When wet or contam N.R. Eyewash	TBAL	Inh Ing Con	Irrit eyes, skin, resp sys; head, dizz, nau, inco, CNS depres; derm, skin sens	Eye: Skin: Breath: Swallow:	Irr immed Water wash immed Resp support Medical attention immed	Eyes, skin, resp sys, CNS
[Hexylene glycol]							

Chemical name, structure/formula, CAS and RTECS Nos., and DOT ID and guide Nos.	Synonyms, trade names, and conversion factors	Exposure limits (TWA unless noted otherwise)	IDLH	Physical description	Chemical and physical properties		Incompatibilities and reactivities	Measurement method (See Table 1)
					MW, BP, SOL FI.P, IP, Sp, Gr, flammability	VP, FRZ UEL, LEL		
Hydrazine H_2NNH_2 302-01-2 MU7175000 2029 132 (anhydrous) 3293 152 (<37% soln.) 2030 153 (37-64% soln.) 2029 132 (>64% soln.)	Diamine, Hydrazine (anhydrous), Hydrazine base 1 ppm = 1.31 mg/m³	NIOSH Ca See Appendix A C 0.03 ppm (0.04 mg/m³) [2-hr] OSHA† 1 ppm (1.3 mg/m³) [skin]	Ca [50 ppm]	Colorless, fuming, oily liquid with an ammonia-like odor. [Note: A solid below 36°F.]	MW: 32.1 BP: 236°F Sol: Miscible FI.P: 99°F IP: 8.93 eV Sp.Gr. 1.01 Class IC Flammable Liquid	VP: 10 mm FRZ: 36°F UEL: 98% LEL: 2.9%	Oxidizers, hydrogen peroxide, nitric acid, metallic oxides, acids [Note: Can ignite SPONTANEOUSLY on contact with oxidizers or porous materials such as earth, wood & cloth.]	Bub; Reagent; Vis; IV [#3503]
Hydrogenated terphenyls $(C_6H_n)_3$ 61788-32-7 WZ6535000	Hydrogenated diphenyl-benzenes, Hydrogenated phenyl-biphenyls, Hydrogenated triphenyls [Note: Complex mixture of terphenyl isomers that are partially hydrogenated.] 1 ppm = 12.19 mg/m³ (40% hydrogenated)	NIOSH 0.5 ppm (5 mg/m³) OSHA† none	N.D.	Clear, oily, pale-yellow liquids with a faint odor. [plasticizer/heat transfer media]	MW: 298 (40% hydro-genated) BP: 644°F (40%) Sol: Insoluble FI.P: 315°F(40%) IP: ? Sp.Gr(77°F): 1.003-1.009 (40% hydrogenated) Class IIIB Combustible Liquids	VP(77°F): 0.1 mm (40%) FRZ: ? UEL: ? LEL: ?	None reported [Note: When heated, irritating vapors will be released.]	None available
Hydrogen bromide HBr 10035-10-6 MW3850000 1048 125 (anhydrous) 1788 154 (solution)	Anhydrous hydrogen bromide; Aqueous hydrogen bromide (i.e., Hydrobromic acid) 1 ppm = 3.31 mg/m³	NIOSH C 3 ppm (10 mg/m³) OSHA† 3 ppm (10 mg/m³)	30 ppm	Colorless gas with a sharp, irritating odor. [Note: Shipped as a liquefied compressed gas. Often used in an aqueous solution.]	MW: 80.9 BP: -88°F Sol: 49% FI.P: NA IP: 11.62 eV RGasD: 2.81 Nonflammable Gas	VP: 20 atm FRZ: -124°F UEL: NA LEL: NA	Strong oxidizers, strong caustics, moisture, copper, brass, zinc [Note: Hydrobromic acid is highly corrosive to most metals.]	Si gel; NaHCO₃/ Na₂CO₃; IC; IV [#7903, Inorganic Acids]
Hydrogen chloride HCl 7647-01-0 MW4025000 1050 125 (anhydrous) 1789 157 (solution)	Anhydrous hydrogen chloride; Aqueous hydrogen chloride (i.e., Hydrochloric acid, Muriatic acid) [Note: Often used in an aqueous solution.] 1 ppm = 1.49 mg/m³	NIOSH/OSHA C 5 ppm (7 mg/m³)	50 ppm	Colorless to slightly yellow gas with a pungent, irritating odor. [Note: Shipped as a liquefied compressed gas.]	MW: 36.5 BP: -121°F Sol(86°F): 67% FI.P: NA IP: 12.74 eV RGasD: 1.27 Nonflammable Gas	VP: 40.5 atm FRZ: -174°F UEL: NA LEL: NA	Hydroxides, amines, alkalis, copper, brass, zinc [Note: Hydrochloric acid is highly corrosive to most metals.]	Si gel; NaHCO₃/ Na₂CO₃; IC; IV [#7903, Inorganic Acids]

Personal protection and sanitation (See Table 3)		Recommendations for respirator selection — maximum concentration for use (MUC) (See Table 4)	Health hazards			
			Route	Symptoms (See Table 5)	First aid (See Table 6)	Target organs (See Table 5)
Skin: Eyes: Wash skin: Remove: Change: Provide:	Prevent skin contact Prevent eye contact When contam When wet (flamm) N.R. Eyewash, Quick drench	NIOSH ¥: SCBAF:PD,PP/SAF:PD,PP:ASCBA Escape: SCBAE	Inh Abs Ing Con	Irrit eyes, skin, nose, throat; temporary blindness; dizz, nau; derm; eye, skin burns; in animals: bron, pulm edema; liver, kidney damage; convuls; [carc]	Eye: Skin: Breath: Swallow:	Irr immed Water flush immed Resp support Medical attention immed	Eyes, skin, resp sys CNS, liver, kidneys [in animals: tumors of the lungs, liver, blood vessels & intestine]
[Hydrazine]						
Skin: Eyes: Wash skin: Remove: Change:	Prevent skin contact Prevent eye contact When contam When wet or contam Daily	TBAL	Inh Ing Con	Irrit eyes, skin, resp sys; liver, kidney, hemato damage	Eye: Skin: Breath: Swallow:	Irr immed Soap wash immed Resp support Medical attention immed	Eyes, skin, resp sys, liver, kidneys, hemato sys
[Hydrogenated terphenyls]						
Skin: Eyes: Wash skin: Remove: Change: Provide:	Prevent skin contact (soln)/Frostbite Prevent eye contact (soln)/Frostbite When contam (soln) When wet or contam (soln) N.R. Eyewash (soln), Quick drench (soln), Frostbite	NIOSH/OSHA 30 ppm: SA:CF£/PAPRAG£/GMFAG/ SCBAF/SAF §: SCBAF:PD,PP/SAF:PD,PP:ASCBA Escape: GMFAG/SCBAE	Inh Ing (soln) Con	Irrit eyes, skin, nose, throat; soln: eye, skin burns; liq: frostbite	Eye: Skin: Breath: Swallow:	Irr immed (soln)/ Frostbite Water flush immed (soln)/Frostbite Resp support Medical attention immed (soln)	Eyes, skin, resp sys
[Hydrogen bromide]						
Skin: Eyes: Wash skin: Remove: Change: Provide:	Prevent skin contact (soln)/ Frostbite Prevent eye contact/Frostbite When contam (soln) When wet or contam N.R. Eyewash (soln), Quick drench (soln), Frostbite	NIOSH/OSHA 50 ppm: CCRS*/GMFS/PAPRS*/ SA*/SCBAF §: SCBAF:PD,PP/SAF:PD,PP:ASCBA Escape: GMFAG/SCBAE	Inh Ing (soln) Con	Irrit nose, throat, larynx; cough, choking; derm; soln: eye, skin burns; liq: frostbite; in animals: lar spasm; pulm edema	Eye: Skin: Breath: Swallow:	Irr immed (soln)/ Frostbite Water flush immed (soln)/Frostbite Resp support Medical attention immed (soln)	Eyes, skin, resp sys
[Hydrogen chloride]						

Chemical name, structure/formula, CAS and RTECS Nos., and DOT ID and guide Nos.	Synonyms, trade names, and conversion factors	Exposure limits (TWA unless noted otherwise)	IDLH	Physical description	Chemical and physical properties		Incompatibilities and reactivities	Measurement method (See Table 1)
					MW, BP, SOL Fl.P, IP, Sp.Gr, flammability	VP, FRZ UEL, LEL		
Hydrogen cyanide HCN 74-90-8 MW6825000 1051 117 (>20% soln.) 1051 117 (anhydrous) 1613 154 (<20% soln.)	Formonitrile, Hydrocyanic acid, Prussic acid 1 ppm = 1.10 mg/m³	NIOSH ST 4.7 ppm (5 mg/m³) [skin] OSHA† 10 ppm (11 mg/m³) [skin]	50 ppm	Colorless or pale-blue liquid or gas (above 78°F) with a bitter, almond-like odor. [Note: Often used as a 96% solution in water.]	MW: 27.0 BP: 78°F (96%) Sol: Miscible Fl.P: 0°F (96%) IP: 13.60 eV Sp.Gr: 0.69 Class IA Flammable Liquid Flammable Gas	VP: 630 mm FRZ: 7°F (96%) UEL: 40.0% LEL: 5.6%	Amines, oxidizers, acids, sodium hydroxide, calcium hydroxide, sodium carbonate, water, caustics, ammonia [Note: Can polymerize at 122-140°F.]	Soda lime; Water; Vis; IV [#6010]
Hydrogen fluoride (as F) HF 7664-39-3 MW7875000 1052 125 (anhydrous) 1790 157 (solution)	Anhydrous hydrogen fluoride; Aqueous hydrogen fluoride (i.e., Hydrofluoric acid); HF-A 1 ppm = 0.82 mg/m³	NIOSH 3 ppm (2.5 mg/m³) C 6 ppm (5 mg/m³) [15-min] OSHA† 3 ppm	30 ppm	Colorless gas or fuming liquid (below 67°F) with a strong, irritating odor. [Note: Shipped in cylinders.]	MW: 20.0 BP: 67°F Sol: Miscible Fl.P: NA IP: 15.98 eV RGasD: 1.86 Sp.Gr: 1.00 (Liquid at 67°F) Nonflammable Gas	VP: 783 mm FRZ: -118°F UEL: NA LEL: NA	Metals, water or steam [Note: Corrosive to metals. Will attack glass and concrete.]	Si gel*; NaHCO₃/ Na₂CO₃; IC; IV [#7903, Inorganic Acids] [Also #7902, #7906]
Hydrogen peroxide H₂O₂ 7722-84-1 MX0900000 2984 140 (8-20% soln.) 2014 140 (20-60% soln.) 2015 143 (>60% soln.)	High-strength hydrogen peroxide, Hydrogen dioxide, Hydrogen peroxide (aqueous), Hydroperoxide, Peroxide 1 ppm = 1.39 mg/m³	NIOSH/OSHA 1 ppm (1.4 mg/m³)	75 ppm	Colorless liquid with a slightly sharp odor. [Note: The pure compound is a crystalline solid below 12°F. Often used in an aqueous solution.]	MW: 34.0 BP: 286°F Sol: Miscible Fl.P: NA IP: 10.54 eV Sp.Gr: 1.39 Noncombustible Liquid, but a powerful oxidizer.	VP(86°F): 5mm FRZ: 12°F UEL: NA LEL: NA	Oxidizable materials, iron, copper, brass, bronze, chromium, zinc, lead, silver, manganese. [Note: Contact with combustible material may result in SPONTANEOUS combustion.]	Bub; TiOSO₄; Vis; OSHA [#ID126SG]
Hydrogen selenide H₂Se 7783-07-5 MX1050000 2202 117 (anhydrous)	Selenium dihydride, Selenium hydride 1 ppm = 3.31 mg/m³	NIOSH/OSHA 0.05 ppm (0.2 mg/m³)	1 ppm	Colorless gas with an odor resembling decayed horse radish. [Note: Shipped as a liquefied compressed gas.]	MW: 81.0 BP: -42°F Sol(73°F): 0.9% Fl.P: NA (Gas) IP: 9.88 eV RGasD: 2.80 Flammable Gas	VP(70°F): 9.5 atm FRZ: -87°F UEL: ? LEL: ?	Strong oxidizers, acids, water, halogenated hydrocarbons	None available

Personal protection and sanitation (See Table 3)		Recommendations for respirator selection — maximum concentration for use (MUC) (See Table 4)	Health hazards				
			Route	Symptoms (See Table 5)	First aid (See Table 6)		Target organs (See Table 5)
Skin:	Prevent skin contact	NIOSH	Inh	Asphy; weak, head, conf;	Eye:	Irr immed	CNS, CVS, thyroid,
Eyes:	Prevent eye contact	47 ppm: SA	Abs	nau, vomit; incr rate and	Skin:	Water flush immed	blood
Wash skin:	When contam	50 ppm: SA:CF/SCBAF/SAF	Ing	depth of respiration or	Breath:	Resp support	
Remove:	When wet (flamm)	§: SCBAF:PD,PP/SAF:PD,PP:ASCBA	Con	respiration slow and	Swallow:	Medical attention	
Change:	N.R.	Escape: GMFS/SCBAE		gasping; thyroid, blood		immed	
Provide:	Eyewash, Quick drench			changes			

[Hydrogen cyanide]

Skin:	Prevent skin contact (liq)	NIOSH/OSHA	Inh	Irrit eyes, skin, nose,	Eye:	Irr immed (soln/liq)	Eyes, skin, resp sys,
Eyes:	Prevent eye contact (liq)	30 ppm: CCRS*/PAPRS*/GMFS/	Abs	throat; pulm edema; eye,	Skin:	Water flush immed	bones
Wash skin:	When contam (liq)	SA*/SCBAF	(liq)	skin burns; rhinitis; bron;		(soln/liq)	
Remove:	When wet or contam (liq)	50 ppm: SA:CF*/SCBAF	Ing	bone changes	Breath:	Resp support	
Change:	N.R.	§: SCBAF:PD,PP/SAF:PD,PP:ASCBA	(soln)		Swallow:	Medical attention	
Provide:	Eyewash (liq), Quick drench (liq)	Escape: GMFS/SCBAE	Con			immed (soln)	

[Hydrogen fluoride (as F)]

Skin:	Prevent skin contact	NIOSH/OSHA	Inh	Irrit eyes, nose, throat;	Eye:	Irr immed	Eyes, skin, resp
Eyes:	Prevent eye contact	10 ppm: SA*	Ing	corn ulcer; eryt, vesic	Skin:	Water flush immed	sys
Wash skin:	When contam	25 ppm: SA:CF*	Con	skin; bleaching hair	Breath:	Resp support	
Remove:	When wet or contam	50 ppm: SCBAF/SAF			Swallow:	Medical attention	
Change:	N.R.	75 ppm: SAF:PD,PP				immed	
Provide:	Eyewash, Quick drench	§: SCBAF:PD,PP/SAF:PD,PP:ASCBA					
		Escape: GMFS/SCBAE					

[Hydrogen peroxide]

Skin:	Frostbite	NIOSH/OSHA	Inh	Irrit eyes, nose, throat;	Eye:	Frostbite	Eyes, resp sys, liver
Eyes:	Frostbite	0.5 ppm: SA	Con	nau, vomit, diarr; metallic	Skin:	Frostbite	
Wash skin:	N.R.	1 ppm: SA:CF*/SCBAF/SAF		taste, garlic breath; dizz,	Breath:	Resp support	
Remove:	When wet (flamm)	§: SCBAF:PD,PP/SAF:PD,PP:ASCBA		lass, ftg; liq: frostbite;			
Change:	N.R.	Escape: GMFS4/SCBAE		in animals: pneuitis; liver			
Provide:	Frostbite			damage			

[Hydrogen selenide]

169

Chemical name, structure/formula, CAS and RTECS Nos., and DOT ID and guide Nos.	Synonyms, trade names, and conversion factors	Exposure limits (TWA unless noted otherwise)	IDLH	Physical description	Chemical and physical properties		Incompatibilities and reactivities	Measurement method (See Table 1)
					MW, BP, SOL Fl.P, IP, Sp, Gr, flammability	VP, FRZ UEL, LEL		
Hydrogen sulfide H_2S 7783-06-4 MX1225000 1053 117	Hydrosulfuric acid, Sewer gas, Sulfuretted hydrogen 1 ppm = 1.40 mg/m³	NIOSH C 10 ppm (15 mg/m³) [10-min] OSHA† C 20 ppm 50 ppm (10-min max peak)	100 ppm	Colorless gas with a strong odor of rotten eggs. [Note: Sense of smell becomes rapidly fatigued & can NOT be relied upon to warn of the continuous presence of H_2S. Shipped as a liquefied compressed gas.]	MW: 34.1 BP: -77°F Sol: 0.4% Fl.P: NA (Gas) IP: 10.46 eV	VP: 17.6 atm FRZ: -122°F UEL: 44.0% LEL: 4.0% RGasD: 1.19 Flammable Gas	Strong oxidizers, strong nitric acid, metals	Char; NH_4OH/H_2O_2; IC; IV [#6013]
Hydroquinone $C_6H_4(OH)_2$ 123-31-9 MX3500000 2662 153	p-Benzenediol; 1,4-Benzenediol; Dihydroxybenzene; 1,4-Dihydroxybenzene; Quinol	NIOSH C 2 mg/m³ [15-min] OSHA 2 mg/m³	50 mg/m³	Light-tan, light-gray, or colorless crystals.	MW: 110.1 BP: 545°F Sol: 7% Fl.P: 329°F (Molten) IP: 7.95 eV Sp.Gr: 1.33 Combustible Solid; dust cloud may explode if ignited in an enclosed area.	VP: 0.00001 mm MLT: 338°F UEL: ? LEL: ?	Strong oxidizers, alkalis	Filter; CH_3COOH; HPLC/UVD; IV [#5004]
2-Hydroxypropyl acrylate $CH_2=CHCOOCH_2CHOHCH_3$ 999-61-1 AT1925000	HPA, ß-Hydroxypropyl acrylate, Propylene glycol monoacrylate 1 ppm = 5.33 mg/m³	NIOSH 0.5 ppm (3 mg/m³) [skin] OSHA† none	N.D.	Clear to light-yellow liquid with a sweetish, solvent odor.	MW: 130.2 BP: 376°F Sol: ? Fl.P: 149°F IP: ? Sp.Gr: 1.05 Class IIIA Combustible Liquid	VP: ? FRZ: ? UEL: ? LEL: 1.8%	Water [Note: Can become unstable at high temperatures & pressures or may react with water with some release of energy, but not violently.]	None available
Indene C_9H_8 95-13-6 NK8225000	Indonaphthene 1 ppm = 4.75 mg/m³	NIOSH 10 ppm (45 mg/m³) OSHA† none	N.D.	Colorless liquid. [Note: A solid below 29°F.]	MW: 116.2 BP: 359°F Sol: Insoluble Fl.P: 173°F IP: 8.81 eV Sp.Gr: 0.997 Class IIIA Combustible Liquid	VP: ? FRZ: 29°F UEL: ? LEL: ?	None reported [Note: Polymerizes & oxidizes on standing. It has exploded during nitration with (H_2SO_4 + HNO_3).]	None available

Personal protection and sanitation (See Table 3)	Recommendations for respirator selection — maximum concentration for use (MUC) (See Table 4)	Route	Symptoms (See Table 5)	First aid (See Table 6)	Target organs (See Table 5)
Skin: Frostbite Eyes: Frostbite Wash skin: N.R. Remove: When wet (flamm) Change: N.R. Provide: Frostbite	NIOSH 100 ppm: PAPRS/GMFS/SA*/SCBAF §: SCBAF:PD,PP/SAF:PD,PP:ASCBA Escape: GMFS/SCBAE	Inh Con	Irrit eyes, resp sys; apnea, coma, convuls; conj, eye pain, lac, photo, corn vesic; dizz, head, ftg, irrity, insom; GI dist	Eye: Frostbite Skin: Frostbite Breath: Resp support	Eyes, resp sys, CNS

[Hydrogen sulfide]

Personal protection and sanitation (See Table 3)	Recommendations for respirator selection — maximum concentration for use (MUC) (See Table 4)	Route	Symptoms (See Table 5)	First aid (See Table 6)	Target organs (See Table 5)
Skin: Prevent skin contact Eyes: Prevent eye contact Wash skin: When contam Remove: When wet or contam Change: Daily Provide: Eyewash (>7%)	NIOSH/OSHA 50 mg/m³: PAPRD£/HiEF/SAT:CF£/ SCBAF/SAF §: SCBAF:PD,PP/SAF:PD,PP:ASCBA Escape: HiEF/SCBAE	Inh Ing Con	Irrit eyes, conj, kera; CNS excitement; colored urine, nau, dizz, suffocation, rapid breath; musc twitch, delirium; collapse; skin irrit, sens, derm	Eye: Irr immed Skin: Water flush Breath: Resp support Swallow: Medical attention immed	Eyes, skin, resp sys, CNS

[Hydroquinone]

Personal protection and sanitation (See Table 3)	Recommendations for respirator selection — maximum concentration for use (MUC) (See Table 4)	Route	Symptoms (See Table 5)	First aid (See Table 6)	Target organs (See Table 5)
Skin: Prevent skin contact Eyes: Prevent eye contact Wash skin: When contam Remove: When wet or contam Change: N.R. Provide: Eyewash, Quick drench	TBAL	Inh Abs Ing Con	Irrit eyes, skin, resp sys; eye, skin burns; cough, dysp	Eye: Irr immed Skin: Soap flush immed Breath: Resp support Swallow: Medical attention immed	Eyes, skin, resp sys

[2-Hydroxypropyl acrylate]

Personal protection and sanitation (See Table 3)	Recommendations for respirator selection — maximum concentration for use (MUC) (See Table 4)	Route	Symptoms (See Table 5)	First aid (See Table 6)	Target organs (See Table 5)
Skin: Prevent skin contact Eyes: Prevent eye contact Wash skin: Daily Remove: When wet or contam Change: N.R.	TBAL	Inh Ing Con	In animals: irrit eyes, skin, muc memb; derm, skin sens; chemical pneu (aspir liq); liver, kidney, spleen inj	Eye: Irr immed Skin: Soap wash Breath: Resp support Swallow: Medical attention immed	Eyes, skin, resp sys, liver, kidneys, spleen

[Indene]

Chemical name, structure/formula, CAS and RTECS Nos., and DOT ID and guide Nos.	Synonyms, trade names, and conversion factors	Exposure limits (TWA unless noted otherwise)	IDLH	Physical description	Chemical and physical properties		Incompatibilities and reactivities	Measurement method (See Table 1)
					MW, BP, SOL Fl.P, IP, Sp, Gr, flammability	VP, FRZ UEL, LEL		
Indium In 7440-74-6 NL1050000	Indium metal	NIOSH* 0.1 mg/m³ [*Note: The REL also applies to other Indium compounds (as In).] OSHA† none	N.D.	Ductile, shiny, silver-white metal that is softer than lead.	MW: 114.8 BP: 3767°F Sol: Insoluble Fl.P: NA IP: NA Sp.Gr: 7.31 Noncombustible Solid in bulk form, but may ignite in powdered or dust form.	VP: 0 mm (approx) MLT: 314°F UEL: NA LEL: NA	(Dinitrogen tetraoxide + acetonitrile), mercury(II) bromide (at 662°F), sulfur (mixtures ignite when heated) [Note: oxidizes readily at higher temperatures.]	Filter; Acid; FAA; II(5) [P&CAM #173]
Iodine I₂ 7553-56-2 NN1575000 1 ppm = 10.38 mg/m³	Iodine crystals, Molecular iodine	NIOSH/OSHA C 0.1 ppm (1 mg/m³)	2 ppm	Violet solid with a sharp, characteristic odor.	MW: 253.8 BP: 365°F Sol: 0.01% Fl.P: NA IP: 9.31 eV Sp.Gr: 4.93 Noncombustible Solid	VP(77°F): 0.3 mm MLT: 236°F UEL: NA LEL: NA	Ammonia, acetylene, acetaldehyde, powdered aluminum, active metals, liquid chlorine	Char*; Na₂CO₃; IC; IV [#6005]
Iodoform CHI₃ 75-47-8 PB7000000 1 ppm = 16.10 mg/m³	Triiodomethane	NIOSH 0.6 ppm (10 mg/m³) OSHA† none	N.D.	Yellow to greenish-yellow powder or crystalline solid with a pungent, disagreeable odor. [antiseptic for external use]	MW: 393.7 BP: 410°F (Decomposes) Sol: 0.01% Fl.P: NA IP: ? Sp.Gr: 4.01 Noncombustible Solid	VP: ? MLT: 246°F UEL: NA LEL: NA	Strong oxidizers, lithium, metallic salts (e.g., mercuric oxide, silver nitrate), strong bases, calomel, tannin	None available
Iron oxide dust and fume (as Fe) Fe₂O₃ 1309-37-1 NO7400000 NO7525000 (fume) 1376 135 (spent)	Ferric oxide, Iron(III) oxide	NIOSH 5 mg/m³ OSHA 10 mg/m³	2500 mg/m³ (as Fe)	Reddish-brown solid. [Note: Exposure to fume may occur during the arc-welding of iron.]	MW: 159.7 BP: ? Sol: Insoluble Fl.P: NA IP: NA Sp.Gr: 5.24 Noncombustible Solid	VP: 0 mm (approx) MLT: 2664°F UEL: NA LEL: NA	Calcium hypochlorite	Filter; Acid; ICP; IV [#7300, Elements]

Personal protection and sanitation (See Table 3)		Recommendations for respirator selection — maximum concentration for use (MUC) (See Table 4)	Health hazards				
			Route	Symptoms (See Table 5)	First aid (See Table 6)		Target organs (See Table 5)
Skin:	N.R.	TBAL	Inh	Irrit eyes, skin, resp	Eye:	Irr immed	Eyes, skin, resp sys,
Eyes:	N.R.		Ing	sys; possible liver,	Skin:	Soap wash	liver, kidneys
Wash skin:	N.R.		Con	kidney, heart, blood	Breath:	Resp support	heart, blood
Remove:	N.R.			effects; pulm edema	Swallow:	Medical attention	
Change:	N.R.					immed	

[Indium]

Skin:	Prevent skin contact	NIOSH/OSHA	Inh	Irrit eyes, skin, nose;	Eye:	Irr immed	Eyes, skin, resp sys,
Eyes:	Prevent eye contact	1 ppm: SA*	Ing	lac; head; chest tight;	Skin:	Soap wash immed	CNS, CVS
Wash skin:	When contam	2 ppm: SA:CF*/SCBAF/SAF	Con	skin burns, rash;	Breath:	Resp support	
Remove:	When wet or contam	§: SCBAF:PD,PP/SAF:PD,PP:ASCBA		cutaneous hypersensitivity	Swallow:	Medical attention	
Change:	Daily	Escape: GMFAGHiE/SCBAE				immed	
Provide:	Eyewash (>7%), Quick drench (>7%)						

[Iodine]

173

Skin:	Prevent skin contact	TBAL	Inh	Irrit eyes, skin; li-head,	Eye:	Irr immed	Eyes, skin, resp sys,
Eyes:	Prevent eye contact		Abs	dizz, nau, inco, CNS	Skin:	Soap wash immed	liver, kidneys,
Wash skin:	When contam		Ing	depres; dysp; liver,	Breath:	Resp support	heart
Remove:	When wet or contam		Con	kidney, heart damage;	Swallow:	Medical attention	
Change:	Daily			vis dist		immed	

[Iodoform]

Skin:	N.R.	NIOSH	Inh	Benign pneumoconiosis	Breath:	Resp support	Resp sys
Eyes:	N.R.	50 mg/m³: DMFu/SA		with X-ray shadows			
Wash skin:	N.R.	125 mg/m³: SA:CF/PAPRDMFu		indistinguishable from			
Remove:	N.R.	250 mg/m³: HiEF/SAT:CF/PAPRTHiE/ SCBAF/SAF		fibrotic pneumoconiosis (siderosis)			
Change:	N.R.	2500 mg/m³: SA:PD,PP					
		§: SCBAF:PD,PP/SAF:PD,PP:ASCBA					
		Escape: HiEF/SCBAE					

[Iron oxide dust and fume (as Fe)]

Chemical name, structure/formula, CAS and RTECS Nos., and DOT ID and guide Nos.	Synonyms, trade names, and conversion factors	Exposure limits (TWA unless noted otherwise)	IDLH	Physical description	Chemical and physical properties		Incompatibilities and reactivities	Measurement method (See Table 1)
					MW, BP, SOL Fl.P, IP, Sp.Gr, flammability	VP, FRZ UEL, LEL		
Iron pentacarbonyl (as Fe) Fe(CO)$_5$ 13463-40-6 NO4900000 1994 131	Iron carbonyl, Pentacarbonyl iron 1 ppm = 2.28 mg/m^3 (as Fe)	NIOSH 0.1 ppm (0.23 mg/m^3) ST 0.2 ppm (0.45 mg/m^3) OSHA† none	N.D.	Colorless to yellow to dark-red, oily liquid.	MW: 195.9 BP(749 mm): 217°F Sol: Insoluble Fl.P: 5°F IP: ? Sp.Gr: 1.46-1.52 Class IB Flammable Liquid	VP(87°F): 40 mm FRZ: -6°F UEL: ? LEL: ?	Oxidizers, nitrogen oxide, (zinc + cobalt halides) [Note: Pyrophoric (i.e., ignites spontaneously in air). Decomposed by light or air, releasing carbon monoxide.]	None available
Iron salts (soluble, as Fe)	FeSO$_4$: Ferrous sulfate, Iron(II) sulfate FeCl$_2$: Ferrous chloride, Iron(II) chloride Fe(NO$_3$)$_3$: Ferric nitrate, Iron(III) nitrate Fe(SO$_4$)$_3$: Ferric sulfate, Iron(III) sulfate FeCl$_3$: Ferric chloride, Iron(III) chloride	NIOSH 1 mg/m^3 OSHA† none	N.D.	Appearance and odor vary depending upon the specific soluble iron salt.	Properties vary depending upon the specific soluble iron salt. Noncombustible Solids		Varies	Filter; Acid; ICP; IV [#7300, Elements]
Isoamyl acetate CH$_3$COOCH$_2$CH$_2$CH(CH$_3$)$_2$ 123-92-2 NS9800000 1 ppm = 5.33 mg/m^3	Banana oil, Isopentyl acetate, 3-Methyl-1-butanol acetate, 3-Methylbutyl ester of acetic acid, 3-Methylbutyl ethanoate	NIOSH/OSHA 100 ppm (525 mg/m^3)	1000 ppm	Colorless liquid with a banana-like odor.	MW: 130.2 BP: 288°F Sol: 0.3% Fl.P: 77°F IP: ? Sp.Gr: 0.87 Class IC Flammable Liquid	VP: 4 mm FRZ: -109°F UEL:7.5% LEL(212°F): 1.0%	Nitrates; strong oxidizers, alkalis & acids	Char; CS$_2$; GC/FID; IV [#1450, Esters I]
Isoamyl alcohol (primary) (CH$_3$)$_2$CHCH$_2$CH$_2$OH 123-51-3 EL5425000 1105 129	Fermentation amyl alcohol, Fusel oil, Isobutyl carbinol, Isopentyl alcohol, 3-Methyl-1-butanol, Primary isoamyl alcohol 1 ppm = 3.61 mg/m^3	NIOSH 100 ppm (360 mg/m^3) ST 125 ppm (450 mg/m^3) OSHA† 100 ppm (360 mg/m^3)	500 ppm	Colorless liquid with a disagreeable odor.	MW: 88.2 BP: 270°F Sol(57°F): 2% Fl.P: 109°F IP: ? Sp.Gr(57°F): 0.81 Class II Combustible Liquid	VP: 28 mm FRZ: -179°F UEL(212°F): 9.0% LEL:1.2%	Strong oxidizers	Char; 2-Propanol/ CS$_2$; GC/FID; IV [#1402, Alcohols III]

Personal protection and sanitation (See Table 3)		Recommendations for respirator selection — maximum concentration for use (MUC) (See Table 4)	Health hazards				
			Route	Symptoms (See Table 5)	First aid (See Table 6)		Target organs (See Table 5)
Skin:	Prevent skin contact	TBAL	Inh	Irrit eyes, muc memb, resp	Eye:	Irr immed	Eyes, resp sys, CNS,
Eyes:	Prevent eye contact		Abs	sys; head, dizz, nau,	Skin:	Soap flush immed	liver, kidneys
Wash skin:	When contam		Ing	vomit; fever, cyan, cough,	Breath:	Resp support	
Remove:	When wet (flamm)		Con	dysp; liver, kidney, lung	Swallow:	Medical attention	
Change:	N.R.			inj; degenerative changes		immed	
Provide:	Quick drench			in CNS			

[Iron pentacarbonyl (as Fe)]

Skin:	Prevent skin contact	TBAL	Inh	Irrit eyes, skin, muc memb;	Eye:	Irr immed	Eyes, skin, resp sys,
Eyes:	Prevent eye contact		Ing	abdom pain, diarr, vomit;	Skin:	Soap wash	liver, GI tract
Wash skin:	Daily		Con	possible liver damage	Breath:	Resp support	
Remove:	N.R.				Swallow:	Medical attention	
Change:	Daily					immed	

175

[Iron salts (soluble, as Fe)]

Skin:	Prevent skin contact	NIOSH/OSHA	Inh	Irrit eyes, skin, nose,	Eye:	Irr immed	Eyes, skin, resp sys,
Eyes:	Prevent eye contact	1000 ppm: CCROV//PAPROV/GMFOV/	Ing	throat; derm;	Skin:	Water flush prompt	CNS
Wash skin:	When contam	SA/SCBAF	Con	in animals: narco	Breath:	Resp support	
Remove:	When wet (flamm)	§: SCBAF:PD,PP/SAF:PD,PP:ASCBA			Swallow:	Medical attention	
Change:	N.R.	Escape: GMFOV/SCBAE				immed	

[Isoamyl acetate]

Skin:	Prevent skin contact	NIOSH/OSHA	Inh	Irrit eyes, skin, nose,	Eye:	Irr immed	Eyes, skin, resp sys,
Eyes:	Prevent eye contact	500 ppm: SA:CF^E/CCRFOV/GMFOV/	Ing	throat; head, dizz; cough,	Skin:	Water flush prompt	CNS
Wash skin:	When contam	PAPROV^E/SCBAF/SAF	Con	dysp, nau, vomit, diarr;	Breath:	Resp support	
Remove:	When wet or contam	§: SCBAF:PD,PP/SAF:PD,PP:ASCBA		skin cracking;	Swallow:	Medical attention	
Change:	N.R.	Escape: GMFOV/SCBAE		in animals: narco		immed	

[Isoamyl alcohol (primary)]

Chemical name, structure/formula, CAS and RTECS Nos., and DOT ID and guide Nos.	Synonyms, trade names, and conversion factors	Exposure limits (TWA unless noted otherwise)	IDLH	Physical description	Chemical and physical properties		Incompatibilities and reactivities	Measurement method (See Table 1)
					MW, BP, SOL Fl.P, IP, Sp, Gr, flammability	VP, FRZ UEL, LEL		
Isoamyl alcohol (secondary) (CH$_3$)$_2$CHCH(OH)CH$_3$ 6032-29-7 1105 129	3-Methyl-2-butanol, Secondary isoamyl alcohol 1 ppm = 3.61 mg/m^3	NIOSH 100 ppm (360 mg/m^3) ST 125 ppm (450 mg/m^3) OSHA† 100 ppm (360 mg/m^3)	500 ppm	Colorless liquid with a disagreeable odor.	MW: 88.2 BP: 234°F Sol: ? Fl.P(oc): 95°F IP: ? Sp.Gr. 0.82 Class IC Flammable Liquid	VP: 1 mm FRZ: ? UEL: ? LEL: ?	Strong oxidizers	Char; 2-Propanol/ CS$_2$; GC/FID; IV [#1402, Alcohols III]
Isobutane CH$_3$CH(CH$_3$)$_2$ 75-28-5 TZ4300000 1075 115 1969 115	2-Methylpropane [Note: Also see specific listing for n-Butane.] 1 ppm = 2.38 mg/m^3	NIOSH 800 ppm (1900 mg/m^3) OSHA† none	N.D.	Colorless gas with a gasoline-like or natural gas odor. [Note: Shipped as a liquefied compressed gas. A liquid below 11°F.]	MW: 58.1 BP: 11°F Sol: Slight Fl.P: NA (Gas) IP: 10.74 eV RGasD: 2.06 Flammable Gas Class IA Flammable Liquid	VP(70°F): 3.1 atm FRZ: -255°F UEL: 8.4% LEL: 1.6%	Strong oxidizers (e.g., nitrates & perchlorates), chlorine, fluorine, (nickel carbonyl + oxygen)	None available
Isobutyl acetate CH$_3$COOCH$_2$CH(CH$_3$)$_2$ 110-19-0 AI4025000 1213 129	Isobutyl ester of acetic acid, 2-Methylpropyl acetate, 2-Methylpropyl ester of acetic acid, ß-Methylpropyl ethanoate 1 ppm = 4.75 mg/m^3	NIOSH/OSHA 150 ppm (700 mg/m^3)	1300 ppm [10%LEL]	Colorless liquid with a fruity, floral odor.	MW: 116.2 BP: 243°F Sol(77°F): 0.6% Fl.P: 64°F IP: 9.97 eV Sp.Gr. 0.87 Class IB Flammable Liquid	VP: 13 mm FRZ: -145°F UEL: 10.5% LEL: 1.3%	Nitrates; strong oxidizers, alkalis & acids	Char; CS$_2$; GC/FID; IV [#1450, Esters I]
Isobutyl alcohol (CH$_3$)$_2$CHCH$_2$OH 78-83-1 NP9625000 1212 129	IBA, Isobutanol, Isopropylcarbinol, 2-Methyl-1-propanol 1 ppm = 3.03 mg/m^3	NIOSH 50 ppm (150 mg/m^3) OSHA† 100 ppm (300 mg/m^3)	1600 ppm	Colorless, oily liquid with a sweet, musty odor.	MW: 74.1 BP: 227°F Sol: 10% Fl.P: 82°F IP: 10.12 eV Sp.Gr. 0.80 Class IC Flammable Liquid	VP: 9 mm FRZ: -162°F UEL(202°F): 10.6% LEL(123°F): 1.7%	Strong oxidizers	Char; 2-Propanol/ CS$_2$; GC/FID; IV [#1401, Alcohols II]

Personal protection and sanitation (See Table 3)	Recommendations for respirator selection — maximum concentration for use (MUC) (See Table 4)	Route	Symptoms (See Table 5)	First aid (See Table 6)	Target organs (See Table 5)
Skin: Prevent skin contact Eyes: Prevent eye contact Wash skin: When contam Remove: When wet (flamm) Change: N.R.	NIOSH/OSHA 500 ppm: SA:CF$^\varepsilon$/CCRFOV/GMFOV/ PAPROV$^\varepsilon$/SCBAF/SAF §: SCBAF:PD,PP/SAF:PD,PP:ASCBA Escape: GMFOV/SCBAE	Inh Ing Con	Irrit eyes, skin, nose, throat; head, dizz; cough, dysp, nau, vomit, diarr; skin cracking; in animals: narco	Eye: Irr immed Skin: Water flush prompt Breath: Resp support Swallow: Medical attention immed	Eyes, skin, resp sys, CNS

[Isoamyl alcohol (secondary)]

Skin: Frostbite Eyes: Frostbite Wash skin: N.R. Remove: When wet (flamm) Change: N.R. Provide: Frostbite	TBAL	Inh Con (liq)	Drow, narco, asphy; liq: frostbite	Eye: Frostbite Skin: Frostbite Breath: Resp support	CNS

[Isobutane]

Skin: Prevent skin contact Eyes: Prevent eye contact Wash skin: When contam Remove: When wet (flamm) Change: N.R.	NIOSH/OSHA 1300 ppm: SA:CF$^\varepsilon$/CCRFOV/GMFOV/ PAPROV$^\varepsilon$/SCBAF/SAF §: SCBAF:PD,PP/SAF:PD,PP:ASCBA Escape: GMFOV/SCBAE	Inh Ing Con	Irrit eyes, skin, upper resp sys; head, drow, anes; in animals: narco	Eye: Irr immed Skin: Water flush prompt Breath: Resp support Swallow: Medical attention immed	Skin, eyes, resp sys, CNS

[Isobutyl acetate]

Skin: Prevent skin contact Eyes: Prevent eye contact Wash skin: When contam Remove: When wet (flamm) Change: N.R.	NIOSH 500 ppm: CCROV*/SA* 1250 ppm: SA:CF*/PAPROV* 1600 ppm: CCRFOV/GMFOV/ PAPRTOV*/SCBAF/SAF §: SCBAF:PD,PP/SAF:PD,PP:ASCBA Escape: GMFOV/SCBAE	Inh Ing Con	Irrit eyes, throat; head, drow; skin cracking; in animals: narco	Eye: Irr immed Skin: Water flush prompt Breath: Resp support Swallow: Medical attention immed	Eyes, skin, resp sys, CNS

[Isobutyl alcohol]

Chemical name, structure/formula, CAS and RTECS Nos., and DOT ID and guide Nos.	Synonyms, trade names, and conversion factors	Exposure limits (TWA unless noted otherwise)	IDLH	Physical description	Chemical and physical properties		Incompatibilities and reactivities	Measurement method (See Table 1)
					MW, BP, SOL Fl.P, IP, Sp, Gr, flammability	VP, FRZ UEL, LEL		
Isobutyronitrile (CH₃)₂CHCN 78-82-0 TZ4900000 2284 131	Isopropyl cyanide, 2-Methylpropanenitrile, 2-Methylpropionitrile 1 ppm = 2.83 mg/m³	NIOSH 8 ppm (22 mg/m³) OSHA none	N.D.	Colorless liquid with an almond-like odor. [Note: Forms cyanide in the body.]	MW: 69.1 BP: 219°F Sol: Slight Fl.P: 47°F IP: ? Sp.Gr: 0.76 Class IB Flammable Liquid	VP(130°F): 100 mm FRZ: -97°F UEL: ? LEL: ?	Oxidizers, reducing agents, strong acids & bases	Char; Benzene; GC/FID; IV [Adapt #1606]
Isooctyl alcohol C₇H₁₅CH₂OH 26952-21-6 NS7700000	Isooctanol, Oxooctyl alcohol [Note: A mixture of closely related isomeric, primary alcohols with branched chains such as 2-Ethyl-hexanol, CH₃(CH₂)₃CH(CH₂CH₃)CH₂OH.] 1 ppm = 5.33 mg/m³	NIOSH 50 ppm (270 mg/m³) [skin] OSHA† none	N.D.	Clear, colorless liquid.	MW: 130.3 BP: 367°F Sol: Insoluble Fl.P(oc): 180°F IP: ? Sp.Gr: 0.83 Class IIIA Combustible Liquid	VP: 0.4 mm FRZ: <-105°F UEL(est.): 5.7% LEL(calc.): 0.9%	None reported	None available
Isophorone C₉H₁₄O 78-59-1 GW7700000 1993 128 (combustible liquid, n.o.s.)	Isoacetophorone; 3,5,5-Trimethyl-2-cyclo-hexenone; 3,5,5-Trimethyl-2-cyclo-hexen-1-one 1 ppm = 5.65 mg/m³	NIOSH 4 ppm (23 mg/m³) OSHA† 25 ppm (140 mg/m³)	200 ppm	Colorless to white liquid with a peppermint-like odor.	MW: 138.2 BP: 419°F Sol: 1% Fl.P: 184°F IP: 9.07 eV Sp.Gr: 0.92 Class IIIA Combustible Liquid	VP: 0.3 mm FRZ: 17°F UEL: 3.8% LEL: 0.8%	Oxidizers, strong alkalis, amines	Char(pet); CS₂; GC/FID; IV [#2508]
Isophorone diisocyanate C₁₂H₁₈N₂O₂ 4098-71-9 NQ9370000 2290 156	IPDI; 3-Isocyanatomethyl-3,5,5-trimethylcyclohexyl-isocyanate; Isophorone diamine diisocyanate 1 ppm = 9.09 mg/m³	NIOSH 0.005 ppm (0.045 mg/m³) ST 0.02 ppm (0.180 mg/m³) [skin] OSHA† none	N.D.	Colorless to slightly yellow liquid with a pungent odor.	MW: 222.3 BP: ? Sol: Decomposes Fl.P: 311°F IP: ? Sp.Gr: 1.06 Class IIIB Combustible Liquid	VP: 0.0003 mm FRZ: -76°F UEL: ? LEL: ?	Water, alcohols, phenols, amines, mercaptans, amides, urethanes, ureas [Note: Reacts with water to form carbon dioxide.]	None available

Personal protection and sanitation (See Table 3)	Recommendations for respirator selection — maximum concentration for use (MUC) (See Table 4)	Health hazards			
		Route	Symptoms (See Table 5)	First aid (See Table 6)	Target organs (See Table 5)
Skin: Prevent skin contact Eyes: Prevent eye contact Wash skin: When contam Remove: When wet (flamm) Change: N.R. Provide: Eyewash, Quick drench	NIOSH 80 ppm: CCROV/SA 200 ppm: SA:CF/PAPROV 400 ppm: CCRFOV/GMFOV/PAPRTOV/ SCBAF/SAF 1000 ppm: SAF:PD,PP §: SCBAF:PD,PP/SAF:PD,PP:ASCBA Escape: GMFOV/SCBAE	Inh Abs Ing Con	Irrit eyes, skin, nose, throat; head, dizz, weak, gidd, conf, convuls; dysp; abdom pain, nau, vomit	Eye: Irr immed Skin: Soap flush immed Breath: Resp support Swallow: Medical attention immed	Eyes, skin, resp sys, CNS, CVS

[Isobutyronitrile]

Skin: Prevent skin contact Eyes: Prevent eye contact Wash skin: When contam/Daily Remove: When wet or contam Change: N.R. Provide: Eyewash	TBAL	Inh Abs Ing Con	Irrit eyes, skin, nose, throat; eye, skin burns	Eye: Irr immed Skin: Soap wash immed Breath: Resp support Swallow: Medical attention immed	Eyes, skin, resp sys

[Isooctyl alcohol]

Skin: Prevent skin contact Eyes: Prevent eye contact Wash skin: When contam Remove: When wet or contam Change: N.R. Provide: Eyewash	NIOSH 40 ppm: CCROV*/SA* 100 ppm: SA:CF*/PAPROV* 200 ppm: CCRFOV/GMFOV/PAPRTOV*/ SAT:CF*/SCBAF/SAF §: SCBAF:PD,PP/SAF:PD,PP:ASCBA Escape: GMFOV/SCBAE	Inh Ing Con	Irrit eyes, nose, throat; head, nau, dizz, ftg, mal, narco; derm; in animals: kidney, liver damage	Eye: Irr immed Skin: Soap wash prompt Breath: Resp support Swallow: Medical attention immed	Eyes, skin, resp sys CNS, liver, kidneys

[Isophorone]

Skin: Prevent skin contact Eyes: Prevent eye contact Wash skin: When contam Remove: When wet or contam Change: Daily Provide: Quick drench	NIOSH 0.05 ppm: SA* 0.125 ppm: SA:CF* 0.25 ppm: SCBAF/SAF 1 ppm: SAF:PD,PP §: SCBAF:PD,PP/SAF:PD,PP:ASCBA Escape: GMFOV/SCBAE	Inh Abs Ing Con	Irrit eyes, skin, resp sys; chest tight, dysp, cough, sore throat; bron, wheez, pulm edema; possible resp sens, asthma	Eye: Irr immed Skin: Water flush immed Breath: Resp support Swallow: Medical attention immed	Eyes, skin, resp sys

[Isophorone diisocyanate]

Chemical name, structure/formula, CAS and RTECS Nos., and DOT ID and guide Nos.	Synonyms, trade names, and conversion factors	Exposure limits (TWA unless noted otherwise)	IDLH	Physical description	Chemical and physical properties		Incompatibilities and reactivities	Measurement method (See Table 1)
					MW, BP, SOL FI.P, IP, Sp, Gr, flammability	VP, FRZ UEL, LEL		
2-Isopropoxyethanol $(CH_3)_2CHOCH_2CH_2OH$ 109-59-1 KL5075000	Ethylene glycol isopropyl ether, ß-Hydroxyethyl isopropyl ether, Isopropyl Cellosolve®, Isopropyl glycol	NIOSH See Appendix D OSHA† none	N.D.	Colorless liquid with a mild, ethereal odor.	MW: 104.2 BP: 283°F Sol: Miscible FI.P(oc): 92°F IP: ? Sp.Gr. 0.90 Class IC Flammable Liquid	VP: 3 mm FRZ: ? UEL: ? LEL: ?	Oxidizers	None available
Isopropyl acetate $CH_3COOCH(CH_3)_2$ 108-21-4 AI4930000 1220 129	Isopropyl ester of acetic acid, 1-Methylethyl ester of acetic acid, 2-Propyl acetate 1 ppm = 4.18 mg/m³	NIOSH See Appendix D OSHA† 250 ppm (950 mg/m³)	1800 ppm	Colorless liquid with a fruity odor.	MW: 102.2 BP: 194°F Sol: 3% FI.P: 36°F IP: 9.95 eV Sp.Gr. 0.87 Class IB Flammable Liquid	VP: 42 mm FRZ: -92°F UEL: 8% LEL(100°F): 1.8%	Nitrates; strong oxidizers, alkalis & acids	Char; CS₂; GC/FID; IV [#1454]
Isopropyl alcohol $(CH_3)_2CHOH$ 67-63-0 NT8050000 1219 129	Dimethyl carbinol, IPA, Isopropanol, 2-Propanol, sec-Propyl alcohol, Rubbing alcohol 1 ppm = 2.46 mg/m³	NIOSH 400 ppm (980 mg/m³) ST 500 ppm (1225 mg/m³) OSHA† 400 ppm (980 mg/m³)	2000 ppm [10%LEL]	Colorless liquid with the odor of rubbing alcohol.	MW: 60.1 BP: 181°F Sol: Miscible FI.P: 53°F IP: 10.10 eV Sp.Gr. 0.79 Class IB Flammable Liquid	VP: 33 mm FRZ: -127°F UEL(200°F): 12% LEL: 2.0%	Strong oxidizers, acetaldehyde, chlorine, ethylene oxide, acids, isocyanates	Char; 2-Butanol/ CS₂; GC/FID; IV [#1400, Alcohols I]
Isopropylamine $(CH_3)_2CHNH_2$ 75-31-0 NT8400000 1221 132	2-Aminopropane, Monoisopropylamine, 2-Propylamine, sec-Propylamine 1 ppm = 2.42 mg/m³	NIOSH See Appendix D OSHA† 5 ppm (12 mg/m³)	750 ppm	Colorless liquid with an ammonia-like odor. [Note: A gas above 91°F.]	MW: 59.1 BP: 91°F Sol: Miscible FI.P(oc): -35°F IP: 8.72 eV Sp.Gr. 0.69 Class IA Flammable Liquid	VP: 460 mm FRZ: -150°F UEL: ? LEL: ?	Strong acids, strong oxidizers, aldehydes, ketones, epoxides	Bub; NaOH; GC/FID; II(3) [#S147]

Personal protection and sanitation (See Table 3)		Recommendations for respirator selection — maximum concentration for use (MUC) (See Table 4)	Health hazards				
			Route	Symptoms (See Table 5)	First aid (See Table 6)		Target organs (See Table 5)
Skin:	Prevent skin contact	TBAL	Inh	In animals: irrit eyes,	Eye:	Irr immed	Eyes, skin, resp
Eyes:	Prevent eye contact		Abs	skin; hemog, anemia,	Skin:	Water wash prompt	sys, blood
Wash skin:	When contam		Ing	pulm edema	Breath:	Resp support	
Remove:	When wet (flamm)		Con		Swallow:	Medical attention	
Change:	N.R.					immed	
[2-Isopropoxyethanol]							
Skin:	Prevent skin contact	OSHA	Inh	Irrit eyes, skin, nose;	Eye:	Irr immed	Eyes, skin, resp
Eyes:	Prevent eye contact	1800 ppm: SA:CF£/SCBAF/SAF	Ing	derm;	Skin:	Water flush prompt	sys, CNS
Wash skin:	When contam	§: SCBAF:PD,PP/SAF:PD,PP:ASCBA	Con	in animals: narco	Breath:	Resp support	
Remove:	When wet (flamm)	Escape: GMFOV/SCBAE			Swallow:	Medical attention	
Change:	N.R.					immed	
[Isopropyl acetate]							
Skin:	Prevent skin contact	NIOSH/OSHA	Inh	Irrit eyes, nose, throat;	Eye:	Irr immed	Eyes, skin, resp
Eyes:	Prevent eye contact	2000 ppm: SA:CF£/CCRFOV/GMFOV/	Ing	drow, dizz, head; dry	Skin:	Water flush	sys, CNS
Wash skin:	When contam	PAPROV£/SCBAF/SAF	Con	cracking skin;	Breath:	Resp support	
Remove:	When wet (flamm)	§: SCBAF:PD,PP/SAF:PD,PP:ASCBA		in animals: narco	Swallow:	Medical attention	
Change:	N.R.	Escape: GMFOV/SCBAE				immed	
[Isopropyl alcohol]							
Skin:	Prevent skin contact	OSHA	Inh	Irrit eyes, nose,	Eye:	Irr immed	Eyes, skin, resp sys
Eyes:	Prevent eye contact	125 ppm: SA:CF£/PAPRS£	Abs	throat; pulm edema; vis	Skin:	Water flush immed	
Wash skin:	When contam	250 ppm: CCRFS/GMFS/PAPRTS£/	Ing	dist; eye, skin burns;	Breath:	Resp support	
Remove:	When wet (flamm)	SCBAF/SAF	Con	derm	Swallow:	Medical attention	
Change:	N.R.	750 ppm: SAF:PD,PP				immed	
Provide:	Eyewash, Quick drench	§: SCBAF:PD,PP/SAF:PD,PP:ASCBA					
		Escape: GMFS/SCBAE					
[Isopropylamine]							

181

Chemical name, structure/formula, CAS and RTECS Nos., and DOT ID and guide Nos.	Synonyms, trade names, and conversion factors	Exposure limits (TWA unless noted otherwise)	IDLH	Physical description	Chemical and physical properties MW, BP, SOL FI.P, IP, Sp, Gr, flammability	VP, FRZ UEL, LEL	Incompatibilities and reactivities	Measurement method (See Table 1)
N-Isopropylaniline $C_6H_5NHCH(CH_3)_2$ 768-52-5 BY4190000	N-IPA, Isopropylaniline, N- (1-Methylethyl)-benzenamine, N-Phenylisopropylamine 1 ppm = 5.53 mg/m³	NIOSH 2 ppm (10 mg/m³) [skin] OSHA† none	N.D.	Clear, yellowish liquid with a sweet, aromatic odor.	MW: 135.2 BP: 397°F Sol: Insoluble FI.P(oc): 190°F IP: ? Sp.Gr(60°F): 0.93 Class IIIB Combustible Liquid	VP(77°F): 0.03 mm FRZ: -58°F UEL: ? LEL: ?	None reported	Filter*(2); Methanol; HPLC/UV; OSHA [#78]
Isopropyl ether $(CH_3)_2CHOCH(CH_3)_2$ 108-20-3 TZ5425000 1159 127	DIisopropyl ether, DIisopropyl oxide, 2-Isopropoxy propane 1 ppm = 4.18 mg/m³	NIOSH/OSHA 500 ppm (2100 mg/m³)	1400 ppm [10%LEL]	Colorless liquid with a sharp, sweet, ether-like odor.	MW: 102.2 BP: 154°F Sol: 0.2% FI.P: -18°F IP: 9.20 eV Sp.Gr: 0.73 Class IB Flammable Liquid	VP:119mm FRZ: -76°F UEL: 7.9% LEL:1.4%	Strong oxidizers, acids [Note: Unstable peroxides may form on long contact of isopropyl ether with air.]	Char; CS₂; GC/FID; IV [#1618]
Isopropyl glycidyl ether $C_6H_{12}O_2$ 4016-14-2 TZ3500000	1,2-Epoxy-3-isopropoxy-propane; IGE; Isopropoxymethyl oxirane 1 ppm = 4.75 mg/m³	NIOSH C 50 ppm (240 mg/m³) [15-min] OSHA† 50 ppm (240 mg/m³)	400 ppm	Colorless liquid.	MW: 116.2 BP: 279°F Sol: 19% FI.P: 92°F IP: ? Sp.Gr: 0.92 Class IC Flammable Liquid	VP(77°F): 9 mm FRZ: ? UEL: ? LEL: ?	Strong oxidizers, strong caustics [Note: May form explosive peroxides upon exposure to air or light.]	Char; CS₂; GC/FID; IV [#1620]
Kaolin 1332-58-7 GF1670500	China clay, Clay, Hydrated aluminum silicate, Hydrite, Porcelain clay [Note: Main constituent of Kaolin is Kaolinite $(Al_2Si_2O_5(OH)_4)$.]	NIOSH 10 mg/m³ (total) 5 mg/m³ (resp) OSHA† 15 mg/m³ (total) 5 mg/m³ (resp)	N.D.	White to yellowish or grayish powder. [Note: When moistened, darkens & develops a clay-like odor.]	MW: varies BP: ? Sol: Insoluble FI.P: NA IP: NA Sp.Gr: 1.8-2.6 Noncombustible Solid	VP: 0 mm (approx) MLT: ? UEL: NA LEL: NA	None reported	Filter; none; Grav; IV [Particulates NOR: #0500 (total), #0600 (resp)] '

Personal protection and sanitation (See Table 3)	Recommendations for respirator selection — maximum concentration for use (MUC) (See Table 4)	Health hazards			
		Route	Symptoms (See Table 5)	First aid (See Table 6)	Target organs (See Table 5)
Skin: Prevent skin contact Eyes: Prevent eye contact Wash skin: When contam Remove: When wet or contam Change: N.R. Provide: Quick drench	TBAL	Inh Abs Ing Con	Irrit eyes, skin; head, weak, dizz; cyan; ataxia; dysp on effort; tacar; methemo	Eye: Irr immed Skin: Soap wash prompt Breath: Resp support Swallow: Medical attention immed	Eyes, skin, resp sys, blood, CVS, liver, kidneys

[N-Isopropylaniline]

| Skin: Prevent skin contact
Eyes: Prevent eye contact
Wash skin: When contam
Remove: When wet (flamm)
Change: N.R. | NIOSH/OSHA
1400 ppm: CCROV*/PAPROV*/GMFOV/
SA*/SCBAF
§: SCBAF:PD,PP/SAF:PD,PP:ASCBA
Escape: GMFOV/SCBAE | Inh
Ing
Con | Irrit eyes, skin, nose; resp discomfort; derm; in animals: drow, dizz, uncon, narco | Eye: Irr immed
Skin: Soap wash prompt
Breath: Resp support
Swallow: Medical attention immed | Eyes, skin, resp sys, CNS |

[Isopropyl ether]

| Skin: Prevent skin contact
Eyes: Prevent eye contact
Wash skin: When contam
Remove: When wet (flamm)
Change: N.R. | NIOSH/OSHA
400 ppm: SA:CF£/SCBAF
§: SCBAF:PD,PP/SAF:PD,PP:ASCBA
Escape: GMFOV/SCBAE | Inh
Ing
Con | Irrit eyes, skin, upper resp sys; skin sens; possible hemato, repro effects | Eye: Irr immed
Skin: Soap wash immed
Breath: Resp support
Swallow: Medical attention immed | Eyes, skin, resp sys, blood, repro sys |

[Isopropyl glycidyl ether]

| Skin: N.R.
Eyes: N.R.
Wash skin: N.R.
Remove: N.R.
Change: N.R. | TBAL | Inh
Con | Chronic pulm fib, stomach granuloma | Eye: Irr immed
Breath: Fresh air | Resp sys, stomach |

[Kaolin]

Chemical name, structure/formula, CAS and RTECS Nos., and DOT ID and guide Nos.	Synonyms, trade names, and conversion factors	Exposure limits (TWA unless noted otherwise)	IDLH	Physical description	Chemical and physical properties		Incompatibilities and reactivities	Measurement method (See Table 1)
					MW, BP, SOL Fl.P, IP, Sp, Gr, flammability	VP, FRZ UEL, LEL		
Kepone $C_{10}Cl_{10}O$ 143-50-0 PC8575000	Chlordecone; Decachlorooctahydro-kepone-2-one; Decachlorooctahydro-1,3,4-metheno-2H-cyclobuta(cd)-pentalen-2-one; Decachlorotetrahydro-4,7-methanoindeneone;	NIOSH Ca See Appendix A 0.001 mg/m³ OSHA none	Ca [N.D.]	Tan to white, crystalline, odorless solid. [insecticide]	MW: 490.6 BP: Sublimes Sol(212°F): 0.5% Fl.P: NA IP: ? Sp.Gr: ? Noncombustible Solid	VP(77°F): <3 x 10⁻⁷ mm MLT: 662°F (Sublimes) UEL: NA LEL: NA	Acids, acid fumes	Filter/ Imp; Benzene/ Methanol; GC/ECD; IV [#5508]
Kerosene 8008-20-6 OA5500000 1223 128	Fuel Oil No. 1, Range oil [Note: A refined petroleum solvent (predominantly C_9-C_{16}), which typically is 25% normal paraffins, 11% branched paraffins, 30% monocycloparaffins, 12% dicycloparaffins, 1% tricycloparaffins, 16% mononuclear aromatics & 5% dinuclear aromatics.]	NIOSH 100 mg/m³ OSHA none	N.D.	Colorless to yellowish, oily liquid with a strong, characteristic odor.	MW: 170(approx) BP: 347-617°F Sol: Insoluble Fl.P: 100-162°F IP: ? Sp.Gr: 0.81 Class II Combustible Liquid	VP(100°F): 5 mm FRZ: -50°F UEL: 5% LEL: 0.7%	Strong oxidizers	Char; CS₂; GC/FID; IV [#1550, Naphthas]
Ketene $CH_2=CO$ 463-51-4 OA7700000 1 ppm = 1.72 mg/m³	Carbomethene, Ethenone, Keto-ethylene	NIOSH 0.5 ppm (0.9 mg/m³) ST 1.5 ppm (3 mg/m³) OSHA† 0.5 ppm (0.9 mg/m³)	5 ppm	Colorless gas with a penetrating odor.	MW: 42.0 BP: -69°F Sol: Reacts Fl.P: NA (Gas) IP: 9.61 eV RGasD: 1.45 Flammable Gas	VP: >1 atm FRZ: -238°F UEL: ? LEL: ?	Water, alcohols, ammonia [Note: Readily polymerizes. Reacts with water to form acetic acid.]	Bub; FeCl₃; Vis; II(2) [#S92]
Lead Pb 7439-92-1 OF7525000	Lead metal, Plumbum	NIOSH* 0.100 mg/m³ See Appendix C OSHA* [1910.1025] 0.050 mg/m³ See Appendix C [*Note: The REL and PEL also apply to other lead compounds (as Pb) -- See Appendix C.]	100 mg/m³ (as Pb)	A heavy, ductile, soft, gray solid.	MW: 207.2 BP: 3164°F Sol: Insoluble Fl.P: NA IP: NA Sp.Gr: 11.34 Noncombustible Solid in bulk form.	VP: 0 mm (approx) MLT: 621°F UEL: NA LEL: NA	Strong oxidizers, hydrogen peroxide, acids	Filter; HNO₃/H₂O₂; AAS; III [#7082] [Also #7105.]

Personal protection and sanitation (See Table 3)	Recommendations for respirator selection — maximum concentration for use (MUC) (See Table 4)	Route	Symptoms (See Table 5)	First aid (See Table 6)	Target organs (See Table 5)
Skin: Prevent skin contact Eyes: Prevent eye contact Wash skin: When contam/Daily Remove: When wet or contam Change: Daily Provide: Eyewash, Quick drench [Kepone]	NIOSH ¥: SCBAF:PD,PP/SAF:PD,PP:ASCBA Escape: GMFOVHiE/SCBAE	Inh Abs Ing Con	Head, ner, tremor, liver, kidney damage; vis dist; ataxia, chest pain, skin eryt; testicular atrophy, low sperm count; [carc]	Eye: Irr immed Skin: Soap wash immed Breath: Resp support Swallow: Medical attention immed	Eyes, skin, resp sys, CNS, liver, kidneys, repro sys [in animals: liver cancer]
Skin: Prevent skin contact Eyes: Prevent eye contact Wash skin: When contam Remove: When wet or contam Change: N.R. Provide: Quick drench [Kerosene]	NIOSH 1000 mg/m³: CCROV/SA 2500 mg/m³: SA:CF/PAPROV 5000 mg/m³: CCRFOV/GMFOV/PAPRTOV/ SCBAF/SAF §: SCBAF:PD,PP/SAF:PD,PP:ASCBA Escape: GMFOV/SCBAE	Inh Ing Con	Irrit eyes, skin, nose, throat; burning sensation in chest; head, nau, weak, restless, inco, conf, drow; vomit, diarr; derm; chemical pneu (aspir liq)	Eye: Irr immed Skin: Soap flush immed Breath: Resp support Swallow: Medical attention immed	Eyes, skin, resp sys, CNS
Skin: N.R. Eyes: N.R. Wash skin: N.R. Remove: N.R. Change: N.R. [Ketene]	NIOSH/OSHA 5 ppm: SA*/SCBAF §: SCBAF:PD,PP/SAF:PD,PP:ASCBA Escape: GMFOV/SCBAE	Inh Con	Irrit eyes, skin, nose, throat, resp sys; pulm edema	Breath: Resp support	Eyes, skin, resp sys
Skin: Prevent skin contact Eyes: Prevent eye contact Wash skin: Daily Remove: When wet or contam Change: Daily [Lead]	OSHA 0.5 mg/m³: HiE/SA 1.25 mg/m³: SA:CF/PAPRHiE 2.5 mg/m³: HiEF/SAT:CF/PAPRTHiE/ SCBAF/SAF 50 mg/m³: SA:PD,PP 100 mg/m³: SAF:PD,PP §: SCBAF:PD,PP/SAF:PD,PP:ASCBA Escape: HiEF/SCBAE	Inh Ing Con	Weak, lass, insom; facial pallor; pal eye, anor, low-wgt, malnut; constip, abdom pain, colic; anemia; gingival lead line; tremor; para wrist, ankles; encephalopathy; kidney disease; irrit eyes; hypotension	Eye: Irr immed Skin: Soap flush prompt Breath: Resp support Swallow: Medical attention immed	Eyes, GI tract, CNS, kidneys, blood, gingival tissue

Chemical name, structure/formula, CAS and RTECS Nos., and DOT ID and guide Nos.	Synonyms, trade names, and conversion factors	Exposure limits (TWA unless noted otherwise)	IDLH	Physical description	Chemical and physical properties		Incompatibilities and reactivities	Measurement method (See Table 1)
					MW, BP, SOL FI.P, IP, Sp, Gr, flammability	VP, FRZ UEL, LEL		
Limestone $CaCO_3$ 1317-65-3 EV9580000	Calcium carbonate, Natural calcium carbonate [Note: Calcite & aragonite are commercially important natural calcium carbonates.]	NIOSH 10 mg/m³ (total) 5 mg/m³ (resp) OSHA 15 mg/m³ (total) 5 mg/m³ (resp)	N.D.	Odorless, white to tan powder.	MW: 100.1 BP: Decomposes Sol: 0.001% FI.P: NA IP: NA Sp.Gr: 2.7-2.9 Noncombustible Solid	VP: 0 mm (approx) MLT:1517-2442°F (Decomposes) UEL: NA LEL: NA	Fluorine, magnesium, acids, alum, ammonium salts	Filter; none; Grav; IV [Particulates NOR: #0500 (total), #0600 (resp)]
Lindane $C_6H_6Cl_6$ 58-89-9 GV4900000 2761 151	BHC; HCH; γ-Hexachlorocyclohexane; gamma-isomer of 1,2,3,4,5,6-Hexachlorocyclohexane	NIOSH/OSHA 0.5 mg/m³ [skin]	50 mg/m³	White to yellow, crystalline powder with a slight, musty odor. [pesticide]	MW: 290.8 BP: 614°F Sol: 0.001% FI.P: NA IP: ? Sp.Gr: 1.85 Noncombustible Solid, but may be dissolved in flammable liquids.	VP: 0.00001 mm MLT: 235°F UEL: NA LEL: NA	Corrosive to metals	Filter/Bub; Isooctane; GC/EConD; IV [#5502]
Lithium hydride LiH 7580-67-8 OJ6300000 1414 138 2805 138 (fused solid)	Lithium monohydride	NIOSH/OSHA 0.025 mg/m³	0.5 mg/m³	Odorless, off-white to gray, translucent, crystalline mass or white powder. Sp.Gr: 0.78 Combustible Solid that can form airborne dust clouds which may explode on contact with flame, heat, or oxidizers.	MW: 7.95 BP: Decomposes Sol: Reacts FI.P: NA IP: NA	VP: 0 mm (approx) MLT:1256°F UEL: NA LEL: NA	Strong oxidizers, halogenated hydrocarbons, acids, water [Note: May ignite SPONTANEOUSLY in air and may reignite after fire is extinguished. Reacts with water to form hydrogen & lithium hydroxide.]	None available
L.P.G. $C_3H_8/C_3H_6/C_4H_{10}/C_4H_8$ 68476-85-7 SE7545000 1075 115	Bottled gas, Compressed petroleum gas, Liquefied hydrocarbon gas, Liquefied petroleum gas, LPG [Note: A fuel mixture of propane, propylene, butanes & butylenes.] 1 ppm = 1.72-2.37 mg/m³	NIOSH/OSHA 1000 ppm (1800 mg/m³)	2000 ppm [10%LEL]	Colorless, noncorrosive, odorless gas when pure. [Note: A foul-smelling odorant is usually added. Shipped as a liquefied compressed gas.]	MW: 42-58 BP: >-44°F Sol: Insoluble FI.P: NA (Gas) IP: 10.95 eV RGasD: 1.45-2.00 Flammable Gas	VP: >1 atm FRZ: ? UEL: 9.5% (Propane) 8.5% (Butane) LEL: 2.1% (Propane) 1.9% (Butane)	Strong oxidizers, chlorine dioxide	Combustible gas meter; none; none; II(2) [#S93]

Personal protection and sanitation (See Table 3)		Recommendations for respirator selection — maximum concentration for use (MUC) (See Table 4)	Health hazards				
			Route	Symptoms (See Table 5)	First aid (See Table 6)		Target organs (See Table 5)
Skin:	N.R.	TBAL	Inh	Irrit eyes, skin, muc memb;	Eye:	Irr immed	Eyes, skin, resp sys
Eyes:	N.R.		Con	cough, sneez, rhin; lac	Skin:	Soap wash	
Wash skin:	N.R.				Breath:	Fresh air	
Remove:	N.R.						
Change:	N.R.						
[Limestone]							
Skin:	Prevent skin contact	NIOSH/OSHA	Inh	Irrit eyes, skin, nose,	Eye:	Irr immed	Eyes, skin, resp sys,
Eyes:	N.R.	5 mg/m³: CCROVDMFu/SA	Abs	throat; head; nau; clonic	Skin:	Soap wash prompt	CNS, blood, liver,
Wash skin:	When contam	12.5 mg/m³: SA:CF*/PAPROVDMFu*	Ing	convuls; resp difficulty;	Breath:	Resp support	kidneys
Remove:	When wet or contam	25 mg/m³: CCRFOVHiE/GMFOVHiE/	Con	cyan; aplastic anemia;	Swallow:	Medical attention	
Change:	Daily	PAPRTOVHiE*/SCBAF/SAF		musc spasm;		immed	
Provide:	Quick drench	50 mg/m³: SAF:PD,PP		in animals: liver, kidney			
		§: SCBAF:PD,PP/SAF:PD,PP:ASCBA		damage			
		Escape: GMFOVHiE/SCBAE					
[Lindane]							
Skin:	Prevent skin contact	NIOSH/OSHA	Inh	Irrit eyes, skin; eye,	Eye:	Irr immed	Eyes, skin, resp sys,
Eyes:	Prevent eye contact	0.25 mg/m³: HiE/SA	Ing	skin burns; mouth,	Skin:	Brush (DO NOT	CNS
Wash skin:	Brush (DO NOT WASH)	0.5 mg/m³: SA:CF*/HiEF/PAPRHiE*/	Con	esophagus burns (if		WASH)	
Remove:	When wet or contam	SCBAF/SAF		ingested); nau; musc	Breath:	Resp support	
Change:	Daily	§: SCBAF:PD,PP/SAF:PD,PP:ASCBA		twitches; mental conf;	Swallow:	Medical attention	
Provide:	Eyewash, Quick	Escape: HiEF/SCBAE		blurred vision		immed	
	drench (>0.5 mg/m³)						
[Lithium hydride]							
Skin:	Frostbite	NIOSH/OSHA	Inh	Li-head, drow, asphy;	Eye:	Frostbite	Resp sys, CNS
Eyes:	Frostbite	2000 ppm: SA/SCBAF	Con	liq: frostbite	Skin:	Frostbite	
Wash skin:	N.R.	§: SCBAF:PD,PP/SAF:PD,PP:ASCBA	(liq)		Breath:	Resp support	
Remove:	When wet (flamm)	Escape: SCBAE					
Change:	N.R.						
Provide:	Frostbite						
[L.P.G.]							

Chemical name, structure/formula, CAS and RTECS Nos., and DOT ID and guide Nos.	Synonyms, trade names, and conversion factors	Exposure limits (TWA unless noted otherwise)	IDLH	Physical description	Chemical and physical properties			Incompatibilities and reactivities	Measurement method (See Table 1)
					MW, BP, SOL FI.P, IP, Sp, Gr, flammability	VP, FRZ UEL, LEL			
Magnesite MgCO₃ 546-93-0 OM2470000	Carbonate magnesium, Hydromagnesite, Magnesium carbonate, Magnesium(II) carbonate [Note: Magnesite is a naturally-occurring form of magnesium carbonate.]	NIOSH 10 mg/m³ (total) 5 mg/m³ (resp) OSHA 15 mg/m³ (total) 5 mg/m³ (resp)	N.D.	White, odorless, crystalline powder.	MW: 84.3 BP: Decomposes Sol: 0.01% FI.P: NA IP: NA Sp.Gr: 2.96 Noncombustible Solid	VP: 0 mm (approx) MLT: 662°F (Decomposes) UEL: NA LEL: NA		Acids, formaldehyde	Filter; none; Grav; IV [Particulates NOR: #0500 (total) & #0600 (resp)]
Magnesium oxide fume MgO 1309-48-4 OM3850000	Magnesia fume	NIOSH See Appendix D OSHA† 15 mg/m³	750 mg/m³	Finely divided white particulate dispersed in air. [Note: Exposure may occur when magnesium is burned, thermally cut, or welded upon.]	MW: 40.3 BP: 6512°F Sol(86°F): 0.009% FI.P: NA IP: NA Sp.Gr: 3.58 Noncombustible Solid	VP: 0 mm (approx) MLT: 5072°F UEL: NA LEL: NA		Chlorine trifluoride, phosphorus penta- chloride	Filter; Acid; ICP; IV [#7300, Elements]
Malathion C₁₀H₁₉O₆PS₂ 121-75-5 WM8400000 2783 152	S-[1,2-bis(ethoxycarbonyl) ethyl]0,0-dimethyl- phosphorodithioate; Diethyl (dimethoxyphosphino- thioylthio) succinate [(CH₃O)₂P(S)SCH(COOC₂H₅)- CH₂COOC₂H₅]	NIOSH 10 mg/m³ [skin] OSHA† 15 mg/m³ [skin]	250 mg/m³	Deep-brown to yellow liquid with a garlic-like odor. [insecticide] [Note: A solid below 37°F.]	MW: 330.4 BP: 140°F (Decomposes) Sol: 0.02% FI.P(oc): >325°F IP: ? Sp.Gr: 1.21 Class IIIB Combustible Liquid, but may be difficult to ignite.	VP: 0.00004 mm FRZ: 37°F UEL: ? LEL: ?		Strong oxidizers, magnesium, alkaline pesticides [Note: Corrosive to metals.]	OVS-2; Toluene/ Acetone; GC/FPD; IV [#5600, Organo- phosphorus Pesticides]
Maleic anhydride C₄H₂O₃ 108-31-6 ON3675000 2215 156	cis-Butenedioic anhydride; 2,5-Furanedione; Maleic acid anhydride; Toxilic anhydride 1 ppm = 4.01 mg/m³	NIOSH/OSHA 1 mg/m³ (0.25 ppm)	10 mg/m³	Colorless needles, white lumps, or pellets with an irritating, choking odor.	MW: 98.1 BP: 396°F Sol: Reacts FI.P: 218°F IP: 9.90 eV Sp.Gr: 1.48 Combustible Solid, but may be difficult to ignite.	VP: 0.2 mm MLT: 127°F UEL: 7.1% LEL: 1.4%		Strong oxidizers, water, alkalis, metals, caustics & amines above 150°F [Note: Reacts slowly with water (hydro- lyzes) to form maleic acid.]	Bub; none; HPLC/UVD; IV [#3512]

Personal protection and sanitation (See Table 3)		Recommendations for respirator selection — maximum concentration for use (MUC) (See Table 4)	Health hazards				
			Route	Symptoms (See Table 5)	First aid (See Table 6)		Target organs (See Table 5)
Skin: Eyes: Wash skin: Remove: Change:	N.R. N.R. N.R. N.R. N.R	TBAL	Inh Con	Irrit eyes, skin, resp sys; cough	Eye: Breath:	Irr immed Fresh air	Eyes, skin, resp sys

[Magnesite]

| Skin:
Eyes:
Wash skin:
Remove:
Change: | N.R.
N.R.
N.R.
N.R.
N.R. | OSHA
150 mg/m³: DMFu/SA
375 mg/m³: SA:CF/PAPRDMFu
750 mg/m³: HiEF/PAPRTHiE*/
SCBAF/SAF
§: SCBAF:PD,PP/SAF:PD,PP:ASCBA
Escape: HiEF/SCBAE | Inh
Con | Irrit eyes, nose; metal fume fever: cough, chest pain, flu-like fever | Breath: | Resp support | Eyes, resp sys |

189

[Magnesium oxide fume]

| Skin:
Eyes:
Wash skin:
Remove:
Change: | Prevent skin contact
Prevent eye contact
When contam
When wet or contam
Daily | NIOSH
100 mg/m³: CCROVDMFu/SA
250 mg/m³: SA:CF*/CCRFOVHiE/
GMFOVHiE/PAPROVDMFu*/
SCBAF/SAF
§: SCBAF:PD,PP/SAF:PD,PP:ASCBA
Escape: GMFOVHiE/SCBAE | Inh
Abs
Ing
Con | Irrit eyes, skin; miosis, aching eyes, blurred vision, lac; salv; anor, nau, vomit, abdom cramps, diarr, gidd, conf, ataxia; rhin, head; chest tight, wheez, lar spasm | Eye:
Skin:
Breath:
Swallow: | Irr immed
Soap wash prompt
Resp support
Medical attention immed | Eyes, skin, resp sys, liver, blood chol, CNS, CVS, GI tract |

[Malathion]

| Skin:
Eyes:
Wash skin:
Remove:
Change:
Provide: | Prevent skin contact
Prevent eye contact
When contam
When wet or contam
N.R.
Eyewash | NIOSH/OSHA
10 mg/m³: SA:CF£/SCBAF/SAF
§: SCBAF:PD,PP/SAF:PD,PP:ASCBA
Escape: GMFOVHiE/SCBAE | Inh
Ing
Con | Irrit nose, upper resp sys; conj; photo, double vision; bronchial asthma; derm | Eye:
Skin:
Breath:
Swallow: | Irr immed
Soap wash immed
Resp support
Medical attention immed | Eyes, skin, resp sys |

[Maleic anhydride]

Chemical name, structure/formula, CAS and RTECS Nos., and DOT ID and guide Nos.	Synonyms, trade names, and conversion factors	Exposure limits (TWA unless noted otherwise)	IDLH	Physical description	Chemical and physical properties		Incompatibilities and reactivities	Measurement method (See Table 1)
					MW, BP, SOL FI.P, IP, Sp, Gr, flammability	VP, FRZ UEL, LEL		
Malonaldehyde CHOCH$_2$CHO 542-78-9 TX6475000	Malonic aldehyde; Malonodialdehyde; Propanedial; 1,3-Propanedial [Note: Pure Malonaldehyde is unstable and may be used as its sodium salt.]	NIOSH Ca See Appendix A See Appendix C (Aldehydes) OSHA none	Ca [N.D.]	Solid (needles).	MW: 72.1 BP: ? Sol: ? FI.P: ? IP: ? Sp.Gr: ?	VP: ? MLT: 161°F UEL: ? LEL: ?	Proteins [Note: Pure compound is stable under neutral conditions, but not under acidic conditions.]	None available
Malononitrile NCCH$_2$CN 109-77-3 OO3150000 2647 153	Cyanoacetonitrile, Dicyanomethane, Malonic dinitrile 1 ppm = 2.70 mg/m^3	NIOSH 3 ppm (8 mg/m^3) OSHA none	N.D.	White powder or colorless crystals. [Note: Melts above 90°F. Forms cyanide in the body.]	MW: 66.1 BP: 426°F Sol: 13% FI.P(oc): 266°F IP: 12.88 eV Sp.Gr: 1.19 Combustible Solid	VP: ? MLT: 90°F UEL: ? LEL: ?	Strong bases [Note: May polymerize violently on prolonged heating at 265°F, or in contact with strong bases at lower temperatures.]	Char; Toluene; GC/FID; NIOSH Nitriles Crit. Doc.
Manganese compounds and fume (as Mn) Mn (Metal) 7439-96-5 (Metal) OO9275000 (Metal)	Manganese metal: Colloidal manganese, Manganese-55 Synonyms of other compounds vary depending upon the specific manganese compound.	NIOSH* 1 mg/m^3 ST 3 mg/m^3 OSHA†* C 5 mg/m^3 [*Note: Also see specific listings for Manganese cyclopentadienyl tricarbonyl, Methyl cyclopentadienyl manganese tricarbonyl, and Manganese tetroxide.]	500 mg/m^3 (as Mn)	Metal: A lustrous, brittle, silvery solid.	MW: 54.9 BP: 3564°F Sol: Insoluble FI.P: NA IP: NA Sp.Gr: 7.20 (Metal) Metal: Combustible Solid	VP: 0 mm (approx) MLT: 2271°F UEL: NA LEL: NA	Oxidizers [Note: Will react with water or steam to produce hydrogen.]	Filter; Acid; ICP; IV [#7300, Elements]
Manganese cyclopenta-dienyl tricarbonyl (as Mn) C$_5$H$_5$Mn(CO)$_3$ 12079-65-1 OO9720000	Cyclopentadienylmanganese tricarbonyl, Cyclopentadienyl tricarbonyl manganese, MCT	NIOSH 0.1 mg/m^3 [skin] OSHA† C 5 mg/m^3	N.D.	Yellow, crystalline solid with a characteristic odor. [Note: An antiknock additive for gasoline. May be found in an oil & gaseous solution.]	MW: 204.1 BP: Sublimes Sol: Slight FI.P: ? IP: ? Sp.Gr: ? Combustible Solid	VP: ? MLT: 167°F (Sublimes) UEL: ? LEL: ?	None reported	None available

190

	Personal protection and sanitation (See Table 3)	Recommendations for respirator selection — maximum concentration for use (MUC) (See Table 4)	Health hazards					
			Route	Symptoms (See Table 5)	First aid (See Table 6)		Target organs (See Table 5)	

Personal protection and sanitation	Recommendations for respirator selection	Route	Symptoms	First aid	Target organs
Skin: Prevent skin contact Eyes: Prevent eye contact Wash skin: When contam/Daily Remove: When wet or contam Change: Daily Provide: Eyewash, Quick drench	NIOSH ¥: SCBAF:PD,PP/SAF:PD,PP:ASCBA Escape: GMFOV/SCBAE	Inh Abs Ing Con	Irrit eyes, skin, resp sys; cough; CNS depres; [carc]	Eye: Irr immed Skin: Water flush immed Breath: Resp support Swallow: Medical attention immed	Eyes, skin, resp sys, CNS [in animals: thyroid gland tumors]

[Malonaldehyde]

Personal protection and sanitation	Recommendations for respirator selection	Route	Symptoms	First aid	Target organs
Skin: Prevent skin contact Eyes: Prevent eye contact Wash skin: When contam Remove: When wet or contam Change: Daily Provide: Eyewash, Quick drench	NIOSH 80 mg/m³: SA 200 mg/m³: SA:CF 400 mg/m³: SCBAF/SAF 667 mg/m³: SAF:PD,PP §: SCBAF:PD,PP/SAF:PD,PP:ASCBA Escape: GMFOV/SCBAE	Inh Abs Ing Con	Irrit eyes, skin, nose, throat; head, dizz, weak, gidd, conf, convuls; dysp; abdom pain, nau, vomit	Eye: Irr immed Skin: Water wash immed Breath: Resp support Swallow: Medical attention immed	Eyes, skin, resp sys, CNS, CVS

[Malononitrile]

Personal protection and sanitation	Recommendations for respirator selection	Route	Symptoms	First aid	Target organs
Skin: N.R. Eyes: N.R. Wash skin: N.R. Remove: N.R. Change: N.R.	NIOSH 10 mg/m³: DMXSQ^/SA 25 mg/m³: SA:CF/PAPRDM^ 50 mg/m³: HiEF/SAT:CF/PAPRTHiE/ SCBAF/SAF/ 500 mg/m³: SA:PD,PP §: SCBAF:PD,PP/SAF:PD,PP:ASCBA Escape: HiEF/SCBAE	Inh Ing	Parkinson's; asthenia, insom, mental conf; metal fume fever: dry throat, cough, chest tight, dysp, rales, flu-like fever; low-back pain; vomit; mal; ftg; kidney damage	Breath: Resp support Swallow: Medical attention immed	Resp sys, CNS, blood, kidneys

[Manganese compounds and fume (as Mn)]

Personal protection and sanitation	Recommendations for respirator selection	Route	Symptoms	First aid	Target organs
Skin: Prevent skin contact Eyes: Prevent eye contact Wash skin: When contam Remove: When wet or contam Change: Daily	TBAL	Inh Abs Ing Con	In animals: irrit skin; pulm edema; convuls; CNS, resp sys, kidney changes; decr resistance to infection	Eye: Irr immed Skin: Soap wash Breath: Resp support Swallow: Medical attention immed	Skin, resp sys, CNS, kidneys

[Manganese cyclopentadienyl tricarbonyl (as Mn)]

Chemical name, structure/formula, CAS and RTECS Nos., and DOT ID and guide Nos.	Synonyms, trade names, and conversion factors	Exposure limits (TWA unless noted otherwise)	IDLH	Physical description	Chemical and physical properties		Incompatibilities and reactivities	Measurement method (See Table 1)
					MW, BP, SOL FI.P, IP, Sp, Gr, flammability	VP, FRZ UEL, LEL		
Manganese tetroxide (as Mn) Mn_3O_4 1317-35-7 OP0895000	Manganese oxide, Manganomanganic oxide, Trimanganese tetraoxide, Trimanganese tetroxide	NIOSH See Appendix D OSHA† C 5 mg/m³	N.D.	Brownish-black powder. [Note: Fumes are generated whenever manganese oxides are heated strongly in air.]	MW: 228.8 BP: ? Sol: Insoluble FI.P: NA IP: NA Sp.Gr: 4.88	VP: 0 mm (approx) MLT: 2847°F UEL: NA LEL: NA	Soluble in hydrochloric acid (liberates chlorine gas)	Filter; Acids; ICP; IV [#7300, Elements]
Marble $CaCO_3$ 1317-65-3 EV9580000	Calcium carbonate, Natural calcium carbonate [Note: Marble is a metamorphic form of calcium carbonate.]	NIOSH 10 mg/m³ (total) 5 mg/m³ (resp) OSHA 15 mg/m³ (total) 5 mg/m³ (resp)	N.D.	Odorless, white powder.	MW: 100.1 BP: Decomposes Sol: 0.001% FI.P: NA IP: NA Sp.Gr: 2.7-2.9 Noncombustible Solid	VP: 0 mm (approx) MLT: 1517-2442°F (Decomposes) UEL: NA LEL: NA	Fluorine, magnesium, acids, alum, ammonium salts	Filter; none; Grav; IV [Particulates NOR: #0500 (total), #0600 (resp)]
Mercury compounds [except (organo) alkyls] (as Hg) Hg (Metal) 7439-97-6 (Metal) OV4550000 (Metal) 2809 172	Mercury metal: Colloidal mercury, Elemental mercury, Metallic mercury, Quicksilver Synonyms of "other" Hg compounds vary depending upon the specific compound.	NIOSH Hg Vapor: 0.05 mg/m³ [skin] Other: C 0.1 mg/m³ [skin] OSHA† C 0.1 mg/m³	10 mg/m³ (as Hg)	Metal: Silver-white, heavy, odorless liquid. [Note: "Other" Hg compounds include all inorganic & aryl Hg compounds except (organo) alkyls.]	MW: 200.6 BP: 674°F Sol: Insoluble FI.P: NA IP: ? Sp.Gr: 13.6 (Metal) Metal: Noncombustible Liquid	VP: 0.0012 mm FRZ: -38°F UEL: NA LEL: NA	Acetylene, ammonia, chlorine dioxide, azides, calcium (amalgam formation), sodium carbide, lithium, rubidium, copper	Hopcalite; Acid; AA cold; IV [#6009, Mercury]
Mercury (organo) alkyl compounds (as Hg)	Synonyms vary depending upon the specific (organo) alkyl mercury compound.	NIOSH 0.01 mg/m³ ST 0.03 mg/m³ [skin] OSHA† 0.01 mg/m³ C 0.04 mg/m³	2 mg/m³ (as Hg)	Appearance and odor vary depending upon the specific (organo) alkyl mercury compound.	Properties vary depending upon the specific (organo) alkyl mercury compound.		Strong oxidizers such as chlorine	None available

Personal protection and sanitation (See Table 3)		Recommendations for respirator selection — maximum concentration for use (MUC) (See Table 4)	Health hazards				
			Route	Symptoms (See Table 5)	First aid (See Table 6)		Target organs (See Table 5)
Skin:	N.R.	TBAL	Inh	Asthenia, insom, mental	Eye:	Irr immed	Resp sys, CNS,
Eyes:	N.R.		Ing	conf; low-back pain, vomit;	Skin:	Soap wash	blood, kidneys
Wash skin:	N.R.		Con	mal, ftg; kidney damage;	Breath:	Resp support	
Remove:	N.R.			pneuitis	Swallow:	Medical attention	
Change:	Daily					immed	

[Manganese tetraoxide (as Mn)]

Skin:	N.R.	TBAL	Inh	Irrit eyes, skin, muc memb,	Eye:	Irr immed	Eyes, skin, resp sys
Eyes:	N.R.		Con	upper resp sys; cough,	Skin:	Soap wash	
Wash skin:	N.R.			sneez, rhin; lac	Breath:	Fresh air	
Remove:	N.R.						
Change:	N.R.						

[Marble]

Skin:	Prevent skin contact	See Appendix E for	Inh	Irrit eyes, skin; cough,	Eye:	Irr immed	Eyes, skin, resp sys,
Eyes:	N.R.	Respirator Recommendations	Abs	chest pain, dysp, bron	Skin:	Soap wash prompt	CNS, kidneys
Wash skin:	When contam	for Mercury compounds	Ing	pneuitis; tremor, insom,	Breath:	Resp support	
Remove:	When wet or contam	[except (organo) alkyls].	Con	irrity, indecision, head,	Swallow:	Medical attention	
Change:	Daily			ftg, weak; stomatitis, salv;		immed	
				GI dist, anor, low-wgt; prot			

[Mercury compounds [except (organo) alkyls] (as Hg)]

Skin:	Prevent skin contact	NIOSH/OSHA	Inh	Pares; ataxia, dysarthria;	Eye:	Irr immed	Eyes, skin, CNS,
Eyes:	Prevent eye contact	0.1 mg/m³: SA	Abs	vision, hearing dist;	Skin:	Soap wash immed	PNS, kidneys
Wash skin:	When contam	0.25 mg/m³: SA:CF	Ing	spasticity, jerking limbs;	Breath:	Resp support	
Remove:	When wet or contam	0.5 mg/m³: SAT:CF/SCBAF/SAF	Con	dizz; salv; lac; nau, vomit,	Swallow:	Medical attention	
Change:	Daily	2 mg/m³: SA:PD,PP		diarr, constip; skin burns;		immed	
Provide:	Eyewash, Quick drench	§: SCBAF:PD,PP/SAF:PD,PP:ASCBA		emotional dist; kidney inj;			
		Escape: SCBAE		possible terato effects			

[Mercury (organo) alkyl compounds (as Hg)]

Chemical name, structure/formula, CAS and RTECS Nos., and DOT ID and guide Nos.	Synonyms, trade names, and conversion factors	Exposure limits (TWA unless noted otherwise)	IDLH	Physical description	Chemical and physical properties		Incompatibilities and reactivities	Measurement method (See Table 1)
					MW, BP, SOL FI.P, IP, Sp, Gr, flammability	VP, FRZ UEL, LEL		
Mesityl oxide (CH₃)₂C=CHCOCH₃ 141-79-7 SB4200000 1229 129	Isobutenyl methyl ketone, Isopropylideneacetone, Methyl isobutenyl ketone, 4-Methyl-3-penten-2-one 1 ppm = 4.02 mg/m³	NIOSH 10 ppm (40 mg/m³) OSHA† 25 ppm (100 mg/m³)	1400 ppm [10%LEL]	Oily, colorless to light-yellow liquid with a peppermint- or honey-like odor.	MW: 98.2 BP: 266°F Sol: 3% FI.P: 87°F IP: 9.08 eV Sp.Gr(59°F): 0.86 Class IC Flammable Liquid	VP: 9 mm FRZ: -52°F UEL: 7.2% LEL:1.4%	Oxidizers, acids	Char; Methanol/ CS₂; GC/FID; IV [#1301, Ketones II]
Methacrylic acid CH₂=C(CH₃)COOH 79-41-4 OZ2975000 2531 153P (inhibited)	Methacrylic acid (glacial), Methacrylic acid (inhibited), α -Methacrylic acid, 2-Methylacrylic acid, 2-Methylpropenoic acid 1 ppm = 3.52 mg/m³	NIOSH 20 ppm (70 mg/m³) [skin] OSHA† none	N.D.	Colorless liquid or solid (below 61°F) with an acrid, repulsive odor.	MW: 86.1 BP: 325°F Sol(77°F): 9% FI.P(oc): 171°F IP: ? Sp.Gr: 1.02 (Liquid) Class IIIA Combustible Liquid	VP: 0.7 mm FRZ: 61°F UEL: ? LEL: ?	Oxidizers, elevated temperatures, hydrochloric acid [Note: Typically contains 100 ppm of the monomethyl ether of hydroquinone to prevent polymerization.]	Anasorb(2) Methanol/ Water; HPLC/UV; OSHA [#28]
Methomyl CH₃C(SCH₃)NOC(O)NHCH₃ 16752-77-5 AK2975000 2757 151 (carbamate pesticide, solid, n.o.s.)	Lannate®, Methyl N-((methylamino)-carbonyl)oxy)ethanimi-dothioate, S-Methyl-N-(methylcarbamoyl-oxy)thioacetimidate	NIOSH 2.5 mg/m³ OSHA† none	N.D.	White, crystalline solid with a slight, sulfur-like odor. [insecticide]	MW: 162.2 BP: ? Sol(77°F):6% FI.P: NA IP: ? Sp.Gr(75°F): 1.29 Noncombustible Solid, but may be dissolved in flammable liquids.	VP(77°F): 0.00005 mm MLT: 172°F UEL: NA LEL: NA	Strong bases	None available
Methoxychlor (C₆H₄OCH₃)₂CHCCl₃ 72-43-5 KJ3675000 2761 151 (organochlorine pesticide, solid, n.o.s.)	p,p'-Dimethoxydiphenyltri-chloroethane; DMDT; Methoxy-DDT; 2,2-bis(p-Methoxyphenyl)-1,1,1-trichloroethane; 1,1,1-Trichloro-2,2-bis-(p-methoxyphenyl)ethane	NIOSH Ca See Appendix A OSHA† 15 mg/m³	Ca [5000 mg/m³]	Colorless to light-yellow crystals with a slight, fruity odor. [insecticide]	MW: 345.7 BP: Decomposes Sol: 0.00001% FI.P: ? IP: ? Sp.Gr: 1.41 Combustible Solid, but difficult to burn.	VP: Very low MLT:171°F UEL: ? LEL: ?	Oxidizers	Filter; Isooctane; GC/ECD; II(4) [#S371]

Personal protection and sanitation (See Table 3)		Recommendations for respirator selection — maximum concentration for use (MUC) (See Table 4)	Route	Health hazards		
				Symptoms (See Table 5)	First aid (See Table 6)	Target organs (See Table 5)
Skin:	Prevent skin contact	NIOSH	Inh	Irrit eyes, skin, muc	Eye: Irr immed	Eyes, skin, resp
Eyes:	Prevent eye contact	250 ppm: SA:CF^E/PAPROV^E	Ing	memb; narco, coma;	Skin: Water flush immed	sys, CNS, liver,
Wash skin:	When contam	500 ppm: CCRFOV/GMFOV/PAPRTOV^E/	Con	in animals: liver, kidney	Breath: Resp support	kidneys
Remove:	When wet (flamm)	SCBAF/SAF		damage; CNS effects	Swallow: Medical attention	
Change:	N.R.	1400 ppm: SAF:PD,PP			immed	
Provide:	Quick drench	§: SCBAF:PD,PP/SAF:PD,PP:ASCBA				
		Escape: GMFOV/SCBAE				

[Mesityl oxide]

Personal protection and sanitation		Recommendations for respirator selection	Route	Health hazards		
Skin:	Prevent skin contact	TBAL	Inh	Irrit eyes, skin, muc memb;	Eye: Irr immed	Eyes, skin, resp sys
Eyes:	Prevent eye contact		Abs	eye, skin burns	Skin: Water flush immed	
Wash skin:	When contam		Ing		Breath: Resp support	
Remove:	When wet or contam		Con		Swallow: Medical attention	
Change:	Daily				immed	
Provide:	Eyewash, Quick drench					

[Methacrylic acid]

Personal protection and sanitation		Recommendations for respirator selection	Route	Health hazards		
Skin:	Prevent skin contact	TBAL	Inh	Irrit eyes; blurred vision,	Eye: Irr immed	Eyes, resp sys, CNS,
Eyes:	Prevent eye contact		Ing	miosis; salv; abdom cramps,	Skin: Water flush immed	CVS, liver, kidneys,
Wash skin:	When contam		Con	nau, vomit; dysp; weak,	Breath: Resp support	blood chol
Remove:	When wet or contam			musc twitch; liver, kidney	Swallow: Medical attention	
Change:	Daily			damage	immed	
Provide:	Quick drench					

[Methomyl]

Personal protection and sanitation		Recommendations for respirator selection	Route	Health hazards		
Skin:	Prevent skin contact	NIOSH	Inh	In animals: fasc, trembling,	Skin: Soap wash	CNS, liver, kidneys
Eyes:	N.R.	¥: SCBAF:PD,PP/SAF:PD,PP:ASCBA	Ing	convuls; kidney, liver	Breath: Fresh air	[in animals:
Wash skin:	When contam/Daily	Escape: GMFOVHiE/SCBAE		damage; [carc]	Swallow: Medical attention	liver & ovarian
Remove:	When wet or contam				immed	cancer]
Change:	Daily					

[Methoxychlor]

Chemical name, structure/formula, CAS and RTECS Nos., and DOT ID and guide Nos.	Synonyms, trade names, and conversion factors	Exposure limits (TWA unless noted otherwise)	IDLH	Physical description	Chemical and physical properties		Incompatibilities and reactivities	Measurement method (See Table 1)
					MW, BP, SOL Fl.P, IP, Sp, Gr, flammability	VP, FRZ UEL, LEL		
Methoxyflurane CHCl$_2$CF$_2$OCH$_3$ 76-38-0 KN7820000	2,2-Dichloro-1,1-difluoro-ethyl methyl ether; 2,2-Dichloro-1,1-difluoro-1-methoxyethane; Methoflurane; Methoxyfluorane; Penthrane 1 ppm = 6.75 mg/m³	NIOSH* C 2 ppm (13.5 mg/m³) [60-min] [*Note: REL for exposure to waste anesthetic gas.] OSHA none	N.D.	Colorless liquid with a fruity odor. [inhalation anesthetic]	MW: 165.0 BP: 220°F Sol: Slight Fl.P: ? IP: ? Sp.Gr(77°F): 1.42 Combustible Liquid	VP: 23 mm FRZ: -31°F UEL: ? LEL(176°F):7%	None reported	None available
4-Methoxyphenol CH$_3$OC$_6$H$_4$OH 150-76-5 SL7700000	Hydroquinone monomethyl ether, p-Hydroxyanisole, Mequinol, p-Methoxyphenol, Monomethyl ether hydroquinone	NIOSH 5 mg/m³ OSHA† none	N.D.	Colorless to white, waxy solid with an odor of caramel & phenol.	MW: 124.2 BP: 469°F Sol(77°F): 4% Fl.P(oc): 270°F IP: 7.50 eV Sp.Gr. 1.55 Combustible Solid; under certain conditions, a dust cloud can probably explode if ignited by a spark or flame.	VP: <0.01 mm MLT: 135°F UEL: ? LEL: ?	Strong oxidizers, strong bases, acid chlorides, acid anhydrides	None available
Methyl acetate CH$_3$COOCH$_3$ 79-20-9 AI9100000 1231 26	Methyl ester of acetic acid, Methyl ethanoate 1 ppm = 3.03 mg/m³	NIOSH 200 ppm (610 mg/m³) ST 250 ppm (760 mg/m³) OSHA† 200 ppm (610 mg/m³)	3100 ppm [10%LEL]	Colorless liquid with a fragrant, fruity odor.	MW: 74.1 BP: 135°F Sol: 25% Fl.P: 14°F IP: 10.27 eV Sp.Gr. 0.93 Class IB Flammable Liquid	VP: 173 mm FRZ: -145°F UEL: 16% LEL: 3.1%	Nitrates; strong oxidizers, alkalis & acids; water [Note: Reacts slowly with water to form acetic acid & methanol.]	Char; CS$_2$; GC/FID; IV [#1458]
Methyl acetylene CH$_3$C≡CH 74-99-7 UK4250000	Allylene, Propine, Propyne, 1-Propyne 1 ppm = 1.64 mg/m³	NIOSH/OSHA 1000 ppm (1650 mg/m³)	1700 ppm [10%LEL]	Colorless gas with a sweet odor. [Note: A fuel that is shipped as a liquefied compressed gas.]	MW: 40.1 BP: -10°F Sol: Insoluble Fl.P: NA (Gas) IP: 10.36 eV RGasD: 1.41 Flammable Gas	VP: 5.2 atm FRZ: -153°F UEL: ? LEL: 1.7%	Strong oxidizers (such as chlorine), copper alloys [Note: Can decompose explosively at 4.5 to 5.6 atmospheres of pressure.]	Bag; none; GC/FID; II(5) [#S84]

Personal protection and sanitation (See Table 3)		Recommendations for respirator selection — maximum concentration for use (MUC) (See Table 4)	Health hazards				
			Route	Symptoms (See Table 5)	First aid (See Table 6)		Target organs (See Table 5)
Skin: Eyes: Wash skin: Remove: Change:	N.R. Prevent eye contact N.R. When wet or contam N.R.	TBAL	Inh Ing Con	Irrit eyes; CNS depres, analgesia; anes, sez, resp depres; liver, kidney inj; in animals: repro, terato effects	Eye: Skin: Breath: Swallow:	Irr immed Soap wash Resp support Medical attention immed	Eyes, CNS, liver, kidneys, repro sys

[Methoxyflurane]

Personal protection and sanitation (See Table 3)		Recommendations for respirator selection — maximum concentration for use (MUC) (See Table 4)	Health hazards				
Skin: Eyes: Wash skin: Remove: Change: Provide:	Prevent skin contact Prevent eye contact When contam When wet or contam Daily Eyewash, Quick drench	TBAL	Inh Abs Ing Con	Irrit eyes, skin, nose, throat, upper resp sys; eye, skin burns; CNS depres	Eye: Skin: Breath: Swallow:	Irr immed Soap flush immed Resp support Medical attention immed	Eyes, skin, resp sys, CNS

[4-Methoxyphenol]

Personal protection and sanitation (See Table 3)		Recommendations for respirator selection — maximum concentration for use (MUC) (See Table 4)	Health hazards				
Skin: Eyes: Wash skin: Remove: Change:	Prevent skin contact Prevent eye contact When contam When wet (flamm) N.R.	NIOSH/OSHA 2000 ppm: CCROV*/SA* 3100 ppm: SA:CF*/CCRFOV/GMFOV/ PAPROV*/SCBAF/SAF §: SCBAF:PD,PP/SAF:PD,PP:ASCBA Escape: GMFOV/SCBAE	Inh Ing Con	Irrit eyes, skin, nose, throat; head, drow; optic nerve atrophy; chest tight; in animals: narco	Eye: Skin: Breath: Swallow:	Irr immed Water flush prompt Resp support Medical attention immed	Eyes, skin, resp sys, CNS

[Methyl acetate]

Personal protection and sanitation (See Table 3)		Recommendations for respirator selection — maximum concentration for use (MUC) (See Table 4)	Health hazards				
Skin: Eyes: Wash skin: Remove: Change: Provide:	Frostbite Frostbite N.R. When wet (flamm) N.R. Frostbite	NIOSH/OSHA 1700 ppm: SA/SCBAF §: SCBAF:PD,PP/SAF:PD,PP:ASCBA Escape: GMFOV/SCBAE	Inh Con (liq)	Irrit resp sys; tremor, hyperexcitability, anes; liq: frostbite	Eye: Skin: Breath:	Frostbite Frostbite Resp support	Resp sys, CNS

[Methyl acetylene]

Chemical name, structure/formula, CAS and RTECS Nos., and DOT ID and guide Nos.	Synonyms, trade names, and conversion factors	Exposure limits (TWA unless noted otherwise)	IDLH	Physical description	Chemical and physical properties		Incompatibilities and reactivities	Measurement method (See Table 1)
					MW, BP, SOL Fl.P, IP, Sp, Gr, flammability	VP, FRZ UEL, LEL		
Methyl acetylene-propadiene mixture CH₃C≡CH/CH₂=C=CH₂ 59355-75-8 UK4920000 1060 116P (stabilized)	MAPP gas, Methyl acetylene-allene mixture, Methyl acetylene-propadiene mixture (stabilized), Propadiene-methyl acetylene, Propyne-allene mixture, Propyne-propadiene mixture 1 ppm = 1.64 mg/m³	NIOSH 1000 ppm (1800 mg/m³) ST 1250 ppm (2250 mg/m³) OSHA† 1000 ppm (1800 mg/m³)	3400 ppm [10%LEL]	Colorless gas with a strong, characteristic, foul odor. [Note: A fuel that is shipped as a liquefied compressed gas.]	MW: 40.1 BP: -36 to -4°F Sol: Insoluble Fl.P: NA (Gas) IP: ? RGasD: 1.48 Flammable Gas	VP:>1 atm FRZ:-213°F UEL:10.8% LEL:3.4%	Strong oxidizers, copper alloys [Note: Forms explosive compounds at high pressure in contact with alloys containing more than 67% copper.]	Bag; none; GC/FID; II(6) [#S85]
Methyl acrylate CH₂=CHCOOCH₃ 96-33-3 AT2800000 1919 129P (inhibited)	Methoxycarbonylethylene, Methyl ester of acrylic acid, Methyl propenoate 1 ppm = 3.52 mg/m³	NIOSH/OSHA 10 ppm (35 mg/m³) [skin]	250 ppm	Colorless liquid with an acrid odor.	MW: 86.1 BP: 176°F Sol: 6% Fl.P: 27°F IP: 9.90 eV Sp.Gr: 0.96 Class IB Flammable Liquid	VP: 65 mm FRZ:-106°F UEL: 25% LEL: 2.8%	Nitrates, oxidizers such as peroxides, strong alkalis [Note: Polymerizes easily; usually contains an inhibitor such as hydroquinone.]	Char; CS₂; GC/FID; IV [#1459]
Methylacrylonitrile CH₂=C(CH₃)CN 126-98-7 UD1400000 3079 131P (inhibited)	2-Cyanopropene-1, 2-Cyano-1-propene, Isoprene cyanide, Isopropenylnitrile, Methacrylonitrile, α–Methylacrylonitrile, 2-Methylpropenenitrile 1 ppm = 2.74 mg/m³	NIOSH 1 ppm (3 mg/m³) [skin] OSHA† none	N.D.	Colorless liquid with an odor like bitter almonds.	MW: 67.1 BP: 195°F Sol: 3% Fl.P: 34°F IP: ? Sp.Gr: 0.80 Class IB Flammable Liquid	VP(77°F): 71mm FRZ: -32°F UEL: 6.8% LEL: 2%	Strong acids, strong oxidizers, alkali, light [Note: Polymerization may occur due to elevated temperature, visible light, or contact with a concentrated alkali.]	None available
Methylal CH₃OCH₂OCH₃ 109-87-5 PA8750000 1234 127	Dimethoxymethane, Formal, Formaldehyde dimethylacetal, Methoxymethyl methyl ether, Methylene dimethyl ether 1 ppm = 3.11 mg/m³	NIOSH/OSHA 1000 ppm (3100 mg/m³)	2200 ppm [10%LEL]	Colorless liquid with a chloroform-like odor.	MW: 76.1 BP: 111°F Sol: 33% Fl.P(oc): -26°F IP: 10.00 eV Sp.Gr: 0.86 Class IB Flammable Liquid	VP: 330 mm FRZ:-157°F UEL: 13.8% LEL: 2.2%	Strong oxidizers, acids	Char; Hexane; GC/FID; IV [#1611]

Personal protection and sanitation (See Table 3)		Recommendations for respirator selection — maximum concentration for use (MUC) (See Table 4)	Health hazards					
			Route	Symptoms (See Table 5)	First aid (See Table 6)		Target organs (See Table 5)	

Personal protection and sanitation (See Table 3)		Recommendations for respirator selection — MUC (See Table 4)	Route	Symptoms (See Table 5)	First aid (See Table 6)		Target organs (See Table 5)
Skin:	Frostbite	NIOSH/OSHA	Inh	Irrit resp sys; excitement,	Eye:	Frostbite	Resp sys, CNS
Eyes:	Frostbite	3400 ppm: SA/SCBAF	Con	conf, anes; liq: frostbite	Skin:	Frostbite	
Wash skin:	N.R.	§: SCBAF:PD,PP/SAF:PD,PP:ASCBA	(liq)		Breath:	Resp support	
Remove:	When wet (flamm)	Escape: GMFS/SCBAE					
Change:	N.R.						
Provide:	Frostbite						

[Methyl acetylene-propadiene mixture]

Skin:	Prevent skin contact	NIOSH/OSHA	Inh	Irrit eyes, skin, upper	Eye:	Irr immed	Eyes, skin, resp sys
Eyes:	Prevent eye contact	100 ppm: SA*	Abs	resp sys	Skin:	Water flush immed	
Wash skin:	When contam	250 ppm: SA:CF*/SCBAF/SAF	Ing		Breath:	Resp support	
Remove:	When wet (flamm)	§: SCBAF:PD,PP/SAF:PD,PP:ASCBA	Con		Swallow:	Medical attention	
Change:	N.R.	Escape: GMFOV/SCBAE				immed	
Provide:	Quick drench						

[Methyl acrylate]

Skin:	Prevent skin contact	TBAL	Inh	Irrit eyes, skin; lac,	Eye:	Irr immed	Eyes, skin, CNS
Eyes:	Prevent eye contact		Abs	in animals: convuls,	Skin:	Soap wash immed	
Wash skin:	When contam		Ing	loss of motor control in	Breath:	Resp support	
Remove:	When wet (flamm)		Con	hind limbs	Swallow:	Medical attention	
Change:	N.R.					immed	

[Methylacrylonitrile]

Skin:	Prevent skin contact	NIOSH/OSHA	Inh	Irrit eyes, skin, upper	Eye:	Irr immed	Eyes, skin, resp sys,
Eyes:	Prevent eye contact	2200 ppm: SA/SCBAF	Ing	resp sys; anes	Skin:	Water flush prompt	CNS
Wash skin:	When contam	§: SCBAF:PD,PP/SAF:PD,PP:ASCBA	Con		Breath:	Resp support	
Remove:	When wet (flamm)	Escape: GMFOV/SCBAE			Swallow:	Medical attention	
Change:	N.R.					immed	

[Methylal]

Chemical name, structure/formula, CAS and RTECS Nos., and DOT ID and guide Nos.	Synonyms, trade names, and conversion factors	Exposure limits (TWA unless noted otherwise)	IDLH	Physical description	Chemical and physical properties		Incompatibilities and reactivities	Measurement method (See Table 1)
					MW, BP, SOL FI.P, IP, Sp, Gr, flammability	VP, FRZ UEL, LEL		
Methyl alcohol CH_3OH 67-56-1 PC1400000 1230 131	Carbinol, Columbian spirits, Methanol, Pyroligneous spirit, Wood alcohol, Wood naphtha, Wood spirit 1 ppm = 1.31 mg/m³	NIOSH 200 ppm (260 mg/m³) ST 250 ppm (325 mg/m³) [skin] OSHA† 200 ppm (260 mg/m³)	6000 ppm	Colorless liquid with a characteristic pungent odor.	MW: 32.1 BP: 147°F Sol: Miscible FI.P: 52°F IP: 10.84 eV Sp.Gr: 0.79 Class IB Flammable Liquid	VP: 96 mm FRZ: -144°F UEL: 36% LEL: 6.0%	Strong oxidizers	Si gel; Water; GC/FID; IV [#2000, Methanol]
Methylamine CH_3NH_2 74-89-5 PF6300000 1061 118 (anhydrous) 1235 132 (aqueous)	Aminomethane, Anhydrous methylamine, Aqueous methylamine, Monomethylamine 1 ppm = 1.27 mg/m³	NIOSH/OSHA 10 ppm (12 mg/m³)	100 ppm	Colorless gas with a fish- or ammonia-like odor. [Note: A liquid below 21°F. Shipped as a liquefied compressed gas.]	MW: 31.1 BP: 21°F Sol: Soluble FI.P: NA (Gas) 14°F (Liq) IP: 8.97 eV RGasD: 1.08 Sp.Gr: 0.70 (Liquid at 13°F) Flammable Gas Class IA Flammable Liquid	VP: 3.0 atm FRZ: -136°F UEL: 20.7% LEL: 4.9%	Mercury, strong oxidizers, nitromethane [Note: Corrosive to copper & zinc alloys, aluminum & galvanized surfaces.]	XAD-7*; THF; HPLC/FLU/vis; OSHA [#40]
Methyl (n-amyl) ketone $CH_3CO[CH_2]_4CH_3$ 110-43-0 MJ5075000 1110 127	Amyl methyl ketone, n-Amyl methyl ketone, 2-Heptanone 1 ppm = 4.67 mg/m³	NIOSH/OSHA 100 ppm (465 mg/m³)	800 ppm	Colorless to white liquid with a banana-like, fruity odor.	MW: 114.2 BP: 305°F Sol: 0.4% FI.P: 102°F IP: 9.33 eV Sp.Gr: 0.81 Class II Combustible Liquid	VP: 3 mm FRZ: -32°F UEL(250°F): 7.9% LEL(151°F): 1.1%	Strong acids, alkalis & oxidizers [Note: Will attack some forms of plastic.]	Char; Methanol/ CS₂; GC/FID; IV [#1301, Ketones II]
Methyl bromide CH_3Br 74-83-9 PA4900000 1062 123	Bromomethane, Monobromomethane 1 ppm = 3.89 mg/m³	NIOSH Ca See Appendix A OSHA† C 20 ppm (80 mg/m³) [skin]	Ca [250 ppm]	Colorless gas with a chloroform-like odor at high concentrations. [Note: A liquid below 38°F. Shipped as a liquefied compressed gas.]	MW: 95.0 BP: 38°F Sol: 2% FI.P: NA (Gas) IP: 10.54 eV RGasD: 3.36 Sp.Gr: 1.73 (Liquid at 32°F) Flammable Gas, but only in presence of a high energy ignition source.	VP: 1.9 atm FRZ: -137°F UEL: 16.0% LEL: 10%	Aluminum, magnesium, strong oxidizers [Note: Attacks aluminum to form aluminum trimethyl, which is SPONTANE-OUSLY flammable.]	Char(pet)(2)/ dry tube; CS₂; GC/FID; IV [#2520]

	Personal protection and sanitation (See Table 3)	Recommendations for respirator selection — maximum concentration for use (MUC) (See Table 4)	Health hazards				
			Route	Symptoms (See Table 5)		First aid (See Table 6)	Target organs (See Table 5)
Skin: Eyes: Wash skin: Remove: Change:	Prevent skin contact Prevent eye contact When contam When wet (flamm) N.R.	NIOSH/OSHA 2000 ppm: SA 5000 ppm: SA:CF 6000 ppm: SAT:CF/SCBAF/SAF §: SCBAF:PD,PP/SAF:PD,PP:ASCBA Escape: SCBAE	Inh Abs Ing Con	Irrit eyes, skin, upper resp sys; head, drow, dizz, verti, li-head, nau, vomit; vis dist, optic nerve damage (blindness); derm		Eye: Irr immed Skin: Water flush prompt Breath: Resp support Swallow: Medical attention immed	Eyes, resp sys, CNS, GI tract
[Methyl alcohol]							

Skin:
Eyes:
Wash skin:
Remove:
Change:
Provide:
	Prevent skin contact (soln)/Frostbite
	Prevent eye contact (soln)/Frostbite
	When contam (soln)
	When wet (flamm)
	N.R.
	Frostbite
		NIOSH/OSHA
		100 ppm: CCRFS/GMFS/PAPRS£/
		            SCBAF/SAF
		§: SCBAF:PD,PP/SAF:PD,PP:ASCBA
		Escape: GMFS/SCBAE
			Inh
			Abs
			(soln)
			Ing
			(soln)
			Con
			(soln/liq)
				Irrit eyes, skin, resp sys; cough; skin, muc memb burns; derm; conj; liq: frostbite		Eye: Irr immed (soln)/
						            Frostbite
						Skin: Water flush immed
						            (soln)/Frostbite
						Breath: Resp support
						Swallow: Medical attention
						            immed (soln)
							Eyes, skin, resp sys

[Methylamine]							

Skin:
Eyes:
Wash skin:
Remove:
Change:
	Prevent skin contact
	Prevent eye contact
	When contam
	When wet or contam
	N.R.
		NIOSH/OSHA
		800 ppm: CCROV*/PAPROV*/GMFOV/
		            SA*/SCBAF
		§: SCBAF:PD,PP/SAF:PD,PP:ASCBA
		Escape: GMFOV/SCBAE
			Inh
			Ing
			Con
				Irrit eyes, skin, muc memb; head; narco; coma; derm		Eye: Irr immed
						Skin: Soap wash
						Breath: Fresh air
						Swallow: Medical attention
						            immed
							Eyes, skin, resp sys, CNS, PNS

[Methyl (n-amyl) ketone]							
Skin: Eyes: Wash skin: Remove: Change: Provide:	Prevent skin contact (liq) Prevent eye contact (liq) When contam When wet (flamm) N.R. Quick drench (liq)	NIOSH ¥: SCBAF:PD,PP/SAF:PD,PP:ASCBA Escape: GMFOV/SCBAE	Inh Abs (liq) Con (liq)	Irrit eyes, skin, resp sys; musc weak, inco, vis dist, verti; nau, vomit, head; mal; hand tremor; convuls; dysp; skin vesic; liq: frostbite; [carc]		Eye: Irr immed (liq) Skin: Water flush immed (liq) Breath: Resp support	Eyes, skin, resp sys, CNS [in animals: lung, kidney & forestomach tumors]
[Methyl bromide]							

Chemical name, structure/formula, CAS and RTECS Nos., and DOT ID and guide Nos.	Synonyms, trade names, and conversion factors	Exposure limits (TWA unless noted otherwise)	IDLH	Physical description	Chemical and physical properties — MW, BP, SOL, Fl.P, IP, Sp.Gr, flammability	VP, FRZ, UEL, LEL	Incompatibilities and reactivities	Measurement method (See Table 1)
Methyl Cellosolve® CH$_3$OCH$_2$CH$_2$OH 109-86-4 KL5775000 1188 127	EGME, Ethylene glycol monomethyl ether, Glycol monomethyl ether, 2-Methoxyethanol 1 ppm = 3.11 mg/m^3	NIOSH 0.1 ppm (0.3 mg/m^3) [skin] OSHA 25 ppm (80 mg/m^3) [skin]	200 ppm	Colorless liquid with a mild, ether-like odor.	MW: 76.1 BP: 256°F Sol: Miscible Fl.P: 102°F IP: 9.60 eV Sp.Gr: 0.96 Class II Combustible Liquid	VP: 6 mm FRZ: -121°F UEL: 14% LEL: 1.8%	Strong oxidizers, caustics	Char; Methanol/ CH$_2$Cl$_2$; GC/FID; IV [#1403, Alcohols IV]
Methyl Cellosolve® acetate CH$_3$COOCH$_2$CH$_2$OCH$_3$ 110-49-6 KL5950000 1189 129	EGMEA, Ethylene glycol monomethyl ether acetate, Glycol monomethyl ether acetate, 2-Methoxyethyl acetate 1 ppm = 4.83 mg/m^3	NIOSH 0.1 ppm (0.5 mg/m^3) [skin] OSHA 25 ppm (120 mg/m^3) [skin]	200 ppm	Colorless liquid with a mild, ether-like odor.	MW: 118.1 BP: 293°F Sol: Miscible Fl.P: 120°F IP: ? Sp.Gr: 1.01 Class II Combustible Liquid	VP: 2 mm FRZ: -85°F UEL: 8.2% LEL: 1.7%	Nitrates; strong oxidizers, alkalis & acids	Char; CS$_2$; GC/FID; IV [#1451]
Methyl chloride CH$_3$Cl 74-87-3 PA6300000 1063 115	Chloromethane, Monochloromethane 1 ppm = 2.07 mg/m^3	NIOSH Ca See Appendix A OSHA† 100 ppm C 200 ppm 300 ppm (5-min max peak in any 3 hrs)	Ca [2000 ppm]	Colorless gas with a faint, sweet odor which is not noticeable at dangerous concentrations. [Note: Shipped as a liquefied compressed gas.]	MW: 50.5 BP: -12°F Sol: 0.5% Fl.P: NA (Gas) IP: 11.28 eV RGasD: 1.78 Flammable Gas	VP: 5.0 atm FRZ: -144°F UEL: 17.4% LEL: 8.1%	Chemically-active metals such as potassium, powdered aluminum, zinc & magnesium; water [Note: Reacts with water (hydrolyzes) to form hydrochloric acid.]	Char(2); CH$_2$Cl$_2$; GC/FID; IV [#1001]
Methyl chloroform CH$_3$CCl$_3$ 71-55-6 KJ2975000 2831 160	Chlorothene; 1,1,1-Trichloroethane; 1,1,1-Trichloroethane (stabilized) 1 ppm = 5.46 mg/m^3	NIOSH C 350 ppm (1900 mg/m^3) [15-min] See Appendix C (Chloroethanes) OSHA† 350 ppm (1900 mg/m^3)	700 ppm	Colorless liquid with a mild, chloroform-like odor.	MW: 133.4 BP: 165°F Sol: 0.4% Fl.P: ? IP: 11.00 eV Sp.Gr: 1.34 Combustible Liquid, but burns with difficulty.	VP: 100 mm FRZ: -23°F UEL: 12.5% LEL: 7.5%	Strong caustics; strong oxidizers; chemically-active metals such as zinc, aluminum, magnesium powders, sodium & potassium; water [Note: Reacts slowly with water to form hydrochloric acid.]	Char; CS$_2$; GC/FID; IV [#1003, Halogenated Hydrocarbons]

Personal protection and sanitation (See Table 3)	Recommendations for respirator selection — maximum concentration for use (MUC) (See Table 4)	Health hazards			
		Route	Symptoms (See Table 5)	First aid (See Table 6)	Target organs (See Table 5)
Skin: Prevent skin contact Eyes: Prevent eye contact Wash skin: When contam Remove: When wet or contam Change: N.R. Provide: Quick drench	NIOSH 1 ppm: SA* 2.5 ppm: SA:CF* 5 ppm: SCBAF/SAF 100 ppm: SA:PD,PP* 200 ppm: SAF:PD,PP §: SCBAF:PD,PP/SAF:PD,PP:ASCBA Escape: GMFOV/SCBAE	Inh Abs Ing Con	Irrit eyes, nose, throat; head, drow, weak; ataxia, tremor, som; anemic pallor, in animals: repro, terato effects	Eye: Irr immed Skin: Water flush prompt Breath: Resp support Swallow: Medical attention immed	Eyes, resp sys, CNS, blood, kidneys, repro sys, hemato sys
[Methyl Cellosolve®]					
Skin: Prevent skin contact Eyes: Prevent eye contact Wash skin: When contam Remove: When wet or contam Change: N.R.	NIOSH 1 ppm: SA* 2.5 ppm: SA:CF* 5 ppm: SCBAF/SAF 100 ppm: SA:PD,PP* 200 ppm: SAF:PD,PP §: SCBAF:PD,PP/SAF:PD,PP:ASCBA Escape: GMFOV/SCBAE	Inh Abs Ing Con	Irrit eyes, nose, throat; kidney, brain damage; in animals: narco; repro, terato effects	Eye: Irr immed Skin: Water flush prompt Breath: Resp support Swallow: Medical attention immed	Eyes, resp sys, kidneys, brain, CNS, PNS, repro sys, hemato sys
[Methyl Cellosolve® acetate]					
Skin: Frostbite Eyes: Frostbite Wash skin: N.R. Remove: When wet (flamm) Change: N.R. Provide: Frostbite	NIOSH ¥: SCBAF:PD,PP/SAF:PD,PP:ASCBA Escape: SCBAE	Inh Con (liq)	Dizz, nau, vomit; vis dist, stagger, slurred speech, convuls, coma; liver, kidney damage; liq: frostbite; repro, terato effects; [carc]	Eye: Frostbite Skin: Frostbite Breath: Resp support	CNS, liver, kidneys, repro sys [in animals: lung, kidney & forestomach tumors]
[Methyl chloride]					
Skin: Prevent skin contact Eyes: Prevent eye contact Wash skin: When contam Remove: When wet or contam Change: N.R.	NIOSH/OSHA 700 ppm: SA*/SCBAF §: SCBAF:PD,PP/SAF:PD,PP:ASCBA Escape: GMFOV/SCBAE	Inh Ing Con	Irrit eyes, skin; head, lass, CNS depres, poor equi; derm; card arrhy; liver damage	Eye: Irr immed Skin: Soap wash prompt Breath: Resp support Swallow: Medical attention immed	Eyes, skin, CNS, CVS, liver
[Methyl chloroform]					

Chemical name, structure/formula, CAS and RTECS Nos., and DOT ID and guide Nos.	Synonyms, trade names, and conversion factors	Exposure limits (TWA unless noted otherwise)	IDLH	Physical description	Chemical and physical properties		Incompatibilities and reactivities	Measurement method (See Table 1)
					MW, BP, SOL FI.P, IP, Sp, Gr, flammability	VP, FRZ UEL, LEL		
Methyl-2-cyano-acrylate $CH_2=C(CN)COOCH_3$ 137-05-3 AS7000000	Mecrylate, Methyl cyanoacrylate, Methyl α-cyanoacrylate, Methyl ester of 2-cyano-acrylic acid	NIOSH 2 ppm (8 mg/m³) ST 4 ppm (16 mg/m³) OSHA† none	N.D.	Colorless liquid with a characteristic odor.	MW:111.1 BP: ? Sol: 30% Fl.P:174°F IP: ? Sp.Gr(81°F):1.10 Class IIIA Combustible Liquid	VP(77°F): 0.2 mm FRZ: ? UEL: ? LEL: ?	Moisture [Note: Contact with moisture causes rapid polymerization.]	XAD-7*; CH₂CN/ H₃PO₄ HPLC/UV; OSHA [#55]
	1 ppm = 4.54 mg/m³							
Methylcyclohexane $CH_3C_6H_{11}$ 108-87-2 GV6125000	Cyclohexylmethane, Hexahydrotoluene	NIOSH 400 ppm (1600 mg/m³) OSHA† 500 ppm (2000 mg/m³)	1200 ppm [10%LEL]	Colorless liquid with a faint, benzene-like odor.	MW: 98.2 BP: 214°F Sol: Insoluble Fl.P: 25°F IP: 9.85 eV Sp.Gr: 0.77 Class IB Flammable Liquid	VP: 37 mm FRZ: -196°F UEL:6.7% LEL:1.2%	Strong oxidizers	Char; CS₂; GC/FID; IV [#1500, Hydro-carbons]
2296 128	1 ppm = 4.02 mg/m³							
Methylcyclohexanol $CH_3C_6H_{10}OH$ 25639-42-3 GW0175000	Hexahydrocresol, Hexahydromethylphenol	NIOSH 50 ppm (235 mg/m³) OSHA† 100 ppm (470 mg/m³)	500 ppm	Straw-colored liquid with a weak odor like coconut oil.	MW: 114.2 BP: 311-356°F Sol: 4% Fl.P: 149-158°F IP: 9.80 eV Sp.Gr: 0.92 Class IIIA Combustible Liquid	VP(86°F): 2 mm FRZ: -58°F UEL: ? LEL: ?	Strong oxidizers	Char; CH₂Cl₂; GC/FID; IV [#1404]
2617 129	1 ppm = 4.67 mg/m³							
o-Methylcyclohexanone $CH_3C_6H_9O$ 583-60-8 GW1750000	2-Methylcyclohexanone	NIOSH 50 ppm (230 mg/m³) ST 75 ppm (345 mg/m³ [skin] OSHA† 100 ppm (460 mg/m³) [skin]	600 ppm	Colorless liquid with a weak, peppermint-like odor.	MW: 112.2 BP: 325°F Sol: Insoluble Fl.P: 118°F IP: ? Sp.Gr: 0.93 Class II Combustible Liquid	VP: 1 mm FRZ: 7°F UEL: ? LEL: ?	Strong oxidizers	Porapak; Acetone; GC/FID; IV [#2521]
2297 127	1 ppm = 4.59 mg/m³							

Personal protection and sanitation (See Table 3)		Recommendations for respirator selection — maximum concentration for use (MUC) (See Table 4)	Health hazards				
			Route	Symptoms (See Table 5)	First aid (See Table 6)		Target organs (See Table 5)
Skin:	Prevent skin contact	TBAL	Inh	Irrit eyes, skin, nose;	Eye:	Irr immed	Eyes, skin, resp sys
Eyes:	Prevent eye contact		Ing	blurred vision, lac; rhinitis	Skin:	Water wash	
Wash skin:	Daily		Con		Breath:	Resp support	
Remove:	N.R.				Swallow:	Medical attention	
Change:	N.R.					immed	
Provide:	Eyewash						
[Methyl-2-cyanoacrylate]							
Skin:	Prevent skin contact	NIOSH	Inh	Irrit eyes, skin, nose,	Eye:	Irr immed	Eyes, skin, resp sys,
Eyes:	Prevent eye contact	1200 ppm: SA/SCBAF	Ing	throat; li-head, drow;	Skin:	Soap wash prompt	CNS
Wash skin:	When contam	§: SCBAF:PD,PP/SAF:PD,PP:ASCBA	Con	in animals: narco	Breath:	Resp support	
Remove:	When wet (flamm)	Escape: GMFOV/SCBAE			Swallow:	Medical attention	
Change:	N.R.					immed	
[Methylcyclohexane]							
Skin:	Prevent skin contact	NIOSH	Inh	Irrit eyes, skin, upper resp	Eye:	Irr immed	Eyes, skin, resp sys,
Eyes:	Prevent eye contact	500 ppm: SA*/SCBAF	Abs	sys; head;	Skin:	Soap wash prompt	CNS, kidneys, liver
Wash skin:	When contam	§: SCBAF:PD,PP/SAF:PD,PP:ASCBA	Ing	in animals: narco;	Breath:	Resp support	
Remove:	When wet or contam	Escape: GMFOV/SCBAE	Con	liver, kidney damage	Swallow:	Medical attention	
Change:	N.R.					immed	
[Methylcyclohexanol]							
Skin:	Prevent skin contact	NIOSH	Inh	In animals: irrit eyes,	Eye:	Irr immed	Skin, resp sys,
Eyes:	Prevent eye contact	500 ppm: SA*	Abs	eyes, muc memb; narco; derm	Skin:	Soap wash prompt	liver, kidneys, CNS
Wash skin:	When contam	600 ppm: SA:CF*/SCBAF/SAF	Ing		Breath:	Resp support	
Remove:	When wet or contam	§: SCBAF:PD,PP/SAF:PD,PP:ASCBA	Con		Swallow:	Medical attention	
Change:	N.R.	Escape: GMFOV/SCBAE				immed	
[o-Methylcyclohexanone]							

Chemical name, structure/formula, CAS and RTECS Nos., and DOT ID and guide Nos.	Synonyms, trade names, and conversion factors	Exposure limits (TWA unless noted otherwise)	IDLH	Physical description	Chemical and physical properties		Incompatibilities and reactivities	Measurement method (See Table 1)
					MW, BP, SOL Fl.P, IP, Sp, Gr, flammability	VP, FRZ UEL, LEL		
Methyl cyclopenta-dienyl manganese tricarbonyl (as Mn) $CH_3C_6H_4Mn(CO)_3$ 12108-13-3 OP1450000	CI-2, Combustion Improver-2, Manganese tricarbonyl-methylcyclopentadienyl, 2-Methylcyclopentadienyl manganese tricarbonyl, M M T	NIOSH 0.2 mg/m³ [skin] OSHA† C 5 mg/m³	N.D.	Yellow to dark-orange liquid with a faint, pleasant odor. [Note: A solid below 36°F.]	MW: 218.1 BP: 449°F Sol: Insoluble Fl.P: 230°F IP: ? Sp.Gr. 1.39 Class IIIB Combustible Liquid	VP(212°F): 7mm FRZ: 36°F UEL: ? LEL: ?	Light (decomposes)	None available
Methyl demeton $C_6H_{15}O_3PS_2$ 8022-00-2 TG1760000	Demeton methyl; O,O-Dimethyl 2-ethylmer-captoethyl thiophosphate; Metasystox®; Methyl mercaptophos; Methyl systox®	NIOSH 0.5 mg/m³ [skin] OSHA† none	N.D.	Oily, colorless to pale-yellow liquid with an unpleasant odor. [insecticide] [Note: Technical grade consists of 2 isomers: thiono & thiolo.]	MW: 230.3 BP: Decomposes Sol: 0.03-0.3% Fl.P: ? IP: ? Sp.Gr. 1.20 Combustible Liquid	VP: 0.0004 mm FRZ: ? UEL: ? LEL: ?	Strong oxidizers, alkalis, water	None available
4,4'-Methylenebis(2-chloroaniline) $CH_2(C_6H_4ClNH_2)_2$ 101-14-4 CY1050000	DACPM; 3,3'-Dichloro-4,4'-diamino-diphenylmethane; MBOCA; 4,4'-Methylenebis(o-chloro-aniline); 4,4'-Methylenebis(2-chloro-benzenamine); MOCA	NIOSH Ca See Appendix A 0.003 mg/m³ [skin] OSHA† none	Ca [N.D.]	Tan-colored pellets or flakes with a faint, amine-like odor.	MW: 267.2 BP: ? Sol: Slight Fl.P: ? IP: ? Sp.Gr. 1.44	VP(77°F): 0.00001 mm MLT: 230°F UEL: ? LEL: ?	Chemically-active metals (e.g., potassium, sodium, magnesium, zinc)	Filters*(2); Water; GC/ECD; OSHA [#71]
Methylene bis(4-cyclo-hexylisocyanate) $CH_2[(C_6H_{10})NCO]_2$ 5124-30-1 NQ9250000	Dicyclohexylmethane 4,4'-diisocyanate; DMDI; bis(4-Isocyanatocyclohexyl)-methane; HMDI; Hydrogenated MDI; Reduced MDI; Saturated MDI 1 ppm = 10.73 mg/m³	NIOSH C 0.01 ppm (0.11 mg/m³) OSHA† none	N.D.	Clear, colorless to light-yellow liquid.	MW: 262.4 BP: ? Sol: Reacts Fl.P: >395°F IP: ? Sp.Gr(77°F): 1.07 Class IIIB Combustible Liquid	VP(77°F): 0.001 mm FRZ: <14°F UEL: ? LEL: ?	Water, ethanol, alcohols, amines, bases, acids, organotin catalysts [Note: May slowly polymerize if heated above 122°F.]	None available

Personal protection and sanitation (See Table 3)		Recommendations for respirator selection — maximum concentration for use (MUC) (See Table 4)	Health hazards					
			Route	Symptoms (See Table 5)	First aid (See Table 6)		Target organs (See Table 5)	

Personal protection and sanitation		Recommendations for respirator selection	Route	Symptoms	First aid		Target organs
Skin:	Prevent skin contact	TBAL	Inh	Irrit eyes; gidd, nau, head;	Eye:	Irr immed	Eyes, CNS, liver, kidneys
Eyes:	Prevent eye contact		Abs	in animals: tremor, severe	Skin:	Soap wash immed	
Wash skin:	When contam		Ing	clonic spasms, weak, slow	Breath:	Resp support	
Remove:	When wet or contam		Con	respiration; liver, kidney inj	Swallow:	Medical attention immed	
Change:	N.R.						

[Methyl cyclopentadienyl manganese tricarbonyl (as Mn)]

Skin:	Prevent skin contact	TBAL	Inh	Irrit eyes, skin; ache eyes,	Eye:	Irr immed	Eyes, skin, resp sys, CNS, CVS, blood chol
Eyes:	Prevent eye contact		Abs	rhin; nau, head, dizz, vomit	Skin:	Soap wash immed	
Wash skin:	When contam		Ing		Breath:	Resp support	
Remove:	When wet or contam		Con		Swallow:	Medical attention immed	
Change:	Daily						
Provide:	Eyewash, Quick drench						

[Methyl demeton]

Skin:	Prevent skin contact	NIOSH	Inh	Hema, cyan, nau, methemo,	Eye:	Irr immed	Liver, blood, kidneys [in animals: liver, lung & bladder tumors]
Eyes:	Prevent eye contact	¥: SCBAF:PD,PP/SAF:PD,PP:ASCBA	Abs	kidney irrit; [carc]	Skin:	Soap wash immed	
Wash skin:	When contam/Daily	Escape: GMFOVHiE/SCBAE	Ing		Breath:	Resp support	
Remove:	When wet or contam		Con		Swallow:	Medical attention immed	
Change:	Daily						
Provide:	Eyewash, Quick drench						

[4,4'-Methylenebis(2-chloroaniline)]

Skin:	Prevent skin contact	NIOSH	Inh	Irrit eyes, skin, resp sys;	Eye:	Irr immed	Eyes, skin, resp sys
Eyes:	Prevent eye contact	0.1 ppm: SA*	Ing	skin, resp sens; chest tight,	Skin:	Water flush immed	
Wash skin:	When contam	0.25 ppm: SA:CF*	Con	dysp, cough, dry throat,	Breath:	Resp support	
Remove:	When wet or contam	0.5 ppm: SCBAF/SAF		wheez, pulm edema; skin	Swallow:	Medical attention immed	
Change:	N.R.	1 ppm: SAF:PD,PP		blisters			
Provide:	Quick drench	§: SCBAF:PD,PP/SAF:PD,PP:ASCBA					
		Escape: GMFOV/SCBAE					

[Methylene bis(4-cyclohexylisocyanate)]

Chemical name, structure/formula, CAS and RTECS Nos., and DOT ID and guide Nos.	Synonyms, trade names, and conversion factors	Exposure limits (TWA unless noted otherwise)	IDLH	Physical description	Chemical and physical properties		Incompatibilities and reactivities	Measurement method (See Table 1)
					MW, BP, SOL Fl.P, IP, Sp, Gr, flammability	VP, FRZ UEL, LEL		
Methylene bisphenyl isocyanate $CH_2(C_6H_4NCO)_2$ 101-68-8 NQ9350000 2489 156	4,4'-Diphenylmethane diisocyanate; MDI; Methylene bis(4-phenyl isocyanate); Methylene di-p-phenylene ester of isocyanic acid 1 ppm = 10.24 mg/m³	NIOSH 0.05 mg/m³ (0.005 ppm) C 0.2 mg/m³ (0.020 ppm) [10-min] OSHA C 0.2 mg/m³ (0.02 ppm)	75 mg/m³	White to light-yellow, odorless flakes. [Note: A liquid above 99°F.]	MW: 250.3 BP: 597°F Sol: 0.2% Fl.P: 390° IP: ? Sp.Gr: 1.23 (Solid at 77°F) 1.19 (Liquid at 122°F) Combustible Solid	VP(77°F): 0.000005 mm MLT: 99°F UEL: ? LEL: ?	Strong alkalis, acids, alcohol [Note: Polymerizes at 450°F.]	Bub; Acetylate/ Methanol; HPLC/UV/ ECD; IV [#5521]
Methylene chloride CH_2Cl_2 75-09-2 PA8050000 1593 160	Dichloromethane, Methylene dichloride 1 ppm = 3.47 mg/m³	NIOSH Ca See Appendix A OSHA [1910.1052] 25 ppm ST 125 ppm	Ca [2300 ppm]	Colorless liquid with a chloroform-like odor. [Note: A gas above 104°F.]	MW: 84.9 BP: 104°F Sol: 2% Fl.P: ? IP: 11.32 eV Sp.Gr: 1.33 Combustible Liquid	VP: 350 mm FRZ: -139°F UEL: 23% LEL: 13%	Strong oxidizers; caustics; chemically-active metals such as aluminum, magnesium powders, potassium & sodium; concentrated nitric acid	Char(2); CS₂; GC/FID; IV [#1005]
4,4'-Methylene-dianiline $CH_2(C_6H_4NH_2)_2$ 101-77-9 BY5425000	4,4'-Diaminodiphenylmethane; para, para'-Diaminodiphenyl-methane; Dianilinomethane; 4,4'-Diphenylmethanediamine; MDA	NIOSH Ca See Appendix A OSHA [1910.1050] 0.010 ppm ST 0.100 ppm	Ca [N.D.]	Pale-brown, crystalline solid with a faint, amine-like odor.	MW: 198.3 BP: 748°F Sol: 0.1% Fl.P: 374°F IP: 10.70 eV Sp.Gr: 1.06 (Liquid at 212°F) Combustible Solid	VP(77°F): 0.0000002 mm MLT: 198°F UEL: ? LEL: ?	Strong oxidizers	Filter*; KOH/ Methanol; HPLC/UV/ ECD IV [#5029]
Methyl ethyl ketone peroxide $C_8H_{16}O_4$ 1338-23-4 EL9450000 2550 147	2-Butanone peroxide, Ethyl methyl ketone peroxide, MEKP, MEK peroxide, Methyl ethyl ketone hydroperoxide 1 ppm = 7.21 mg/m³	NIOSH C 0.2 ppm (1.5 mg/m³) OSHA† none	N.D.	Colorless liquid with a character-istic odor. [Note: Explosive decomposition occurs at 230°F.]	MW: 176.2 BP: 244°F (Decomposes) Sol: Soluble Fl.P(oc): 125-200°F (60% MEKP) IP: ? Sp.Gr(59°F): 1.12 Combustible Liquid	VP: ? FRZ: ? UEL: ? LEL: ?	Organic materials, heat, flames, sunlight, trace contaminants [Note: A strong oxidiz-ing agent. Pure MEKP is shock sensitive. Commercial product is diluted with 40% dimethyl phthalate, cyclohexane peroxide, or diallyl phthalate to reduce sensitivity to shock.]	Imp; Reagent; Vis; IV [#3508]

Personal protection and sanitation (See Table 3)		Recommendations for respirator selection — maximum concentration for use (MUC) (See Table 4)	Health hazards					
			Route	Symptoms (See Table 5)		First aid (See Table 6)		Target organs (See Table 5)

Personal protection and sanitation		Respirator selection (MUC)	Route	Symptoms	First aid		Target organs
Skin:	Prevent skin contact	NIOSH	Inh	Irrit eyes, nose, throat;	Eye:	Irr immed	Eyes, resp sys
Eyes:	Prevent eye contact	0.5 mg/m³: SA*	Ing	resp sens, cough, pulm	Skin:	Soap wash immed	
Wash skin:	When contam	1.25 mg/m³: SA:CF*	Con	secretions, chest pain,	Breath:	Resp support	
Remove:	When wet or contam	2.5 mg/m³: SCBAF/SAF		dysp; asthma	Swallow:	Medical attention	
Change:	Daily	75 mg/m³: SAF:PD,PP				immed	
		§: SCBAF:PD,PP/SAF:PD,PP:ASCBA					
		Escape: GMFOVHiE/SCBAE					

[Methylene bisphenyl isocyanate]

Skin:	Prevent skin contact	NIOSH	Inh	Irrit eyes, skin; ftg,	Eye:	Irr immed	Eyes, skin, CVS, CNS
Eyes:	Prevent eye contact	¥: SCBAF:PD,PP/SAF:PD,PP:ASCBA	Abs	weak, som, li-head; numb	Skin:	Soap wash prompt	[in animals:
Wash skin:	When contam	Escape: GMFOV/SCBAE	Ing	tingle limbs; nau; [carc]	Breath:	Resp support	lung, liver,
Remove:	When wet or contam		Con		Swallow:	Medical attention	salivary &
Change:	N.R.					immed	mammary gland
Provide:	Eyewash, Quick drench						tumors]

[Methylene chloride]

Skin:	Prevent skin contact	NIOSH	Inh	Irrit eyes; jaun, hepatitis;	Eye:	Irr immed	Eyes, liver, CVS,
Eyes:	Prevent eye contact	¥: SCBAF:PD,PP/SAF:PD,PP:ASCBA	Abs	myocardial damage;	Skin:	Soap wash immed	spleen
Wash skin:	When contam/Daily	Escape: GMFOVHiE/SCBAE	Ing	in animals: heart, liver,	Breath:	Resp support	[in animals:
Remove:	When wet or contam		Con	spleen damage; [carc]	Swallow:	Medical attention	bladder cancer]
Change:	Daily					immed	
Provide:	Eyewash, Quick drench						

[4,4'-Methylenedianiline]

Skin:	Prevent skin contact	TBAL	Inh	Irrit eyes, skin, nose,	Eye:	Irr immed	Eyes, skin, resp sys,
Eyes:	Prevent eye contact		Ing	throat; cough, dysp, pulm	Skin:	Water wash immed	liver, kidneys
Wash skin:	When contam		Con	edema; blurred vision;	Breath:	Resp support	
Remove:	When wet or contam			blisters, scars skin;	Swallow:	Medical attention	
Change:	N.R.			abdom pain, vomit, diarr;		immed	
Provide:	Eyewash, Quick drench			derm;			
				in animals: liver, kidney			
				damage			

[Methyl ethyl ketone peroxide]

Chemical name, structure/formula, CAS and RTECS Nos., and DOT ID and guide Nos.	Synonyms, trade names, and conversion factors	Exposure limits (TWA unless noted otherwise)	IDLH	Physical description	Chemical and physical properties		Incompatibilities and reactivities	Measurement method (See Table 1)
					MW, BP, SOL Fl.P, IP, Sp, Gr, flammability	VP, FRZ UEL, LEL		
Methyl formate HCOOCH$_3$ 107-31-3 LQ8925000 1243 129	Methyl ester of formic acid, Methyl methanoate 1 ppm = 2.46 mg/m^3	NIOSH 100 ppm (250 mg/m^3) ST 150 ppm (375 mg/m^3) OSHA† 100 ppm (250 mg/m^3)	4500 ppm	Colorless liquid with a pleasant odor. [Note: A gas above 89°F.]	MW: 60.1 BP: 89°F Sol: 30% Fl.P: -2°F IP: 10.82 eV Sp.Gr: 0.98 Class IA Flammable Liquid	VP: 476 mm FRZ: -148°F UEL: 23% LEL: 4.5%	Strong oxidizers [Note: Reacts slowly with water to form methanol & formic acid.]	Carbo-B(2); Ethyl acetate; GC/FID; II(5) [#S291]
5-Methyl-3-heptanone C$_2$H$_5$COCH$_2$CH(CH$_3$)CH$_2$CH$_3$ 541-85-5 MJ7350000 2271 127	Amyl ethyl ketone, Ethyl amyl ketone, 3-Methyl-5-heptanone 1 ppm = 5.24 mg/m^3	NIOSH/OSHA 25 ppm (130 mg/m^3)	100 ppm	Colorless liquid with a pungent odor.	MW: 128.2 BP: 315°F Sol: Insoluble Fl.P: 138°F IP: ? Sp.Gr: 0.82 Class II Combustible Liquid	VP: 2 mm FRZ: -70°F UEL: ? LEL: ?	Strong oxidizers	Char; Methanol/ CS$_2$; GC/FID; IV [#1301, Ketones II]
Methyl hydrazine CH$_3$NHNH$_2$ 60-34-4 MV5600000 1244 131	MMH, Monomethylhydrazine 1 ppm = 1.89 mg/m^3	NIOSH Ca See Appendix A C 0.04 ppm (0.08 mg/m^3) [2-hr] OSHA C 0.2 ppm (0.35 mg/m^3) [skin]	Ca [20 ppm]	Fuming, colorless liquid with an ammonia-like odor.	MW: 46.1 BP: 190°F Sol: Miscible Fl.P: 17°F IP: 8.00 eV Sp.Gr(77°F): 0.87 Class IB Flammable Liquid	VP: 38 mm FRZ: -62°F UEL: 92% LEL: 2.5%	Oxides of iron; copper; manganese; lead; copper alloys; porous materials such as earth, asbestos, wood & cloth; strong oxidizers such as fluorine & chlorine; nitric acid; hydrogen peroxide	Bub; Pho-acid; Vis; [#3510]
Methyl iodide CH$_3$I 74-88-4 PA9450000 2644 151	Iodomethane, Monoiodomethane 1 ppm = 5.80 mg/m^3	NIOSH Ca See Appendix A 2 ppm (10 mg/m^3) [skin] OSHA† 5 ppm (28 mg/m^3) [skin]	Ca [100 ppm]	Colorless liquid with a pungent, ether-like odor. [Note: Turns yellow, red, or brown on exposure to light & moisture.]	MW: 141.9 BP: 109°F Sol: 1% Fl.P: NA IP: 9.54 eV Sp.Gr: 2.28 Noncombustible Liquid	VP: 400 mm FRZ: -88°F UEL: NA LEL: NA	Strong oxidizers [Note: Decomposes at 518°F.]	Char; Toluene; GC/FID; IV [#1014]

Personal protection and sanitation (See Table 3)		Recommendations for respirator selection — maximum concentration for use (MUC) (See Table 4)	Health hazards					
			Route	Symptoms (See Table 5)		First aid (See Table 6)		Target organs (See Table 5)
Skin:	Prevent skin contact	NIOSH/OSHA	Inh	Irrit eyes, nose; chest	Eye:	Irr immed	Eyes, resp sys, CNS
Eyes:	Prevent eye contact	1000 ppm: SA*	Abs	tight, dysp; vis dist;	Skin:	Soap wash immed	
Wash skin:	When contam	2500 ppm: SA:CF*	Ing	CNS depres;	Breath:	Resp support	
Remove:	When wet (flamm)	4500 ppm: SCBAF/SAF	Con	in animals: pulm edema;	Swallow:	Medical attention	
Change:	N.R.	§: SCBAF:PD,PP/SAF:PD,PP:ASCBA		narco		immed	
		Escape: GMFOV/SCBAE					

[Methyl formate]

Skin:	Prevent skin contact	NIOSH/OSHA	Inh	Irrit eyes, skin, muc memb;	Eye:	Irr immed	Eyes, skin, resp sys,
Eyes:	Prevent eye contact	100 ppm: CCROV*/PAPROV*/GMFOV/	Ing	head; narco, coma; derm	Skin:	Water flush	CNS
Wash skin:	When contam	SA*/SCBAF	Con		Breath:	Resp support	
Remove:	When wet or contam	§: SCBAF:PD,PP/SAF:PD,PP:ASCBA			Swallow:	Medical attention	
Change:	N.R.	Escape: GMFOV/SCBAE				immed	

[5-Methyl-3-heptanone]

Skin:	Prevent skin contact	NIOSH	Inh	Irrit eyes, skin, resp sys;	Eye:	Irr immed	Eyes, skin, resp sys,
Eyes:	Prevent eye contact	¥: SCBAF:PD,PP/SAF:PD,PP:ASCBA	Abs	vomit, diarr, tremor,	Skin:	Water flush immed	CNS, liver, blood,
Wash skin:	When contam	Escape: SCBAE	Ing	ataxia; anoxia, cyan;	Breath:	Resp support	CVS
Remove:	When wet (flamm)		Con	convuls; [carc]	Swallow:	Medical attention	[in animals:
Change:	N.R.					immed	lung, liver,
Provide:	Eyewash, Quick drench						blood vessel
							& intestine
							tumors]

[Methyl hydrazine]

Skin:	Prevent skin contact	NIOSH	Inh	Irrit eyes, skin, resp sys;	Eye:	Irr immed	Eyes, skin, resp sys,
Eyes:	Prevent eye contact	¥: SCBAF:PD,PP/SAF:PD,PP:ASCBA	Abs	nau, vomit; verti, ataxia;	Skin:	Soap flush immed	CNS
Wash skin:	When contam	Escape: GMFOV/SCBAE	Ing	slurred speech, drow;	Breath:	Resp support	[in animals:
Remove:	When wet or contam		Con	derm; [carc]	Swallow:	Medical attention	lung, kidney
Change:	N.R.					immed	& forestomach
Provide:	Eyewash, Quick drench						tumors]

[Methyl iodide]

Chemical name, structure/formula, CAS and RTECS Nos., and DOT ID and guide Nos.	Synonyms, trade names, and conversion factors	Exposure limits (TWA unless noted otherwise)	IDLH	Physical description	Chemical and physical properties		Incompatibilities and reactivities	Measurement method (See Table 1)
					MW, BP, SOL Fl.P, IP, Sp, Gr, flammability	VP, FRZ UEL, LEL		
Methyl isoamyl ketone $CH_3COCH_2CH_2CH(CH_3)_2$ 110-12-3 MP3850000 2302 127	Isoamyl methyl ketone, Isopentyl methyl ketone, 2-Methyl-5-hexanone, 5-Methyl-2-hexanone, MIAK 1 ppm = 4.67 mg/m³	NIOSH 50 ppm (240 mg/m³) OSHA† 100 ppm (475 mg/m³)	N.D.	Colorless, clear liquid with a pleasant, fruity odor.	MW: 114.2 BP: 291°F Sol: 0.5% Fl.P: 97°F IP: 9.284 eV Sp.Gr. 0.81 Class IC Flammable Liquid	VP: 5 mm FRZ: -101°F UEL(200°F): 8.2% LEL(200°F): 1.0%	Oxidizers	None available
Methyl isobutyl carbinol $(CH_3)_2CHCH_2CH(OH)CH_3$ 108-11-2 SA7350000 2053 129	Isobutylmethylcarbinol, Methyl amyl alcohol, 4-Methyl-2-pentanol, MIBC 1 ppm = 4.18 mg/m³	NIOSH 25 ppm (100 mg/m³) ST 40 ppm (165 mg/m³) [skin] OSHA† 25 ppm (100 mg/m³) [skin]	400 ppm	Colorless liquid with a mild odor.	MW: 102.2 BP: 271°F Sol: 2% Fl.P: 106°F IP: ? Sp.Gr. 0.81 Class II Combustible Liquid	VP: 3 mm FRZ: -130°F UEL: 5.5% LEL: 1.0%	Strong oxidizers	Char; 2-Propanol/ CS₂; GC/FID; IV [#1402, Alcohols III]
Methyl isocyanate CH_3NCO 624-83-9 NQ9450000 2480 155	Methyl ester of isocyanic acid, MIC 1 ppm = 2.34 mg/m³	NIOSH/OSHA 0.02 ppm (0.05 mg/m³) [skin]	3 ppm	Colorless liquid with a sharp, pungent odor.	MW: 57.1 BP: 139°F Sol(59°F): 10% Fl.P: 19°F IP: 10.67 eV Sp.Gr. 0.96 Class IB Flammable Liquid	VP: 348 mm FRZ: -49°F UEL: 26% LEL: 5.3%	Water, oxidizers, acids, alkalis, amines, iron, tin, copper [Note: Usually contains inhibitors to prevent polymerization.]	XAD-7*; CH₃CN; HPLC/FLD; OSHA [#54]
Methyl isopropyl ketone $CH_3COCH(CH_3)_2$ 563-80-4 EL9100000 2397 127	2-Acetyl propane, Isopropyl methyl ketone, 3-Methyl-2-butanone, 3-Methyl butan-2-one, MIPK 1 ppm = 3.53 mg/m³	NIOSH 200 ppm (705 mg/m³) OSHA† none	N.D.	Colorless liquid with an acetone-like odor.	MW: 86.2 BP: 199°F Sol: Very slight Fl.P: ? IP: 9.32 eV Sp.Gr. 0.81 Combustible Liquid	VP: 42 mm FRZ: -134°F UEL: ? LEL: ?	Oxidizers	None available

Personal protection and sanitation (See Table 3)		Recommendations for respirator selection — maximum concentration for use (MUC) (See Table 4)	Health hazards					
			Route	Symptoms (See Table 5)	First aid (See Table 6)		Target organs (See Table 5)	

Personal protection and sanitation (See Table 3)		Recommendations for respirator selection — maximum concentration for use (MUC) (See Table 4)	Route	Symptoms (See Table 5)	First aid (See Table 6)		Target organs (See Table 5)
Skin:	Prevent skin contact	NIOSH	Inh	Irrit eyes, skin, muc memb;	Eye:	Irr immed	Eyes, skin, resp sys,
Eyes:	Prevent eye contact	500 ppm: CCROV*/SA*	Ing	head, narco, coma; derm;	Skin:	Soap flush prompt	CNS, liver, kidneys
Wash skin:	When contam	1250 ppm: SA:CF*/PAPROV*	Con	in animals: liver, kidney	Breath:	Resp support	
Remove:	When wet (flamm)	2500 ppm: CCRFOV/GMFOV/PAPRTOV*/		damage	Swallow:	Medical attention	
Change:	N.R.	SAT:CF*/SCBAF/SAF				immed	
		5000 ppm: SAF:PD,PP					
		§: SCBAF:PD,PP/SAF:PD,PP:ASCBA					
		Escape: GMFOV/SCBAE					

[Methyl isoamyl ketone]

Skin:	Prevent skin contact	NIOSH/OSHA	Inh	Irrit eyes, skin; head,	Eye:	Irr immed	Eyes, skin, CNS
Eyes:	Prevent eye contact	250 ppm: SA*	Abs	drow; derm;	Skin:	Water flush prompt	
Wash skin:	When contam	400 ppm: SA:CF*/SCBAF/SAF	Ing	in animals: narco	Breath:	Resp support	
Remove:	When wet or contam	§: SCBAF:PD,PP/SAF:PD,PP:ASCBA	Con		Swallow:	Medical attention	
Change:	N.R.	Escape: GMFOV/SCBAE				immed	

[Methyl isobutyl carbinol]

Skin:	Prevent skin contact	NIOSH/OSHA	Inh	Irrit eyes, skin, nose,	Eye:	Irr immed	Eyes, skin, resp sys
Eyes:	Prevent eye contact	0.2 ppm: SA*	Abs	throat; resp sens, cough,	Skin:	Water flush immed	
Wash skin:	When contam	0.5 ppm: SA:CF*	Ing	pulm secretions, chest pain,	Breath:	Resp support	
Remove:	When wet (flamm)	1 ppm: SCBAF/SAF	Con	dysp; asthma; eye, skin	Swallow:	Medical attention	
Change:	N.R.	3 ppm: SAF:PD,PP		damage;		immed	
Provide:	Eyewash, Quick drench	§: SCBAF:PD,PP/SAF:PD,PP:ASCBA		in animals: pulm edema			
		Escape: GMFOV/SCBAE					

[Methyl isocyanate]

Skin:	Prevent skin contact	TBAL	Inh	Irrit eyes, skin, muc memb;	Eye:	Irr immed	Eyes, skin, resp sys
Eyes:	Prevent eye contact		Ing	resp sys; cough	Skin:	Soap wash immed	
Wash skin:	When contam		Con		Breath:	Resp support	
Remove:	When wet or contam				Swallow:	Medical attention	
Change:	N.R.					immed	

[Methyl isopropyl ketone]

Chemical name, structure/formula, CAS and RTECS Nos., and DOT ID and guide Nos.	Synonyms, trade names, and conversion factors	Exposure limits (TWA unless noted otherwise)	IDLH	Physical description	Chemical and physical properties		Incompatibilities and reactivities	Measurement method (See Table 1)
					MW, BP, SOL FI.P, IP, Sp, Gr, flammability	VP, FRZ UEL, LEL		
Methyl mercaptan CH₃SH 74-93-1 PB4375000 1064 117	Mercaptomethane, Methanethiol, Methyl sulfhydrate 1 ppm = 1.97 mg/m³	NIOSH C 0.5 ppm (1 mg/m³) [15-min] OSHA† C 10 ppm (20 mg/m³)	150 ppm	Colorless gas with a disagreeable odor like garlic or rotten cabbage. [Note: A liquid below 43°F. Shipped as a liquefied compressed gas.]	MW: 48.1 BP: 43°F Sol: 2% FI.P: NA (Gas) (oc) 0°F (Liq) IP: 9.44 eV RGasD: 1.66 Sp.Gr: 0.90 (Liquid at 32°F) Flammable Gas Class IA Flammable Liquid	VP: 1.7 atm FRZ: -186°F UEL: 21.8% LEL: 3.9%	Strong oxidizers, bleaches, copper, aluminum, nickel-copper alloys	Filter*; HCI/DCE; GC/FPD; IV [#2542]
Methyl methacrylate CH₂=C(CH₃)COOCH₃ 80-62-6 OZ5075000 1247 129P (inhibited)	Methacrylate monomer, Methyl ester of methacrylic acid, Methyl-2-methyl-2-propenoate 1 ppm = 4.09 mg/m³	NIOSH/OSHA 100 ppm (410 mg/m³)	1000 ppm	Colorless liquid with an acrid, fruity odor.	MW: 100.1 BP: 214°F Sol: 1.5% FI.P(oc): 50°F IP: 9.70 eV Sp.Gr: 0.94 Class IB Flammable Liquid	VP: 29 mm FRZ: -54°F UEL: 8.2% LEL: 1.7%	Nitrates, oxidizers, peroxides, strong alkalis, moisture [Note: May polymerize if subjected to heat, oxidizers, or ultraviolet light. Usually contains an inhibitor such as hydroquinone.]	XAD-2; CS₂; GC/FID; IV [#2537]
Methyl parathion (CH₃O)₂P(S)OC₆H₄NO₂ 298-00-0 TG0175000 2783 152	Azophos®; O,O-Dimethyl-O-p-nitro-phenylphosphorothioate; Parathion methyl	NIOSH 0.2 mg/m³ [skin] OSHA† none	N.D.	White to tan, crystalline solid or powder with a pungent, garlic-like odor. [pesticide] [Note: The commercial product in xylene is a tan liquid.]	MW: 263.2 BP: 289°F Sol(77°F): 0.006% FI.P: ? IP: ? Sp.Gr: 1.36 Combustible Solid	VP: 0.00001 mm MLT: 99°F UEL: ? LEL: ?	Strong oxidizers, water [Note: Explosive risk when heated above 122°F.]	OVS-2; Toluene/ Acetone; GC/FPD; IV [#5600, Organo-phosphorus Pesticides]
Methyl silicate (CH₃O)₄Si 681-84-5 VV9800000 2606 155	Methyl orthosilicate, Tetramethoxysilane, Tetramethyl ester of silicic acid, Tetramethyl silicate 1 ppm = 6.23 mg/m³	NIOSH 1 ppm (6 mg/m³) OSHA† none	N.D.	Clear, colorless liquid. [Note: A solid below 28°F.]	MW: 152.3 BP: 250°F Sol: Soluble FI.P: 205°F IP: ? Sp.Gr: 1.02 Class IIIB Combustible Liquid	VP(77°F): 12 mm FRZ: 28°F UEL: ? LEL: ?	Oxidizers; hexa-fluorides of rhenium, molybdenum & tungsten	None available

Personal protection and sanitation (See Table 3)	Recommendations for respirator selection — maximum concentration for use (MUC) (See Table 4)	Route	Symptoms (See Table 5)	First aid (See Table 6)	Target organs (See Table 5)
Skin: Prevent skin contact (liq)/Frostbite Eyes: Prevent eye contact (liq)/Frostbite Wash skin: N.R. Remove: When wet (flamm) Change: N.R. Provide: Eyewash (liq), Quick drench (liq), Frostbite [Methyl mercaptan]	NIOSH 5 ppm: CCROV/SA 12.5 ppm: SA:CF/PAPROV 25 ppm: CCRFOV/GMFOV/PAPRTOV/SAT:CF/SCBAF/SAF 150 ppm: SA:PD,PP §: SCBAF:PD,PP/SAF:PD,PP:ASCBA Escape: GMFOV/SCBAE	Inh Con (liq)	Irrit eyes, skin, resp sys; narco; cyan; convuls; liq: frostbite	Eye: Irr immed (liq)/Frostbite Skin: Water flush immed (liq)/Frostbite Breath: Resp support	Eyes, skin, resp sys, CNS, blood
Skin: Prevent skin contact Eyes: Prevent eye contact Wash skin: When contam Remove: When wet (flamm) Change: N.R. [Methyl methacrylate]	NIOSH/OSHA 1000 ppm: SA:CF$^£$/CCRFOV/GMFOV/PAPROV$^£$/SCBAF/SAF §: SCBAF:PD,PP/SAF:PD,PP:ASCBA Escape: GMFOV/SCBAE	Inh Ing Con	Irrit eyes, skin, nose, throat; derm	Eye: Irr immed Skin: Water flush prompt Breath: Resp support Swallow: Medical attention immed	Eyes, skin, resp sys
Skin: Prevent skin contact Eyes: Prevent eye contact Wash skin: When contam/Daily Remove: When wet or contam Change: Daily Provide: Eyewash, Quick drench [Methyl parathion]	NIOSH 2 mg/m³: CCROVDMFu/SA 5 mg/m³: SA:CF/PAPROVDMFu 10 mg/m³: CCRFOVHiE/GMFOVHiE/PAPRTOVHiE/SAT:CF/SCBAF/SAF 200 mg/m³: SAF:PD,PP §: SCBAF:PD,PP/SAF:PD,PP:ASCBA Escape: GMFOVHiE/SCBAE	Inh Abs Ing Con	Irrit eyes, skin; nau, vomit, abdom cramps, diarr, salv; head, gidd, verti, weak; rhin, chest tight; blurred vision, miosis; card irreg; musc fasc; dysp	Eye: Irr immed Skin: Soap wash immed Breath: Resp support Swallow: Medical attention immed	Eyes, skin, resp sys, CNS, CVS, blood chol
Skin: Prevent skin contact Eyes: Prevent eye contact Wash skin: Daily Remove: When wet or contam Change: N.R. Provide: Eyewash [Methyl silicate]	TBAL	Inh Ing Con (vap/liq)	Irrit eyes, corn damage (following even short-term exposure to the vapor); lung, kidney inj; pulm edema	Eye: Irr immed (vap/liq) Skin: Soap wash Breath: Resp support Swallow: Medical attention immed	Eyes, resp sys, kidneys

Chemical name, structure/formula, CAS and RTECS Nos., and DOT ID and guide Nos.	Synonyms, trade names, and conversion factors	Exposure limits (TWA unless noted otherwise)	IDLH	Physical description	Chemical and physical properties		Incompatibilities and reactivities	Measurement method (See Table 1)
					MW, BP, SOL Fl.P, IP, Sp, Gr, flammability	VP, FRZ UEL, LEL		
α-Methyl styrene $C_6H_5C(CH_3)=CH_2$ 98-83-9 WL5075300	AMS, Isopropenyl benzene, 1-Methyl-1-phenylethylene, 2-Phenyl propylene 1 ppm = 4.83 mg/m³	NIOSH 50 ppm (240 mg/m³) ST 100 ppm (485 mg/m³) OSHA† C 100 ppm (480 mg/m³)	700 ppm	Colorless liquid with a characteristic odor.	MW: 118.2 BP: 330°F Sol: Insoluble Fl.P: 129°F IP: 8.35 eV Sp.Gr: 0.91 Class II Combustible Liquid	VP: 2 mm FRZ: -10°F UEL:6.1% LEL:1.9%	Oxidizers, peroxides, halogens, catalysts for vinyl or ionic polymers; aluminum, iron chloride, copper [Note: Usually contains an inhibitor such as tert-butyl catechol.]	Char; CS₂; GC/FID; IV [#1501, Aromatic Hydrocarbons]
Metribuzin $C_8H_{14}N_4OS$ 21087-64-9 XZ2990000	4-Amino-6-(1,1-dimethyl-ethyl)-3-(methylthio)-1,2,4-triazin-5(4H)-one; Sencor®	NIOSH 5 mg/m³ OSHA† none	N.D.	Colorless, crystalline solid. [herbicide]	MW: 214.3 BP: ? Sol: 0.1% Fl.P: NA IP: ? Sp.Gr: 1.31 Noncombustible Solid	VP: 0.0000004 mm MLT: 257°F UEL: NA LEL: NA	None reported	None available
Mica (containing less than 1% quartz) 12001-26-2 VV8760000	Biotite, Lepidolite, Margarite, Muscovite, Phlogopite, Roscoelite, Zimmwaldite	NIOSH 3 mg/m³ (resp) OSHA† 20 mppcf	1500 mg/m³	Colorless, odorless flakes or sheets of hydrous silicates.	MW: 797 (approx) BP: ? Sol: Insoluble Fl.P: NA IP: NA Sp.Gr: 2.6-3.2 Noncombustible Solid	VP: 0 mm (approx) MLT: ? UEL: NA LEL: NA	None reported	Filter; none; Grav; IV [#0600, Particulates NOR resp)]
Mineral wool fiber PY8070000	Manmade mineral fibers, Rock wool, Slag wool, Synthetic vitreous fibers [Note: Produced by blowing steam or air through molten rock (rock wool) or various furnace slags that are by-products of metal smelting or refining processes (slag wool).]	NIOSH 3 fibers/cm³ (fibers ≤ 3.5 µm diameter & ≥ 10 µm in length) 5 mg/m³ (total) OSHA 15 mg/m³ (total) 5 mg/m³ (resp)	N.D.	Typically, a mineral "wool" with diameters >0.5 µm & >1.5 µm in length.	MW: varies BP: NA Sol: Insoluble Fl.P: NA IP: NA Sp.Gr: ? Noncombustible Fibers	VP: 0 mm (approx) MLT: ? UEL: NA LEL: NA	None reported	Filter; none; Grav; IV [#0500, Particulates NOR (total)] [Also #7400]

Personal protection and sanitation (See Table 3)	Recommendations for respirator selection — maximum concentration for use (MUC) (See Table 4)	Health hazards			
		Route	Symptoms (See Table 5)	First aid (See Table 6)	Target organs (See Table 5)

Skin: Prevent skin contact
Eyes: Prevent eye contact
Wash skin: When contam
Remove: When wet or contam
Change: N.R.
 	
[α-Methyl styrene]
	NIOSH
	500 ppm: CCROV*/SA*
	700 ppm: SA:CF*/CCRFOV/GMFOV/
	    PAPROV*/SCBAF/SAF
	§: SCBAF:PD,PP/SAF:PD,PP:ASCBA
	Escape: GMFOV/SCBAE
		Inh
		Ing
		Con
			Irrit eyes, skin, nose, throat; drow; derm	Eye: Irr immed
				Skin: Water flush prompt
				Breath: Resp support
				Swallow: Medical attention
				    immed
					Eyes, skin, resp sys, CNS

Skin: Prevent skin contact Eyes: Prevent eye contact Wash skin: When contam/Daily Remove: When wet or contam Change: Daily [Metribuzin]	TBAL	Inh Ing Con	In animals: CNS depres; thyroid, liver, enzyme changes	Eye: Irr immed Skin: Soap wash Breath: Fresh air Swallow: Medical attention immed	CNS, thyroid, liver
Skin: N.R. Eyes: N.R. Wash skin: N.R. Remove: N.R. Change: N.R. [Mica (containing less than 1% quartz)]	NIOSH 15 mg/m³: DM 30 mg/m³: DMXSQ/SA 75 mg/m³: SA:CF/PAPRDM 150 mg/m³: HiEF/SAT:CF/PAPRTHiE/ SCBAF/SAF 1500 mg/m³: SA:PD,PP §: SCBAF:PD,PP/SAF:PD,PP:ASCBA Escape: HiEF/SCBAE	Inh Con	Irrit eyes; pneumoconiosis, cough, dysp; weak; low-wgt	Eye: Irr immed Breath: Fresh air	Resp sys
Skin: Prevent skin contact Eyes: Prevent eye contact Wash skin: Daily Remove: N.R. Change: Daily [Mineral Wool]	NIOSH 5X REL: D 10X REL: DXSQ/HiE/SA 25X REL: SA:CF/PAPRD 50X REL: HiEF/PAPRTHiE/SCBAF/SAF 1000X REL: SAF:PD,PP §: SCBAF:PD,PP/SAF:PD,PP:ASCBA Escape: HiEF/SCBAE	Inh Con	Irrit eyes, skin, resp sys; dysp	Eye: Irr immed Skin: Soap wash Breath: Fresh air	Eyes, skin, resp sys

Chemical name, structure/formula, CAS and RTECS Nos., and DOT ID and guide Nos.	Synonyms, trade names, and conversion factors	Exposure limits (TWA unless noted otherwise)	IDLH	Physical description	Chemical and physical properties		Incompatibilities and reactivities	Measurement method (See Table 1)
					MW, BP, SOL Fl.P, IP, Sp.Gr, flammability	VP, FRZ UEL, LEL		
Molybdenum M o 7439-98-7 QA4680000	Molybdenum metal	NIOSH* See Appendix D OSHA†* 15 mg/m³ [*Note: The REL and PEL also apply to other insoluble molybdenum compounds (as Mo).]	5000 mg/m³ (as Mo)	Dark gray or black powder with a metallic luster.	MW: 95.9 BP: 8717°F Sol: Insoluble Fl.P: NA IP: NA Sp.Gr: 10.28 Combustible Solid in form of dust or powder.	VP: 0 mm (approx) MLT: 4752°F UEL: NA LEL: NA	Strong oxidizers	Filter; Acid; ICP; IV [#7300, Elements]
Molybdenum (soluble compounds, as Mo)	Synonyms vary depending upon the specific soluble molybdenum compound.	NIOSH See Appendix D OSHA 5 mg/m³	1000 mg/m³ (as Mo)	Appearance and odor vary depending upon the specific soluble molybdenum compound.	Properties vary depending upon the specific soluble molybdenum compound.		Varies	Filter; Acid; ICP; IV [#7300, Elements]
Monocrotophos C₇H₁₄NO₅P 6923-22-4 TC4375000 2783 152 (organophosphorus pesticide, solid)	3-Hydroxy-N-methylcrotonamide dimethylphosphate, Monocron [(CH₃O)₂P(O)OC(CH₃)=CHC(O)NHCH₃]	NIOSH 0.25 mg/m³ OSHA† none	N.D.	Colorless to reddish-brown solid with a mild, ester odor. [insecticide]	MW: 223.2 BP: 257°F Sol: Miscible Fl.P: >200°F IP: ? Sp.Gr: ? Combustible Solid	VP: 0.000007 mm MLT: 129°F UEL: ? LEL: ?	Metals, low molecular weight alcohols & glycols [Note: Corrosive to black iron, drum steel, stainless steel 304 & brass. Should be stored at 70-80°F.]	OVS-2; Toluene/ Acetone; GC/FPD; IV [#5600, Organophosphorus Pesticides]
Monomethyl aniline C₆H₅NHCH₃ 100-61-8 BY4550000 2294 153	MA, (Methylamino)benzene, N-Methyl aniline, Methylphenylamine, N-Phenylmethylamine 1 ppm = 4.38 mg/m³	NIOSH 0.5 ppm (2 mg/m³) [skin] OSHA† 2 ppm (9 mg/m³) [skin]	100 ppm	Yellow to light-brown liquid with a weak, ammonia-like odor.	MW: 107.2 BP: 384°F Sol: Insoluble Fl.P: 175°F IP: 7.32 eV Sp.Gr: 0.99 Class IIIA Combustible Liquid	VP: 0.3 mm FRZ: -71°F UEL: ? LEL: ?	Strong acids, strong oxidizers	Bub; NaOH; GC/FID; IV [#3511]

Personal protection and sanitation (See Table 3)		Recommendations for respirator selection — maximum concentration for use (MUC) (See Table 4)	Health hazards				
			Route	Symptoms (See Table 5)	First aid (See Table 6)		Target organs (See Table 5)
Skin:	N.R.	OSHA	Inh	In animals: irrit eyes,	Eye:	Irr immed	Eyes, resp sys,
Eyes:	N.R.	75 mg/m³: DM^	Ing	nose, throat; anor, diarr,	Breath:	Resp support	liver, kidneys
Wash skin:	N.R.	150 mg/m³: DMXSQ^/SA	Con	low-wgt; listlessness;	Swallow:	Medical attention	
Remove:	N.R.	375 mg/m³: SA:CF/PAPRDM^		liver, kidney damage		immed	
Change:	N.R.	750 mg/m³: HiEF/SAT:CF/PAPRTHiE/ SCBAF/SAF					
		5000 mg/m³: SA:PD,PP					
		§: SCBAF:PD,PP/SAF:PD,PP:ASCBA					
		Escape: HiEF/SCBAE					
[Molybdenum]							
Skin:	Prevent skin contact	OSHA	Inh	In animals: irrit eyes,	Eye:	Irr immed	Eyes, resp sys,
Eyes:	Prevent eye contact	25 mg/m³: DM*	Ing	nose, throat; anor; inco;	Skin:	Water flush	kidneys, blood
Wash skin:	When contam	50 mg/m³: DMXSQ*/SA*	Con	dysp; anemia	Breath:	Resp support	
Remove:	When wet or contam	125 mg/m³: SA:CF*/PAPRDM*			Swallow:	Medical attention	
Change:	N.R.	250 mg/m³: HiEF/SAT:CF*/PAPRTHiE*/ SCBAF/SAF				immed	
		1000 mg/m³: SAF:PD,PP					
		§: SCBAF:PD,PP/SAF:PD,PP:ASCBA					
		Escape: HiEF/SCBAE					
[Molybdenum (soluble compounds, as Mo)]							
Skin:	Prevent skin contact	TBAL	Inh	Irrit eyes, miosis, blurred	Eye:	Irr immed	Eyes, resp sys, CNS,
Eyes:	Prevent eye contact		Abs	vision; dizz, convuls; dysp;	Skin:	Water flush immed	CVS, blood chol,
Wash skin:	When contam		Ing	salv, abdom cramps, nau,	Breath:	Resp support	repro sys
Remove:	When wet or contam		Con	diarr, vomit;	Swallow:	Medical attention	
Change:	Daily			in animals: possible terato		immed	
				effects			
[Monocrotophos]							
Skin:	Prevent skin contact	NIOSH	Inh	Weak, dizz, head; dysp,	Eye:	Irr immed	Resp sys, liver,
Eyes:	Prevent eye contact	5 ppm: SA	Abs	cyan; methemo; pulm	Skin:	Soap wash immed	kidneys, blood, CNS
Wash skin:	When contam	12.5 ppm: SA:CF	Ing	edema; liver, kidney	Breath:	Resp support	
Remove:	When wet or contam	25 ppm: SAT:CF/SCBAF/SAF	Con	damage	Swallow:	Medical attention	
Change:	N.R.	100 ppm: SAF:PD,PP				immed	
		§: SCBAF:PD,PP/SAF:PD,PP:ASCBA					
		Escape: GMFS/SCBAE					
[Monomethyl aniline]							

Chemical name, structure/formula, CAS and RTECS Nos., and DOT ID and guide Nos.	Synonyms, trade names, and conversion factors	Exposure limits (TWA unless noted otherwise)	IDLH	Physical description	Chemical and physical properties		Incompatibilities and reactivities	Measurement method (See Table 1)
					MW, BP, SOL Fl.P, IP, Sp, Gr, flammability	VP, FRZ UEL, LEL		
Morpholine C_4H_9ON 110-91-8 QD6475000 1760 154 (aqueous) 2054 132	Diethylene imidoxide; Diethylene oximide; Tetrahydro-1,4-oxazine; Tetrahydro-p-oxazine 1 ppm = 3.56 mg/m³	NIOSH 20 ppm (70 mg/m³) ST 30 ppm (105 mg/m³) [skin] OSHA† 20 ppm (70 mg/m³) [skin]	1400 ppm [10%LEL]	Colorless liquid with a weak, ammonia- or fish-like odor. [Note: A solid below 23°F.]	MW: 87.1 BP: 264°F Sol: Miscible Fl.P(oc): 98°F IP: 8.88 eV Sp.Gr: 1.007 Class IC Flammable Liquid	VP: 6 mm FRZ: 23°F UEL: 11.2% LEL: 1.4%	Strong acids, strong oxidizers, metals, nitro compounds [Note: Corrosive to metals.]	Si gel; H_2SO_4/NaOH; GC/FID; II(3) [#S150]
Naphtha (coal tar) 8030-30-6 DE3030000 1256 128 (solvent) 2553 128	Crude solvent coal tar naphtha, High solvent naphtha, Naphtha 1 ppm = 4.50 mg/m³ (approx)	NIOSH/OSHA 100 ppm (400 mg/m³)	1000 ppm [10%LEL]	Reddish-brown, mobile liquid with an aromatic odor.	MW: 110 (approx) BP: 320-428°F Sol: Insoluble Fl.P: 100-109°F IP: ? Sp.Gr: 0.89-0.97 Class II Combustible Liquid	VP: <5 mm FRZ: ? UEL: ? LEL: 1%	Strong oxidizers	Char; CS_2; GC/FID; IV [#1550]
Naphthalene $C_{10}H_8$ 91-20-3 QJ0525000 1334 133 (crude or refined) 2304 133 (molten)	Naphthalin, Tar camphor, White tar 1 ppm = 5.24 mg/m³	NIOSH 10 ppm (50 mg/m³) ST 15 ppm (75 mg/m³) OSHA† 10 ppm (50 mg/m³)	250 ppm	Colorless to brown solid with an odor of mothballs. [Note: Shipped as a molten solid.]	MW: 128.2 BP: 424°F Sol: 0.003% Fl.P: 174°F IP: 8.12 eV Sp.Gr: 1.15 Combustible Solid, but will take some effort to ignite.	VP: 0.08 mm MLT: 176°F UEL: 5.9% LEL: 0.9%	Strong oxidizers, chromic anhydride	Char; CS_2; GC/FID; IV [#1501, Aromatic Hydrocarbons]
Naphthalene diisocyanate $C_{10}H_6(NCO)_2$ 3173-72-6 NQ9600000	1,5-Diisocyanatonaphtha-lene; 1,5-Naphthalene diiso-cyanate; 1,5-Naphthalene ester of isocyanic acid; NDI 1 ppm = 8.60 mg/m³	NIOSH 0.040 mg/m³ (0.005 ppm) C 0.170 mg/m³ (0.020 ppm) [10-min] OSHA none	N.D.	White to light-yellow, crystalline flakes.	MW: 210.2 BP: 505°F Sol: ? Fl.P(oc): 311°F IP: ? Sp.Gr: ? Combustible Solid	VP(75°F): 0.003 mm MLT: 261°F UEL: ? LEL: ?	None reported	None available

Personal protection and sanitation (See Table 3)		Recommendations for respirator selection — maximum concentration for use (MUC) (See Table 4)	Route	Symptoms (See Table 5)	First aid (See Table 6)		Target organs (See Table 5)

Skin: Prevent skin contact
Eyes: Prevent eye contact
Wash skin: When contam
Remove: When wet (flamm)
Change: N.R.
Provide: Eyewash (>15%), Quick drench (>25%)

NIOSH/OSHA
500 ppm: SA:CF^ε/PAPROV^ε
1000 ppm: CCRFOV/GMFOV/PAPRTOV^ε/SCBAF/SAF
1400 ppm: SAF:PD,PP
§: SCBAF:PD,PP/SAF:PD,PP:ASCBA
Escape: GMFOV/SCBAE

Inh Abs Ing Con

Irrit eyes, skin, nose, resp sys; vis dist; cough; in animals: liver, kidney damage

Eye: Irr immed
Skin: Water flush immed
Breath: Resp support
Swallow: Medical attention immed

Eyes, skin, resp sys, liver, kidneys

[Morpholine]

Skin: Prevent skin contact
Eyes: Prevent eye contact
Wash skin: When contam
Remove: When wet or contam
Change: N.R.

NIOSH/OSHA
1000 ppm: SA:CF^ε/CCRFOV/GMFOV/PAPROV^ε/SCBAF/SAF
§: SCBAF:PD,PP/SAF:PD,PP:ASCBA
Escape: GMFOV/SCBAE

Inh Ing Con

Irrit eyes, skin, nose; li-head, drow; derm; in animals: liver, kidney damage

Eye: Irr immed
Skin: Soap wash prompt
Breath: Resp support
Swallow: Medical attention immed

Eyes, skin, resp sys, CNS, liver, kidneys

221

[Naphtha (coal tar)]

Skin: Prevent skin contact
Eyes: Prevent eye contact
Wash skin: When contam
Remove: When wet or contam
Change: Daily

NIOSH/OSHA
100 ppm: CCROVDM*/SA*
250 ppm: SA:CF*/CCRFOVHiE/PAPROVDM*/SCBAF/SAF
§: SCBAF:PD,PP/SAF:PD,PP:ASCBA
Escape: GMFOVHiE/SCBAE

Inh Abs Ing Con

Irrit eyes; head, conf, excitement, mal; nau; vomit, abdom pain; irrit bladder; profuse sweat; jaun; hema, hemog, renal shutdown; derm; optical neuritis, corn damage

Eye: Irr immed
Skin: Molten flush immed/sol-liq soap wash prompt
Breath: Resp support
Swallow: Medical attention immed

Eyes, skin, blood, liver, kidneys, CNS

[Naphthalene]

Skin: Prevent skin contact
Eyes: Prevent eye contact
Wash skin: When contam
Remove: When wet or contam
Change: Daily

NIOSH
0.05 ppm: SA*
0.125 ppm: SA:CF*
0.25 ppm: SCBAF/SAF
1 ppm: SAF:PD,PP
§: SCBAF:PD,PP/SAF:PD,PP:ASCBA
Escape: GMFOV/SCBAE

Inh Ing Con

Irrit eyes, nose, throat; resp sens, cough, pulm secretions, chest pain, dysp; asthma

Eye: Irr immed
Skin: Soap wash immed
Breath: Resp support
Swallow: Medical attention immed

Eyes, resp sys

[Naphthalene diisocyanate]

Chemical name, structure/formula, CAS and RTECS Nos., and DOT ID and guide Nos.	Synonyms, trade names, and conversion factors	Exposure limits (TWA unless noted otherwise)	IDLH	Physical description	Chemical and physical properties		Incompatibilities and reactivities	Measurement method (See Table 1)
					MW, BP, SOL Fl.P, IP, Sp, Gr, flammability	VP, FRZ UEL, LEL		
α-Naphthylamine $C_{10}H_7NH_2$ 134-32-7 QM1400000 2077 153	1-Aminonaphthalene, 1-Naphthylamine	NIOSH Ca See Appendix A OSHA [1910.1004] See Appendix B	Ca [N.D.]	Colorless crystals with an ammonia-like odor. [Note: Darkens in air to a reddish-purple color.]	MW: 143.2 BP: 573°F Sol: 0.002% Fl.P: 315°F IP: 7.30 eV Sp.Gr: 1.12 Combustible Solid	VP(220°F): 1 mm MLT: 122°F UEL: ? LEL: ?	Oxidizes in air	Filter/ Si gel; CH_3COOH/ 2-Pro-panol; GC/FID; IV [#5518]
ß-Naphthylamine $C_{10}H_7NH_2$ 91-59-8 QM2100000 1650 153	2-Aminonaphthalene, 2-Naphthylamine	NIOSH Ca See Appendix A OSHA [1910.1009] See Appendix B	Ca [N.D.]	Odorless, white to red crystals with a faint, aromatic odor. [Note: Darkens in air to a reddish-purple color.]	MW: 143.2 BP: 583°F Sol: Miscible in hot water Fl.P: 315°F IP: 9.71 eV Sp.Gr(208°F): 1.06 Combustible Solid	VP(226°F): 1mm MLT: 232°F UEL: ? LEL: ?	None reported	Filter/ Si gel; CH_3COOH/ 2-Pro-panol; GC/FID; IV [#5518]
Niax® Catalyst ESN 62765-93-9 QR3900000	None [Note: A Mixture of 95% dimethylaminopropio-nitrile & 5% bis(2-dimethylamino)ethyl ether.]	NIOSH/OSHA See Appendix C	N.D.	A liquid mixture. [Note: Used in the past as a catalyst in the manufacture of flexible poly-urethane foams.]	MW: mixture BP: ? Sol: ? Fl.P: ? IP: ? Sp.Gr: ?	VP: ? FRZ: ? UEL: ? LEL: ?	Oxidizers	None available
Nickel carbonyl $Ni(CO)_4$ 13463-39-3 QR6300000 1259 131	Nickel tetracarbonyl, Tetracarbonyl nickel 1 ppm = 6.98 mg/m³	NIOSH Ca See Appendix A 0.001 ppm (0.007 mg/m³) OSHA 0.001 ppm (0.007 mg/m³)	Ca [2 ppm]	Colorless to yellow liquid with a musty odor. [Note: A gas above 110°F.]	MW: 170.7 BP: 110°F Sol: 0.05% Fl.P: <-4°F IP: 8.28 eV Sp.Gr(63°F): 1.32 Class IB Flammable Liquid	VP: 315mm FRZ: -13°F UEL: ? LEL: 2%	Nitric acid, bromine, chlorine & other oxidizers; flammable materials	Char(low Ni) HNO_3; GFAAS; IV [#6007]

Personal protection and sanitation (See Table 3)		Recommendations for respirator selection — maximum concentration for use (MUC) (See Table 4)	Health hazards			
			Route	Symptoms (See Table 5)	First aid (See Table 6)	Target organs (See Table 5)
Skin:	Prevent skin contact	NIOSH	Inh	Derm; hemorrhagic	Eye: Irr immed	Bladder, skin
Eyes:	Prevent eye contact	¥: SCBAF:PD,PP/SAF:PD,PP:ASCBA	Abs	cystitis; dysp, ataxia,	Skin: Soap wash immed	[bladder cancer]
Wash skin:	When contam/Daily	Escape: HiEF/SCBAE	Ing	methemo; hema; dysuria;	Breath: Resp support	
Remove:	When wet or contam		Con	[carc]	Swallow: Medical attention	
Change:	Daily				immed	
Provide:	Eyewash, Quick drench					

[α-Naphthylamine]

Skin:	Prevent skin contact	NIOSH	Inh	Derm; hemorrhagic	Eye: Irr immed	Bladder, skin
Eyes:	Prevent eye contact	¥: SCBAF:PD,PP/SAF:PD,PP:ASCBA	Abs	cystitis; dysp; ataxia;	Skin: Soap wash immed	[bladder cancer]
Wash skin:	When contam/Daily	Escape: HiEF/SCBAE	Ing	methemo, hema; dysuria;	Breath: Resp support	
Remove:	When wet or contam		Con	[carc]	Swallow: Medical attention	
Change:	Daily				immed	
Provide:	Eyewash, Quick drench					

[ß-Naphthylamine]

Skin:	Prevent skin contact	NIOSH	Inh	Irrit eyes, skin; urinary	Eye: Irr immed	Eyes, skin, urinary
Eyes:	Prevent eye contact	¥: SCBAF:PD,PP/SAF:PD,PP:ASCBA	Abs	dysfunc; neurological	Skin: Soap flush immed	tract, PNS
Wash skin:	When contam	Escape: GMFOV/SCBAE	Ing	disorders; pins & needles	Breath: Resp support	
Remove:	When wet or contam		Con	sensation in hands & feet;	Swallow: Medical attention	
Change:	Daily			musc weak, lass, nau, vomit;	immed	
Provide:	Eyewash, Quick drench			decr nerve conduction times		
				of lower legs		

[NIAX® Catalyst ESN]

Skin:	Prevent skin contact	NIOSH	Inh	Head, verti; nau, vomit,	Eye: Irr immed	Lungs, paranasal
Eyes:	Prevent eye contact	¥: SCBAF:PD,PP/SAF:PD,PP:ASCBA	Abs	epigastric pain; subs pain;	Skin: Soap wash immed	sinus, CNS, repro sys
Wash skin:	When contam	Escape: GMFS/SCBAE	Ing	cough, hyperpnea; cyan;	Breath: Resp support	[lung & nasal
Remove:	When wet (flamm)		Con	weak; leucyt; pneuitis;	Swallow: Medical attention	cancer]
Change:	N.R.			delirium; convuls; [carc];	immed	
Provide:	Eyewash, Quick drench			in animals: repro, terato		
				effects		

[Nickel carbonyl]

Chemical name, structure/formula, CAS and RTECS Nos., and DOT ID and guide Nos.	Synonyms, trade names, and conversion factors	Exposure limits (TWA unless noted otherwise)	IDLH	Physical description	Chemical and physical properties		Incompatibilities and reactivities	Measurement method (See Table 1)
					MW, BP, SOL Fl.P, IP, Sp, Gr, flammability	VP, FRZ UEL, LEL		
Nickel metal and other compounds (as Ni) Ni (Metal) 7440-02-0 (Metal) QR5950000 (Metal)	Nickel metal: Elemental metal, Nickel catalyst Synonyms of other nickel compounds vary depending upon the specific compound.	NIOSH* Ca See Appendix A 0.015 mg/m³ OSHA†* 1 mg/m³ [*Note: The REL and PEL do not apply to Nickel carbonyl.]	Ca [10 mg/m³ (as Ni)]	Metal: Lustrous, silvery, odorless solid.	MW: 58.7 BP: 5139°F Sol: Insoluble Fl.P: NA IP: NA Sp.Gr: 8.90 (Metal) Metal: Combustible Solid; nickel sponge catalyst may ignite SPONTANEOUSLY in air.	VP: 0 mm (approx) MLT: 2831°F UEL: NA LEL: NA	Strong acids, sulfur, selenium, wood & other combustibles, nickel nitrate	Filter; Acid; ICP; IV [#7300, Elements]
Nicotine C₅H₄NC₄H₇NCH₃ 54-11-5 QS5250000 1654 151	3-(1-Methyl-2-pyrrolidyl)-pyridine	NIOSH/OSHA 0.5 mg/m³ [skin]	5 mg/m³	Pale-yellow to dark brown liquid with a fish-like odor when warm. [insecticide]	MW: 162.2 BP: 482°F (Decomposes) Sol: Miscible Fl.P: 203°F IP: 8.01 eV Sp.Gr: 1.01 Class IIIB Combustible Liquid	VP: 0.08 mm FRZ: -110°F UEL: 4.0% LEL: 0.7%	Strong oxidizers, strong acids	XAD-2; Ethyl acetate; GC/NPD; IV [#2544]
Nitric acid HNO₃ 7697-37-2 QU5775000 1760 154 (≤40% acid) 2031 157 (>40% acid) 2032 157 (fuming)	Aqua fortis, Engravers acid, Hydrogen nitrate, Red fuming nitric acid (RFNA), White fuming nitric acid (WFNA) 1 ppm = 2.58 mg/m³	NIOSH/OSHA 2 ppm (5 mg/m³) ST 4 ppm (10 mg/m³) OSHA† 2 ppm (5 mg/m³) [Note: Often used in an aqueous solution. Fuming nitric acid is concentrated nitric acid that contains dissolved nitrogen dioxide.]	25 ppm	Colorless, yellow, or red, fuming liquid with an acrid, suffocating odor.	MW: 63.0 BP: 181°F Sol: Miscible Fl.P: NA IP: 11.95 eV Sp.Gr(77°F): 1.50 Noncombustible Liquid, but increases the flammability of combustible materials.	VP: 48 mm FRZ: -44°F UEL: NA LEL: NA	Combustible materials, metallic powders, hydrogen sulfide, carbides, alcohols [Note: Reacts with water to produce heat. Corrosive to metals.]	Si gel; NaHCO₃/ Na₂CO₃; IC; IV [#7903, Inorganic Acids]
Nitric oxide NO 10102-43-9 QX0525000 1660 124	Mononitrogen monoxide, Nitrogen monoxide 1 ppm = 1.23 mg/m³	NIOSH/OSHA 25 ppm (30 mg/m³)	100 ppm	Colorless gas. [Note: Shipped as a nonliquefied compressed gas.]	MW: 30.0 BP: -241°F Sol: 5% Fl.P: NA IP: 9.27 eV RGasD: 1.04 Nonflammable Gas, but will accelerate the burning of combustible materials.	VP: 34.2 atm FRZ: -263°F UEL: NA LEL: NA	Fluorine, combustible materials, ozone, NH₃, chlorinated hydro-carbons, metals, carbon disulfide [Note: Reacts with water to form nitric acid. Rapidly converted] in air to nitrogen dioxide.]	Mol-sieve*; Reagent; Vis; IV [#6014]

Personal protection and sanitation (See Table 3)		Recommendations for respirator selection — maximum concentration for use (MUC) (See Table 4)	Health hazards			
			Route	Symptoms (See Table 5)	First aid (See Table 6)	Target organs (See Table 5)
Skin:	Prevent skin contact	NIOSH	Inh	Sens derm, allergic asthma, pneuitis; [carc]	Skin: Water flush immed	Nasal cavities, lungs, skin, [lung & nasal cancer]
Eyes:	N.R.	¥: SCBAF:PD,PP/SAF:PD,PP:ASCBA	Ing		Breath: Resp support	
Wash skin:	When contam/Daily	Escape: HiEF/SCBAE	Con		Swallow: Medical attention immed	
Remove:	When wet or contam					
Change:	Daily					

[Nickel metal and other compounds (as Ni)]

Skin:	Prevent skin contact	NIOSH/OSHA	Inh	Nau, salv, abdom pain, vomit, diarr; head, dizz, hearing, vis dist; conf, weak, inco; paroxysmal atrial fibrl; convuls; dysp; in animals: terato effects	Eye: Irr immed	CNS, CVS, lungs, GI tract, repro sys
Eyes:	Prevent eye contact	5 mg/m³: SA/SCBAF	Abs		Skin: Water flush immed	
Wash skin:	When contam	§: SCBAF:PD,PP/SAF:PD,PP:ASCBA	Ing		Breath: Resp support	
Remove:	When wet or contam	Escape: GMFOV/SCBAE	Con		Swallow: Medical attention immed	
Change:	N.R.					
Provide:	Eyewash, Quick drench					

225

[Nicotine]

Skin:	Prevent skin contact	NIOSH/OSHA	Inh	Irrit eyes, skin, muc memb; delayed pulm edema, pneuitis, bron; dental erosion	Eye: Irr immed	Eyes, skin, resp sys, teeth
Eyes:	Prevent eye contact	25 ppm: SA:CF*/CCRFS⁴/GMFS⁴/ SCBAF/SAF	Ing		Skin: Water flush immed	
Wash skin:	When contam	§: SCBAF:PD,PP/SAF:PD,PP:ASCBA	Con		Breath: Resp support	
Remove:	When wet or contam	Escape: GMFS⁴/SCBAE			Swallow: Medical attention immed	
Change:	N.R.					
Provide:	Eyewash (pH<2.5), Quick drench (pH<2.5)					

[Nitric acid]

Skin:	N.R.	NIOSH/OSHA	Inh	Irrit eyes, wet skin, nose, throat; drow, uncon; methemo	Breath: Resp support	Eyes, skin, resp sys, blood, CNS
Eyes:	N.R.	100 ppm: SA:CF*/CCRFS⁴/PAPRS*⁴/ GMFS⁴/SA*/SCBAF				
Wash skin:	N.R.	§: SCBAF:PD,PP/SAF:PD,PP:ASCBA				
Remove:	N.R.	Escape: GMFS⁴/SCBAE				
Change:	N.R.					

[Nitric oxide]

Chemical name, structure/formula, CAS and RTECS Nos., and DOT ID and guide Nos.	Synonyms, trade names, and conversion factors	Exposure limits (TWA unless noted otherwise)	IDLH	Physical description	Chemical and physical properties		Incompatibilities and reactivities	Measurement method (See Table 1)
					MW, BP, SOL Fl.P, IP, Sp, Gr, flammability	VP, FRZ UEL, LEL		
p-Nitroaniline $NO_2C_6H_4NH_2$ 100-01-6 BY7000000 1661 153	para-Aminonitrobenzene, 4-Nitroaniline, 4-Nitrobenzenamine, p-Nitrophenylamine, PNA	NIOSH 3 mg/m³ [skin] OSHA† 6 mg/m³ (1 ppm) [skin]	300 mg/m³	Bright yellow, crystalline powder with a slight, ammonia-like odor.	MW: 138.1 BP: 630°F Sol: 0.08% Fl.P: 390°F IP: 8.85 eV Sp.Gr: 1.42 Combustible Solid	VP: 0.00002 mm MLT: 295°F UEL: ? LEL: ?	Strong oxidizers, strong reducers [Note: May result in spontaneous heating of organic materials in the presence of moisture.]	Filter; 2-Propanol; HPLC/UVD; IV [#5033]
Nitrobenzene $C_6H_5NO_2$ 98-95-3 DA6475000 1662 152	Essence of mirbane, Nitrobenzol, Oil of mirbane 1 ppm = 5.04 mg/m³	NIOSH/OSHA 1 ppm (5 mg/m³) [skin]	200 ppm	Yellow, oily liquid with a pungent odor like paste shoe polish. [Note: A solid below 42°F.]	MW: 123.1 BP: 411°F Sol: 0.2% Fl.P: 190°F IP: 9.92 eV Sp.Gr: 1.20 Class IIIA Combustible Liquid	VP(77°F): 0.3 mm FRZ: 42°F UEL: ? LEL(200°F): 1.8%	Concentrated nitric acid, nitrogen tetroxide, caustics, phosphorus pentachloride, chemically-active metals such as tin or zinc	Si gel; Methanol; GC/FID; IV [#2005]
4-Nitrobiphenyl $C_6H_5C_6H_4NO_2$ 92-93-3 DV5600000	p-Nitrobipheny, p-Nitrodiphenyl, 4-Nitrodiphenyl, p-Phenylnitrobenzene, 4-Phenylnitrobenzene, PNB	NIOSH Ca See Appendix A OSHA [1910.1003] See Appendix B	Ca [N.D.]	White to yellow, needle-like, crystalline solid with a sweetish odor.	MW: 199.2 BP: 644°F Sol: Insoluble Fl.P: 290°F IP: ? Sp.Gr: ? Combustible Solid	VP: ? MLT: 237°F UEL: ? LEL: ?	Strong reducers	Filter/ Si gel(2); 2-Propanol; GC/FID; II(4) [P&CAM #273]
p-Nitrochlorobenzene $ClC_6H_4NO_2$ 100-00-5 CZ1050000 1578 152	p-Chloronitrobenzene, 4-Chloronitrobenzene, 1-Chloro-4-nitrobenzene, 4-Nitrochlorobenzene, PCNB, PNCB	NIOSH Ca See Appendix A [skin] OSHA 1 mg/m³ [skin]	Ca [100 mg/m³]	Yellow, crystalline solid with a sweet odor.	MW: 157.6 BP: 468°F Sol: Slight Fl.P: 261°F IP: 9.96 eV Sp.Gr: 1.52 Solid that does not burn, or burns with difficulty.	VP(86°F): 0.2 mm MLT: 182°F UEL: ? LEL: ?	Strong oxidizers, alkalis	Si gel; Methanol; GC/FID; IV [#2005, Nitrobenzenes]

Personal protection and sanitation (See Table 3)	Recommendations for respirator selection — maximum concentration for use (MUC) (See Table 4)	Health hazards			
		Route	Symptoms (See Table 5)	First aid (See Table 6)	Target organs (See Table 5)
Skin: Prevent skin contact Eyes: Prevent eye contact Wash skin: When contam/Daily Remove: When wet or contam Change: Daily Provide: Quick drench	NIOSH 30 mg/m³: SA* 75 mg/m³: SA:CF* 150 mg/m³: SCBAF/SAF 300 mg/m³: SAF:PD,PP §: SCBAF:PD,PP/SAF:PD,PP:ASCBA Escape: GMFOVDMFu/SCBAE	Inh Abs Ing Con	Irrit nose, throat; cyan, ataxia; tacar, tachypnea; dysp; irrity; vomit, diarr; convuls; resp arrest; anemia; methemo; jaundice	Eye: Irr immed Skin: Water flush immed Breath: Resp support Swallow: Medical attention immed	Resp sys, blood, heart, liver
[p-Nitroaniline]					
Skin: Prevent skin contact Eyes: Prevent eye contact Wash skin: N.R. Remove: When wet or contam Change: Daily Provide: Quick drench	NIOSH/OSHA 10 ppm: CCROV*/SA* 25 ppm: SA:CF*/PAPROV* 50 ppm: CCRFOV/GMFOV/PAPRTOV*/SCBAF/SAF 200 ppm: SAF:PD,PP §: SCBAF:PD,PP/SAF:PD,PP:ASCBA Escape: GMFOV/SCBAE	Inh Abs Ing Con	Irrit eyes, skin, anoxia; derm; anemia; methemo; in animals: liver, kidney damage; testicular effects	Eye: Irr immed Skin: Soap wash immed Breath: Resp support Swallow: Medical attention immed	Eyes, skin, blood, liver, kidneys CVS, repro sys
[Nitrobenzene]					
Skin: Prevent skin contact Eyes: Prevent eye contact Wash skin: When contam/Daily Remove: When wet or contam Change: Daily Provide: Eyewash, Quick drench	NIOSH ¥: SCBAF:PD,PP/SAF:PD,PP:ASCBA Escape: HiEF/SCBAE	Inh Abs Ing Con	Head, leth, dizz; dysp; ataxia, weak; methemo; urinary burning; acute hemorrhagic cystitis; [carc]	Eye: Irr immed Skin: Soap wash immed Breath: Resp support Swallow: Medical attention immed	Bladder, blood [in animals: bladder tumors]
[4-Nitrobiphenyl]					
Skin: Prevent skin contact Eyes: Prevent eye contact Wash skin: When contam/Daily Remove: When wet or contam Change: Daily Provide: Eyewash, Quick drench	NIOSH ¥: SCBAF:PD,PP/SAF:PD,PP:ASCBA Escape: HiEF/SCBAE	Inh Abs Ing Con	Anoxia; unpleasant taste; anemia; methemo; in animals: hema, hemog; spleen, kidney, bone marrow changes; repro effects; [carc]	Eye: Irr immed Skin: Soap wash immed Breath: Resp support Swallow: Medical attention immed	Blood, liver, kidneys, CVS, spleen, bone marrow, repro sys [in animals: vascular & liver tumors]
[p-Nitrochlorobenzene]					

Chemical name, structure/formula, CAS and RTECS Nos., and DOT ID and guide Nos.	Synonyms, trade names, and conversion factors	Exposure limits (TWA unless noted otherwise)	IDLH	Physical description	Chemical and physical properties		Incompatibilities and reactivities	Measurement method (See Table 1)
					MW, BP, SOL Fl.P, IP, Sp, Gr, flammability	VP, FRZ UEL, LEL		
Nitroethane $CH_3CH_2NO_2$ 79-24-3 K15600000 2842 129	Nitroetan 1 ppm = 3.07 mg/m³	NIOSH/OSHA 100 ppm (310 mg/m³)	1000 ppm	Colorless, oily liquid with a mild, fruity odor.	MW: 75.1 BP: 237°F Sol: 5% Fl.P: 82°F IP: 10.88 eV Sp.Gr: 1.05 Class IC Flammable Liquid	VP(77°F): 21mm FRZ: -130°F UEL: ? LEL: 3.4%	Amines; strong acids, alkalis & oxidizers; hydrocarbons; combustibles; metal oxides	XAD-2(2); Ethyl acetate; GC/FID; IV [#2526]
Nitrogen dioxide NO_2 10102-44-0 QW9800000 1067 124	Dinitrogen tetroxide (N_2O_4), Nitrogen peroxide 1 ppm = 1.88 mg/m³	NIOSH ST 1 ppm (1.8 mg/m³) OSHA† C 5 ppm (9 mg/m³)	20 ppm	Yellowish-brown liquid or reddish-brown gas (above 70°F) with a pungent, acrid odor. [Note: In solid form (below 15°F) it is found structurally as N_2O_4.]	MW: 46.0 BP: 70°F Sol: Reacts Fl.P: NA IP: 9.75 eV Sp.Gr: 1.44 (Liquid at 68°F) RGasD: 2.62 Noncombustible Liquid/Gas, but will accelerate the burning of combustible materials.	VP: 720 mm FRZ: 15°F UEL: NA LEL: NA	Combustible material, water, chlorinated hydrocarbons, carbon disulfide, ammonia [Note: Reacts with water to form nitric acid.]	Mol-sieve*; Reagent; Vis; IV [#6014]
Nitrogen trifluoride NF_3 7783-54-2 QX1925000 2451 122	Nitrogen fluoride, Trifluoramine, Trifluorammonia 1 ppm = 2.90 mg/m³	NIOSH/OSHA 10 ppm (29 mg/m³)	1000 ppm	Colorless gas with a moldy odor. [Note: Shipped as a nonliquefied compressed gas.]	MW: 71.0 BP: -200°F Sol: Slight Fl.P: NA IP: 12.97 eV RGasD: 2.46 Nonflammable Gas	VP: >1 atm FRZ: -340°F UEL: NA LEL: NA	Water, oil, grease, oxidizable materials, ammonia, carbon monoxide, methane, hydrogen, hydrogen sulfide, activated charcoal, diborane	None available
Nitroglycerine $CH_2NO_3CHNO_3CH_2NO_3$ 55-63-0 QX2100000 1204 127 (≤1% soln. in alcohol) 3064 127 (1-5% soln. in alcohol)	Glyceryl trinitrate; NG; 1,2,3-Propanetriol trinitrate; Trinitroglycerine 1 ppm = 9.29 mg/m³	NIOSH ST 0.1 mg/m³ [skin] OSHA† C 0.2 ppm (2 mg/m³) [skin]	75 mg/m³	Colorless to pale-yellow, viscous liquid or solid (below 56°F). [Note: An explosive ingredient in dynamite (20-40%) with ethylene glycol dinitrate (80-60%).]	MW: 227.1 BP: Begins to decompose at 122-140°F Sol: 0.1% Fl.P: Explodes IP: ? Sp.Gr: 1.60 Explosive Liquid	VP: 0.0003 mm FRZ: 56°F UEL: ? LEL: ?	Heat, ozone, shock, acids [Note: An OSHA Class A Explosive (1910.109).]	Tenax GC; Ethanol; GC/ECD; IV [#2507]

Personal protection and sanitation (See Table 3)		Recommendations for respirator selection — maximum concentration for use (MUC) (See Table 4)	Health hazards				
			Route	Symptoms (See Table 5)	First aid (See Table 6)		Target organs (See Table 5)
Skin:	Prevent skin contact	NIOSH/OSHA	Inh	Derm;	Eye:	Irr immed	Skin, resp sys, CNS, kidneys, liver
Eyes:	Prevent eye contact	1000 ppm: SCBAF/SAF	Ing	in animals: lac; dysp,	Skin:	Soap wash prompt	
Wash skin:	When contam	§: SCBAF:PD,PP/SAF:PD,PP:ASCBA	Con	pulm rales, edema; liver,	Breath:	Resp support	
Remove:	When wet (flamm)	Escape: SCBAE		kidney inj; narco	Swallow:	Medical attention	
Change:	N.R.					immed	

[Nitroethane]

Personal protection and sanitation		Recommendations for respirator selection	Route	Symptoms	First aid		Target organs
Skin:	Prevent skin contact	NIOSH	Inh	Irrit eyes, nose, throat;	Eye:	Irr immed	Eyes, resp sys, CVS
Eyes:	Prevent eye contact	20 ppm: SA:CF£/SCBAF/SAF	Ing	cough, mucoid frothy	Skin:	Water flush immed	
Wash skin:	When contam	§: SCBAF:PD,PP/SAF:PD,PP:ASCBA	Con	sputum, decr pulm func,	Breath:	Resp support	
Remove:	When wet or contam	Escape: GMFS♩/SCBAE		chronic bron, dysp; chest	Swallow:	Medical attention	
Change:	N.R.			pain; pulm edema, cyan,		immed	
Provide:	Eyewash, Quick drench			tachypnea, tacar			

[Nitrogen dioxide]

Personal protection and sanitation		Recommendations for respirator selection	Route	Symptoms	First aid		Target organs
Skin:	N.R.	NIOSH/OSHA	Inh	In animals: anoxia, cyan;	Breath:	Resp support	Blood, liver, kidneys
Eyes:	N.R.	100 ppm: CCRS/SA		methemo; weak, dizz;			
Wash skin:	N.R.	250 ppm: SA:CF/PAPRS		head; liver, kidney inj			
Remove:	N.R.	500 ppm: CCRFS/GMFS/PAPRTS*/					
Change:	N.R.	SAT:CF*/SCBAF/SAF					
		1000 ppm: SAF:PD,PP					
		§: SCBAF:PD,PP/SAF:PD,PP:ASCBA					
		Escape: GMFS/SCBAE					

[Nitrogen trifluoride]

Personal protection and sanitation		Recommendations for respirator selection	Route	Symptoms	First aid		Target organs
Skin:	Prevent skin contact	NIOSH	Inh	Throb head; dizz; nau,	Eye:	Irr immed	CVS, blood, skin, CNS
Eyes:	Prevent eye contact	1 mg/m³: SA*	Abs	vomit, abdom pain;	Skin:	Soap wash immed	
Wash skin:	When contam	2.5 mg/m³: SA:CF*	Ing	hypotension; flush;	Breath:	Resp support	
Remove:	When wet (flamm)	5 mg/m³: SAT:CF*/SCBAF/SAF	Con	palp; methemo; delirium,	Swallow:	Medical attention	
Change:	Daily	75 mg/m³: SAF:PD,PP		CNS depres; angina;		immed	
Provide:	Quick drench	§: SCBAF:PD,PP/SAF:PD,PP:ASCBA		skin irrit			
		Escape: GMFOVHiE/SCBAE					

[Nitroglycerine]

Chemical name, structure/formula, CAS and RTECS Nos., and DOT ID and guide Nos.	Synonyms, trade names, and conversion factors	Exposure limits (TWA unless noted otherwise)	IDLH	Physical description	Chemical and physical properties		Incompatibilities and reactivities	Measurement method (See Table 1)
					MW, BP, SOL Fl.P, IP, Sp, Gr, flammability	VP, FRZ UEL, LEL		
Nitromethane CH₃NO₂ 75-52-5 PA9800000 1261 129	Nitrocarbol 1 ppm = 2.50 mg/m³	NIOSH See Appendix D OSHA 100 ppm (250 mg/m³)	750 ppm	Colorless, oily liquid with a disagreeable odor.	MW: 61.0 BP: 214°F Sol: 10% Fl.P: 95°F IP: 11.08 eV Sp.Gr. 1.14 Class IC Flammable Liquid	VP: 28 mm FRZ: -20°F UEL: ? LEL: 7.3%	Amines; strong acids, alkalis & oxidizers; hydrocarbons & other combustible materials; metallic oxides [Note: Slowly corrodes steel & copper when wet.]	Chrom-106; Ethyl acetate; GC/FPD; IV [#2527]
2-Nitronaphthalene C₁₀H₇NO₂ 581-89-5 QJ9760000 2538 133	ß-Nitronaphthalene	NIOSH Ca* See Appendix A [*Note: Since metabolized to ß-Naphthylamine.] OSHA none	Ca [N.D.]	Colorless solid.	MW: 178.2 BP: ? Sol: Insoluble Fl.P: ? IP: 8.67 eV Sp.Gr. ? Combustible Solid	VP: ? MLT: 174°F UEL: ? LEL: ?	For "Nitrates" in general: Aluminum, cyanides, esters, phosphorus, tin chlorides, thiocyanates, sodium hypophosphite	None available
1-Nitropropane CH₃CH₂CH₂NO₂ 108-03-2 TZ5075000 2608 129	Nitropropane, 1-NP 1 ppm = 3.64 mg/m³	NIOSH/OSHA 25 ppm (90 mg/m³)	1000 ppm	Colorless liquid with a somewhat disagreeable odor.	MW: 89.1 BP: 269°F Sol: 1% Fl.P: 96°F IP: 10.81 eV Sp.Gr. 1.00 Class IC Flammable Liquid	VP: 8 mm FRZ: -162°F UEL: ? LEL: 2.2%	Amines; strong acids, alkalis & oxidizers; hydrocarbons & other combustible materials; metal oxides	XAD-4; CS₂; GC/NPD; OSHA [#46]
2-Nitropropane (CH₃)₂CHNO₂ 79-46-9 TZ5250000 2608 129	Dimethylnitromethane, iso-Nitropropane, 2-NP 1 ppm = 3.64 mg/m³	NIOSH Ca See Appendix A OSHA† 25 ppm (90 mg/m³)	Ca [100 ppm]	Colorless liquid with a pleasant, fruity odor.	MW: 89.1 BP: 249°F Sol: 2% Fl.P: 75°F IP: 10.71 eV Sp.Gr. 0.99 Class IC Flammable Liquid	VP: 13 mm FRZ: -135°F UEL: 11.0% LEL: 2.6%	Amines; strong acids, alkalis & oxidizers; metal oxides; combustible materials	Chrom-106; Ethyl acetate; GC/FID; IV [#2528]

Personal protection and sanitation (See Table 3)		Recommendations for respirator selection — maximum concentration for use (MUC) (See Table 4)	Health hazards			
			Route	Symptoms (See Table 5)	First aid (See Table 6)	Target organs (See Table 5)
Skin: Eyes: Wash skin: Remove: Change:	Prevent skin contact Prevent eye contact When contam When wet (flamm) N.R.	OSHA 750 ppm: SA:CF£/SCBAF/SAF §: SCBAF:PD,PP/SAF:PD,PP:ASCBA Escape: SCBAE	Inh Ing Con	Derm; in animals: irrit eyes, resp sys; convuls, narco; liver damage	Eye: Skin: Breath: Swallow:	Irr immed Soap wash prompt Resp support Medical attention immed	Eyes, skin, CNS, liver

[Nitromethane]

| Skin:
Eyes:
Wash skin:
Remove:
Change:
Provide: | Prevent skin contact
Prevent eye contact
When contam/Daily
When wet or contam
Daily
Eyewash, Quick drench | NIOSH
¥: SCBAF:PD,PP/SAF:PD,PP:ASCBA
Escape: GMFOVHiE/SCBAE | Inh
Abs
Ing
Con | Irrit skin, resp sys; derm; [carc] | Eye:
Skin:
Breath:
Swallow: | Irr immed
Soap wash immed
Resp support
Medical attention immed | Skin, resp sys [bladder cancer] |

231

[2-Nitronaphthalene]

| Skin:
Eyes:
Wash skin:
Remove:
Change: | N.R.
Prevent eye contact
N.R.
When wet (flamm)
N.R. | NIOSH/OSHA
250 ppm: SA*
625 ppm: SA:CF*
1000 ppm: SCBAF/SAF
§: SCBAF:PD,PP/SAF:PD,PP:ASCBA
Escape: SCBAE | Inh
Ing
Con | Irrit eyes; head, nau, vomit, diarr; in animals: liver, kidney damage | Eye:
Skin:
Breath:
Swallow: | Irr immed
Soap wash prompt
Resp support
Medical attention immed | Eyes, CNS, liver, kidneys |

[1-Nitropropane]

| Skin:
Eyes:
Wash skin:
Remove:
Change: | Prevent skin contact
Prevent eye contact
When contam
When wet (flamm)
N.R. | NIOSH
¥: SCBAF:PD,PP/SAF:PD,PP:ASCBA
Escape: SCBAE | Inh
Ing
Con | Irrit eyes, skin, nose, resp sys; head, añor, nau, vomit, diarr; kidney, liver damage; [carc] | Eye:
Skin:
Breath:
Swallow: | Irr immed
Soap wash prompt
Resp support
Medical attention immed | Eyes, skin, resp sys, CNS, kidneys, liver [in animals: liver tumors] |

[2-Nitropropane]

Chemical name, structure/formula, CAS and RTECS Nos., and DOT ID and guide Nos.	Synonyms, trade names, and conversion factors	Exposure limits (TWA unless noted otherwise)	IDLH	Physical description	Chemical and physical properties		Incompatibilities and reactivities	Measurement method (See Table 1)
					MW, BP, SOL, Fl.P, IP, Sp, Gr, flammability	VP, FRZ, UEL, LEL		
N-Nitrosodimethylamine $(CH_3)_2N_2O$ 62-75-9 IQ0525000	Dimethylnitrosamine; N,N-Dimethylnitrosamine; DMNA; N-Methyl-N-nitroso-methanamine; NDMA; N-Nitroso-N,N-dimethylamine	NIOSH Ca See Appendix A OSHA[1910.1016] See Appendix B	Ca [N.D.]	Yellow, oily liquid with a faint, characteristic odor.	MW: 74.1 BP: 306°F Sol: Soluble Fl.P: ? IP: 8.69 eV Sp.Gr: 1.005 Combustible Liquid	VP: 3 mm FRZ: ? UEL: ? LEL: ?	Strong oxidizers [Note: Should be stored in dark bottles.]	T-Sorb; Methanol/ CH_2Cl_2; GC/FID; IV [#2522]
o-Nitrotoluene $NO_2C_6H_4CH_3$ 88-72-2 XT3150000 1664 152	o-Methylnitrobenzene, 2-Methylnitrobenzene, ortho-Nitrotoluene, 2-Nitrotoluene 1 ppm = 5.61 mg/m³	NIOSH 2 ppm (11 mg/m³) [skin] OSHA† 5 ppm (30 mg/m³) [skin]	200 ppm	Yellow liquid with a weak, aromatic odor. [Note: A solid below 25°F.]	MW: 137.1 BP: 432°F Sol: 0.07% Fl.P: 223°F IP: 9.43 eV Sp.Gr: 1.16 Class IIIB Combustible Liquid	VP: 0.1 mm FRZ: 25°F UEL: ? LEL: 2.2%	Strong oxidizers, sulfuric acid	Si gel; Methanol; GC/FID; IV [#2005, Nitro-benzenes]
m-Nitrotoluene $NO_2C_6H_4CH_3$ 99-08-1 XT2975000 1664 152	m-Methylnitrobenzene, 3-Methylnitrobenzene, meta-Nitrotoluene, 3-Nitrotoluene 1 ppm = 5.61 mg/m³	NIOSH 2 ppm (11 mg/m³) [skin] OSHA† 5 ppm (30 mg/m³) [skin]	200 ppm	Yellow liquid with a weak, aromatic odor. [Note: A solid below 59°F.]	MW: 137.1 BP: 450°F Sol: 0.05% Fl.P: 223°F IP: 9.48 eV Sp.Gr: 1.16 Class IIIB Combustible Liquid	VP: 0.1 mm FRZ: 59°F UEL: ? LEL: 1.6%	Strong oxidizers, sulfuric acid	Si gel; Methanol; GC/FID; IV [#2005, Nitro-benzenes]
p-Nitrotoluene $NO_2C_6H_4CH_3$ 99-99-0 XT3325000 1664 152	p-Methylnitrobenzene, 4-Methylnitrobenzene, para-Nitrotoluene, 4-Nitrotoluene 1 ppm = 5.61 mg/m³	NIOSH 2 ppm (11 mg/m³) [skin] OSHA† 5 ppm (30 mg/m³) [skin]	200 ppm	Crystalline solid with a weak, aromatic odor.	MW: 137.1 BP: 460°F Sol: 0.04% Fl.P: 223°F IP: 9.50 eV Sp.Gr: 1.12 Combustible Solid	VP: 0.1 mm MLT: 126°F UEL: ? LEL: 1.6%	Strong oxidizers, sulfuric acid	Si gel; Methanol; GC/FID; IV [#2005, Nitro-benzenes]

Personal protection and sanitation (See Table 3)		Recommendations for respirator selection — maximum concentration for use (MUC) (See Table 4)	Health hazards				
			Route	Symptoms (See Table 5)	First aid (See Table 6)	Target organs (See Table 5)	
Skin:	Prevent skin contact	NIOSH	Inh	Nau, vomit, diarr,	Eye:	Irr immed	Liver, kidneys,
Eyes:	Prevent eye contact	¥: SCBAF:PD,PP/SAF:PD,PP:ASCBA	Abs	abdom cramps; head;	Skin:	Soap wash immed	lungs
Wash skin:	When contam/Daily	Escape: HiEF/SCBAE	Ing	fever; enlarged liver,	Breath:	Resp support	[in animals:
Remove:	When wet or contam		Con	jaun; decr liver, kidney,	Swallow:	Medical attention	lung, kidney,
Change:	Daily			pulm func; [carc]		immed	liver & nasal
Provide:	Eyewash, Quick drench						cavity tumors]
[N-Nitrosodimethylamine]							
Skin:	Prevent skin contact	NIOSH	Inh	Anoxia, cyan; head,	Eye:	Irr immed	Blood, CNS, CVS,
Eyes:	Prevent eye contact	20 ppm: SA*	Abs	weak, dizz; ataxia;	Skin:	Soap wash immed	skin, GI tract
Wash skin:	When contam	50 ppm: SA:CF*	Ing	dysp; tacar; nau, vomit	Breath:	Resp support	
Remove:	When wet or contam	100 ppm: SAT:CF*/SCBAF/SAF	Con		Swallow:	Medical attention	
Change:	N.R.	200 ppm: SAF:PD,PP				immed	
		§: SCBAF:PD,PP/SAF:PD,PP:ASCBA					
		Escape: GMFOVHiE/SCBAE					
[o-Nitrotoluene]							
Skin:	Prevent skin contact	NIOSH	Inh	Anoxia, cyan; head,	Eye:	Irr immed	Blood, CNS, CVS,
Eyes:	Prevent eye contact	20 ppm: SA*	Abs	weak, dizz; ataxia;	Skin:	Soap wash immed	skin, GI tract
Wash skin:	When contam	50 ppm: SA:CF*	Ing	dysp; tacar; nau, vomit	Breath:	Resp support	
Remove:	When wet or contam	100 ppm: SAT:CF*/SCBAF/SAF	Con		Swallow:	Medical attention	
Change:	N.R.	200 ppm: SAF:PD,PP				immed	
		§: SCBAF:PD,PP/SAF:PD,PP:ASCBA					
		Escape: GMFOVHiE/SCBAE					
[m-Nitrotoluene]							
Skin:	Prevent skin contact	NIOSH	Inh	Anoxia, cyan; head,	Eye:	Irr immed	Blood, CNS, CVS,
Eyes:	Prevent eye contact	20 ppm: SA*	Abs	weak, dizz; ataxia;	Skin:	Soap wash immed	skin, GI tract
Wash skin:	When contam	50 ppm: SA:CF*	Ing	dysp; tacar; nau, vomit	Breath:	Resp support	
Remove:	When wet or contam	100 ppm: SAT:CF*/SCBAF/SAF	Con		Swallow:	Medical attention	
Change:	Daily	200 ppm: SAF:PD,PP				immed	
		§: SCBAF:PD,PP/SAF:PD,PP:ASCBA					
		Escape: GMFOVHiE/SCBAE					
[p-Nitrotoluene]							

Chemical name, structure/formula, CAS and RTECS Nos., and DOT ID and guide Nos.	Synonyms, trade names, and conversion factors	Exposure limits (TWA unless noted otherwise)	IDLH	Physical description	Chemical and physical properties		Incompatibilities and reactivities	Measurement method (See Table 1)
					MW, BP, SOL Fl.P, IP, Sp, Gr, flammability	VP, FRZ UEL, LEL		
Nitrous oxide N₂O 10024-97-2 QX1350000 1070 122 (compressed) 2201 122 (refrigerated liquid)	Dinitrogen monoxide, Hyponitrous acid anhydride, Laughing gas	NIOSH* 25 ppm (46 mg/m³) (TWA over the time exposed) [*Note: REL for exposure to waste anesthetic gas.] OSHA none 1 ppm = 1.80 mg/m³	N.D.	Colorless gas with a slightly sweet odor. [inhalation anesthetic] [Note: Shipped as a liquefied compressed gas.]	MW: 44.0 BP: -127°F Sol(77°F):0.1% Fl.P: NA IP: 12.89 eV RGasD: 1.53 Nonflammable Gas, but supports combustion at elevated temperatures.	VP: 51.3 atm FRZ: -132°F UEL: NA LEL: NA	Aluminum, boron, hydrazine, lithium hydride, phosphine, sodium	Bag; none; IR; IV [#6600]
Nonane CH₃(CH₂)₇CH₃ 111-84-2 RA6115000 1920 128	n-Nonane, Nonyl hydride	NIOSH 200 ppm (1050 mg/m³) OSHA† none 1 ppm = 5.25 mg/m³	N.D.	Colorless liquid with a gasoline-like odor.	MW: 128.3 BP: 303°F Sol: Insoluble Fl.P: 88°F IP: 10.21 eV Sp.Gr: 0.72 Class IC Flammable Liquid	VP: 3 mm FRZ: -60°F UEL: 2.9% LEL: 0.8%	Strong oxidizers (e.g., peroxides, nitrates, perchlorates)	None available
1-Nonanethiol CH₃(CH₂)₈SH 1455-21-6 1228 131	1-Mercaptononane, n-Nonyl mercaptan, Nonylthiol	NIOSH C 0.5 ppm (3.3 mg/m³) [15-min] OSHA none 1 ppm = 6.56 mg/m³	N.D.	Liquid.	MW: 160.3 BP: ? Sol: Insoluble Fl.P: ? IP: ? Sp.Gr: ? Combustible Liquid	VP: ? FRZ: ? UEL: ? LEL: ?	Oxidizers, reducing agents, strong acids & bases, alkali metals	None available
Octachloronaphthalene C₁₀Cl₈ 2234-13-1 QK0250000	Halowax® 1051; 1,2,3,4,5,6,7,8-Octa-chloronaphthalene; Perchloronaphthalene	NIOSH 0.1 mg/m³ ST 0.3 mg/m³ [skin] OSHA† 0.1 mg/m³ [skin]	Unknown	Waxy, pale-yellow solid with an aromatic odor.	MW: 403.7 BP: 770°F Sol: Insoluble Fl.P: NA IP: ? Sp.Gr: 2.00 Noncombustible Solid	VP: <1 mm MLT: 365°F UEL: NA LEL: NA	Strong oxidizers	Filter; Hexane; GC/FID; II(2) [#S97]

Personal protection and sanitation (See Table 3)		Recommendations for respirator selection — maximum concentration for use (MUC) (See Table 4)	Health hazards					
			Route	Symptoms (See Table 5)	First aid (See Table 6)		Target organs (See Table 5)	
Skin:	Frostbite	TBAL	Inh	Dysp; drow, head; asphy; repro effects; liq: frostbite	Eye:	Frostbite	Resp sys, CNS, repro sys	
Eyes:	Frostbite		Con		Skin:	Frostbite		
Wash skin:	N.R.		(liq)		Breath:	Fresh air		
Remove:	N.R.							
Change:	N.R.							
Provide:	Frostbite							

[Nitrous oxide]

Skin:	N.R.	TBAL	Inh	Irrit eyes, skin, nose, throat; head, drow, dizz, conf, nau, tremor, inco; dysp; chemical pneu (aspir liq)	Eye:	Irr immed	Eyes, skin, resp sys, CNS
Eyes:	Prevent eye contact		Ing		Skin:	Soap wash immed	
Wash skin:	Daily		Con		Breath:	Resp support	
Remove:	When wet (flamm)				Swallow:	Medical attention immed	
Change:	N.R.						
Provide:	Eyewash						

[Nonane]

Skin:	Prevent skin contact	NIOSH	Inh	Irrit eyes, skin, nose, throat; weak, cyan, incr respiration, nau, drow, head, vomit	Eye:	Irr immed	Eyes, skin, resp sys, blood, CNS
Eyes:	Prevent eye contact	5 ppm: CCROV/SA	Ing		Skin:	Soap wash	
Wash skin:	When contam	12.5 ppm: SA:CF/PAPROV	Con		Breath:	Resp support	
Remove:	When wet or contam	25 ppm: CCRFOV/GMFOV/PAPRTOV/ SCBAF/SAF			Swallow:	Medical attention immed	
Change:	N.R.	§ : SCBAF:PD,PP/SAF:PD,PP:ASCBA					
		Escape: GMFOV/SCBAE					

[1-Nonanethiol]

Skin:	Prevent skin contact	NIOSH/OSHA	Inh	Acne-form derm; liver damage, jaun	Eye:	Irr immed	Skin, liver
Eyes:	Prevent eye contact	1 mg/m³: SA/SCBAF	Abs		Skin:	Water flush immed	
Wash skin:	When contam/Daily	§ : SCBAF:PD,PP/SAF:PD,PP:ASCBA	Ing		Breath:	Resp support	
Remove:	When wet or contam	Escape: GMFOVHiE/SCBAE	Con		Swallow:	Medical attention immed	
Change:	Daily						

[Octachloronaphthalene]

Chemical name, structure/formula, CAS and RTECS Nos., and DOT ID and guide Nos.	Synonyms, trade names, and conversion factors	Exposure limits (TWA unless noted otherwise)	IDLH	Physical description	Chemical and physical properties		Incompatibilities and reactivities	Measurement method (See Table 1)
					MW, BP, SOL Fl.P, IP, Sp, Gr, flammability	VP, FRZ UEL, LEL		
1-Octadecanethiol CH₃(CH₂)₁₇SH 2885-00-9	1-Mercaptooctadecane, Octadecyl mercaptan, Stearyl mercaptan	NIOSH C 0.5 ppm (5.9 mg/m³) [15-min] OSHA none 1 ppm = 11.72 mg/m³	N.D.	Solid or liquid (above 77°F).	MW: 286.6 BP: ? Sol: Insoluble Fl.P: ? IP: ? Sp.Gr: 0.85 Combustible Solid Combustible Liquid	VP: ? MLT: 77°F UEL: ? LEL: ?	Oxidizers, reducing agents, strong acids & bases, alkali metals	None available
Octane CH₃[CH₂]₆CH₃ 111-65-9 RG8400000 1262 128	n-Octane, normal-Octane	NIOSH 75 ppm (350 mg/m³) C 385 ppm (1800 mg/m³) [15-min] OSHA† 500 ppm (2350 mg/m³) 1 ppm = 4.67 mg/m³	1000 ppm [10%LEL]	Colorless liquid with a gasoline-like odor.	MW: 114.2 BP: 258°F Sol(77°F): 0.00007% Fl.P: 56°F IP: 9.82 eV Sp.Gr: 0.70 Class IB Flammable Liquid	VP: 10 mm FRZ: -70°F UEL: 6.5% LEL: 1.0%	Strong oxidizers	Char; CS₂; GC/FID; IV [#1500, Hydro-carbons]
1-Octanethiol CH₃(CH₂)₇SH 111-88-6	1-Mercaptooctane, n-Octyl mercaptan, Octylthiol, 1-Octylthiol	NIOSH C 0.5 ppm (3.0 mg/m³) [15-min] OSHA none 1 ppm = 5.98 mg/m³	N.D.	Water-white liquid with a mild odor.	MW: 146.3 BP: 390°F Sol: Insoluble Fl.P(oc): 115°F IP: ? Sp.Gr: 0.84 Class II Combustible Liquid	VP(212°F): 3 mm FRZ: -57°F UEL: ? LEL: ?	Oxidizers, reducing agents, strong acids & bases, alkali metals	Tenax GC; Acetone; GC/FPD; IV [#2510]
Oil mist (mineral) 8012-95-1 PY8030000	Heavy mineral oil mist, Paraffin oil mist, White mineral oil mist	NIOSH 5 mg/m³ ST 10 mg/m³ OSHA 5 mg/m³	2500 mg/m³	Colorless, oily liquid aerosol dispersed in air. [Note: Has an odor like burned lubricating oil.]	MW: Varies BP: 680°F Sol: Insoluble Fl.P(oc): 380°F IP: ? Sp.Gr: 0.90 Class IIIB Combustible Liquid	VP: <0.5 mm FRZ: 0°F UEL: ? LEL: ?	None reported	Filter; CCl₄; IR; IV [#5026]

Personal protection and sanitation (See Table 3)		Recommendations for respirator selection — maximum concentration for use (MUC) (See Table 4)	Route	Symptoms (See Table 5)	First aid (See Table 6)		Target organs (See Table 5)
Skin: Eyes: Wash skin: Remove: Change:	Prevent skin contact Prevent eye contact When contam When wet or contam Daily	NIOSH 5 ppm: CCROV/SA 12.5 ppm: SA:CF/PAPROV 25 ppm: CCRFOV/GMFOV/PAPRTOV/ SCBAF/SAF §: SCBAF:PD,PP/SAF:PD,PP:ASCBA Escape: GMFOV/SCBAE	Inh Abs Ing Con	Irrit eyes, skin, resp sys; head, dizz, weak, cyan, nau, convuls	Eye: Skin: Breath: Swallow:	Irr immed Soap wash immed Resp support Medical attention immed	Eyes, skin, resp sys, CNS, blood
[1-Octadecanethiol]							
Skin: Eyes: Wash skin: Remove: Change:	Prevent skin contact Prevent eye contact When contam When wet (flamm) N.R.	NIOSH 750 ppm: SA* 1000 ppm: SA:CF*/SCBAF/SAF §: SCBAF:PD,PP/SAF:PD,PP:ASCBA Escape: GMFOV/SCBAE	Inh Ing Con	Irrit eyes, nose; drow; derm; chemical pneu (aspir liq); in animals: narco	Eye: Skin: Breath: Swallow:	Irr immed Soap wash prompt Resp support Medical attention immed	Eyes, skin, resp sys, CNS
[Octane]							
Skin: Eyes: Wash skin: Remove: Change:	Prevent skin contact Prevent eye contact When contam When wet or contam N.R.	NIOSH 5 ppm: CCROV/SA 12.5 ppm: SA:CF/PAPROV 25 ppm: CCRFOV/GMFOV/PAPRTOV/ SCBAF/SAF §: SCBAF:PD,PP/SAF:PD,PP:ASCBA Escape: GMFOV/SCBAE	Inh Ing Con	Irrit eyes, skin, nose, throat; weak, cyan, incr respiration, nau, drow, head, vomit	Eye: Skin: Breath: Swallow:	Irr immed Soap wash immed Resp support Medical attention immed	Eyes, skin, resp sys, blood, CNS
[1-Octanethiol]							
Skin: Eyes: Wash skin: Remove: Change:	Prevent skin contact N.R. When contam When wet or contam Daily	NIOSH/OSHA 50 mg/m³: HiE/SA 125 mg/m³: SA:CF/PAPRHiE 250 mg/m³: HiEF/SAT:CF/PAPRTHiE/ SCBAF/SAF 2500 mg/m³: SA:PD,PP §: SCBAF:PD,PP/SAF:PD,PP:ASCBA Escape: HiEF/SCBAE	Inh Con	Irrit eyes, skin, resp sys	Skin: Breath:	Soap wash Fresh air	Eyes, skin, resp sys
[Oil mist (mineral)]							

Chemical name, structure/formula, CAS and RTECS Nos., and DOT ID and guide Nos.	Synonyms, trade names, and conversion factors	Exposure limits (TWA unless noted otherwise)	IDLH	Physical description	Chemical and physical properties		Incompatibilities and reactivities	Measurement method (See Table 1)
					MW, BP, SOL Fl.P, IP, Sp, Gr, flammability	VP, FRZ UEL, LEL		
Osmium tetroxide OsO₄ 20816-12-0 RN1140000 2471 154	Osmic acid anhydride, Osmium oxide 1 ppm = 10.40 mg/m³	NIOSH 0.002 mg/m³ (0.0002 ppm) ST 0.006 mg/m³ (0.0006 ppm) OSHA† 0.002 mg/m³	1 mg/m³	Colorless, crystalline solid or pale-yellow mass with an unpleasant, acrid, chlorine-like odor. [Note: A liquid above 105°F.]	MW: 254.2 BP: 266°F Sol(77°F): 6% Fl.P: NA IP: 12.60 eV Sp.Gr: 5.10 Noncombustible Solid	VP: 7 mm MLT: 105°F UEL: NA UEL: NA	Hydrochloric acid, easily oxidized organic materials [Note: Begins to sublime below BP. Contact with other materials may cause fire.]	None available
Oxalic acid HOOCCOOH•2H₂O 144-62-7 RO2450000	Ethanedioic acid, Oxalic acid (aqueous), Oxalic acid dihydrate	NIOSH 1 mg/m³ ST 2 mg/m³ OSHA† 1 mg/m³	500 mg/m³	Colorless, odorless powder or granular solid. [Note: The anhydrous form (COOH)₂ is an odorless, white solid.]	MW: 126.1 BP: Sublimes Sol: 14% Fl.P: ? IP: ? Sp.Gr: 1.90 Combustible Solid	VP: <0.001 mm MLT: 215°F (Sublimes) UEL: ? LEL: ?	Strong oxidizers, silver compounds, strong alkalis, chlorites [Note: Gives off water of crystallization at 215°F and begins to sublime.]	None available
Oxygen difluoride OF₂ 7783-41-7 RS2100000 2190 124	Difluorine monoxide, Fluorine monoxide, Oxygen fluoride 1 ppm = 2.21 mg/m³	NIOSH C 0.05 ppm (0.1 mg/m³) OSHA† 0.05 ppm (0.1 mg/m³)	0.5 ppm	Colorless gas with a peculiar, foul odor. [Note: Shipped as a nonliquefied compressed gas.]	MW: 54.0 BP: -230°F Sol: 0.02% Fl.P: NA IP: 13.11 eV RGasD: 1.88 Nonflammable Gas, but a strong oxidizer.	VP: >1 atm FRZ: -371°F UEL: NA LEL: NA	Combustible materials, chlorine, bromine, iodine, platinum, metal oxides, moist air, hydrogen sulfide, hydrocarbons, water [Note: Reacts very slowly with water to form hydrofluoric acid.]	None available
Ozone O₃ 10028-15-6 RS8225000 1 ppm = 1.96 mg/m³	Triatomic oxygen	NIOSH C 0.1 ppm (0.2 mg/m³) OSHA† 0.1 ppm (0.2 mg/m³)	5 ppm	Colorless to blue gas with a very pungent odor.	MW: 48.0 BP: -169°F Sol(32°F): 0.001% Fl.P: NA IP: 12.52 eV RGasD: 1.66 Nonflammable Gas, but a powerful oxidizer.	VP: >1 atm FRZ: -315°F UEL: NA LEL: NA	All oxidizable materials (both organic & inorganic)	Filters*(2)/ Oxidizer; Water; IC; OSHA [#ID214]

Personal protection and sanitation (See Table 3)		Recommendations for respirator selection — maximum concentration for use (MUC) (See Table 4)	Health hazards			
			Route	Symptoms (See Table 5)	First aid (See Table 6)	Target organs (See Table 5)
Skin:	Prevent skin contact	NIOSH/OSHA	Inh	Irrit eyes, resp sys; lac,	Eye: Irr immed	Eyes, skin, resp sys
Eyes:	Prevent eye contact	0.1 mg/m³: CCRFSHiE/GMFSHiE/	Ing	vis dist; conj; head;	Skin: Soap wash immed	
Wash skin:	When contam	SCBAF/SAF	Con	cough, dysp; derm	Breath: Resp support	
Remove:	When wet or contam	1 mg/m³: SAF:PD,PP			Swallow: Medical attention	
Change:	Daily	§: SCBAF:PD,PP/SAF:PD,PP:ASCBA			immed	
Provide:	Eyewash	Escape: GMFSHiE/SCBAE				

[Osmium tetroxide]

Skin:	Prevent skin contact	NIOSH/OSHA	Inh	Irrit eyes, skin, muc memb;	Eye: Irr immed	Eyes, skin, resp sys,
Eyes:	Prevent eye contact	25 mg/m³: SA:CFᴱ/PAPRDMᴱ	Ing	eye burns; local pain,	Skin: Water flush prompt	kidneys
Wash skin:	When contam	50 mg/m³: HiEF/SCBAF/SAF	Con	cyan; shock, collapse,	Breath: Resp support	
Remove:	When wet or contam	500 mg/m³: SAF:PD,PP		convuls; kidney damage	Swallow: Medical attention	
Change:	Daily	§: SCBAF:PD,PP/SAF:PD,PP:ASCBA			immed	
Provide:	Eyewash	Escape: HiEF/SCBAE				

[Oxalic acid]

Skin:	N.R.	NIOSH/OSHA	Inh	Irrit eyes, skin, resp sys;	Eye: Irr immed	Eyes, skin, resp sys
Eyes:	N.R.	0.5 ppm: SA/SCBAF	Con	head; pulm edema; eye,	Skin: Water flush immed	
Wash skin:	N.R.	§: SCBAF:PD,PP/SAF:PD,PP:ASCBA		skin burns (from contact	Breath: Resp support	
Remove:	N.R.	Escape: GMFS⊥/SCBAE		with the gas under pressure)		
Change:	N.R.					

[Oxygen difluoride]

Skin:	N.R.	NIOSH/OSHA	Inh	Irrit eyes, muc memb;	Eye: Medical attention	Eyes, resp sys
Eyes:	N.R.	1 ppm: CCRS⊥/SA	Con	pulm edema; chronic	Breath: Fresh air; 100% O₂	
Wash skin:	N.R.	2.5 ppm: SA:CF/PAPRS⊥		resp disease		
Remove:	N.R.	5 ppm: CCRFS⊥/GMFS⊥/SAT:CF/				
Change:	N.R.	SCBAF/SAF				
		§: SCBAF:PD,PP/SAF:PD,PP:ASCBA				
		Escape: GMFS⊥/SCBAE				

[Ozone]

Chemical name, structure/formula, CAS and RTECS Nos., and DOT ID and guide Nos.	Synonyms, trade names, and conversion factors	Exposure limits (TWA unless noted otherwise)	IDLH	Physical description	Chemical and physical properties		Incompatibilities and reactivities	Measurement method (See Table 1)
					MW, BP, SOL FI.P, IP, Sp, Gr, flammability	VP, FRZ UEL, LEL		
Paraffin wax fume C_nH_{2n+2} 8002-74-2 RV0350000	Paraffin fume, Paraffin scale fume	NIOSH 2 mg/m³ OSHA† none	N.D.	Paraffin wax is a white to slightly yellowish, odorless solid. [Note: Consists of a mixture of high molecular weight hydrocarbons (e.g., $C_{35}H_{74}$).]	MW: 350-420 BP: ? Sol: Insoluble FI.P: 390°F IP: ? Sp.Gr: 0.88-0.92 Combustible Solid	VP: ? MLT: 115-154°F UEL: ? LEL: ?	None reported	None available
Paraquat (Paraquat dichloride) $CH_3(C_5H_4N)_2CH_3\cdot2Cl$ 1910-42-5 DW2275000	1,1'-Dimethyl-4,4'-bipyridinium dichloride; N,N'-Dimethyl-4,4'-bipyridinium dichloride; Paraquat chloride; Paraquat dichloride [Note: Paraquat is a cation ($C_{12}H_{14}N_2^{++}$; 1,1-dimethyl-4,4'-bipyridinium ion); the commercial product is the dichloride salt of paraquat.]	NIOSH 0.1 mg/m³ (resp) [skin] OSHA† 0.5 mg/m³ (resp) [skin]	1 mg/m³	Yellow solid with a faint, ammonia-like odor. [herbicide]	MW: 257.2 BP: Decomposes Sol: Miscible FI.P: NA IP: ? Sp.Gr: 1.24 Noncombustible Solid	VP: <0.0000001 mm MLT: 572°F (Decomposes) UEL: NA LEL: NA	Strong oxidizers, alkylaryl-sulfonate wetting agents [Note: Corrosive to metals. Decomposes in presence of ultraviolet light.]	Filter; Water; HPLC/UVD; IV [#5003]
Parathion $(C_2H_5O)_2P(S)OC_6H_4NO_2$ 56-38-2 TF4550000 2783 152	O,O-Diethyl-O(p-nitrophenyl) phosphorothioate; Diethyl parathion; Ethyl parathion; Parathion-ethyl	NIOSH 0.05 mg/m³ [skin] OSHA 0.1 mg/m³ [skin]	10 mg/m³	Pale-yellow to dark-brown liquid with a garlic-like odor. [Note: A solid below 43°F. Pesticide that may be absorbed on a dry carrier.]	MW: 291.3 BP: 707°F Sol: 0.001% FI.P(oc): 392°F IP: ? Sp.Gr: 1.27 Class IIIB Combustible Liquid	VP: 0.00004 mm FRZ: 43°F UEL: ? LEL: ?	Strong oxidizers, alkaline materials	OVS-2; Toluene/ Acetone; GC/FPD; IV [#5600, Organo-phosphorus Pesticides]
Particulates not otherwise regulated	"Inert" dusts, Nuisance dusts, PNOR [Note: Includes all inert or nuisance dusts, whether mineral, inorganic, or organic, not listed specifically in 1910.1000.]	NIOSH See Appendix D OSHA 15 mg/m³ (total) 5 mg/m³ (resp)	N.D.	Dusts from solid substances without specific occupational exposure standards.	Properties vary depending upon the specific solid.		Varies	Filter; none; Grav; IV [Particulates NOR: #0500 (total), #0600 (resp)]

Personal protection and sanitation (See Table 3)		Recommendations for respirator selection — maximum concentration for use (MUC) (See Table 4)	Health hazards					
			Route	Symptoms (See Table 5)	First aid (See Table 6)		Target organs (See Table 5)	

Skin:	N.R.	TBAL	Inh	Irrit eyes, skin, resp sys;	Eye:	Irr immed	Eyes, skin, resp sys
Eyes:	Prevent eye contact		Con	discomfort, nau	Breath:	Resp support	
Wash skin:	N.R.						
Remove:	N.R.						
Change:	N.R.						

[Paraffin wax fume]

Skin:	Prevent skin contact	NIOSH	Inh	Irrit eyes, skin, nose,	Eye:	Irr immed	Eyes, skin, resp sys,
Eyes:	Prevent eye contact	1 mg/m³: CCROVDMFu*/PAPROVDMFu*/	Abs	throat, resp sys; epis;	Skin:	Water flush immed	heart, liver,
Wash skin:	When contam	SA*/SCBAF	Ing	derm; fingernail damage;	Breath:	Resp support	kidneys, GI tract
Remove:	When wet or contam	§: SCBAF:PD,PP/SAF:PD,PP:ASCBA	Con	irrit GI tract; heart,	Swallow:	Medical attention	
Change:	N.R.	Escape: GMFOVHiE/SCBAE		liver, kidney damage		immed	
Provide:	Quick drench						

241

[Paraquat]

Skin:	Prevent skin contact	NIOSH	Inh	Irrit eyes, resp sys;	Eye:	Irr immed	Eyes, skin, resp sys,
Eyes:	Prevent eye contact	0.5 mg/m³: CCROVDMFu/SA	Abs	miosis; rhin; head; chest	Skin:	Soap wash immed	CNS, CVS, blood chol
Wash skin:	When contam	1.25 mg/m³: SA:CF/PAPROVDMFu	Ing	tight, wheez, lar spasm,	Breath:	Resp support	
Remove:	When wet or contam	2.5 mg/m³: CCRFOVHiE/SAT:CF/	Con	salv, cyan; anor, nau,	Swallow:	Medical attention	
Change:	Daily	PAPRTOVHiE/SCBAF/SAF		vomit, abdom cramps, diarr;		immed	
Provide:	Eyewash, Quick drench	10 mg/m³: SA:PD,PP		sweat; musc fasc, weak,			
		§: SCBAF:PD,PP/SAF:PD,PP:ASCBA		para; gidd, conf, ataxia;			
		Escape: GMFOVHiE/SCBAE		convuls, coma; low BP;			
				card irreg			

[Parathion]

Skin:	N.R.	TBAL	Inh	Irrit eyes, skin, throat,	Eye:	Irr immed	Eyes, skin, resp sys
Eyes:	N.R.		Con	upper resp sys	Breath:	Fresh air	
Wash skin:	N.R.						
Remove:	N.R.						
Change:	N.R.						

[Particulates not otherwise regulated]

Chemical name, structure/formula, CAS and RTECS Nos., and DOT ID and guide Nos.	Synonyms, trade names, and conversion factors	Exposure limits (TWA unless noted otherwise)	IDLH	Physical description	Chemical and physical properties		Incompatibilities and reactivities	Measurement method (See Table 1)
					MW, BP, SOL Fl.P, IP, Sp, Gr, flammability	VP, FRZ UEL, LEL		
Pentaborane B_5H_9 19624-22-7 RY8925000 1380 135	Pentaboron nonahydride 1 ppm = 2.58 mg/m^3	NIOSH 0.005 ppm (0.01 mg/m^3) ST 0.015 ppm (0.03 mg/m^3) OSHA† 0.005 ppm (0.01 mg/m^3)	1 ppm	Colorless liquid with a pungent odor like sour milk.	MW: 63.1 BP: 140°F Sol: Reacts Fl.P: 86°F IP: 9.90 eV Sp.Gr. 0.62 Class IC Flammable Liquid	VP: 171 mm FRZ: -52°F UEL: ? LEL: 0.42%	Oxidizers, halogens, water, halogenated hydrocarbons [Note: May ignite SPONTANEOUSLY in moist air. Corrosive to natural rubber. Hydrolyzes slowly with heat in water to form boric acid.]	None available
Pentachloroethane $CHCl_2CCl_3$ 76-01-7 KI6300000 1669 151	Ethane pentachloride, Pentalin	NIOSH Handle with caution in the workplace. See Appendix C (Chloroethanes) OSHA none	N.D.	Colorless liquid with a sweetish, chloroform-like odor.	MW: 202.3 BP: 322°F Sol: 0.05% Fl.P: ? IP: 11.28 eV Sp.Gr. 1.68 Combustible Liquid	VP: 3 mm MLT: -20°F UEL: ? LEL: ?	(Sodium-potassium alloy + bromoform), alkalis, metals, water [Note: Hydrolysis produces dichloro-acetic acid. Reaction with alkalis & metals produces spontaneously explosive chloroacetylenes.]	Porapak; Hexane; GC/ECD; IV [#2517]
Pentachloronaphthalene $C_{10}H_3Cl_5$ 1321-64-8 QK0300000	Halowax® 1013; 1,2,3,4,5-Pentachloro-naphthalene	NIOSH/OSHA 0.5 mg/m^3 [skin]	Unknown	Pale-yellow or white solid or powder with an aromatic odor.	MW: 300.4 BP: 636°F Sol: Insoluble Fl.P: NA IP: ? Sp.Gr. 1.67 Noncombustible Solid	VP: <1 mm MLT: 248°F UEL: NA LEL: NA	Strong oxidizers	Filter/Bub; Isooctane; GC/ECD; II(2) [#S96]
Pentachlorophenol C_6Cl_5OH 87-86-5 SM6300000 2020 154	PCP; Penta; 2,3,4,5,6-Pentachlorophenol	NIOSH/OSHA 0.5 mg/m^3 [skin]	2.5 mg/m^3	Colorless to white, crystalline solid with a benzene-like odor. [fungicide]	MW: 266.4 BP: 588°F (Decomposes) Sol: 0.001% Fl.P: NA IP: NA Sp.Gr. 1.98 Noncombustible Solid	VP(77°F): 0.0001 mm MLT: 374°F UEL: NA LEL: NA	Strong oxidizers, acids, alkalis	Filter/Bub; Methanol; HPLC/UVD; IV [#5512]

Personal protection and sanitation (See Table 3)		Recommendations for respirator selection — maximum concentration for use (MUC) (See Table 4)	Health hazards				
			Route	Symptoms (See Table 5)	First aid (See Table 6)		Target organs (See Table 5)
Skin:	Prevent skin contact	NIOSH/OSHA	Inh	Irrit eyes, skin, dizz,	Eye:	Irr immed	Eyes, skin, CNS
Eyes:	Prevent eye contact	0.05 ppm: SA	Abs	head, drow, li-head, inco,	Skin:	Soap wash immed	
Wash skin:	When contam	0.125 ppm: SA:CF	Ing	tremor, convuls, behavioral	Breath:	Resp support	
Remove:	When wet (flamm)	0.25 ppm: SAT:CF/SCBAF/SAF	Con	changes; tonic spasm face,	Swallow:	Medical attention	
Change:	N.R.	1 ppm: SA:PD,PP		neck, abdom, limbs		immed	
Provide:	Eyewash, Quick drench	§: SCBAF:PD,PP/SAF:PD,PP:ASCBA					
		Escape: GMFS/SCBAE					

[Pentaborane]

Personal protection and sanitation (See Table 3)		Recommendations for respirator selection — maximum concentration for use (MUC) (See Table 4)	Health hazards				
Skin:	Prevent skin contact	TBAL	Inh	In animals: irrit eyes,	Eye:	Irr immed	Eyes, skin, resp sys,
Eyes:	Prevent eye contact		Ing	skin; weak, restless, irreg	Skin:	Soap wash	CNS, liver, kidneys
Wash skin:	When contam		Con	respiration, musc inco;	Breath:	Resp support	
Remove:	When wet or contam			liver, kidney, lung changes	Swallow:	Medical attention	
Change:	N.R.					immed	
Provide:	Eyewash, Quick drench						

243

[Pentachloroethane]

Personal protection and sanitation (See Table 3)		Recommendations for respirator selection — maximum concentration for use (MUC) (See Table 4)	Health hazards				
Skin:	Prevent skin contact	NIOSH/OSHA	Inh	Head, ftg, verti, anor;	Eye:	Irr immed	Skin, liver, CNS
Eyes:	Prevent eye contact	5 mg/m³: SA*/SCBAF	Abs	pruritus, acne-form skin	Skin:	Soap prompt/molten	
Wash skin:	When contam	§: SCBAF:PD,PP/SAF:PD,PP:ASCBA	Ing	eruptions; jaun, liver nec		flush immed	
Remove:	When wet or contam	Escape: GMFOVHiE/SCBAE	Con		Breath:	Resp support	
Change:	Daily				Swallow:	Medical Attention	
						immed	

[Pentachloronaphthalene]

Personal protection and sanitation (See Table 3)		Recommendations for respirator selection — maximum concentration for use (MUC) (See Table 4)	Health hazards				
Skin:	Prevent skin contact	NIOSH/OSHA	Inh	Irrit eyes, nose, throat;	Eye:	Irr immed	Eyes, skin, resp sys,
Eyes:	Prevent eye contact	2.5 mg/m³: CCROVDMFu*/PAPROVDMFu*/	Abs	sneez, cough; weak,	Skin:	Soap wash immed	CVS, liver, kidneys,
Wash skin:	When contam	SA*/SCBAF	Ing	anor, low-wgt; sweat;	Breath:	Resp support	CNS
Remove:	When wet or contam	§: SCBAF:PD,PP/SAF:PD,PP:ASCBA	Con	head, dizz; nau, vomit;	Swallow:	Medical attention	
Change:	Daily	Escape: GMFOVHiE/SCBAE		dysp, chest pain; high		immed	
Provide:	Eyewash, Quick drench			fever; derm			

[Pentachlorophenol]

<table>
Chemical name, structure/formula, CAS and RTECS Nos., and DOT ID and guide Nos.	Synonyms, trade names, and conversion factors	Exposure limits (TWA unless noted otherwise)	IDLH	Physical description	Chemical and physical properties		Incompatibilities and reactivities	Measurement method (See Table 1)
					MW, BP, SOL FI.P, IP, Sp, Gr, flammability	VP, FRZ UEL, LEL		
Pentaerythritol C(CH₂OH)₄ 115-77-5 RZ2490000	2,2-bis(Hydroxymethyl)-1,3-propanediol; Methane tetramethylol; Monopentaerythritol; PE; Tetrahydroxymethylmethane; Tetramethylolmethane	NIOSH 10 mg/m³ (total) 5 mg/m³ (resp) OSHA† 15 mg/m³ (total) 5 mg/m³ (resp)	N.D.	Colorless to white, crystalline, odorless powder. [Note: Technical grade is 88% monopentaerythritol & 12% dipentaerythritol.]	MW: 136.2 BP: Sublimes Sol(59°F): 6% FI.P: ? IP: ? Sp.Gr. 1.38 Combustible Solid	VP: 0 mm (approx) MLT: 500°F (Sublimes) UEL: ? LEL: ?	Organic acids, oxidizers [Note: Explosive compound is formed when a mixture of PE & thiophosphoryl chloride is heated.]	Filter; none; Grav; IV [Particulates NOR: #0500 (total), #0600 (resp)]
n-Pentane CH₃[CH₂]₃CH₃ 109-66-0 RZ9450000 1265 128	Pentane, normal-Pentane 1 ppm = 2.95 mg/m³	NIOSH 120 ppm (350 mg/m³) C 610 ppm (1800 mg/m³) [15-min] OSHA† 1000 ppm (2950 mg/m³)	1500 ppm [10%LEL]	Colorless liquid with a gasoline-like odor. [Note: A gas above 97°F. May be utilized as a fuel.]	MW: 72.2 BP: 97°F Sol: 0.04% FI.P: -57°F IP: 10.34 eV Sp.Gr. 0.63 Class IA Flammable Liquid	VP: 420 mm FRZ: -202°F UEL: 7.8% LEL: 1.5%	Strong oxidizers	Char; CS₂; GC/FID; IV [#1500, Hydrocarbons]
1-Pentanethiol CH₃(CH₂)₄SH 110-66-7 SA3150000 1111 130	Amyl hydrosulfide, Amyl mercaptan, Amyl sulfhydrate, Pentyl mercaptan 1 ppm = 4.26 mg/m³	NIOSH C 0.5 ppm (2.1 mg/m³) [15-min] OSHA none	N.D.	Water-white to yellowish liquid with a strong, garlic-like odor.	MW: 104.2 BP: 260°F Sol: Insoluble FI.P(oc): 65°F IP: ? Sp.Gr. 0.84 Class IB Flammable Liquid	VP(77°F): 14mm FRZ: -104°F UEL: ? LEL: ?	Oxidizers, reducing agents, alkali metals, calcium hypochlorite, concentrated nitric acid	None available
2-Pentanone CH₃COCH₂CH₂CH₃ 107-87-9 SA7875000 1249 127	Ethyl acetone, Methyl propyl ketone, MPK 1 ppm = 3.52 mg/m³	NIOSH 150 ppm (530 mg/m³) OSHA† 200 ppm (700 mg/m³)	1500 ppm	Colorless to water-white liquid with a characteristic acetone-like odor.	MW: 86.1 BP: 215°F Sol: 6% FI.P: 45°F IP: 9.39 eV Sp.Gr. 0.81 Class IB Flammable Liquid	VP: 27 mm FRZ: -108°F UEL: 8.2% LEL: 1.5%	Oxidizers, bromine trifluoride	Char; CS₂; GC/FID; IV [#1300, Ketones I]
</table>

244

Personal protection and sanitation (See Table 3)		Recommendations for respirator selection — maximum concentration for use (MUC) (See Table 4)	Health hazards			
			Route	Symptoms (See Table 5)	First aid (See Table 6)	Target organs (See Table 5)
Skin: N.R. Eyes: N.R. Wash skin: N.R. Remove: N.R. Change: N.R.		TBAL	Inh Ing Con	Irrit eyes, resp sys	Eye: Irr immed Skin: Water wash Breath: Fresh air Swallow: Medical attention immed	Eyes, resp sys
[Pentaerythritol]						
Skin: Prevent skin contact Eyes: Prevent eye contact Wash skin: When contam Remove: When wet (flamm) Change: N.R.		NIOSH 1200 ppm: SA 1500 ppm: SA:CF/SCBAF/SAF §: SCBAF:PD,PP/SAF:PD,PP/ASCBA Escape: GMFOV/SCBAE	Inh Ing Con	Irrit eyes, skin, nose; derm; chemical pneu; (aspir liq); drow; in animals: narco	Eye: Irr immed Skin: Water wash prompt Breath: Resp support Swallow: Medical attention immed	Eyes, skin, resp sys, CNS
[n-Pentane]						
Skin: Prevent skin contact Eyes: Prevent eye contact Wash skin: When contam Remove: When wet (flamm) Change: N.R.		NIOSH 5 ppm: CCRFOV/SA 12.5 ppm: SA:CF/PAPROV 25 ppm: CCRFOV/GMFOV/PAPRTOV/ SCBAF/SAF §: SCBAF:PD,PP/SAF:PD,PP/ASCBA Escape: GMFOV/SCBAE	Inh Ing Con	Irrit eyes, skin, nose, throat, resp sys; head, nau, dizz; vomit, diarr; derm, skin sens	Eye: Irr immed Skin: Soap wash immed Breath: Resp support Swallow: Medical attention immed	Eyes, skin, resp sys, CNS
[1-Pentanethiol]						
Skin: Prevent skin contact Eyes: Prevent eye contact Wash skin: When contam Remove: When wet (flamm) Change: N.R.		NIOSH 1500 ppm: CCROV*/PAPROV*/GMFOV/ SA*/SCBAF §: SCBAF:PD,PP/SAF:PD,PP/ASCBA Escape: GMFOV/SCBAE	Inh Ing Con	Irrit eyes, skin, muc memb; head; derm; narco, coma	Eye: Irr immed Skin: Water flush Breath: Resp support Swallow: Medical attention immed	Eyes, skin, resp sys, CNS
[2-Pentanone]						

Chemical name, structure/formula, CAS and RTECS Nos., and DOT ID and guide Nos.	Synonyms, trade names, and conversion factors	Exposure limits (TWA unless noted otherwise)	IDLH	Physical description	Chemical and physical properties		Incompatibilities and reactivities	Measurement method (See Table 1)
					MW, BP, SOL FI.P, IP, Sp, Gr, flammability	VP, FRZ UEL, LEL		
Perchloromethyl mercaptan Cl₃CSCl 594-42-3 PB0370000 1670 157	PCM, PMM, Tricholoromethane sulfenyl chloride, Trichloromethyl sulfur chloride 1 ppm = 7.60 mg/m³	NIOSH/OSHA 0.1 ppm (0.8 mg/m³)	10 ppm	Pale-yellow, oily liquid with an unbearable, acrid odor.	MW: 185.9 BP: 297°F (Decomposes) Sol: insoluble FI.P: NA IP: ? Sp.Gr: 1.69 Noncombustible Liquid, but will support combustion.	VP: 3 mm FRZ: ? UEL: NA LEL: NA	Alkalis, amines, hot iron, water [Note: Corrosive to most metals. Forms HCl, sulfur & CO₂ on contact with water.]	None available
Perchloryl fluoride ClO₃F 7616-94-6 SD1925000 3083 124	Chlorine fluoride oxide, Chlorine oxyfluoride, Trioxychlorofluoride 1 ppm = 4.19 mg/m³	NIOSH 3 ppm (14 mg/m³) ST 6 ppm (28 mg/m³) OSHA† 3 ppm (13.5 mg/m³)	100 ppm	Colorless gas with a characteristic, sweet odor. [Note: Shipped as a liquefied compressed gas.]	MW: 102.5 BP: -52°F Sol: 0.06% FI.P: NA IP: 13.60 eV RGasD: 3.64 Nonflammable Gas, but will support combustion.	VP: 10.5 atm FRZ: -234°F UEL: NA LEL: NA	Combustibles, strong bases, amines, finely divided metals, reducing agents, alcohols	None available
Perlite 93763-70-3 SO5254000	Expanded perlite [Note: An amorphous material consisting of fused sodium potassium aluminum silicate.]	NIOSH 10 mg/m³ (total) 5 mg/m³ (resp) OSHA 15 mg/m³ (total) 5 mg/m³ (resp)	N.D.	Odorless, light-gray to glassy-black solid. [Note: Expanded perlite is a fluffy, white particulate.]	MW: varies BP: ? Sol:<1% FI.P: NA IP: NA Sp.Gr: 2.2-2.4 (crude) 0.05-0.3 (expanded) Noncombustible Solid	VP: 0 mm (approx) MLT: >2000°F UEL: NA LEL: NA	None reported	Filter; none; Grav; IV [Particulates NOR: #0500 (total), #0600 (resp)]
Petroleum distillates (naphtha) 8002-05-9 SE7449000 1255 128	Aliphatic petroleum naphtha, Petroleum naphtha, Rubber solvent 1 ppm = 4.05 mg/m³ (approx)	NIOSH 350 mg/m³ C 1800 mg/m³ [15-min] OSHA† 500 ppm (2000 mg/m³)	1100 ppm [10%LEL]	Colorless liquid with a gasoline- or kerosene-like odor. [Note: A mixture of paraffins (C₅ to C₁₃) that may contain a small amount of aromatic hydrocarbons.]	MW: 99 (approx) BP: 86-460°F Sol: Insoluble FI.P: -40 to -86°F IP: ? Sp.Gr: 0.63-0.66 Flammable Liquid	VP: 40 mm (approx) FRZ: -99°F UEL: 5.9% LEL: 1.1%	Strong oxidizers	Char; CS₂; GC/FID; IV [#1550, Naphthas]

Personal protection and sanitation (See Table 3)		Recommendations for respirator selection — maximum concentration for use (MUC) (See Table 4)	Health hazards				
			Route	Symptoms (See Table 5)	First aid (See Table 6)		Target organs (See Table 5)
Skin:	Prevent skin contact	NIOSH/OSHA	Inh	Irrit eyes, skin, nose,	Eye:	Irr immed	Eyes, skin, resp sys,
Eyes:	Prevent eye contact	1 ppm: CCROV*/SA*	Abs	throat; lac; cough,	Skin:	Soap wash immed	liver, kidneys
Wash skin:	When contam	2.5 ppm: SA:CF*/PAPROV*	Ing	dysp, deep breath pain,	Breath:	Resp support	
Remove:	When wet or contam	5 ppm: CCRFOV/GMFOV/PAPRTOV*/	Con	coarse rales; vomit;	Swallow:	Medical attention	
Change:	N.R.	SAT:CF*/SCBAF/SAF		pallor, tacar; acidosis;		immed	
		10 ppm: SAF:PD,PP		anuria; liver, kidney			
		§: SCBAF:PD,PP/SAF:PD,PP:ASCBA		damage			
		Escape: GMFOV/SCBAE					

[Perchloromethyl mercaptan]

Personal protection and sanitation (See Table 3)		Recommendations for respirator selection — maximum concentration for use (MUC) (See Table 4)	Health hazards				
			Route	Symptoms (See Table 5)	First aid (See Table 6)		Target organs (See Table 5)
Skin:	Frostbite	NIOSH/OSHA	Inh	Irrit resp sys;	Eye:	Frostbite	Skin, resp sys, blood
Eyes:	Frostbite	30 ppm: SA	Con	liq: frostbite;	Skin:	Frostbite	
Wash skin:	N.R.	75 ppm: SA:CF*	(liq)	in animals: methemo;	Breath:	Resp support	
Remove:	N.R.	100 ppm: SCBAF/SAF		cyan; weak, dizz, head;			
Change:	N.R.	§: SCBAF:PD,PP/SAF:PD,PP:ASCBA		pulm edema; pneuitis;			
Provide:	Frostbite	Escape: GMFS⁴/SCBAE		anoxia			

[Perchloryl fluoride]

Personal protection and sanitation (See Table 3)		Recommendations for respirator selection — maximum concentration for use (MUC) (See Table 4)	Health hazards				
			Route	Symptoms (See Table 5)	First aid (See Table 6)		Target organs (See Table 5)
Skin:	N.R.	TBAL	Inh	Irrit eyes, skin, throat,	Eye:	Irr immed	Eyes, skin, resp sys
Eyes:	N.R.		Con	upper resp sys	Breath:	Fresh air	
Wash skin:	N.R.						
Remove:	N.R.						
Change:	N.R.						

[Perlite]

Personal protection and sanitation (See Table 3)		Recommendations for respirator selection — maximum concentration for use (MUC) (See Table 4)	Health hazards				
			Route	Symptoms (See Table 5)	First aid (See Table 6)		Target organs (See Table 5)
Skin:	Prevent skin contact	NIOSH	Inh	Irrit eyes, nose, throat;	Eye:	Irr immed	Eyes, skin, resp sys,
Eyes:	Prevent eye contact	850 ppm: SA	Ing	dizz, drow, head, nau;	Skin:	Soap wash prompt	CNS
Wash skin:	When contam	1100 ppm: SA:CF*/SCBAF/SAF	Con	dry cracked skin; chemical	Breath:	Resp support	
Remove:	When wet (flamm)	§: SCBAF:PD,PP/SAF:PD,PP:ASCBA		pneu (aspir liq)	Swallow:	Medical Attention	
Change:	N.R.	Escape: GMFOV/SCBAE				immed	

[Petroleum distillates (naphtha)]

Chemical name, structure/formula, CAS and RTECS Nos., and DOT ID and guide Nos.	Synonyms, trade names, and conversion factors	Exposure limits (TWA unless noted otherwise)	IDLH	Physical description	Chemical and physical properties: MW, BP, SOL Fl.P, IP, Sp, Gr, flammability	VP, FRZ UEL, LEL	Incompatibilities and reactivities	Measurement method (See Table 1)
Phenol C_6H_5OH 108-95-2 SJ3325000 1671 153 (solid) 2312 153 (molten) 2821 153 (solution)	Carbolic acid, Hydroxybenzene, Monohydroxybenzene, Phenyl alcohol, Phenyl hydroxide 1 ppm = 3.85 mg/m³	NIOSH 5 ppm (19 mg/m³) C 15.6 ppm (60 mg/m³) [15-min] [skin] OSHA 5 ppm (19 mg/m³) [skin]	250 ppm	Colorless to light-pink, crystalline solid with a sweet, acrid odor. [Note: Phenol liquefies by mixing with about 8% water.]	MW: 94.1 BP: 359°F Sol(77°F): 9% Fl.P: 175°F IP: 8.50 eV Sp.Gr: 1.06 Combustible Solid	VP: 0.4 mm MLT: 109°F UEL: 8.6% LEL: 1.8%	Strong oxidizers, calcium hypochlorite, aluminum chloride, acids	XAD-7; Methanol; GC/FID; IV [#2546, Cresols and Phenol]
Phenothiazine $S(C_6H_4)_2NH$ 92-84-2 SN5075000	Dibenzothiazine, Fenothiazine, Thiodiphenylamine	NIOSH 5 mg/m³ [skin] OSHA† none	N.D.	Grayish-green to greenish-yellow solid. [insecticide]	MW: 199.3 BP: 700°F Sol: Insoluble Fl.P: ? IP: ? Sp.Gr: ? Combustible Solid, but not a high fire risk.	VP: 0 mm (approx) MLT: 365°F UEL: ? LEL: ?	None reported	None available
p-Phenylene diamine $C_6H_4(NH_2)_2$ 106-50-3 SS8050000 1673 153	4-Aminoaniline; 1,4-Benzenediamine; p-Diaminobenzene; 1,4-Diaminobenzene; 1,4-Phenylene diamine	NIOSH/OSHA 0.1 mg/m³ [skin]	25 mg/m³	White to slightly red, crystalline solid.	MW: 108.2 BP: 513°F Sol(75°F): 4% Fl.P: 312°F IP: 6.89 eV Sp.Gr: ? Combustible Solid	VP: <1 mm MLT: 295°F UEL: ? LEL: ?	Strong oxidizers	Filter*; EDTA; HPLC/UVD; OSHA [#87]
Phenyl ether (vapor) $C_6H_5OC_6H_5$ 101-84-8 KN8970000	Diphenyl ether, Diphenyl oxide, Phenoxy benzene, Phenyl oxide 1 ppm = 6.96 mg/m³	NIOSH/OSHA 1 ppm (7 mg/m³)	100 ppm	Colorless, crystalline solid or liquid (above 82°F) with a geranium-like odor.	MW: 170.2 BP: 498°F Sol: Insoluble Fl.P: 239°F IP: 8.09 eV Sp.Gr: 1.08 Combustible Solid Class IIIB Combustible Liquid	VP(77°F): 0.02 mm MLT: 82°F UEL: 6.0% LEL: 0.7%	Strong oxidizers	Char; CS₂; GC/FID; IV [#1617]

Personal protection and sanitation (See Table 3)		Recommendations for respirator selection — maximum concentration for use (MUC) (See Table 4)	Health hazards				
			Route	Symptoms (See Table 5)	First aid (See Table 6)		Target organs (See Table 5)
Skin:	Prevent skin contact	NIOSH/OSHA	Inh	Irrit eyes, nose, throat;	Eye:	Irr immed	Eyes, skin, resp sys,
Eyes:	Prevent eye contact	50 ppm: CCROVDM/SA	Abs	anor, low-wgt; weak,	Skin:	Soap wash immed	liver, kidneys
Wash skin:	When contam	125 ppm: SA:CF/PAPROVDM	Ing	musc ache, pain; dark	Breath:	Resp support	
Remove:	When wet or contam	250 ppm: CCRFOVHiE/GMFOVHiE/	Con	urine; cyan; liver, kidney	Swallow:	Medical attention	
Change:	Daily	PAPRTOVHiE/SCBAF/SAF		damage; skin burns; derm;		immed	
Provide:	Eyewash, Quick drench	§: SCBAF:PD,PP/SAF:PD,PP:ASCBA		ochronosis; tremor,			
		Escape: GMFOVHiE/SCBAE		convuls, twitch			

[Phenol]

Personal protection and sanitation (See Table 3)		Recommendations for respirator selection — maximum concentration for use (MUC) (See Table 4)	Health hazards				
			Route	Symptoms (See Table 5)	First aid (See Table 6)		Target organs (See Table 5)
Skin:	Prevent skin contact	TBAL	Inh	Itching, irrit, reddening	Eye:	Irr immed	Skin, CVS, liver,
Eyes:	N.R.		Abs	skin; hepatitis, hemolytic	Skin:	Soap wash prompt	kidneys
Wash skin:	When contam/Daily		Ing	anemia, abdom cramps, tacar;	Breath:	Resp support	
Remove:	When wet or contam		Con	kidney damage; skin photo	Swallow:	Medical attention	
Change:	Daily			sens		immed	

[Phenothiazine]

Personal protection and sanitation (See Table 3)		Recommendations for respirator selection — maximum concentration for use (MUC) (See Table 4)	Health hazards				
			Route	Symptoms (See Table 5)	First aid (See Table 6)		Target organs (See Table 5)
Skin:	Prevent skin contact	NIOSH/OSHA	Inh	Irrit pharynx, larynx;	Eye:	Irr immed	Resp sys, skin
Eyes:	Prevent eye contact	2.5 mg/m³: SA:CF£	Abs	bronchial asthma; sens	Skin:	Soap wash prompt	
Wash skin:	When contam/Daily	5 mg/m³: SCBAF/SAF	Ing	derm	Breath:	Resp support	
Remove:	When wet or contam	25 mg/m³: SAF:PD,PP	Con		Swallow:	Medical attention	
Change:	Daily	§: SCBAF:PD,PP/SAF:PD,PP:ASCBA				immed	
		Escape: GMFSHiE/SCBAE					

[p-Phenylene diamine]

Personal protection and sanitation (See Table 3)		Recommendations for respirator selection — maximum concentration for use (MUC) (See Table 4)	Health hazards				
			Route	Symptoms (See Table 5)	First aid (See Table 6)		Target organs (See Table 5)
Skin:	Prevent skin contact	NIOSH/OSHA	Inh	Irrit eyes, nose, skin; nau	Eye:	Irr immed	Eyes, skin, resp sys
Eyes:	Prevent eye contact	25 ppm: SA:CF£/PAPROVDM£	Con		Skin:	Soap wash prompt	
Wash skin:	When contam	50 ppm: CCRFOVHiE/GMFOVHiE/			Breath:	Resp support	
Remove:	When wet or contam	SCBAF/SAF					
Change:	N.R.	100 ppm: SAF:PD,PP					
		§: SCBAF:PD,PP/SAF:PD,PP:ASCBA					
		Escape: GMFOVHiE/SCBAE					

[Phenyl ether (vapor)]

Chemical name, structure/formula, CAS and RTECS Nos., and DOT ID and guide Nos.	Synonyms, trade names, and conversion factors	Exposure limits (TWA unless noted otherwise)	IDLH	Physical description	Chemical and physical properties		Incompatibilities and reactivities	Measurement method (See Table 1)
					MW, BP, SOL Fl.P, IP, Sp, Gr, flammability	VP, FRZ UEL, LEL		
Phenyl ether-biphenyl mixture (vapor) $C_6H_5OC_6H_5/C_6H_5C_6H_5$ 8004-13-5 DV1500000	Diphenyl oxide-diphenyl mixture, Dowtherm® A 1 ppm 6.79 mg/m³ (approx)	NIOSH/OSHA 1 ppm (7 mg/m³)	10 ppm	Colorless to straw-colored liquid or solid (below 54°F) with a disagreeable, aromatic odor. [Note: A mixture typically contains 75% phenyl ether & 25% biphenyl.]	MW: 166 (approx) BP: 495°F Sol: Insoluble Fl.P: 239°F IP: ? Sp.Gr(77°F): 1.06 Class IIIB Combustible Liquid	VP(77°F): 0.08 mm FRZ: 54°F UEL: ? LEL: ?	Strong oxidizers	Si gel; Benzene; GC/FID; IV [#2013]
Phenyl glycidyl ether $C_9H_{10}O_2$ 122-60-1 TZ3675000	1,2-Epoxy-3-phenoxy propane; Glycidyl phenyl ether; PGE; Phenyl 2,3-epoxypropyl ether 1 ppm = 6.14 mg/m³	NIOSH Ca See Appendix A C 1 ppm (6 mg/m³) [15-min] OSHA† 10 ppm (60 mg/m³)	Ca [100 ppm]	Colorless liquid. [Note: A solid below 38°F.]	MW: 150.1 BP: 473°F Sol: 0.2% Fl.P: 248°F IP: ? Sp.Gr: 1.11 Class IIIB Combustible Liquid	VP: 0.01 mm FRZ: 38°F UEL: ? LEL: ?	Strong oxidizers, amines, strong acids, strong bases	Char; CS₂; GC/FID; IV [#1619]
Phenylhydrazine $C_6H_5NHNH_2$ 100-63-0 MW8925000 2572 153	Hydrazinobenzene, Monophenylhydrazine 1 ppm = 4.42 mg/m³	NIOSH Ca See Appendix A C 0.14 ppm [skin] (0.6 mg/m³) [2-hr] OSHA† 5 ppm (22 mg/m³) [skin]	Ca [15 ppm]	Colorless to pale-yellow liquid or solid (below 67°F) with a faint, aromatic odor.	MW: 108.1 BP: 470°F (Decomposes) Sol: Slight Fl.P: 190°F IP: 7.64 eV Sp.Gr: 1.10 Class IIIA Combustible Liquid Combustible Solid	VP(77°F): 0.04 mm FRZ: 67°F UEL: ? LEL: ?	Strong oxidizers, lead dioxide	Bub; Pho-acid; Vis; IV [#3518]
N-Phenyl-ß-naphthyl-amine $C_{10}H_7NHC_6H_5$ 135-88-6 QM4550000	2-Anilinonaphthalene, ß-Naphthylphenylamine, PBNA, 2-Phenylaminonaphthalene, Phenyl-ß-naphthylamine	NIOSH Ca* See Appendix A [*Note: Since metabolized to ß-Naphthylamine.] OSHA none	Ca [N.D.]	White to yellow crystals or gray to tan flakes or powder. [Note: Commercial product may con-tain 20-30 ppm of ß-Naphthylamine.]	MW: 219.3 BP: 743°F Sol: Insoluble Fl.P: ? IP: ? Sp.Gr: 1.24 Combustible Solid	VP: ? MLT: 226°F UEL: ? LEL: ?	Oxidizers	Filter*; Methanol; HPLC/FLD; OSHA [#96]

Personal protection and sanitation (See Table 3)		Recommendations for respirator selection — maximum concentration for use (MUC) (See Table 4)	Route	Symptoms (See Table 5)	First aid (See Table 6)		Target organs (See Table 5)
					Health hazards		

Personal protection and sanitation	Recommendations for respirator selection — MUC	Route	Symptoms (See Table 5)	First aid (See Table 6)	Target organs (See Table 5)
Skin: Prevent skin contact Eyes: Prevent eye contact Wash skin: When contam Remove: When wet or contam Change: N.R.	NIOSH/OSHA 10 ppm: SA:CF^E/CCRFOVHiE/ GMFOVHiE/PAPROVDM^E/ SCBAF/SAF §: SCBAF:PD,PP/SAF:PD,PP:ASCBA Escape: GMFOVHiE/SCBAE	Inh Con	Irrit eyes, nose, skin; nau	Eye: Irr immed Skin: Soap wash prompt Breath: Resp support	Eyes, skin, resp sys
[Phenyl ether-biphenyl mixture (vapor)]					
Skin: Prevent skin contact Eyes: Prevent eye contact Wash skin: When contam Remove: When wet or contam Change: N.R. Provide: Eyewash, Quick drench	NIOSH ¥: SCBAF:PD,PP/SAF:PD,PP:ASCBA Escape: GMFOV/SCBAE	Inh Abs Ing Con	Irrit eyes, skin, upper resp sys; skin sens; narco; possible hemato, repro effects; [carc]	Eye: Irr immed Skin: Soap wash prompt Breath: Resp support Swallow: Medical attention immed	Eyes, skin, CNS, hemato sys, repro sys [in animals: nasal cancer]
[Phenyl glycidyl ether]					
Skin: Prevent skin contact Eyes: Prevent eye contact Wash skin: When contam/Daily Remove: When wet or contam Change: Daily Provide: Eyewash, Quick drench	NIOSH ¥: SCBAF:PD,PP/SAF:PD,PP:ASCBA Escape: SCBAE	Inh Abs Ing Con	Skin sens, hemolytic anemia, dysp, cyan; jaun; kidney damage; vascular thrombosis; [carc]	Eye: Irr immed Skin: Soap wash immed Breath: Resp support Swallow: Medical attention immed	Blood, resp sys, liver, kidneys, skin [in animals: tumors of the lungs, liver, blood vessels & intestine]
[Phenylhydrazine]					
Skin: Prevent skin contact Eyes: Prevent eye contact Wash skin: When contam/Daily Remove: When wet or contam Change: Daily Provide: Eyewash, Quick drench	NIOSH ¥: SCBAF:PD,PP/SAF:PD,PP:ASCBA Escape: GMFOVHiE/SCBAE	Inh Abs Ing Con	Irritation; leucoplakia; acne; hypersensitivity to sunlight; [carc]	Eye: Irr immed Skin: Soap wash immed Breath: Resp support Swallow: Medical attention immed	Eyes, skin, bladder [bladder cancer]
[N-Phenyl-ß-naphthylamine]					

Chemical name, structure/formula, CAS and RTECS Nos., and DOT ID and guide Nos.	Synonyms, trade names, and conversion factors	Exposure limits (TWA unless noted otherwise)	IDLH	Physical description	Chemical and physical properties MW, BP, SOL FI.P, IP, Sp, Gr, flammability	VP, FRZ UEL, LEL	Incompatibilities and reactivities	Measurement method (See Table 1)
Phenylphosphine $C_6H_5PH_2$ 638-21-1 SZ2100000	Fenylfosfin, PF, Phosphaniline 1 ppm = 4.50 mg/m³	NIOSH C 0.05 ppm (0.25 mg/m³) OSHA† none	N.D.	Clear, colorless liquid with a foul odor.	MW: 110.1 BP: 320°F Sol: Insoluble FI.P: ? IP: ? Sp.Gr(59°F): 1.001 Combustible Liquid	VP: ? FRZ: ? UEL: ? LEL: ?	None reported [Note: Spontaneously combustible in high concentrations in air. Potential exposure to gaseous phenylphosphine when polyphosphinates are heated above 392°F.]	None available
Phorate $(C_2H_5O)_2P(S)SCH_2SC_2H_5$ 298-02-2 TD9450000 3018 152 (organo-phosphorus pesticide, liquid)	O,O-Diethyl S-(ethylthio)-methylphosphorodithioate, O,O-Diethyl S-ethylthio-methylthiothionophosphate; Thimet; Timet	NIOSH 0.05 mg/m³ ST 0.2 mg/m³ [skin] OSHA† none	N.D.	Clear liquid with a skunk-like odor. [insecticide]	MW: 260.4 BP: ? Sol: 0.005% FI.P(oc): 320°F IP: ? Sp.Gr(77°F): 1.16 Class IIIB Combustible Liquid, but does not readily ignite.	VP: 0.0008 mm FRZ: -45°F UEL: ? LEL: ?	Water, alkalis [Note: Hydrolyzed in the presence of moisture and by alkalis.]	OVS-2; Toluene/ Acetone; GC/FPD; IV [#5600, Organo-phosphorus Pesticides]
Phosdrin® $C_7H_{13}PO_6$ 7786-34-7 GQ5250000 2783 152	2-Carbomethoxy-1-methylvinyl dimethyl phosphate, Mevinphos [Note: Commercial product is a mixture of the cis- & trans isomers.] $(CH_3O)_2P(O)OC(CH_3)=CHCOOCH_3$ 1 ppm = 9.17 mg/m³	NIOSH 0.01 ppm (0.1 mg/m³) ST 0.03 ppm (0.3 mg/m³) [skin] OSHA† 0.1 mg/m³ [skin]	4 ppm	Pale-yellow to orange liquid with a weak odor. [Note: Insecticide that may be absorbed on a dry carrier.]	MW: 224.2 BP: Decomposes Sol: Miscible FI.P(oc): 347°F IP: ? Sp.Gr: 1.25 Class IIIB Combustible Liquid	VP: 0.003 mm FRZ: 44°F (trans-) 70°F (cis-) UEL: ? LEL: ?	Strong oxidizers [Note: Corrosive to cast iron, some stainless steels & brass.]	OVS-2; Toluene/ Acetone GC/FPD; IV [#5600, Organo-phosphorus Pesticides]
Phosgene COCl₂ 75-44-5 SY5600000 1076 125	Carbon oxychloride, Carbonyl chloride, Carbonyl dichloride, Chloroformyl chloride 1 ppm = 4.05 mg/m³	NIOSH 0.1 ppm (0.4 mg/m³) C 0.2 ppm (0.8 mg/m³) [15-min] OSHA 0.1 ppm (0.4 mg/m³)	2 ppm	Colorless gas with a suffocating odor like musty hay. [Note: A fuming liquid below 47°F. Shipped as a liquefied compressed gas.]	MW: 98.9 BP: 47°F Sol: Slight FI.P: NA IP: 11.55 eV RGasD: 3.48 Sp.Gr: 1.43 (Liquid at 32°F) Nonflammable Gas	VP: 1.6 atm FRZ: -198°F UEL: NA LEL: NA	Moisture, alkalis, ammonia, alcohols, copper [Note: Reacts slowly in water to form hydrochloric acid & carbon dioxide.]	XAD-2*; Toluene; GC/NPD; OSHA [#61]

Personal protection and sanitation (See Table 3)		Recommendations for respirator selection — maximum concentration for use (MUC) (See Table 4)	Health hazards				
			Route	Symptoms (See Table 5)	First aid (See Table 6)		Target organs (See Table 5)
Skin:	**Prevent skin contact**	**TBAL**	**Inh**	In animals: blood changes, anemia, testicular degeneration; loss of appetite, diarr, lac, hind leg tremor; derm	**Eye:**	**Irr immed**	**Blood, CNS, skin, repro sys**
Eyes:	**Prevent eye contact**		**Ing**		**Skin:**	**Soap wash**	
Wash skin:	**Daily**		**Con**		**Breath:**	**Resp support**	
Remove:	**When wet or contam**				**Swallow:**	**Medical attention immed**	
Change:	**N.R.**						

[Phenylphosphine]

Skin:	Prevent skin contact	TBAL	Inh	Irrit eyes, skin, resp sys; miosis; rhin; head, chest tight, wheez, lar spasm, salv, cyan; anor, nau, vomit, abdom cramps, diarr; sweat; musc fasc, weak, para; gidd, conf, ataxia; convuls, coma; low BP; card irreg	Eye:	Irr immed	Eyes, skin, resp sys, CNS, CVS, blood chol
Eyes:	Prevent eye contact		Abs		Skin:	Soap flush immed	
Wash skin:	When contam		Ing		Breath:	Resp support	
Remove:	When wet or contam		Con		Swallow:	Medical attention immed	
Change:	N.R.						
Provide:	Eyewash, Quick drench						

253

[Phorate]

Skin:	Prevent skin contact	NIOSH/OSHA	Inh	Irrit eyes, skin, resp sys; miosis; rhin; head; chest tight, wheez, lar spasm, salv, cyan; anor, nau, vomit, abdom cramps, diarr; para; ataxia, convuls; low BP, card irreg	Eye:	Irr immed	Eyes, skin, resp sys, CNS, CVS, blood chol
Eyes:	Prevent eye contact	0.1 ppm: SA	Abs		Skin:	Soap wash immed	
Wash skin:	When contam	0.25 ppm: SA:CF	Ing		Breath:	Resp support	
Remove:	When wet or contam	0.5 ppm: SAT:CF/SCBAF/SAF	Con		Swallow:	Medical attention immed	
Change:	N.R.	4 ppm: SA:PD,PP					
Provide:	Eyewash, Quick drench	§: SCBAF:PD,PP/SAF:PD,PP:ASCBA					
		Escape: GMFOVHiE/SCBAE					

[Phosdrin®]

Skin:	Prevent skin contact (liq)	NIOSH/OSHA	Inh	Irrit eyes; dry burning throat; vomit; cough, foamy sputum, dysp, chest pain, cyan; liq: frostbite	Eye:	Irr immed (liq)	Eyes, skin, resp sys
Eyes:	Prevent eye contact (liq)	1 ppm: SA*	Con		Skin:	Water flush immed (liq)	
Wash skin:	When contam (liq)	2 ppm: SCBAF/SAF	(liq)				
Remove:	When wet or contam (liq)	§: SCBAF:PD,PP/SAF:PD,PP:ASCBA			Breath:	Resp support	
Change:	N.R.	Escape: GMFS/SCBAE					
Provide:	Quick drench (liq)						

[Phosgene]

Chemical name, structure/formula, CAS and RTECS Nos., and DOT ID and guide Nos.	Synonyms, trade names, and conversion factors	Exposure limits (TWA unless noted otherwise)	IDLH	Physical description	Chemical and physical properties		Incompatibilities and reactivities	Measurement method (See Table 1)
					MW, BP, SOL Fl.P, IP, Sp, Gr, flammability	VP, FRZ UEL, LEL		
Phosphine PH₃ 7803-51-2 SY7525000 2199 119	Hydrogen phosphide, Phosphorated hydrogen, Phosphorus hydride, Phosphorus trihydride 1 ppm = 1.39 mg/m³	NIOSH 0.3 ppm (0.4 mg/m³) ST 1 ppm (1 mg/m³) OSHA† 0.3 ppm (0.4 mg/m³)	50 ppm	Colorless gas with a fish- or garlic-like odor. [pesticide] [Note: Shipped as a liquefied compressed gas. Pure compound is odorless.]	MW: 34.0 BP: -126°F Sol: Slight Fl.P: NA (Gas) IP: 9.96 eV RGasD: 1.18 Flammable Gas	VP: 41.3 atm FRZ: -209°F UEL: ? LEL:1.79%	Air, oxidizers, chlorine, acids, moisture, halogenated hydrocarbons, copper [Note: May ignite SPONTANEOUSLY on contact with air.]	Beaded carbon*; H₂O/ buffer; IC; OSHA [#ID180]
Phosphoric acid H₃PO₄ 7664-38-2 TB6300000 1805 154	Orthophosphoric acid, Phosphoric acid (aqueous), White phosphoric acid	NIOSH 1 mg/m³ ST 3 mg/m³ OSHA† 1 mg/m³	1000 mg/m³	Thick, colorless, odorless, crystalline solid. [Note: Often used in an aqueous solution.]	MW: 98.0 BP: 415°F Sol: Miscible Fl.P: NA IP: ? Sp.Gr(77°F): 1.87 (pure) 1.33 (50% soln.) Noncombustible Solid	VP: 0.03 mm MLT: 108°F UEL: NA LEL: NA	Strong caustics, most metals [Note: Readily reacts with metals to form flammable hydrogen gas. DO NOT MIX WITH SOLUTIONS CONTAINING BLEACH OR AMMONIA.]	Si gel*; NaHCO₃/ Na₂CO₃; IC; IV [#7903, Inorganic Acids]
Phosphorus (yellow) P₄ 7723-14-0 TH3500000 1381 136	Elemental phosphorus, White phosphorus	NIOSH/OSHA 0.1 mg/m³	5 mg/m³	White to yellow, soft, waxy solid with acrid fumes in air. [Note: Usually shipped or stored in water.]	MW: 124.0 BP: 536°F Sol: 0.0003% Fl.P: ? IP: ? Sp.Gr: 1.82 Flammable Solid	VP: 0.03 mm MLT: 111°F UEL: ? LEL: ?	Air, oxidizers (including elemental sulfur & strong caustics), halogens [Note: Ignites SPONTANEOUSLY in moist air.]	Tenax GC; Xylene; GC/FPD; IV [#7905]
Phosphorus oxychloride POCl₃ 10025-87-3 TH4897000 1810 137	Phosphorus chloride, Phosphorus oxytrichloride, Phosphoryl chloride 1 ppm = 6.27 mg/m³	NIOSH 0.1 ppm (0.6 mg/m³) ST 0.5 ppm (3 mg/m³) OSHA† none	N.D.	Clear, colorless to yellow, oily liquid with a pungent & musty odor. [Note: A solid below 34°F.]	MW: 153.3 BP: 222°F Sol: Decomposes Fl.P: NA IP: ? Sp.Gr(77°F): 1.65 Noncombustible Liquid, but may set fire to combustible materials.	VP(81°F): 40 mm FRZ: 34°F UEL: NA LEL: NA	Water, combustible materials, carbon disulfide, dimethyl-formamide, metals (except nickel & lead) [Note: Decomposes in water to hydrochloric & phosphoric acids.]	None available

Personal protection and sanitation (See Table 3)		Recommendations for respirator selection — maximum concentration for use (MUC) (See Table 4)	Route	Symptoms (See Table 5)	First aid (See Table 6)		Target organs (See Table 5)
					Health hazards		

Personal protection and sanitation		Recommendations for respirator selection (MUC)	Route	Symptoms	First aid		Target organs
Skin: Eyes: Wash skin: Remove: Change: Provide:	Frostbite Frostbite N.R. When wet (flamm) N.R. Frostbite	NIOSH/OSHA 3 ppm: SA 7.5 ppm: SA:CF 15 ppm: GMFS/SCBAF/SAF 50 ppm: SA:PD,PP §: SCBAF:PD,PP/SAF:PD,PP:ASCBA Escape: GMFS/SCBAE	Inh Con (liq)	Nau, vomit, abdom pain, diarr; thirst; chest tight, dysp; musc pain, chills; stupor or syncope; pulm edema; liq: frostbite	Eye: Skin: Breath:	Frostbite Frostbite Resp support	Resp sys
[Phosphine]							
Skin: Eyes: Wash skin: Remove: Change: Provide:	Prevent skin contact Prevent eye contact When contam When wet or contam Daily Eyewash (>1.6%), Quick drench (>1.6%)	NIOSH/OSHA 25 mg/m³: SA:CF* 50 mg/m³: HiEF/SCBAF/SAF 1000 mg/m³: SAF:PD,PP §: SCBAF:PD,PP/SAF:PD,PP:ASCBA Escape: HiEF/SCBAE	Inh Ing Con	Irrit eyes, skin, upper resp sys; eye, skin burns; derm	Eye: Skin: Breath: Swallow:	Irr immed Water flush Immed Resp support Medical attention immed	Eyes, skin, resp sys
[Phosphoric acid]							
Skin: Eyes: Wash skin: Remove: Change: Provide:	Prevent skin contact* Prevent eye contact When contam When wet or contam Daily Eyewash, Quick drench [*Note: Flame retardant personal protective equipment should be provided.]	NIOSH/OSHA 1 mg/m³: SA 2.5 mg/m³: SA:CF£ 5 mg/m³: SCBAF/SAF §: SCBAF:PD,PP/SAF:PD,PP:ASCBA Escape: SCBAE	Inh Ing Con	Irrit eyes, resp tract; eye, skin burns; abdom pain, nau, jaun; anemia; cachexia; dental pain, salv, jaw pain, swell	Eye: Skin: Breath: Swallow:	Irr immed Water flush immed Resp support Medical attention immed	Eyes, skin, resp sys, liver, kidneys, jaw, teeth, blood
[Phosphorus (yellow)]							
Skin: Eyes: Wash skin: Remove: Change: Provide:	Prevent skin contact Prevent eye contact When contam When wet or contam N.R. Eyewash, Quick drench	TBAL	Inh Ing Con	Irrit eyes, skin, resp sys; eye, skin burns; dysp, cough, lung edema; dizz, head, weak; abdom pain, nau, vomit; neph	Eye: Skin: Breath: Swallow:	Irr immed Water flush immed Resp support Medical attention immed	Eyes, skin, resp sys, CNS, kidneys
[Phosphorus oxychloride]							

Chemical name, structure/formula, CAS and RTECS Nos., and DOT ID and guide Nos.	Synonyms, trade names, and conversion factors	Exposure limits (TWA unless noted otherwise)	IDLH	Physical description	Chemical and physical properties		Incompatibilities and reactivities	Measurement method (See Table 1)
					MW, BP, SOL Fl.P, IP, Sp, Gr, flammability	VP, FRZ UEL, LEL		
Phosphorus pentachloride PCl$_5$ 10026-13-8 TB6125000 1806 137	Pentachlorophosphorus, Phosphoric chloride, Phosphorus perchloride	NIOSH/OSHA 1 mg/m^3	70 mg/m^3	White to pale-yellow, crystalline solid with a pungent, unpleasant odor.	MW: 208.3 BP: Sublimes Sol: Reacts Fl.P: NA IP: ? Sp.Gr: 3.60 Noncombustible Solid	VP(132°F): 1mm MLT: 324°F (Sublimes) UEL: NA LEL: NA	Water, magnesium oxide, chemically-active metals such as sodium & potassium, alkalis, amines [Note: Hydrolyzes in water (even in humid air) to form hydrochloric acid & phosphoric acid. Corrosive to metals.]	Filter/Bub; Reagent; Vis; II(5) [#S257]
Phosphorus pentasulfide P$_2$S$_5$/P$_4$S$_{10}$ 1314-80-3 TH4375000 1340 139	Phosphorus persulfide, Phosphorus sulfide, Sulfur phosphide	NIOSH 1 mg/m^3 ST 3 mg/m^3 OSHA† 1 mg/m^3	250 mg/m^3	Greenish-gray to yellow, crystalline solid with an odor of rotten eggs.	MW: 222.3/ 444.6 BP: 957°F Sol: Reacts Fl.P: ? IP: ? Sp.Gr: 2.09 Flammable Solid, which may SPONTANEOUSLY ignite in presence of moisture.	VP(572°F): 1mm MLT: 550°F UEL: ? LEL: ?	Water, alcohols, strong oxidizers, acids, alkalis [Note: Reacts with water to form hydrogen sulfide, sulfur dioxide, and phosphoric acid.]	None available
Phosphorus trichloride PCl$_3$ 7719-12-2 TH3675000 1809 137	Phosphorus chloride	NIOSH 0.2 ppm (1.5 mg/m^3) ST 0.5 ppm (3 mg/m^3) OSHA† 0.5 ppm (3 mg/m^3) 1 ppm = 5.62 mg/m^3	25 ppm	Colorless to yellow, fuming liquid with an odor like hydrochloric acid.	MW: 137.4 BP: 169°F Sol: Reacts Fl.P: NA IP: 9.91 eV Sp.Gr: 1.58 Noncombustible Liquid; however, a strong oxidizer that may ignite combustibles upon contact.	VP: 100 mm FRZ: -170°F UEL: NA LEL: NA	Water, chemically-active metals such as sodium & potassium, aluminum, strong nitric acid, acetic acid, organic matter [Note: Hydrolyzes in water to form hydrochloric acid and phosphoric acid.]	Bub; Reagent; Vis; IV [#6402]
Phthalic anhydride C$_6$H$_4$(CO)$_2$O 85-44-9 TI3150000 2214 156	1,2-Benzenedicarboxylic anhydride; PAN; Phthalic acid anhydride	NIOSH 6 mg/m^3 (1 ppm) OSHA† 12 mg/m^3 (2 ppm) 1 ppm = 6.06 mg/m^3	60 mg/m^3	White solid (flake) or a clear, colorless liquid (molten) with a characteristic, acrid odor.	MW: 148.1 BP: 563°F Sol: 0.6% Fl.P: 305°F IP: 10.00 eV Sp.Gr: 1.53 (Flake) 1.20 (Molten) Combustible Solid	VP: 0.0015 mm MLT: 267°F UEL: 10.5% LEL: 1.7%	Strong oxidizers, water [Note: Converted to phthalic acid in hot water.]	Filter; NH$_4$OH; HPLC/UVD; II(3) [#S179]

Personal protection and sanitation (See Table 3)	Recommendations for respirator selection — maximum concentration for use (MUC) (See Table 4)	Route	Symptoms (See Table 5)	First aid (See Table 6)	Target organs (See Table 5)
Skin: Prevent skin contact Eyes*: Prevent eye contact Wash skin: When contam Remove: When wet or contam Change: Daily Provide: Eyewash, Quick drench	NIOSH/OSHA 10 mg/m³: SA* 25 mg/m³: SA:CF* 50 mg/m³: SCBAF/SAF 70 mg/m³: SAF:PD,PP §: SCBAF:PD,PP/SAF:PD,PP:ASCBA Escape: GMFOVHiE/SCBAE	Inh Ing Con	Irrit eyes, skin, resp sys; bron; derm	Eye: Irr immed Skin: Water flush immed Breath: Resp support Swallow: Medical attention immed	Eyes, skin, resp sys

[Phosphorus pentachloride]

Personal protection and sanitation (See Table 3)	Recommendations for respirator selection — maximum concentration for use (MUC) (See Table 4)	Route	Symptoms (See Table 5)	First aid (See Table 6)	Target organs (See Table 5)
Skin: Prevent skin contact Eyes: Prevent eye contact Wash skin: When contam Remove: When wet or contam Change: Daily	NIOSH/OSHA 10 mg/m³: SA* 25 mg/m³: SA:CF* 50 mg/m³: SCBAF/SAF 250 mg/m³: SAF:PD,PP §: SCBAF:PD,PP/SAF:PD,PP:ASCBA Escape: GMFSHiE/SCBAE	Inh Ing Con	Irrit eyes, skin, resp sys; apnea, coma, convuls; conj pain, lac, photo, kerato-conj, corn vesic; dizz; head; ftg; irrity, insom; GI dist	Eye: Irr immed Skin: Dust off solid; water flush Breath: Resp support Swallow: Medical attention immed	Eyes, skin, resp sys, CNS

[Phosphorus pentasulfide]

Personal protection and sanitation (See Table 3)	Recommendations for respirator selection — maximum concentration for use (MUC) (See Table 4)	Route	Symptoms (See Table 5)	First aid (See Table 6)	Target organs (See Table 5)
Skin: Prevent skin contact Eyes: Prevent eye contact Wash skin: When contam Remove: When wet or contam Change: N.R. Provide: Eyewash, Quick drench	NIOSH 10 ppm: SCBAF/SAF 25 ppm: SAF:PD,PP §: SCBAF:PD,PP/SAF:PD,PP:ASCBA Escape: GMFS⁴/SCBAE	Inh Ing Con	Irrit eyes, skin, nose, throat; pulm edema; eye, skin burns	Eye: Irr immed Skin: Water flush immed Breath: Resp support Swallow: Medical attention immed	Eyes, skin, resp sys

[Phosphorus trichloride]

Personal protection and sanitation (See Table 3)	Recommendations for respirator selection — maximum concentration for use (MUC) (See Table 4)	Route	Symptoms (See Table 5)	First aid (See Table 6)	Target organs (See Table 5)
Skin: Prevent skin contact Eyes: Prevent eye contact Wash skin: When contam Remove: When wet or contam Change: Daily	NIOSH 30 mg/m³: DM* 60 mg/m³: DMXSQ*/HiEF/PAPRDM*/ SA*/SCBAF §: SCBAF:PD,PP/SAF:PD,PP:ASCBA Escape: HiEF/SCBAE	Inh Ing Con	Irrit eyes, skin, upper resp sys; conj; nasal ulcer bleeding; bron, bronchial asthma; derm; in animals: liver, kidney damage	Eye: Irr immed Skin: Soap wash prompt Breath: Resp support Swallow: Medical attention immed	Eyes, skin, resp sys, liver, kidneys

[Phthalic anhydride]

Chemical name, structure/formula, CAS and RTECS Nos., and DOT ID and guide Nos.	Synonyms, trade names, and conversion factors	Exposure limits (TWA unless noted otherwise)	IDLH	Physical description	Chemical and physical properties		Incompatibilities and reactivities	Measurement method (See Table 1)
					MW, BP, SOL Fl.P, IP, Sp, Gr, flammability	VP, FRZ UEL, LEL		
m-Phthalodinitrile C₆H₄(CN)₂ 626-17-5 CZ1900000	1,3-Benzenedicarbonitrile; m-Dicyanobenzene; 1,3-Dicyanobenzene; Isophthalodinitrile; m-PDN	NIOSH 5 mg/m³ OSHA† none	N.D.	Needle-like, colorless to white, crystalline, flaky solid with an almond-like odor.	MW: 128.1 BP: Sublimes Sol: Slight Fl.P: ? IP: ? Sp.Gr. 4.42 Combustible Solid and a severe explosion hazard.	VP: 0.01 mm MLT: 324°F (Sublimes) UEL: ? LEL: ?	Strong oxidizers (e.g., chlorine, bromine, fluorine)	None available
Picloram C₆H₃Cl₃O₂N₂ 1918-02-1 TJ7525000	4-Amino-3,5,6-trichloro-picolinic acid; 4-Amino-3,5,6-trichloro-2-picolinic acid; ATCP; Grazon®; Tordon®	NIOSH See Appendix D OSHA† 15 mg/m³ (total) 5 mg/m³ (resp)	N.D.	Colorless to white crystals with a chlorine-like odor. [herbicide]	MW: 241.5 BP: Decomposes Sol: 0.04% Fl.P: ? IP: ? Sp.Gr: ? Combustible Solid	VP(95°F): 0.0000006 mm MLT: 424°F (Decomposes) UEL: ? LEL: ?	Hot concentrated alkali (hydrolyzes)	Filter; none; Grav; IV [Particulates NOR: #500 (total), #600 (resp)]
Picric acid (NO₂)₃C₆H₂OH 88-89-1 TJ7875000 1344 113 (>10% water)	Phenol trinitrate; 2,4,6-Trinitrophenol [Note: An OSHA Class A Explosive (1910.109).] 1 ppm = 9.37 mg/m³	NIOSH 0.1 mg/m³ ST 0.3 mg/m³ [skin] OSHA 0.1 mg/m³ [skin]	75 mg/m³	Yellow, odorless solid. [Note: Usually used as an aqueous solution.]	MW: 229.1 BP: Explodes above 572°F Sol:1% Fl.P: 302°F IP: ? Sp.Gr. 1.76 Combustible Solid	VP(383°F): 1mm MLT: 252°F UEL: ? LEL: ?	Copper, lead, zinc & other metals; salts; plaster; concrete; ammonia [Note: Corrosive to metals. An explosive mixture results when the aqueous solution crystallizes.]	Filter; Methanol/ Water; HPLC/UVD; II(4) [#S228]
Pindone C₉H₅O₂C(O)C(CH₃)₃ 83-26-1 NK6300000	tert-Butyl valone; 1,3-Dioxo-2-pivaloy-lindane; Pival®; Pivalyl; 2-Pivalyl-1,3-indandione	NIOSH/OSHA 0.1 mg/m³	100 mg/m³	Bright-yellow powder with almost no odor. [rodenticide]	MW: 230.3 BP: Decomposes Sol(77°F): 0.002% Fl.P: ? IP: ? Sp.Gr. 1.06	VP: Very low MLT: 230°F . UEL: ? LEL: ?	None reported	None available

Personal protection and sanitation (See Table 3)		Recommendations for respirator selection — maximum concentration for use (MUC) (See Table 4)	Health hazards				
			Route	Symptoms (See Table 5)	First aid (See Table 6)		Target organs (See Table 5)
Skin:	Prevent skin contact	TBAL	Inh	Head, nau, conf;	Eye:	Irr immed	Eyes, skin, CNS
Eyes:	Prevent eye contact		Abs	in animals: irrit eyes, skin	Skin:	Soap wash immed	
Wash skin:	Daily		Ing		Breath:	Resp support	
Remove:	When wet or contam		Con		Swallow:	Medical attention	
Change:	Daily					immed	

[m-Phthalodinitriie]

Skin:	Prevent skin contact	TBAL	Inh	Irrit eyes, skin, resp sys;	Eye:	Irr immed	Eyes, skin, resp sys,
Eyes:	Prevent eye contact		Ing	nau;	Skin:	Soap wash	liver, kidneys
Wash skin:	When contam		Con	in animals: liver, kidney	Breath:	Fresh air	
Remove:	N.R.			changes	Swallow:	Medical attention	
Change:	Daily					immed	

259

[Picloram]

Skin:	Prevent skin contact	NIOSH/OSHA	Inh	Irrit eyes, skin; sens derm;	Eye:	Irr immed	Eyes, skin, kidneys,
Eyes:	Prevent eye contact	0.5 mg/m³: DM	Abs	yellow-stained hair, skin;	Skin:	Soap wash prompt	liver, blood
Wash skin:	When contam/Daily	1 mg/m³: DMXSQ/SA	Ing	weak, myalgia, anuria,	Breath:	Resp support	
Remove:	When wet or contam	2.5 mg/m³: SA:CF/PAPRDM	Con	polyuria; bitter taste, GI	Swallow:	Medical attention	
Change:	Daily	5 mg/m³: HiEF/SAT:CF/PAPRTHiE/		dist; hepatitis, hema,		immed	
		SCBAF/SAF		album, neph			
		75 mg/m³: SAF:PD,PP					
		§: SCBAF:PD,PP/SAF:PD,PP:ASCBA					
		Escape: HiEF/SCBAE					

[Picric acid]

Skin:	N.R.	NIOSH/OSHA	Inh	Epis, excess bleeding	Eye:	Irr immed	Blood
Eyes:	N.R.	0.5 mg/m³: DM	Ing	from minor cuts, bruises;	Breath:	Resp support	prothrombin
Wash skin:	N.R.	1 mg/m³: DMXSQ/SA		smoky urine, black tarry	Swallow:	Medical attention	
Remove:	N.R.	2.5 mg/m³: SA:CF/PAPRDM		stools; abdom, back pain		immed	
Change:	Daily	5 mg/m³: HiEF/SAT:CF/PAPRTHiE/					
		SCBAF/SAF					
		100 mg/m³: SAF:PD,PP					
		§: SCBAF:PD,PP/SAF:PD,PP:ASCBA					
		Escape: HiEF/SCBAE					

[Pindone]

Chemical name, structure/formula, CAS and RTECS Nos., and DOT ID and guide Nos.	Synonyms, trade names, and conversion factors	Exposure limits (TWA unless noted otherwise)	IDLH	Physical description	Chemical and physical properties		Incompatibilities and reactivities	Measurement method (See Table 1)
					MW, BP, SOL FI.P, IP, Sp, Gr, flammability	VP, FRZ UEL, LEL		
Piperazine dihydro-chloride $C_4H_{10}N_2 \cdot 2HCl$ 142-64-3 TL4025000	Piperazine hydrochloride [Note: The monochloride, $C_4H_{10}N_2 \cdot HCl$ is also commercially available.]	NIOSH 5 mg/m^3 OSHA† none	N.D.	White to cream-colored needles or powder.	MW: 159.1 BP: ? Sol: 41% FI.P: ? IP: ? Sp.Gr: ? Combustible Solid, but does not ignite easily.	VP: ? MLT: 635°F UEL: ? LEL: ?	Water [Note: Slightly hygroscopic (i.e., absorbs moisture from the air).]	None available
Plaster of Paris $CaSO_4 \cdot 0.5H_2O$ 26499-65-0 TP0700000	Calcium sulfate hemihydrate, Dried calcium sulfate, Gypsum hemihydrate, Hemihydrate gypsum [Note: Plaster of Paris is the hemihydrate form of Calcium Sulfate & Gypsum is the dihydrate form.]	NIOSH 10 mg/m^3 (total) 5 mg/m^3 (resp) OSHA 15 mg/m^3 (total) 5 mg/m^3 (resp)	N.D.	White or yellowish, finely divided, odorless powder.	MW: 145.2 BP: ? Sol(77°F): 0.3% FI.P: NA IP: NA Sp.Gr: 2.5 Noncombustible Solid	VP: 0 mm (approx) MLT: 325°F (Loses H$_2$O) UEL: NA LEL: NA	Moisture, water [Note: Hygroscopic (i.e., absorbs moisture from the air). Reacts with water to form Gypsum.]	Filter; none; Grav; IV [Particulates NOR: #0500 (total), #0600 (resp)]
Platinum Pt 7440-06-4 TP2160000	Platinum black, Platinum metal, Platinum sponge	NIOSH 1 mg/m^3 OSHA† none	N.D.	Silvery, whitish-gray, malleable, ductile metal.	MW: 195.1 BP: 6921°F Sol: Insoluble FI.P: NA IP: NA Sp.Gr: 21.45 Noncombustible Solid in bulk form, but finely divided powder can be dangerous to handle.	VP: 0 mm (approx) MLT: 3222°F UEL: NA LEL: NA	Aluminum, acetone, arsenic, ethane, hydrazine, hydrogen peroxide, lithium, phosphorus, selenium, tellurium, various fluorides	Filter; Acids; ICP; IV [#7300, Elements]
Platinum (soluble salts, as Pt)	Synonyms vary depending upon the specific soluble platinum salt.	NIOSH/OSHA 0.002 mg/m^3	4 mg/m^3 (as Pt)	Appearance and odor vary depending upon the specific soluble platinum salt.	Properties vary depending upon the specific soluble platinum salt.		Varies	Filter; Acid/ Reagent; GFAAS; II(7) [#S191]

Personal protection and sanitation (See Table 3)		Recommendations for respirator selection — maximum concentration for use (MUC) (See Table 4)	Health hazards				
			Route	Symptoms (See Table 5)	First aid (See Table 6)		Target organs (See Table 5)
Skin:	Prevent skin contact	TBAL	Inh	Irrit eyes, skin, resp sys;	Eye:	Irr immed	Eyes, skin, resp sys,
Eyes:	Prevent eye contact		Abs	skin burns, sens; asthma;	Skin:	Water flush immed	CNS
Wash skin:	When contam		Ing	GI upset, head, nau, vomit,	Breath:	Resp support	
Remove:	When wet or contam		Con	inco, musc weak	Swallow:	Medical attention	
Change:	Daily					immed	
Provide:	Eyewash, Quick drench						

[Piperazine dihydrochloride]

Personal protection and sanitation (See Table 3)		Recommendations for respirator selection — maximum concentration for use (MUC) (See Table 4)	Health hazards				
			Route	Symptoms	First aid		Target organs
Skin:	N.R.	TBAL	Inh	Irrit eyes, skin, muc memb,	Eye:	Irr immed	Eyes, skin, resp sys
Eyes:	N.R.		Ing	resp sys; cough	Breath:	Resp support	
Wash skin:	N.R.		Con		Swallow:	Medical attention	
Remove:	N.R.					immed	
Change:	N.R.						

[Plaster of Paris]

Personal protection and sanitation (See Table 3)		Recommendations for respirator selection — maximum concentration for use (MUC) (See Table 4)	Health hazards				
			Route	Symptoms	First aid		Target organs
Skin:	N.R.	TBAL	Inh	Irrit eyes, skin, resp sys;	Eye:	Irr immed	Eyes, skin, resp sys
Eyes:	N.R.		Ing	derm	Skin:	Soap wash	
Wash skin:	N.R.		Con		Breath:	Resp support	
Remove:	N.R.				Swallow:	Medical attention	
Change:	Daily					immed	

[Platinum]

Personal protection and sanitation (See Table 3)		Recommendations for respirator selection — maximum concentration for use (MUC) (See Table 4)	Health hazards				
			Route	Symptoms	First aid		Target organs
Skin:	Prevent skin contact	NIOSH/OSHA	Inh	Irrit eyes, nose; cough,	Eye:	Irr immed	Eyes, skin, resp sys
Eyes:	Prevent eye contact	0.05 mg/m^3: SA:CF$^£$	Ing	dysp, wheez, cyan; derm,	Skin:	Water flush immed	
Wash skin:	When contam	0.1 mg/m^3: HiEF/SCBAF/SAF	Con	sens skin; lymphocytosis	Breath:	Resp support	
Remove:	When wet or contam	4 mg/m^3: SAF:PD,PP			Swallow:	Medical attention	
Change:	Daily	§: SCBAF:PD,PP/SAF:PD,PP:ASCBA				immed	
		Escape: HiEF/SCBAE					

[Platinum (soluble salts, as Pt)]

Chemical name, structure/formula, CAS and RTECS Nos., and DOT ID and guide Nos.	Synonyms, trade names, and conversion factors	Exposure limits (TWA unless noted otherwise)	IDLH	Physical description	Chemical and physical properties		Incompatibilities and reactivities	Measurement method (See Table 1)
					MW, BP, SOL Fl.P, IP, Sp, Gr, flammability	VP, FRZ UEL, LEL		
Portland cement 65997-15-1 VV8770000	Cement, Hydraulic cement, Portland cement silicate [Note: A class of hydraulic cements containing tri- and dicalcium silicate in addition to alumina, tricalcium aluminate, and iron oxide.]	NIOSH 10 mg/m³ (total) 5 mg/m³ (resp) OSHA† 15 mg/m³ (total) 5 mg/m³ (resp)	5000 mg/m³	Gray, odorless powder.	MW: ? BP: NA Sol: Insoluble Fl.P: NA IP: NA Sp.Gr: ? Noncombustible Solid	VP: 0 mm (approx) MLT: NA UEL: NA LEL: NA	None reported	Filter; none; Grav; IV [#0500, Particulates NOR (total)]
Potassium cyanide (as CN) KCN 151-50-8 TS8750000 1680 157 (solution)	Potassium salt of hydrocyanic acid	NIOSH* C 5 mg/m³ (4.7 ppm) [10-min] OSHA* 5 mg/m³ [*Note: The REL and PEL also apply to other cyanides (as CN) except Hydrogen cyanide.]	25 mg/m³ (as CN)	White, granular or crystalline solid with a faint, almond-like odor.	MW: 65.1 BP: 2957°F Sol(77°F): 72% Fl.P: NA IP: NA Sp.Gr: 1.55 Noncombustible Solid, but contact with acids releases highly flammable hydrogen cyanide.	VP: 0 mm (approx) MLT: 1173°F UEL: NA LEL: NA	Strong oxidizers (such as acids, acid salts, chlorates & nitrates) [Note: Absorbs moisture from the air forming a syrup.]	Filter/Bub; KOH; ISE; IV [#7904, Cyanides] [Also #6010, Hydrogen Cyanide.]
Potassium hydroxide KOH 1310-58-3 TT2100000 1813 154 (dry, solid) 1814 154 (solution)	Caustic potash, Lye, Potassium hydrate	NIOSH 2 mg/m³ OSHA† none	N.D.	Odorless, white or slightly yellow lumps, rods, flakes, sticks, or pellets. [Note: May be used as an aqueous solution.]	MW: 56.1 BP: 2415°F Sol(59°F): 107% Fl.P: NA IP: ? Sp.Gr: 2.04 Noncombustible Solid; however, may react with H₂O & other substances and generate sufficient heat to ignite combustible materials.	VP(1317°F): 1 mm MLT: 716°F UEL: NA LEL: NA	Acids, water, metals (when wet), halogenated hydrocarbons, maleic anhydride [Note: Heat is generated if KOH comes in contact with H₂O & CO₂ from the air.]	Filter; HCl; Titrate; IV [#7401, Alkaline Dusts]
Propane CH₃CH₂CH₃ 74-98-6 TX2275000 1075 115 1978 115	Bottled gas, Dimethyl methane, n-Propane, Propyl hydride	NIOSH/OSHA 1000 ppm (1800 mg/m³) 1 ppm = 1.80 mg/m³	2100 ppm [10%LEL]	Colorless, odorless gas. [Note: A foul-smelling odorant is often added when used for fuel purposes. Shipped as a liquefied compressed gas.]	MW: 44.1 BP: -44°F Sol: 0.01% Fl.P: NA (Gas) IP: 11.07 eV RGasD: 1.55 Flammable Gas	VP(70°F): 8.4 atm FRZ: -306°F UEL: 9.5% LEL: 2.1%	Strong oxidizers	Combustible gas meter; none; none; II(2) [#S87]

MW: Portland cement — formulas as shown. H_2O, CO_2 appear in notes.

Personal protection and sanitation (See Table 3)	Recommendations for respirator selection — maximum concentration for use (MUC) (See Table 4)	Health hazards			
		Route	Symptoms (See Table 5)	First aid (See Table 6)	Target organs (See Table 5)
Skin: Prevent skin contact Eyes: Prevent eye contact Wash skin: When contam Remove: When wet or contam Change: N.R. [Portland cement]	NIOSH 50 mg/m³: D 100 mg/m³: DXSQ/SA 250 mg/m³: SA:CF/PAPRD 500 mg/m³: HiEF/SAT:CF/PAPRTHiE/ SCBAF/SAF 5000 mg/m³: SA:PD,PP §: SCBAF:PD,PP/SAF:PD,PP:ASCBA Escape: HiEF/SCBAE	Inh Ing Con	Irrit eyes, skin, nose; cough, expectoration; exertional dysp, wheez, chronic bron; derm	Eye: Irr immed Skin: Soap wash prompt Breath: Fresh air Swallow: Medical attention immed	Eyes, skin, resp sys
Skin: Prevent skin contact Eyes: Prevent eye contact Wash skin: When contam Remove: When wet or contam Change: Daily Provide: Eyewash, Quick drench [Potassium cyanide (as CN)]	NIOSH/OSHA 25 mg/m³: SA/SCBAF §: SCBAF:PD,PP/SAF:PD,PP:ASCBA Escape: GMFSHiE/SCBAE	Inh Abs Ing Con	Irrit eyes, skin, upper resp sys; asphy; weak, head, conf; nau, vomit; incr rate resp; slow gasping resp; thyroid, blood changes	Eye: Irr immed Skin: Soap wash immed Breath: Resp support Swallow: Medical attention immed	Eyes, skin, resp sys, CVS, CNS, thyroid, blood
Skin: Prevent skin contact Eyes: Prevent eye contact Wash skin: When contam Remove: When wet or contam Change: Daily Provide: Eyewash, Quick drench [Potassium hydroxide]	TBAL	Inh Ing Con	Irrit eyes, skin, resp sys; cough, sneez; eye, skin burns; vomit, diarr	Eye: Irr immed Skin: Water flush immed Breath: Resp support Swallow: Medical attention immed	Eyes, skin, resp sys
Skin: Frostbite Eyes: Frostbite Wash skin: N.R. Remove: When wet (flamm) Change: N.R. Provide: Frostbite [Propane]	NIOSH/OSHA 2100 ppm: SA/SCBAF §: SCBAF:PD,PP/SAF:PD,PP:ASCBA Escape: SCBAE	Inh Con (liq)	Dizz, conf, excitation, asphy; liq: frostbite	Eye: Frostbite Skin: Frostbite Breath: Resp support	CNS

263

Chemical name, structure/formula, CAS and RTECS Nos., and DOT ID and guide Nos.	Synonyms, trade names, and conversion factors	Exposure limits (TWA unless noted otherwise)	IDLH	Physical description	Chemical and physical properties		Incompatibilities and reactivities	Measurement method (See Table 1)
					MW, BP, SOL FI.P, IP, Sp, Gr, flammability	VP, FRZ UEL, LEL		
Propane sultone C₃H₆O₃S 1120-71-4 RP5425000	3-Hydroxy-1-propanesul-phonic acid sultone; 1,3-Propane sultone	NIOSH Ca See Appendix A OSHA none	Ca [N.D.]	White, crystalline solid or a colorless liquid (above 86°F). [Note: Releases a foul odor as it melts.]	MW: 122.2 BP: ? Sol: 10% FI.P: >235°F IP: ? Sp.Gr: 1.39 Combustible Solid	VP: ? MLT: 86°F UEL: ? LEL: ?	None reported	None available
1-Propanethiol CH₃CH₂CH₂SH 107-03-9 TZ7300000 2402 130	3-Mercaptopropane, Propane-1-thiol, Propyl mercaptan, n-Propyl mercaptan 1 ppm = 3.12 mg/m³	NIOSH C 0.5 ppm (1.6 mg/m³) [15-min] OSHA none	N.D.	Colorless liquid with an offensive, cabbage-like odor.	MW: 76.2 BP: 153°F Sol: Slight FI.P: -5°F IP: 9.195 eV Sp.Gr: 0.84 Class IB Flammable Liquid	VP(77°F): 155mm FRZ: -172°F UEL: ? LEL: ?	Oxidizers, reducing agents, strong acids & bases, alkali metals, calcium hypochlorite	None available
Propargyl alcohol HC≡CCH₂OH 107-19-7 UK5075000 1986 131	1-Propyn-3-ol; 2-Propyn-1-ol; 2-Propynyl alcohol 1 ppm = 2.29 mg/m³	NIOSH 1 ppm (2 mg/m³) [skin] OSHA† none	N.D.	Colorless to straw-colored liquid with a mild, geranium odor.	MW: 56.1 BP: 237°F Sol: Miscible FI.P(oc): 97°F IP: 10.51 eV Sp.Gr: 0.97 Class IC Flammable Liquid	VP: 12mm FRZ: -62°F UEL: ? LEL: ?	Phosphorus pentoxide, oxidizers	Char(pet)*; Toluene; GC/ECD; OSHA [#97]
ß-Propiolactone C₃H₄O₂ 57-57-8 RQ7350000	BPL; Hydroacrylic acid, ß-lactone; 3-Hydroxy-ß-lactone; 3-Hydroxy-propionic acid; ß-Lactone; 2-Oxetanone; 3-Propiolacetone	NIOSH Ca See Appendix A OSHA [1910.1013] See Appendix B	Ca [N.D.]	Colorless liquid with a slightly sweet odor.	MW: 72.1 BP: 323°F (Decomposes) Sol: 37% FI.P: 165°F IP: ? Sp.Gr: 1.15 Class IIIA Combustible Liquid	VP(77°F): 3 mm FRZ: -28°F UEL: ? LEL: 2.9%	Acetates, halogens, thiocyanates, thiosulfates [Note: May polymerize upon storage.]	None available

Personal protection and sanitation (See Table 3)		Recommendations for respirator selection — maximum concentration for use (MUC) (See Table 4)	Health hazards				
			Route	Symptoms (See Table 5)	First aid (See Table 6)		Target organs (See Table 5)
Skin:	Prevent skin contact	NIOSH	Inh	In animals: irrit eyes,	Eye:	Irr immed	Eyes, skin, resp sys
Eyes:	Prevent eye contact	¥: SCBAF:PD,PP/SAF:PD,PP:ASCBA	Abs	skin, muc memb; [carc]	Skin:	Water flush immed	[in animals:
Wash skin:	When contam/Daily	Escape: GMFOVHiE/SCBAE	Ing		Breath:	Resp support	skin tumors,
Remove:	When wet or contam		Con		Swallow:	Medical attention	leukemia,
Change:	Daily					immed	gliomas]
Provide:	Eyewash, Quick drench						
[Propane sultone]							
Skin:	N.R.	NIOSH	Inh	Irrit eyes, skin, nose,	Eye:	Irr immed	Eyes, skin, resp sys,
Eyes:	Prevent eye contact	5 ppm: CCROV/SA	Ing	throat, resp sys; head, nau,	Skin:	Soap wash	CNS, blood, liver,
Wash skin:	N.R.	12.5 ppm: SA:CF/PAPROV	Con	dizz, cyan;	Breath:	Resp support	kidneys
Remove:	When wet (flamm)	25 ppm: CCRFOV/GMFOV/PAPRTOV/		in animals: liver, kidney	Swallow:	Medical attention	
Change:	N.R.	SCBAF/SAF		damage		immed	
Provide:	Eyewash	§: SCBAF:PD,PP/SAF:PD,PP:ASCBA					
		Escape: GMFOV/SCBAE					
[1-Propanethiol]							
Skin:	Prevent skin contact	TBAL	Inh	Irrit skin, muc memb;	Eye:	Irr immed	Skin, resp sys, CNS,
Eyes:	Prevent eye contact		Abs	CNS depres;	Skin:	Water flush prompt	liver, kidneys
Wash skin:	When contam		Ing	in animals: liver, kidney	Breath:	Resp support	
Remove:	When wet or contam		Con	damage	Swallow:	Medical attention	
Change:	N.R.					immed	
Provide:	Eyewash, Quick drench						
[Propargyl alcohol]							
Skin:	Prevent skin contact	NIOSH	Inh	Skin irrit, blistering,	Eye:	Irr immed	Kidneys, skin,
Eyes:	Prevent eye contact	¥: SCBAF:PD,PP/SAF:PD,PP:ASCBA	Abs	burns; corn opac;	Skin:	Soap wash immed	lungs, eyes
Wash skin:	When contam/Daily	Escape: GMFOV/SCBAE	Ing	frequent urination;	Breath:	Resp support	[in animals:
Remove:	When wet or contam		Con	dysuria; hema; [carc]	Swallow:	Medical attention	tumors of the
Change:	Daily					immed	liver, skin &
Provide:	Eyewash, Quick drench						stomach]
[ß-Propiolactone]							

Chemical name, structure/formula, CAS and RTECS Nos., and DOT ID and guide Nos.	Synonyms, trade names, and conversion factors	Exposure limits (TWA unless noted otherwise)	IDLH	Physical description	Chemical and physical properties		Incompatibilities and reactivities	Measurement method (See Table 1)
					MW, BP, SOL FI.P, IP, Sp, Gr, flammability	VP, FRZ UEL, LEL		
Propionic acid CH_3CH_2COOH 79-09-4 UE5950000 1848 132	Carboxyethane, Ethanecarboxylic acid, Ethylformic acid, Metacetonic acid, Methyl acetic acid, Propanoic acid 1 ppm = 3.03 mg/m³	NIOSH 10 ppm (30 mg/m³) ST 15 ppm (45 mg/m³) OSHA† none	N.D.	Colorless, oily liquid with a pungent, disagreeable, rancid odor. [Note: A solid below 5°F.]	MW: 74.1 BP: 286°F Sol: Miscible FI.P: 126°F IP: 10.24 eV Sp.Gr. 0.99 Class II Combustible Liquid	VP: 3 mm FRZ: 5°F UEL: 12.1% LEL: 2.9%	Alkalis, strong oxidizers (e.g., chromium trioxide) [Note: Corrosive to steel.]	None available
Propionitrile CH_3CH_2CN 107-12-0 UF9625000 2404 131	Cyanoethane, Ethyl cyanide, Propanenitrile, Propionic nitrile, Propiononitrile 1 ppm = 2.25 mg/m³	NIOSH 6 ppm (14 mg/m³) OSHA none	N.D.	Colorless liquid with a pleasant, sweetish, ethereal odor. [Note: Forms cyanide in the body.]	MW: 55.1 BP: 207°F Sol: 11.9% FI.P: 36°F IP: 11.84 eV Sp.Gr. 0.78 Class IB Flammable Liquid	VP: 35 mm FRZ: -133°F UEL: ? LEL: 3.1%	Strong oxidizers & reducing agents, strong acids & bases [Note: Hydrogen cyanide is produced when propionitrile is heated to decomposition.]	Char; Benzene; GC/FID; IV [Adapt #1606]
Propoxur $CH_3NHCOOC_6H_4OCH(CH_3)_2$ 114-26-1 FC3150000	Aprocarb®, Baygon®, o-Isopropoxyphenyl-N-methylcarbamate, N-Methyl-2-isopropoxyphenyl-carbamate	NIOSH 0.5 mg/m³ OSHA† none	N.D.	White to tan, crystalline powder with a faint, characteristic odor. [insecticide]	MW: 209.3 BP: Decomposes Sol: 0.2% FI.P: >300°F IP: ? Sp.Gr. ? Class IIIB Combustible Liquid	VP: 0.000007 mm MLT: 197°F UEL: ? LEL: ?	Strong oxidizers, alkalis [Note: Emits highly toxic methyl isocyanate fumes when heated to decomposition.]	None available
n-Propyl acetate $CH_3COOCH_2CH_2CH_3$ 109-60-4 AJ3675000 1276 129	Propylacetate, n-Propyl ester of acetic acid 1 ppm = 4.18 mg/m³	NIOSH 200 ppm (840 mg/m³) ST 250 ppm (1050 mg/m³) OSHA† 200 ppm (840 mg/m³)	1700 ppm	Colorless liquid with a mild, fruity odor.	MW: 102.2 BP: 215°F Sol: 2% FI.P: 55°F IP: 10.04 eV Sp.Gr. 0.84 Class IB Flammable Liquid	VP: 25 mm FRZ: -134°F UEL: 8% LEL(100°F): 1.7%	Nitrates; strong oxidizers, alkalis & acids	Char; CS_2; GC/FID; IV [#1450, Esters I]

Personal protection and sanitation (See Table 3)		Recommendations for respirator selection — maximum concentration for use (MUC) (See Table 4)	Health hazards				
			Route	Symptoms (See Table 5)	First aid (See Table 6)		Target organs (See Table 5)
Skin: Eyes: Wash skin: Remove: Change: Provide:	Prevent skin contact Prevent eye contact When contam When wet or contam N.R. Eyewash, Quick drench	TBAL	Inh Abs Ing Con	Irrit eyes, skin, nose, throat; blurred vision, corn burns; skin burns; abdom pain, nau, vomit	Eye: Skin: Breath: Swallow:	Irr immed Water flush immed Resp support Medical attention immed	Eyes, skin, resp sys

[Propionic acid]

| Skin:
Eyes:
Wash skin:
Remove:
Change:
Provide: | Prevent skin contact
Prevent eye contact
When contam
When wet or contam
N.R.
Quick drench | NIOSH
60 ppm: CCROV/SA
150 ppm: SA:CF/PAPROV
300 ppm: CCRFOV/GMFOV/PAPRTOV/
      SCBAF/SAF
1000 ppm: SAF:PD,PP
§: SCBAF:PD,PP/SAF:PD,PP:ASCBA
Escape: GMFOV/SCBAE | Inh
Abs
Ing
Con | Irrit eyes, skin, resp sys; nau, vomit; chest pain; weak; stupor, convuls; in animals: liver, kidney damage | Eye:
Skin:
Breath:
Swallow: | Irr immed
Water flush immed
Resp support
Medical attention immed | Eyes, skin, resp sys, CVS, CNS, liver, kidneys |

[Propionitrile]

| Skin:
Eyes:
Wash skin:
Remove:
Change: | Prevent skin contact
Prevent eye contact
Daily
When wet or contam
Daily | TBAL | Inh
Abs
Ing
Con | Miosis, blurred vision; sweat, salv; abdom cramps, nau, diarr, vomit; head, weak, musc twitch | Eye:
Skin:
Breath:
Swallow: | Irr immed
Soap wash immed
Resp support
Medical attention immed | CNS, liver, kidneys, GI tract, blood chol |

[Propoxur]

| Skin:
Eyes:
Wash skin:
Remove:
Change: | Prevent skin contact
Prevent eye contact
When contam
When wet (flamm)
N.R. | NIOSH/OSHA
1700 ppm: SA:CF£/CCRFOV/GMFOV/
      PAPROV£/SCBAF/SAF
§: SCBAF:PD,PP/SAF:PD,PP:ASCBA
Escape: GMFOV/SCBAE | Inh
Ing
Con | In animals: irrit eyes, nose, throat; derm; narco | Eye:
Skin:
Breath:
Swallow: | Irr immed
Water flush prompt
Resp support
Medical attention immed | Eyes, skin, resp sys, CNS |

[n-Propyl acetate]

Chemical name, structure/formula, CAS and RTECS Nos., and DOT ID and guide Nos.	Synonyms, trade names, and conversion factors	Exposure limits (TWA unless noted otherwise)	IDLH	Physical description	Chemical and physical properties		Incompatibilities and reactivities	Measurement method (See Table 1)
					MW, BP, SOL FI.P, IP, Sp, Gr, flammability	VP, FRZ UEL, LEL		
n-Propyl alcohol $CH_3CH_2CH_2OH$ 71-23-8 UH8225000 1274 129	Ethyl carbinol, 1-Propanol, n-Propanol, Propyl alcohol 1 ppm = 2.46 mg/m³	NIOSH/OSHA 200 ppm (500 mg/m³) ST 250 ppm (625 mg/m³) [skin] OSHA† 200 ppm (500 mg/m³)	800 ppm	Colorless liquid with a mild, alcohol-like odor.	MW: 60.1 BP: 207°F Sol: Miscible FI.P: 72°F IP: 10.15 eV Sp.Gr: 0.81 Class IB Flammable Liquid	VP: 15 mm FRZ: -196°F UEL: 13.7% LEL: 2.2%	Strong oxidizers	Char; 2-Propanol/ CS₂; GC/FID; IV [#1401, Alcohols II]
Propylene dichloride $CH_3CHClCH_2Cl$ 78-87-5 TX9625000 1279 130	Dichloro-1,2-propane; 1,2-Dichloropropane 1 ppm = 4.62 mg/m³	NIOSH Ca See Appendix A OSHA† 75 ppm (350 mg/m³)	Ca [400 ppm]	Colorless liquid with a chloroform-like odor. [pesticide]	MW: 113.0 BP: 206°F Sol: 0.3% FI.P: 60°F IP: 10.87 eV Sp.Gr: 1.16 Class IB Flammable Liquid	VP: 40 mm FRZ: -149°F UEL: 14.5% LEL: 3.4%	Strong oxidizers, strong acids, active metals	Char(pet); Acetone/ Cyclo-hexane; GC/ECD; IV [#1013, 1,2-Di-chloro-propane]
Propylene glycol dinitrate $CH_3CNO_2OHCHNO_2OH$ 6423-43-4 TY6300000	PGDN; Propylene glycol-1,2-dinitrate; 1,2-Propylene glycol dinitrate 1 ppm = 6.79 mg/m³	NIOSH 0.05 ppm (0.3 mg/m³) [skin] OSHA† none	N.D.	Colorless liquid with a disagreeable odor. [Note: A solid below 18°F.]	MW: 166.1 BP: ? Sol: 0.1% FI.P: ? IP: ? Sp.Gr(77°F): 1.23 Combustible Liquid	VP(72°F): 0.07 mm FRZ: 18°F UEL: ? LEL: ?	Ammonia compounds, amines, oxidizers, reducing agents, combustible materials [Note: Similar to Ethylene glycol dinitrate in explosion potential.]	None available
Propylene glycol monomethyl ether $CH_3OCH_2CHCH_3$ 107-98-2 UB7700000	Dowtherm® 209, 1-Methoxy-2-hydroxypropane, 1-Methoxy-2-propanol, 2-Methoxy-1-methylethanol, Propylene glycol methyl ether 1 ppm = 3.69 mg/m³	NIOSH 100 ppm (360 mg/m³) ST 150 ppm (540 mg/m³) OSHA† none	N.D.	Clear, colorless liquid with a mild, ethereal odor.	MW: 90.1 BP: 248°F Sol: Miscible FI.P: 97°F IP: ? Sp.Gr: 0.96 Class IC Flammable Liquid	VP(77°F): 12 mm FRZ: -139°F (Sets to glass) UEL(calc): 13.8% LEL(calc.): 1.6%	Oxidizers, strong acids [Note: Hygroscopic (i.e. absorbs moisture from the air). May slowly form reactive peroxides during prolonged storage.]	None available

Personal protection and sanitation (See Table 3)		Recommendations for respirator selection — maximum concentration for use (MUC) (See Table 4)	Health hazards					
			Route	Symptoms (See Table 5)	First aid (See Table 6)		Target organs (See Table 5)	

Personal protection and sanitation	Respirator selection	Route	Symptoms	First aid	Target organs
Skin: Prevent skin contact Eyes: Prevent eye contact Wash skin: When contam Remove: When wet (flamm) Change: N.R.	NIOSH/OSHA 800 ppm: CCROV*/PAPROV*/GMFOV/ SA*/SCBAF §: SCBAF:PD,PP/SAF:PD,PP:ASCBA Escape: GMFOV/SCBAE	Inh Abs Ing Con	Irrit eyes, nose, throat; dry cracking skin; drow, head; ataxia, GI pain; abdom cramps, nau, vomit, vomit, diarr; in animals: narco	Eye: Irr immed Skin: Water flush Breath: Resp support Swallow: Medical attention immed	Eyes, skin, resp sys, GI tract, CNS

[n-Propyl alcohol]

Personal protection and sanitation	Respirator selection	Route	Symptoms	First aid	Target organs
Skin: Prevent skin contact Eyes: Prevent eye contact Wash skin: When contam Remove: When wet (flamm) Change: N.R. Provide: Eyewash, Quick drench	NIOSH ¥: SCBAF:PD,PP/SAF:PD,PP:ASCBA Escape: GMFOV/SCBAE	Inh Abs Ing Con	Irrit eyes, skin, resp sys; drow, li-head; liver, kidney damage; in animals: CNS depres; [carc]	Eye: Irr immed Skin: Soap wash prompt Breath: Resp support Swallow: Medical attention immed	Eyes, skin, resp sys, liver, kidneys, CNS [in animals: liver & mammary gland tumors]

[Propylene dichloride]

Personal protection and sanitation	Respirator selection	Route	Symptoms	First aid	Target organs
Skin: Prevent skin contact Eyes: Prevent eye contact Wash skin: N.R. Remove: N.R. Change: N.R.	TBAL	Inh Abs Ing Con	Irrit eyes; conj; methemo; head, impaired balance, vis dist; in animals: liver, kidney damage	Eye: Irr immed Skin: Soap wash Breath: Resp support Swallow: Medical attention immed	Eyes, CNS, blood, liver, kidneys

[Propylene glycol dinitrate]

Personal protection and sanitation	Respirator selection	Route	Symptoms	First aid	Target organs
Skin: N.R. Eyes: Prevent eye contact Wash skin: N.R. Remove: When wet (flamm) Change: N.R.	TBAL	Inh Ing Con	Irrit eyes, skin, nose, throat; head, nau, li-head, drow, inco; vomit, diarr	Eye: Irr immed Skin: Water wash Breath: Resp support Swallow: Medical attention immed	Eyes, skin, resp sys, CNS

[Propylene glycol monomethyl ether]

Chemical name, structure/formula, CAS and RTECS Nos., and DOT ID and guide Nos.	Synonyms, trade names, and conversion factors	Exposure limits (TWA unless noted otherwise)	IDLH	Physical description	Chemical and physical properties		Incompatibilities and reactivities	Measurement method (See Table 1)
					MW, BP, SOL FI.P, IP, Sp, Gr, flammability	VP, FRZ UEL, LEL		
Propylene imine C_3H_7N 75-55-8 CM8050000 1921 131P (inhibited)	2-Methylaziridine, 2-Methylethyleneimine, Propyleneimine, Propylene imine (inhibited), Propylenimine 1 ppm = 2.34 mg/m³	NIOSH Ca See Appendix A 2 ppm (5 mg/m³) [skin] OSHA 2 ppm (5 mg/m³) [skin]	Ca [100 ppm]	Colorless, oily liquid with an ammonia-like odor.	MW: 57.1 BP: 152°F Sol: Miscible FI.P: 25°F IP: 9.00 eV Sp.Gr: 0.80 Class IB Flammable Liquid	VP: 112mm FRZ: -85°F UEL: ? LEL: ?	Acids, strong oxidizers, water, carbonyl compounds, quinones, sulfonyl halides [Note: Subject to violent polymerization in contact with acids. Hydrolyzes in water to form methylethanolamine.]	None available
Propylene oxide C_3H_6O 75-56-9 TZ2975000 1280 127P	1,2-Epoxy propane; Methyl ethylene oxide; Methyloxirane; Propene oxide; 1,2-Propylene oxide 1 ppm = 2.38 mg/m³	NIOSH Ca See Appendix A OSHA† 100 ppm (240 mg/m³)	Ca [400 ppm]	Colorless liquid with a benzene-like odor. [Note: A gas above 94°F.]	MW: 58.1 BP: 94°F Sol:41% FI.P: -35°F IP: 9.81 eV Sp.Gr: 0.83 Class IA Flammable Liquid	VP: 445 mm FRZ: -170°F UEL: 36% LEL: 2.3%	Anhydrous metal chlorides; iron; strong acids, caustics & peroxides [Note: Polymerization may occur due to high temperatures or contamination with alkalis, aqueous acids, amines & acidic alcohols.]	Char; CS₂; GC/FID; IV [#1612]
n-Propyl nitrate $CH_3CH_2CH_2ONO_2$ 627-13-4 UK0350000 1865 131	Propyl ester of nitric acid 1 ppm = 4.30 mg/m³	NIOSH 25 ppm (105 mg/m³) ST 40 ppm (170 mg/m³) OSHA† 25 ppm (110 mg/m³)	500 ppm	Colorless to straw-colored liquid with an ether-like odor.	MW: 105.1 BP: 231°F Sol: Slight FI.P: 68°F IP: 11.07 eV Sp.Gr: 1.07 Class IB Flammable Liquid	VP: 18 mm FRZ: -148°F UEL: 100% LEL: 2%	Strong oxidizers, combustible materials [Note: Forms explosive mixtures with combustible materials.]	Char; CS₂; GC/FID; II(3) [#S227]
Pyrethrum $C_{20}H_{28}O_3/C_{21}H_{28}O_5$ $C_{21}H_{30}O_3/C_{22}H_{30}O_5$ $C_{21}H_{28}O_3/C_{22}H_{28}O_5$ 8003-34-7 UR4200000	Cinerin I or II, Jasmolin I or II, Pyrethrin I or II, Pyrethrum I or II [Note: Pyrethrum is a variable mixture of Cinerin, Jasmolin, and Pyrethrin.]	NIOSH/OSHA 5 mg/m³	5000 mg/m³	Brown, viscous oil or solid. [insecticide]	MW: 316-374 BP: ? Sol: Insoluble FI.P: 180-190°F IP: ? Sp.Gr: 1 (approx) Class IIIA Combustible Liquid	VP: Low MLT: ? UEL: ? LEL: ?	Strong oxidizers	Filter; CH₃CN; HPLC/UVD; IV [#5008]

Personal protection and sanitation (See Table 3)		Recommendations for respirator selection — maximum concentration for use (MUC) (See Table 4)	Health hazards					
			Route	Symptoms (See Table 5)	First aid (See Table 6)		Target organs (See Table 5)	

Skin:	Prevent skin contact	NIOSH	Inh	Eye, skin burns; [carc]	Eye:	Irr immed	Eyes, skin	
Eyes:	Prevent eye contact	¥: SCBAF:PD,PP/SAF:PD,PP:ASCBA	Abs		Skin:	Water flush immed	[in animals:	
Wash skin:	When contam	Escape: GMFS/SCBAE	Ing		Breath:	Resp support	nasal tumors]	
Remove:	When wet (flamm)		Con		Swallow:	Medical attention		
Change:	N.R.					immed		
Provide:	Eyewash, Quick drench							

[Propylene imine]

Skin:	Prevent skin contact	NIOSH	Inh	Irrit eyes, skin, resp sys;	Eye:	Irr immed	Eyes, skin, resp	
Eyes:	Prevent eye contact	¥: SCBAF:PD,PP/SAF:PD,PP:ASCBA	Ing	blisters, burns; [carc]	Skin:	Water flush immed	sys	
Wash skin:	When contam	Escape: GMFS/SCBAE	Con		Breath:	Resp support	[in animals:	
Remove:	When wet (flamm)				Swallow:	Medical attention	nasal tumors]	
Change:	N.R.					immed		
Provide:	Quick drench							

[Propylene oxide]

Skin:	Prevent skin contact	NIOSH/OSHA	Inh	In animals: irrit eyes,	Eye:	Irr immed	Eyes, skin,	
Eyes:	Prevent eye contact	250 ppm: SA	Ing	skin; methemo, anoxia,	Skin:	Soap wash prompt	blood	
Wash skin:	When contam	500 ppm: SA:CF/SCBAF/SAF	Con	cyan; dysp, weak, dizz,	Breath:	Resp support		
Remove:	When wet (flamm)	§: SCBAF:PD,PP/SAF:PD,PP:ASCBA		head	Swallow:	Medical attention		
Change:	N.R.	Escape: GMFS⁴/SCBAE				immed		

[n-Propyl nitrate]

Skin:	Prevent skin contact	NIOSH/OSHA	Inh	Erythema, derm, papules,	Eye:	Irr immed	Resp sys, skin,	
Eyes:	Prevent eye contact	50 mg/m³: CCROVDMFu*/SA*	Ing	pruritus; rhin; sneez;	Skin:	Soap wash immed	CNS	
Wash skin:	When contam	125 mg/m³: SA:CF*/PAPROVDMFu*	Con	asthma	Breath:	Resp support		
Remove:	When wet or contam	250 mg/m³: CCRFOVHiE/PAPRTOVHiE*/			Swallow:	Medical attention		
Change:	Daily	SCBAF/SAF				immed		
		5000 mg/m³: SAF:PD,PP						
		§: SCBAF:PD,PP/SAF:PD,PP:ASCBA						
		Escape: GMFOVHiE/SCBAE						

[Pyrethrum]

Chemical name, structure/formula, CAS and RTECS Nos., and DOT ID and guide Nos.	Synonyms, trade names, and conversion factors	Exposure limits (TWA unless noted otherwise)	IDLH	Physical description	Chemical and physical properties		Incompatibilities and reactivities	Measurement method (See Table 1)
					MW, BP, SOL FI.P, IP, Sp, Gr, flammability	VP, FRZ UEL, LEL		
Pyridine C_5H_5N 110-86-1 UR8400000 1282 129	Azabenzene; Azine 1 ppm = 3.24 mg/m³	NIOSH/OSHA 5 ppm (15 mg/m³)	1000 ppm	Colorless to yellow liquid with a nauseating, fish-like odor.	MW: 79.1 BP: 240°F Sol: Miscible FI.P: 68°F IP: 9.27 eV Sp.Gr: 0.98 Class IB Flammable Liquid	VP: 16 mm FRZ: -44°F UEL: 12.4% UEL: 1.8%	Strong oxidizers, strong acids	Char; CH₂Cl₂; GC/FID; IV [#1613]
Quinone OC_6H_4O 106-51-4 DK2625000 2587 153	1,4-Benzoquinone; p-Benzoquinone; 1,4-Cyclohexadiene dioxide; p-Quinone 1 ppm = 4.42 mg/m³	NIOSH/OSHA 0.4 mg/m³ (0.1 ppm)	100 mg/m³	Pale-yellow solid with an acrid, chlorine-like odor.	MW: 108.1 BP: Sublimes Sol: Slight FI.P: 100-200°F IP: 9.68 eV Sp.Gr: 1.32 Combustible Solid	VP(77°F): 0.1mm MLT: 240°F UEL: ? LEL: ?	Strong oxidizers	XAD-2; Ethanol/ Hexane; HPLC/UVD; II(4) [#S181]
Resorcinol $C_6H_4(OH)_2$ 108-46-3 VG9625000 2876 153	1,3-Benzenediol; m-Benzenediol; 1,3-Dihydroxybenzene; m-Dihydroxybenzene; 3-Hydroxyphenol; m-Hydroxyphenol 1 ppm = 4.50 mg/m³	NIOSH 10 ppm (45 mg/m³) ST 20 ppm (90 mg/m³) OSHA† none	N.D.	White needles, plates, crystals, flakes, or powder with a faint odor. [Note: Turns pink on exposure to air or light, or contact with iron.]	MW: 110.1 BP: 531°F Sol: 110% FI.P: 261°F IP: 8.63 eV Sp.Gr: 1.27 Class IIIB Combustible Liquid, but may be difficult to ignite.	VP(77°F): 0.0002 mm MLT: 228°F UEL: ? LEL (392°F): 1.4%	Acetanilide, albumin, alkalis, antipyrine, camphor, ferric salts, menthol, spirit nitrous ether, strong oxidizers & bases [Note: Hygroscopic (i.e., absorbs moisture from the air).]	None available
Rhodium (metal fume and insoluble compounds, as Rh) Rh (Metal) 7440-16-6 (Metal) VI9069000 (Metal)	Rhodium metal: Elemental rhodium Synonyms of other insoluble rhodium compounds vary depending upon the specific compound.	NIOSH/OSHA 0.1 mg/m³	100 mg/m³ (as Rh)	Metal: White, hard, ductile, malleable solid with a bluish-gray luster.	MW: 102.9 BP: 6741°F Sol: Insoluble FI.P: NA IP: NA Sp.Gr: 12.41 (Metal) Metal: Noncombustible Solid in bulk form, but flammable as dust or powder.	VP: 0 mm (approx) MLT: 3571°F UEL: NA LEL: NA	Chlorine trifluoride, Oxygen difluoride	Filter; Acid; AAS; II(3) [#S188]

	Personal protection and sanitation (See Table 3)	Recommendations for respirator selection — maximum concentration for use (MUC) (See Table 4)	Health hazards				
			Route	Symptoms (See Table 5)	First aid (See Table 6)		Target organs (See Table 5)

Personal protection and sanitation (See Table 3)		Recommendations for respirator selection — maximum concentration for use (MUC) (See Table 4)	Route	Symptoms (See Table 5)	First aid (See Table 6)		Target organs (See Table 5)
Skin:	Prevent skin contact	NIOSH/OSHA	Inh	Irrit eyes; head, ner, dizz,	Eye:	Irr immed	Eyes, skin, CNS,
Eyes:	Prevent eye contact	125 ppm: SA:CF£/PAPROV£	Abs	insom; nau, anor; derm;	Skin:	Water flush immed	liver, kidneys,
Wash skin:	When contam	250 ppm: CCRFOV/GMFOV/PAPRTOV£/	Con	liver, kidney damage	Breath:	Resp support	GI tract
Remove:	When wet (flamm)	SCBAF/SAF			Swallow:	Medical attention	
Change:	N.R.	1000 ppm: SAF:PD,PP				immed	
Provide:	Eyewash, Quick drench	§: SCBAF:PD,PP/SAF:PD,PP:ASCBA					
		Escape: GMFOV/SCBAE					
[Pyridine]							
Skin:	Prevent skin contact	NIOSH/OSHA	Inh	Eye irrit, conj; kera;	Eye:	Irr immed	Eyes, skin
Eyes:	Prevent eye contact	10 mg/m³: SA:CF£	Ing	skin irrit	Skin:	Soap wash immed	
Wash skin:	When contam	20 mg/m³: SCBAF/SAF	Con		Breath:	Resp support	
Remove:	When wet or contam	100 mg/m³: SAF:PD,PP			Swallow:	Medical attention	
Change:	Daily	§: SCBAF:PD,PP/SAF:PD,PP:ASCBA				immed	
Provide:	Eyewash, Quick drench	Escape: GMFOVHiE/SCBAE					
[Quinone]							
Skin:	Prevent skin contact	TBAL	Inh	Irrit eyes, skin, nose,	Eye:	Irr immed	Eyes, skin, resp sys,
Eyes:	Prevent eye contact		Ing	throat, upper resp sys;	Skin:	Water wash immed	CVS, CNS, blood,
Wash skin:	When contam		Con	methemo, cyan, convuls;	Breath:	Resp support	spleen, liver,
Remove:	When wet or contam			restless, bluish skin,	Swallow:	Medical attention	kidneys
Change:	Daily			incr heart rate, dysp;		immed	
Provide:	Eyewash			dizz, drow, hypothermia,			
				hemog; spleen, kidney,			
				liver changes; derm			
[Resorcinol]							
Skin:	N.R.	NIOSH/OSHA	Inh	Possible resp sens	Breath:	Resp support	Resp sys
Eyes:	N.R.	0.5 mg/m³: DM^			Swallow:	Medical attention	
Wash skin:	N.R.	1 mg/m³: DMXSQ^/SA				immed	
Remove:	N.R.	2.5 mg/m³: SA:CF/PAPRDMFu					
Change:	N.R.	5 mg/m³: HiEF/SAT:CF/PAPRTHiE/					
		SCBAF/SAF					
		100 mg/m³: SA:PD,PP					
		§: SCBAF:PD,PP/SAF:PD,PP:ASCBA					
[Rhodium (metal fume and insoluble compounds, as Rh)]		Escape: HiEF/SCBAE					

Chemical name, structure/formula, CAS and RTECS Nos., and DOT ID and guide Nos.	Synonyms, trade names, and conversion factors	Exposure limits (TWA unless noted otherwise)	IDLH	Physical description	Chemical and physical properties		Incompatibilities and reactivities	Measurement method (See Table 1)
					MW, BP, SOL Fl.P, IP, Sp, Gr, flammability	VP, FRZ UEL, LEL		
Rhodium (soluble compounds, as Rh)	Synonyms vary depending upon the specific soluble rhodium compound.	NIOSH/OSHA 0.001 mg/m³	2 mg/m³ (as Rh)	Appearance and odor vary depending upon the specific soluble rhodium compound.	Properties vary depending upon the specific soluble rhodium compound.		Varies	Filter; Acid; GFAAS; II(3) [#S189]
Ronnel $(CH_3O)_2P(S)OC_6H_2Cl_3$ 299-84-3 TG0525000	O,O-Dimethyl O-(2,4,5-tri-chlorophenyl) phosphoro-thioate; Fenchlorophos	NIOSH 10 mg/m³ OSHA† 15 mg/m³	300 mg/m³	White to light tan, crystalline solid. [insecticide] [Note: A liquid above 106°F.]	MW: 321.6 BP: Decomposes Sol(77°F): 0.004% Fl.P: NA IP: ? Sp.Gr: 1.49 Noncombustible Solid	VP(77°F): 0.0008 mm MLT: 106°F UEL: NA LEL: NA	Strong oxidizers	OVS-2; Toluene/ Acetone; GC/FPD; IV [#5600, Organo-phosphorus Pesticides]
Rosin core solder, pyrolysis products (as formaldehyde)	Rosin flux pyrolysis products, Rosin core soldering flux pyrolysis products	NIOSH° 0.1 mg/m³ [°Note: "Ca" in the presence of formaldehyde, acetaldehyde, or malonaldehyde. See Appendices A & C (Aldehydes).] OSHA† none	N.D.	Pyrolysis products of rosin core solder include acetone, aliphatic aldehydes, methyl alcohol, methane, ethane, various abietic acids (the major components of rosin), CO & CO_2.	Properties vary depending upon the specific rosin core solder being used.		Varies	Filter/ Imp(2); none; Vis; IV [#3500, Formalde-hyde] [Also #2541]
Rotenone $C_{23}H_{22}O_6$ 83-79-4 DJ2800000	1,2,12,12a-Tetrahydro-8,9-dimethoxy-2-(1-methyl-ethenyl)-[1]benzopyrano [3,4-b]furo[2,3-h][1] benzopyran-6(6aH)-one	NIOSH/OSHA 5 mg/m³	2500 mg/m³	Colorless to red, odorless, crystalline solid. [insecticide]	MW: 394.4 BP: Decomposes Sol: Insoluble Fl.P: ? IP: ? Sp.Gr: 1.27 Combustible Solid	VP: <0.00004 mm MLT: 330°F UEL: ? LEL: ?	Strong oxidizers, alkalis	Filter; CH_3CN; HPLC/UVD; IV [#5007]

Personal protection and sanitation (See Table 3)	Recommendations for respirator selection — maximum concentration for use (MUC) (See Table 4)	Health hazards			
		Route	Symptoms (See Table 5)	First aid (See Table 6)	Target organs (See Table 5)
Skin: Prevent skin contact Eyes: Prevent eye contact Wash skin: When contam Remove: When wet or contam Change: N.R.	NIOSH/OSHA 0.010 mg/m³: HiE*/SA* 0.025 mg/m³: SA:CF*/PAPRHiE* 0.050 mg/m³: HiEF/PAPRTHiE*/ SCBAF/SAF 2 mg/m³: SAF:PD,PP §: SCBAF:PD,PP/SAF:PD,PP:ASCBA Escape: HiEF/SCBAE	Inh Ing Con	In animals: irrit eyes; CNS damage	Eye: Irr immed Skin: Water flush Breath: Resp support Swallow: Medical attention immed	Eyes, CNS
[Rhodium (soluble compounds, as Rh)]					
Skin: Prevent skin contact Eyes: Prevent eye contact Wash skin: When contam Remove: When wet or contam Change: Daily	NIOSH 100 mg/m³: CCROVDMFu/SA 250 mg/m³: SA:CF/PAPROVDMFu 300 mg/m³: CCRFOVHiE/GMFOVHiE/ PAPRTOVHiE*/SCBAF/SAF §: SCBAF:PD,PP/SAF:PD,PP:ASCBA Escape: GMFOVHiE/SCBAE	Inh Ing Con	In animals: irrit eyes; chol inhibition; liver, kidney damage	Eye: Irr immed Skin: Soap wash prompt Breath: Resp support Swallow: Medical attention immed	Eyes, liver, kidneys, blood plasma
[Ronnel]					
Skin: N.R. Eyes: N.R. Wash skin: N.R. Remove: N.R. Change: N.R.	TBAL In presence of Formaldehyde, Acetaldehyde, or Malonaldehyde: NIOSH ¥: SCBAF:PD,PP/SAF:PD,PP:ASCBA Escape: GMFOVHiE/SCBAE	Inh	Irrit eyes, nose, throat, upper resp sys	Eye: Irr immed Breath: Resp support	Eyes, resp sys [nasal cancer; thyroid gland tumors in animals (in presence of Formaldehyde, Acetaldehyde, or Malonaldehyde)]
[Rosin core solder, pyrolysis products (as formaldehyde)]					
Skin: Prevent skin contact Eyes: Prevent eye contact Wash skin: When contam Remove: When wet or contam Change: Daily	NIOSH/OSHA 50 mg/m³: CCROVDMFu/SA 125 mg/m³: SA:CF/PAPROVDMFu 250 mg/m³: CCRFOVHiE/GMFOVHiE/ PAPRTOVHiE/SAT:CF/ SCBAF/SAF 2500 mg/m³: SA:PD,PP §: SCBAF:PD,PP/SAF:PD,PP:ASCBA Escape: GMFOVHiE/SCBAE	Inh Ing Con	Irrit eyes, skin, resp sys; numb muc memb; nau, vomit, abdom pain; musc tremor, inco, clonic convuls, stupor	Eye: Irr immed Skin: Soap wash prompt Breath: Resp support Swallow: Medical attention immed	Eyes, skin, resp sys, CNS
[Rotenone]					

Chemical name, structure/formula, CAS and RTECS Nos., and DOT ID and guide Nos.	Synonyms, trade names, and conversion factors	Exposure limits (TWA unless noted otherwise)	IDLH	Physical description	Chemical and physical properties		Incompatibilities and reactivities	Measurement method (See Table 1)
					MW, BP, SOL Fl.P, IP, Sp, Gr, flammability	VP, FRZ UEL, LEL		
Rouge Fe_2O_3 1309-37-1 NO7400000	Iron(III)oxide, Iron oxide red, Red iron oxide, Red oxide	NIOSH See Appendix D OSHA† 15 mg/m³ (total) 5 mg/m³ (resp)	N.D.	A fine, red powder of ferric oxide. [Note: Usually used in cake form or impregnated in paper or cloth.]	MW: 159.7 BP: ? Sol: Insoluble Fl.P: NA IP: NA Sp.Gr: 5.24 Noncombustible Solid	VP: 0 mm (approx) MLT: 2849°F UEL: NA LEL: NA	Calcium hypochlorite, carbon monoxide, hydrogen peroxide	Filter; none; Grav; IV [Particulates NOR: #0500 (total), #0600 (resp)]
Selenium Se 7782-49-2 VS7700000 2658 152 (powder)	Elemental selenium, Selenium alloy	NIOSH*/OSHA* 0.2 mg/m³ [*Note: The REL and PEL also apply to other selenium compounds (as Se) except Selenium hexafluoride.]	1 mg/m³ (as Se)	Amorphous or crystalline, red to gray solid. [Note: Occurs as an impurity in most sulfide ores.]	MW: 79.0 BP: 1265°F Sol: Insoluble Fl.P: NA IP: NA Sp.Gr: 4.28 Combustible Solid	VP: 0 mm (approx) MLT: 392°F UEL: NA LEL: NA	Acids, strong oxidizers, chromium trioxide, potassium bromate, cadmium	Filter; Acid; ICP; IV [#7300, Elements] [Also II(7) #S190]
Selenium hexafluoride SeF_6 7783-79-1 VS9450000 2194 125	Selenium fluoride 1 ppm = 7.89 mg/m³	NIOSH 0.05 ppm OSHA 0.05 ppm (0.4 mg/m³)	2 ppm	Colorless gas.	MW: 193.0 BP: -30°F Sol: Insoluble Fl.P: NA IP: ? RGasD: 6.66 Nonflammable Gas	VP: >1 atm FRZ: -59°F UEL: NA LEL: NA	Water [Note: Hydrolyzes very slowly in cold water.]	None available
Silica, amorphous SiO_2 7631-86-9 VV7310000	Diatomaceous earth, Diatomaceous silica, Diatomite, Precipitated amorphous silica, Silica gel, Silicon dioxide (amorphous)	NIOSH 6 mg/m³ OSHA† See Appendix C (Mineral Dusts)	3000 mg/m³	Transparent to gray, odorless powder. [Note: Amorphous silica is the non-crystalline form of SiO_2.]	MW: 60.1 BP: 4046°F Sol: Insoluble Fl.P: NA IP: NA Sp.Gr: 2.20 Noncombustible Solid	VP: 0 mm (approx) MLT: 3110°F UEL: NA LEL: NA	Fluorine, oxygen difluoride, chlorine trifluoride	Filter; LTA; XRD; IV [#7501]

Personal protection and sanitation (See Table 3)		Recommendations for respirator selection — maximum concentration for use (MUC) (See Table 4)	Health hazards			
			Route	Symptoms (See Table 5)	First aid (See Table 6)	Target organs (See Table 5)
Skin:	N.R.	TBAL	Inh	Irrit eyes, skin, resp sys	Eye: Irr immed	Eyes, skin, resp sys
Eyes:	N.R.		Con		Breath: Fresh air	
Wash skin:	N.R.					
Remove:	N.R.					
Change:	N.R.					
[Rouge]						
Skin:	Prevent skin contact	NIOSH/OSHA	Inh	Irrit eyes, skin, nose,	Eye: Irr immed	Eyes, skin, resp sys,
Eyes:	N.R.	1 mg/m³: DM^*/DMFu*/HiEF/PAPRDM^*/	Ing	throat; vis dist; head;	Skin: Soap wash immed	liver, kidneys,
Wash skin:	When contam	PAPRDMFu*/SA*/SCBAF	Con	chills, fever; dysp, bron;	Breath: Resp support	blood, spleen
Remove:	When wet or contam	§: SCBAF:PD,PP/SAF:PD,PP:ASCBA		metallic taste, garlic	Swallow: Medical attention	
Change:	N.R.	Escape: HiEF/SCBAE		breath, GI dist; derm; eye,	immed	
Provide:	Quick drench			skin burns;		
				in animals: anemia; liver		
				nec, cirr; kidney, spleen		
				damage		
[Selenium]						
Skin:	N.R.	NIOSH/OSHA	Inh	In animals: pulm irrit,	Breath: Resp support	Resp sys
Eyes:	N.R.	0.5 ppm: SA		edema		
Wash skin:	N.R.	1.25 ppm: SA:CF				
Remove:	N.R.	2 ppm: SAT:CF/SCBAF/SAF				
Change:	N.R.	§: SCBAF:PD,PP/SAF:PD,PP:ASCBA				
		Escape: GMFS/SCBAE				
[Selenium hexafluoride]						
Skin:	N.R.	NIOSH	Inh	Irrit eyes, pneumoconiosis	Eye: Irr immed	Eyes, resp sys
Eyes:	N.R.	30 mg/m³: DM	Con		Breath: Fresh air	
Wash skin:	N.R.	60 mg/m³: DMXSQ/SA				
Remove:	N.R.	150 mg/m³: SA:CF/PAPRDM				
Change:	N.R.	300 mg/m³: HiEF/SAT:CF/PAPRTHiE/				
		SCBAF/SAF				
		3000 mg/m³: SA:PD,PP				
		§: SCBAF:PD,PP/SAF:PD,PP:ASCBA				
		Escape: HiEF/SCBAE				
[Silica, amorphous]						

Chemical name, structure/formula, CAS and RTECS Nos., and DOT ID and guide Nos.	Synonyms, trade names, and conversion factors	Exposure limits (TWA unless noted otherwise)	IDLH	Physical description	Chemical and physical properties		Incompatibilities and reactivities	Measurement method (See Table 1)
					MW, BP, SOL Fl.P, IP, Sp, Gr, flammability	VP, FRZ UEL, LEL		
Silica, crystalline (as respirable dust) SiO$_2$ 14808-60-7 VV7330000	Cristobalite, Quartz, Tridymite, Tripoli	NIOSH Ca See Appendix A 0.05 mg/m^3 OSHA† See Appendix C (Mineral Dusts)	Ca [*] *IDLHs: 50 mg/m^3 (quartz, tripoli) 25 mg/m^3 (cristobalite, tridymite)	Colorless, odorless solid. [Note: A component of many mineral dusts.]	MW: 60.1 BP: 4046°F Sol: Insoluble Fl.P: NA IP: NA Sp.Gr: 2.66 Noncombustible Solid	VP: 0 mm (approx) MLT: 3110°F UEL: NA LEL: NA	Powerful oxidizers: fluorine, chlorine trifluoride, manganese trioxide, oxygen difluoride, hydrogen peroxide, etc.; acetylene; ammonia	Filter; LTA; XRD; IV [#7500] [Also #7601, #7602]
Silicon Si 7440-21-3 VW0400000 1346 170 (amorphous powder)	Elemental silicon [Note: Does not occur free in nature, but is found in silicon dioxide (silica) & in various silicates.]	NIOSH 10 mg/m^3 (total) 5 mg/m^3 (resp) OSHA† 15 mg/m^3 (total) 5 mg/m^3 (resp)	N.D.	Black to gray, lustrous, needle-like crystals. [Note: The amorphous form is a dark-brown powder.]	MW: 28.1 BP: 4271°F Sol: Insoluble Fl.P: NA IP: NA Sp.Gr: 2.33 Combustible Solid in powder form.	VP: 0 mm (approx) MLT: 2570°F UEL: NA LEL: NA MEC: 160 g/m^3	Chlorine, fluorine, oxidizers, calcium, cesium carbide, alkaline carbonates	Filter; none; Grav; IV [Particulates NOR: #0500 (total) #0600 (resp)]
Silicon carbide SiC 409-21-2 VW0450000	Carbon silicide, Carborundum®, Silicon monocarbide	NIOSH 10 mg/m^3 (total) 5 mg/m^3 (resp) OSHA† 15 mg/m^3 (total) 5 mg/m^3 (resp)	N.D.	Yellow to green to bluish-black, iridescent crystals.	MW: 40.1 BP: Sublimes Sol: Insoluble Fl.P: NA IP: 9.30 eV Sp.Gr: 3.23 Noncombustible Solid	VP: 0 mm (approx) MLT: 4892°F (Sublimes) UEL: NA LEL: NA	None reported [Note: Sublimes with decomposition at 4892°F.]	Filter; none; Grav; IV [Particulates NOR: #0500 (total) #0600 (resp)]
Silicon tetrahydride SiH$_4$ 7803-62-5 VV1400000 2203 116	Monosilane, Silane, Silicane 1 ppm = 1.31 mg/m^3	NIOSH 5 ppm (7 mg/m^3) OSHA† none	N.D.	Colorless gas with a repulsive odor.	MW: 32.1 BP: -169°F Sol: Decomposes Fl.P: NA (Gas) IP: ? RGasD: 1.11 Flammable Gas (may ignite SPONTANEOUSLY in air).	VP: >1 atm FRZ: -301°F UEL: ? LEL: ?	Halogens (bromine, chlorine, carbonyl chloride, antimony pentachloride, tin(IV) chloride), water	None available

Personal protection and sanitation (See Table 3)		Recommendations for respirator selection — maximum concentration for use (MUC) (See Table 4)	Health hazards				
			Route	Symptoms (See Table 5)	First aid (See Table 6)		Target organs (See Table 5)
Skin:	N.R.	NIOSH	Inh	Cough, dysp, wheez; decr	Eye:	Irr immed	Eyes, resp sys
Eyes:	N.R.	0.5 mg/m³: HiE	Con	pulm func, progressive	Breath:	Fresh air	[in animals:
Wash skin:	N.R.	1.25 mg/m³: PAPRHiE/SA:CF		resp symptoms (silicosis);			lung cancer]
Remove:	N.R.	2.5 mg/m³: HiEF/PAPRTHiE			irrit eyes; [carc]		
Change:	N.R.	25 mg/m³: SA:PD,PP					
		§: SCBAF:PD,PP/SAF:PD,PP:ASCBA					
		Escape: HiEF/SCBAE					
[Silica, crystalline (as respirable dust)]							
Skin:	N.R.	TBAL	Inh	Irrit eyes, skin, upper	Eye:	Irr immed	Eyes, skin, resp sys
Eyes:	Prevent eye contact		Ing	resp sys; cough	Breath:	Fresh air	
Wash skin:	N.R.		Con		Swallow:	Medical attention	
Remove:	N.R.					immed	
Change:	N.R.						
[Silicon]							
Skin:	N.R.	TBAL	Inh	Irrit eyes, skin, upper	Eye:	Irr immed	Eyes, skin, resp sys
Eyes:	N.R.		Ing	resp sys; cough	Breath:	Fresh air	
Wash skin:	N.R.		Con		Swallow:	Medical attention	
Remove:	N.R.					immed	
Change:	N.R.						
[Silicon carbide]							
Skin:	N.R.	TBAL	Inh	Irrit eyes, skin, muc memb;	Breath:	Resp support	Eyes, skin, resp sys,
Eyes:	N.R.			nau, head			CNS
Wash skin:	N.R.						
Remove:	N.R.						
Change:	N.R.						
[Silicon tetrahydride]							

Chemical name, structure/formula, CAS and RTECS Nos., and DOT ID and guide Nos.	Synonyms, trade names, and conversion factors	Exposure limits (TWA unless noted otherwise)	IDLH	Physical description	Chemical and physical properties		Incompatibilities and reactivities	Measurement method (See Table 1)
					MW, BP, SOL Fl.P, IP, Sp, Gr, flammability	VP, FRZ UEL, LEL		
Silver (metal dust and soluble compounds, as Ag) Ag (Metal) 7440-22-4 (Metal) VW3500000 (Metal)	Silver metal: Argentum Synonyms of soluble silver compounds such as Silver nitrate (AgNO$_3$) vary depending upon the specific compound.	NIOSH/OSHA 0.01 mg/m^3	10 mg/m^3 (as Ag)	Metal: White, lustrous solid.	MW: 107.9￼ BP: 3632°F Sol: Insoluble Fl.P: NA IP: NA Sp.Gr: 10.49 (Metal) Metal: Noncombustible Solid, but flammable in form of dust or powder.	VP: 0 mm (approx) MLT: 1761°F UEL: NA LEL: NA	Acetylene, ammonia, hydrogen peroxide, bromoazide, chlorine trifluoride, ethyleneimine, oxalic acid, tartaric acid	Filter; Acid; ICP; IV [#7300, Elements]
Soapstone (containing less than 1% quartz) 3MgO-4SiO$_2$-H$_2$O VV8780000	Massive talc, Soapstone silicate, Steatite	NIOSH 6 mg/m^3 (total) 3 mg/m^3 (resp) OSHA† 20 mppcf	3000 mg/m^3	Odorless, white-gray powder.	MW: 379.3 BP: ? Sol: Insoluble Fl.P: NA IP: NA Sp.Gr: 2.7-2.8 Noncombustible Solid	VP: 0 mm (approx) MLT: ? UEL: NA LEL: NA	None reported	Filter; none; Grav; IV [#0500, Particulates NOR (total)]
Sodium aluminum fluoride (as F) Na$_3$AlF$_6$ 15096-52-3 WA9625000	Cryocide, Cryodust, Cryolite, Sodium hexafluoroaluminate	NIOSH*/OSHA* 2.5 mg/m^3 [*Note: The REL and PEL also apply to other inorganic, solid fluorides (as F).]	250 mg/m^3 (as F)	Colorless to dark, odorless solid. [pesticide] [Note: Loses color on heating.]	MW: 209.9 BP: Decomposes Sol: 0.04% Fl.P: NA IP: NA Sp.Gr: 2.90 Noncombustible Solid	VP: 0 mm (approx) MLT: 1832°F UEL: NA LEL: NA	Strong oxidizers	Pad*/pre-Filter; NaOH; ISE; IV [#7902, Fluorides]
Sodium azide NaN$_3$ 26628-22-8 VY8050000 1687 153	Azide, Azium, Sodium salt of hydrazoic acid	NIOSH C 0.1 ppm (as HN$_3$) [skin] C 0.3 mg/m^3 (as NaN$_3$) [skin] OSHA† none	N.D.	Colorless to white, odorless, crystalline solid. [pesticide] [Note: Forms hydrazoic acid (HN$_3$) in water.]	MW: 65.0 BP: Decomposes Sol(63°F): 42% Fl.P: ? IP: 11.70 eV Sp.Gr: 1.85 Combustible Solid (if heated above 572°F).	VP: ? MLT: 527°F (Decomposes) UEL: ? LEL: ?	Acids, metals, water	Filter/ Si gel* NaHCO$_3$/ Na$_2$CO$_3$; IC/UV-vis; OSHA [#ID121]

Personal protection and sanitation (See Table 3)		Recommendations for respirator selection — maximum concentration for use (MUC) (See Table 4)	Health hazards					
			Route	Symptoms (See Table 5)	First aid (See Table 6)		Target organs (See Table 5)
Skin:	Prevent skin contact	NIOSH/OSHA	Inh	Blue-gray eyes, nasal	Eye:	Irr immed	Nasal septum,
Eyes:	Prevent eye contact	0.25 mg/m³: SA:CF^E/PAPRHiE^E	Ing	septum, throat, skin;	Skin:	Water flush	skin, eyes
Wash skin:	When contam	0.5 mg/m³: HiEF/SCBAF/SAF	Con	irrit, ulceration skin;	Breath:	Resp support	
Remove:	When wet or contam (AgNO₃)	10 mg/m³: SAF:PD,PP		GI dist	Swallow:	Medical attention	
Change:	Daily	§: SCBAF:PD,PP/SAF:PD,PP:ASCBA				immed	
Provide:	Eyewash	Escape: HiEF/SCBAE					

[Silver (metal dust and soluble compounds, as Ag)]

Skin:	N.R.	NIOSH	Inh	Pneumoconiosis: cough,	Eye:	Irr immed	Resp sys, CVS
Eyes:	N.R.	30 mg/m³: DM	Con	dysp; digital clubbing;	Breath:	Resp support	
Wash skin:	N.R.	60 mg/m³: DMXSQ/SA		cyan; basal crackles,			
Remove:	N.R.	150 mg/m³: PAPRDM		cor pulmonale			
Change:	N.R.	300 mg/m³: HiEF/SAT:CF*/PAPRTHiE*/					
		SCBAF/SAF					
		3000 mg/m³: SAF:PD,PP					
		§: SCBAF:PD,PP/SAF:PD,PP:ASCBA					
		Escape: HiEF/SCBAE					

281

[Soapstone (containing less than 1% quartz)]

Skin:	Prevent skin contact	NIOSH/OSHA	Inh	Irrit eyes, resp sys;	Eye:	Irr immed	Eyes, skin, resp sys,
Eyes:	Prevent eye contact	12.5 mg/m³: DM	Ing	nau, abdom pain, diarr;	Skin:	Soap wash prompt	CNS, skeleton,
Wash skin:	When contam	25 mg/m³: DMXSQ*/SA*	Con	salv, thirst, sweat;	Breath:	Fresh air	kidneys
Remove:	When wet or contam	62.5 mg/m³: SA:CF*/PAPRDM*+		stiff spine; derm;	Swallow:	Medical attention	
Change:	Daily	125 mg/m³: HiEF+/SCBAF/SAF		calcification of		immed	
		250 mg/m³: SAF:PD,PP		ligaments of ribs, pelvis			
		§: SCBAF:PD,PP/SAF:PD,PP:ASCBA					
		Escape: HiEF+/SCBAE					

[Sodium aluminum fluoride (as F)] · +Note: May need acid gas sorbent

Skin:	Prevent skin contact	TBAL	Inh	Irrit eyes, skin; head,	Eye:	Irr immed	Eyes, skin, CNS,
Eyes:	Prevent eye contact		Abs	dizz, weak, blurred vision;	Skin:	Water flush immed	CVS, kidneys
Wash skin:	When contam		Ing	dysp; low BP, bradycardia;	Breath:	Resp support	
Remove:	When wet or contam		Con	kidney changes	Swallow:	Medical attention	
Change:	Daily					immed	
Provide:	Eyewash, Quick drench						

[Sodium azide]

Chemical name, structure/formula, CAS and RTECS Nos., and DOT ID and guide Nos.	Synonyms, trade names, and conversion factors	Exposure limits (TWA unless noted otherwise)	IDLH	Physical description	Chemical and physical properties		Incompatibilities and reactivities	Measurement method (See Table 1)
					MW, BP, SOL FI.P, IP, Sp, Gr, flammability	VP, FRZ UEL, LEL		
Sodium bisulfite NaHSO₃ 7631-90-5 VZ2000000 2693 154 (solution)	Monosodium salt of sulfurous acid, Sodium acid bisulfite, Sodium bisulphite, Sodium hydrogen sulfite	NIOSH 5 mg/m³ OSHA† none	N.D.	White crystals or powder with a slight odor of sulfur dioxide.	MW: 104.1 BP: Decomposes Sol: 29% FI.P: NA IP: NA Sp.Gr: 1.48 Noncombustible Solid	VP: ? MLT: Decomposes UEL: NA LEL: NA	Heat (decomposes) [Note: Slowly oxidized to the sulfate on exposure to air.]	Filter; none; Grav; IV [#0500, Particulates NOR (total)]
Sodium cyanide (as CN) NaCN 143-33-9 VZ7530000 1689 157	Sodium salt of hydrocyanic acid	NIOSH* C 5 mg/m³ (4.7 ppm) [10-min] OSHA* 5 mg/m³ [*Note: The REL and PEL also apply to other cyanides (as CN) except Hydrogen cyanide.]	25 mg/m³ (as CN)	White, granular or crystalline solid with a faint, almond-like odor.	MW: 49.0 BP: 2725°F Sol(77°F): 58% FI.P: NA IP: NA Sp.Gr: 1.60 Noncombustible Solid, but contact with acids releases highly flammable hydrogen cyanide.	VP: 0 mm (approx) MLT: 1047°F UEL: NA LEL: NA	Strong oxidizers (such as acids, acid salts, chlorates & nitrates) [Note: Absorbs moisture from the air forming a syrup.]	Filter/Bub; KOH; ISE; IV [#7904, Cyanides] [Also #6010, Hydrogen Cyanide.]
Sodium fluoride (as F) NaF 7681-49-4 WB0350000 1690 154	Floridine, Sodium monofluoride	NIOSH/OSHA 2.5 mg/m³ [*Note: The REL and PEL also apply to other inorganic, solid fluorides (as F).]	250 mg/m³ (as F)	Odorless, white powder or colorless crystals. [pesticide] [Note: Pesticide grade is often dyed blue.]	MW: 42.0 BP: 3099°F Sol: 4% FI.P: NA IP: NA Sp.Gr: 2.78 Noncombustible Solid	VP: 0 mm (approx) MLT: 1819°F UEL: NA LEL: NA	Strong oxidizers	Pad*/pre-Filter; NaOH; ISE; IV [#7902, Fluorides] [Also #7906]
Sodium fluoroacetate FCH₂COONa 62-74-8 AH9100000 2629 151	SFA, Sodium monofluoroacetate	NIOSH 0.05 mg/m³ ST 0.15 mg/m³ [skin] OSHA† 0.05 mg/m³ [skin]	2.5 mg/m³	Fluffy, colorless to white (sometimes dyed black), odorless powder. [rodenticide] [Note: A liquid above 95°F.]	MW: 100.0 BP: Decomposes Sol: Miscible FI.P: NA IP: ? Sp.Gr: ? Noncombustible Solid	VP: Low MLT: 392°F UEL: NA LEL: NA	None reported	Filter; Water; IC; II(5) [#S301]

Personal protection and sanitation (See Table 3)		Recommendations for respirator selection — maximum concentration for use (MUC) (See Table 4)	Health hazards				
			Route	Symptoms (See Table 5)	First aid (See Table 6)		Target organs (See Table 5)

Skin:	N.R.	TBAL	Inh	Irrit eyes, skin, muc memb	Eye:	Irr immed	Eyes, skin, resp sys
Eyes:	N.R.		Ing		Breath:	Fresh air	
Wash skin:	N.R.		Con		Swallow:	Medical attention immed	
Remove:	N.R.						
Change:	N.R.						

[Sodium bisulfite]

Skin:	Prevent skin contact	NIOSH/OSHA	Inh	Irrit eyes, skin; asphy;	Eye:	Irr immed	Eyes, skin, CVS, CNS,
Eyes:	Prevent eye contact	25 mg/m³: SA/SCBAF	Abs	weak, head, conf; nau;	Skin:	Soap wash immed	thyroid, blood
Wash skin:	When contam	§: SCBAF:PD,PP/SAF:PD,PP:ASCBA	Ing	vomit; incr resp rate;	Breath:	Resp support	
Remove:	When wet or contam	Escape: GMFSHiE/SCBAE	Con	slow gasping respiration;	Swallow:	Medical attention	
Change:	Daily			thyroid, blood changes		immed	
Provide:	Eyewash, Quick drench						

[Sodium cyanide (as CN)]

Skin:	Prevent skin contact	NIOSH/OSHA	Inh	Irrit eyes, resp sys; nau,	Eye:	Irr immed	Eyes, skin, resp sys,
Eyes:	Prevent eye contact	12.5 mg/m³: DM	Ing	abdom pain, diarr; salv,	Skin:	Soap wash prompt	CNS, skeleton,
Wash skin:	When contam	25 mg/m³: DMXSQ*/SA*	Con	thirst, sweat; stiff spine;	Breath:	Fresh air	kidneys
Remove:	When wet or contam	62.5 mg/m³: SA:CF*/PAPRDM*+		derm; calcification of	Swallow:	Medical attention	
Change:	Daily	125 mg/m³: HiEF+/SCBAF/SAF		ligaments of ribs, pelvis		immed	
		250 mg/m³: SAF:PD,PP					
		§: SCBAF:PD,PP/SAF:PD,PP:ASCBA					
		Escape: HiEF+/SCBAE					

[Sodium fluoride (as F)] +Note: May need acid gas sorbent

Skin:	Prevent skin contact	NIOSH/OSHA	Inh	Vomit; appre, auditory	Eye:	Irr immed	Resp sys, CVS, liver,
Eyes:	Prevent eye contact	0.25 mg/m³: DM	Abs	halu; facial pares; twitch	Skin:	Water flush immed	kidneys, CNS
Wash skin:	When contam	0.5 mg/m³: DMXSQ/SA	Ing	face musc; pulsus altenans,	Breath:	Resp support	
Remove:	When wet or contam	1.25 mg/m³: SA:CF/PAPRDM	Con	ectopic heartbeat, tacar,	Swallow:	Medical attention	
Change:	Daily	2.5 mg/m³: HiEF/SAT:CF/PAPRTHiE/		venfib; pulm edema;		immed	
Provide:	Quick drench	SCBAF/SAF		nystagmus; convuls;			
		§: SCBAF:PD,PP/SAF:PD,PP:ASCBA		liver, kidney damage			
		Escape: HiEF/SCBAE					

[Sodium fluoroacetate]

Chemical name, structure/formula, CAS and RTECS Nos., and DOT ID and guide Nos.	Synonyms, trade names, and conversion factors	Exposure limits (TWA unless noted otherwise)	IDLH	Physical description	Chemical and physical properties		Incompatibilities and reactivities	Measurement method (See Table 1)
					MW, BP, SOL FI.P, IP, Sp, Gr, flammability	VP, FRZ UEL, LEL		
Sodium hydroxide NaOH 1310-73-2 WB4900000 1823 154 (solid) 1824 154 (solution)	Caustic soda, Lye, Soda lye, Sodium hydrate	NIOSH C 2 mg/m^3 OSHA† 2 mg/m^3	10 mg/m^3	Colorless to white, odorless solid (flakes, beads, granular form).	MW: 40.0 BP: 2534°F Sol:111% FI.P: NA IP: NA Sp.Gr: 2.13 Noncombustible Solid, but when in contact with water may generate sufficient heat to ignite combustible materials.	VP: 0 mm (approx) MLT: 605°F UEL: NA LEL: NA	Water; acids; flammable liquids; organic halogens; metals such as aluminum, tin & zinc; nitromethane [Note: Corrosive to metals.]	Filter; HCl; Titrate; IV [#7401, Alkaline Dusts]
Sodium metabisulfite Na$_2$S$_2$O$_5$ 7681-57-4 UX8225000	Disodium pyrosulfite, Sodium metabisulphite, Sodium pyrosulfite	NIOSH 5 mg/m^3 OSHA† none	N.D.	White to yellowish crystals or powder with an odor of sulfur dioxide.	MW: 190.1 BP: Decomposes Sol: 54% FI.P: NA IP: NA Sp.Gr: 1.4 Noncombustible Solid	VP: ? MLT: >302°F (Decomposes) UEL: NA LEL: NA	Heat (decomposes) [Note: Slowly oxidized to the sulfate on exposure to air & moisture.]	Filter; none; Grav; IV [#0500, Particulates NOR (total)]
Starch (C$_6$H$_{10}$O$_5$)$_n$ 9005-25-8 GM5090000	Corn starch, Rice starch, Sorghum gum, α-Starch, Starch gum, Tapioca starch	NIOSH 10 mg/m^3 (total) 5 mg/m^3 (resp) OSHA 15 mg/m^3 (total) 5 mg/m^3 (resp)	N.D.	Fine, white, odorless powder. [Note: A carbohydrate polymer composed of 25% amylose & 75% amylpectin.]	MW: varies BP: Decomposes Sol: Insoluble FI.P: NA IP: NA Sp.Gr: 1.45 Noncombustible Solid, but may form explosive mixture with air.	VP: 0 mm (approx) MLT: Decomposes UEL: NA LEL: NA MEC: 50 g/m^3	Oxidizers, acids, iodine, alkalis	Filter; none; Grav; IV [Particulates NOR: #0500 (total), #0600 (resp)]
Stibine SbH$_3$ 7803-52-3 WJ0700000 2676 119	Antimony hydride, Antimony trihydride, Hydrogen antimonide 1 ppm = 5.10 mg/m^3	NIOSH/OSHA 0.1 ppm (0.5 mg/m^3)	5 ppm	Colorless gas with a disagreeable odor like hydrogen sulfide.	MW: 124.8 BP: -1°F Sol: Slight FI.P: NA (Gas) IP: 9.51 eV RGasD: 4.31 Flammable Gas	VP: >1 atm FRZ: -126°F UEL: ? LEL: ?	Acids, halogenated hydrocarbons, oxidizers, moisture, chlorine, ozone, ammonia	Si gel*; HCl; Vis; IV [#6008]

Personal protection and sanitation (See Table 3)		Recommendations for respirator selection — maximum concentration for use (MUC) (See Table 4)	Health hazards				
			Route	Symptoms (See Table 5)	First aid (See Table 6)		Target organs (See Table 5)
Skin:	Prevent skin contact	NIOSH/OSHA	Inh	Irrit eyes, skin, muc memb;	Eye:	Irr immed	Eyes, skin, resp sys
Eyes:	Prevent eye contact	10 mg/m³: SA:CF£/HiEF/PAPRDM£/	Ing	pneuitis; eye, skin burns;	Skin:	Water flush immed	
Wash skin:	When contam	SCBAF/SAF	Con	temporary loss of hair	Breath:	Resp support	
Remove:	When wet or contam	§: SCBAF:PD,PP/SAF:PD,PP:ASCBA			Swallow:	Medical attention	
Change:	Daily	Escape: HiEF/SCBAE				immed	
Provide:	Eyewash, Quick drench						

[Sodium hydroxide]

Personal protection and sanitation		Recommendations for respirator selection	Health hazards				
Skin:	N.R.	TBAL	Inh	Irrit eyes, skin, muc memb	Eye:	Irr immed	Eyes, skin, resp sys
Eyes:	N.R.		Ing		Breath:	Fresh air	
Wash skin:	N.R.		Con		Swallow:	Medical attention	
Remove:	N.R.					immed	
Change:	N.R.						

[Sodium metabisulfite]

Personal protection and sanitation		Recommendations for respirator selection	Health hazards				
Skin:	Prevent skin contact	TBAL	Inh	Irrit eyes, skin, muc memb;	Eye:	Irr immed	Eyes, skin, resp sys
Eyes:	Prevent eye contact		Ing	cough, chest pain; derm;	Skin:	Soap wash	
Wash skin:	Daily		Con	rhin	Breath:	Fresh air	
Remove:	When wet or contam				Swallow:	Medical attention	
Change:	Daily					immed	

[Starch]

Personal protection and sanitation		Recommendations for respirator selection	Health hazards				
Skin:	N.R.	NIOSH/OSHA	Inh	Head, weak; nau, abdom	Breath:	Resp support	Blood, liver
Eyes:	N.R.	1 ppm: SA		pain; lumbar pain, hemog,			kidneys, resp sys
Wash skin:	N.R.	2.5 ppm: SA:CF		hema, hemolytic anemia;			
Remove:	N.R.	5 ppm: SAT:CF/SCBAF/SAF		jaun; pulm irrit			
Change:	N.R.	§: SCBAF:PD,PP/SAF:PD,PP:ASCBA					
		Escape: GMFS/SCBAE					

[Stibine]

Chemical name, structure/formula, CAS and RTECS Nos., and DOT ID and guide Nos.	Synonyms, trade names, and conversion factors	Exposure limits (TWA unless noted otherwise)	IDLH	Physical description	Chemical and physical properties		Incompatibilities and reactivities	Measurement method (See Table 1)
					MW, BP, SOL FI.P, IP, Sp, Gr, flammability	VP, FRZ UEL, LEL		
Stoddard solvent 8052-41-3 WJ8925000 1268 128 (petroleum distillate)	Dry cleaning safety solvent, Mineral spirits, Petroleum solvent, Spotting naphtha [Note: A refined petroleum solvent with a flash point of 102-110°F, boiling point of 309-396°F, and containing >65% C$_{10}$ or higher hydrocarbons.]	NIOSH 350 mg/m^3 C 1800 mg/m^3 [15-min] OSHA† 500 ppm (2900 mg/m^3)	20,000 mg/m^3	Colorless liquid with a kerosene-like odor.	MW: Varies BP: 309-396°F Sol: Insoluble FI.P: 102-110°F IP: ? Sp.Gr: 0.78 Class II Combustible Liquid	VP: ? FRZ: ? UEL: ? LEL: ?	Strong oxidizers	Char; CS$_2$; GC/FID; IV [#1550, Naphthas]
Strychnine C$_{21}$H$_{22}$N$_2$O$_2$ 57-24-9 WL2275000 1692 151	Nux vomica, Strynchnos	NIOSH/OSHA 0.15 mg/m^3	3 mg/m^3	Colorless to white, odorless, crystalline solid. [pesticide]	MW: 334.4 BP: Decomposes Sol: 0.02% FI.P: ? IP: ? Sp.Gr: 1.36 Combustible Solid, but difficult to ignite.	VP: Low MLT: 514°F UEL: ? LEL: ?	Strong oxidizers	Filter; Reagent; HPLC/UVD; IV [#5016]
Styrene C$_6$H$_5$CH=CH$_2$ 100-42-5 WL3675000 2055 128 (inhibited)	Ethenyl benzene, Phenylethylene, Styrene monomer, Styrol, Vinyl benzene 1 ppm = 4.26 mg/m^3	NIOSH 50 ppm (215 mg/m^3) ST 100 ppm (425 mg/m^3) OSHA† 100 ppm C 200 ppm 600 ppm (5-min max peak in any 3 hrs)	700 ppm	Colorless to yellow, oily liquid with a sweet, floral odor.	MW: 104.2 BP: 293°F Sol: 0.03% FI.P: 88°F IP: 8.40 eV Sp.Gr: 0.91 Class IC Flammable Liquid	VP: 5 mm FRZ: -23°F UEL: 6.8% LEL: 0.9%	Oxidizers, catalysts for vinyl polymers, peroxides, strong acids, aluminum chloride [Note: May polymerize if contaminated or subjected to heat. Usually contains an inhibitor such as tert-butylcatechol.]	Char; CS$_2$; GC/FID; IV [#1501, Aromatic Hydro-carbons]
Subtilisins 1395-21-7 (BPN) 9014-01-1 (Carlsburg) CO9450000 (BPN) CO9550000 (Carlsburg)	Bacillus subtilis, Bacillus subtilis BPN, Bacillus subtilis Carlsburg, Proteolytic enzymes, Subtilisin BPN, Subtilisin Carlsburg [Note: Commercial proteolytic enzymes are used in laundry detergents.]	NIOSH ST 0.00006 mg/m^3 [60-min] OSHA† none	N.D.	Light-colored, free-flowing powders. [Note: A protein containing numerous amino acids.]	MW: 28,000 (approx) BP: ? Sol: ? FI.P: NA IP: NA Sp.Gr: ?	VP: 0 mm (approx) MLT: ? UEL: NA LEL: NA	None reported	None available

Personal protection and sanitation (See Table 3)		Recommendations for respirator selection — maximum concentration for use (MUC) (See Table 4)	Health hazards			
			Route	Symptoms (See Table 5)	First aid (See Table 6)	Target organs (See Table 5)
Skin:	Prevent skin contact	NIOSH	Inh	Irrit eyes, nose, throat;	Eye: Irr immed	Eyes, skin, resp sys,
Eyes:	Prevent eye contact	3500 mg/m³: CCROV*/SA*	Ing	dizz; derm; chemical pneu	Skin: Soap wash prompt	CNS, kidneys
Wash skin:	When contam	8750 mg/m³: SA:CF*/PAPROV*	Con	(aspir liq);	Breath: Resp support	
Remove:	When wet or contam	17,500 mg/m³: CCRFOV/GMFOV/		in animals: kidney damage	Swallow: Medical attention	
Change:	N.R.	PAPRTOV*/SCBAF/SAF			immed	
		20,000 mg/m³: SAF:PD,PP				
		§: SCBAF:PD,PP/SAF:PD,PP:ASCBA				
		Escape: GMFOV/SCBAE				

[Stoddard solvent]

Skin:	Prevent skin contact	NIOSH/OSHA	Inh	Stiff neck, facial musc;	Eye: Irr immed	CNS
Eyes:	N.R.	0.75 mg/m³: DM	Ing	restless, appre, incr	Skin: Soap wash prompt	
Wash skin:	When contam	1.5 mg/m³: DMXSQ/SA	Con	acuity of perception; incr	Breath: Resp support	
Remove:	N.R.	3 mg/m³: SA:CF/PAPRDM/HiEF/		reflex excitability; cyan;	Swallow: Medical attention	
Change:	Daily	SCBAF/SAF		tetanic convuls with	immed	
		§: SCBAF:PD,PP/SAF:PD,PP:ASCBA		opisthotonos		
		Escape: HiEF/SCBAE				

287

[Strychnine]

Skin:	Prevent skin contact	NIOSH	Inh	Irrit eyes, nose; resp sys;	Eye: Irr immed	Eyes, skin, resp sys,
Eyes:	Prevent eye contact	500 ppm: CCROV*/SA*	Abs	head, ftg, dizz, conf, mal,	Skin: Water flush	CNS, liver, repro sys
Wash skin:	When contam	700 ppm: SA:CF*/CCRFOV/GMFOV/	Ing	drow, weak, unsteady gait;	Breath: Resp support	
Remove:	When wet (flamm)	PAPROV*/SCBAF/SAF	Con	narco; defatting derm;	Swallow: Medical attention	
Change:	N.R.	§: SCBAF:PD,PP/SAF:PD,PP:ASCBA		possible liver inj, repro	immed	
		Escape: GMFOV/SCBAE		effects		

[Styrene]

Skin:	Prevent skin contact	TBAL	Inh	Irrit eyes, skin, resp sys;	Eye: Irr immed	Eyes, skin, resp sys
Eyes:	Prevent eye contact		Ing	resp sens (enzyme asthma):	Skin: Soap wash	
Wash skin:	When contam		Con	sweat, head, chest pain,	Breath: Resp support	
Remove:	When wet or contam			flu-like symptoms, cough,	Swallow: Medical attention	
Change:	Daily			breathlessness, wheez	immed	

[Subtilisins]

Chemical name, structure/formula, CAS and RTECS Nos., and DOT ID and guide Nos.	Synonyms, trade names, and conversion factors	Exposure limits (TWA unless noted otherwise)	IDLH	Physical description	Chemical and physical properties		Incompatibilities and reactivities	Measurement method (See Table 1)
					MW, BP, SOL Fl.P, IP, Sp, Gr, flammability	VP, FRZ UEL, LEL		
Succinonitrile NCCH₂CH₂CN 110-61-2 WN3850000 1 ppm = 3.28 mg/m³	Butanedinitrile; 1,2-Dicyanoethane;, Dinile; Ethylene cyanide; Ethylene dicyanide; Succinic dinitrile	NIOSH 6 ppm (20 mg/m³) OSHA none	N.D.	Colorless, waxy solid. [Note: Forms cyanide in the body.]	MW: 80.1 BP: 509°F Sol: 13% Fl.P: 270°F IP: ? Sp.Gr: 0.99 Combustible Solid	VP(212°F): 2 mm MLT: 134°F UEL: ? LEL: ?	Oxidizers	Char; Toluene; GC/FID; NIOSH Nitriles Crit. Doc.
Sucrose C₁₂H₂₂O₁₁ 57-50-1 WN6500000	Beet sugar, Cane sugar, Confectioner's sugar, Granulated sugar, Rock candy, Saccarose, Sugar, Table sugar	NIOSH 10 mg/m³ (total) 5 mg/m³ (resp) OSHA 15 mg/m³ (total) 5 mg/m³ (resp)	N.D.	Hard, white, odorless crystals, lumps, or powder. [Note: May have a characteristic, caramel odor when heated.]	MW: 342.3 BP: Decomposes Sol: 200% Fl.P: NA IP: NA Sp.Gr: 1.59 Noncombustible Solid, but fine airborne dust may explode.	VP: 0 mm (approx) MLT: 320-367°F (Decomposes) UEL: NA LEL: NA MEC: 45 g/m³	Oxidizers, sulfuric acid, nitric acid	Filter; none; Grav; IV [Particulates NOR: #0500 (total), #0600 (resp)]
Sulfur dioxide SO₂ 7446-09-5 WS4550000 1079 125 1 ppm = 2.62 mg/m³	Sulfurous acid anhydride, Sulfurous oxide, Sulfur oxide	NIOSH 2 ppm (5 mg/m³) ST 5 ppm (13 mg/m³) OSHA† 5 ppm (13 mg/m³)	100 ppm	Colorless gas with a characteristic, irritating, pungent odor. [Note: A liquid below 14°F. Shipped as a liquefied compressed gas.]	MW: 64.1 BP: 14°F Sol: 10% Fl.P: NA IP: 12.30 eV RGasD: 2.26 Nonflammable Gas	VP: 3.2 atm FRZ: -104°F UEL: NA LEL: NA	Powdered alkali metals (such as sodium & potassium), water, ammonia, zinc, aluminum, brass, copper [Note: Reacts with water to form sulfurous acid (H₂SO₃).]	Filter/pad*; NaHCO₃/ Na₂CO₃; IC; IV [#6004]
Sulfur hexafluoride SF₆ 2551-62-4 WS4900000 1080 126 1 ppm = 5.98 mg/m³	Sulfur fluoride [Note: May contain highly toxic sulfur pentafluoride as an impurity.]	NIOSH/OSHA 1000 ppm (6000 mg/m³)	N.D.	Colorless, odorless gas. [Note: Shipped as a liquefied compressed gas. Condenses directly to a solid upon cooling.]	MW: 146.1 BP: Sublimes Sol(77°F): 0.003% Fl.P: NA IP: 19.30 eV RGasD: 5.11 Nonflammable Gas	VP: 21.5 atm FRZ: -83°F (Sublimes) UEL: NA LEL: NA	Disilane	Bag; none; GC portable; IV [#6602]

Personal protection and sanitation (See Table 3)		Recommendations for respirator selection — maximum concentration for use (MUC) (See Table 4)	Health hazards				
			Route	Symptoms (See Table 5)	First aid (See Table 6)	Target organs (See Table 5)	

Personal protection and sanitation (See Table 3)		Recommendations for respirator selection (See Table 4)	Route	Symptoms (See Table 5)	First aid (See Table 6)	Target organs (See Table 5)
Skin: Eyes: Wash skin: Remove: Change: Provide:	Prevent skin contact Prevent eye contact When contam When wet or contam Daily Eyewash	NIOSH 60 ppm: SA 150 ppm: SA:CF 250 ppm: SCBAF/SAF §: SCBAF:PD,PP/SAF:PD,PP:ASCBA Escape: GMFOV/SCBAE	Inh Abs Ing Con	Irrit eyes, skin, resp sys; head, dizz, weak, gidd, conf, convuls; blurred vision; dysp; abdom pain, nau, vomit	Eye: Skin: Breath: Swallow:	Irr immed Water flush immed Resp support Medical attention immed	Eyes, skin, resp sys, CNS, CVS

[Succinonitrile]

Skin: Eyes: Wash skin: Remove: Change:	N.R. N.R. N.R. N.R. N.R.	TBAL	Inh Con	Irrit eyes, skin, upper resp sys; cough	Eye: Breath:	Irr immed Fresh air	Eyes, resp sys

[Sucrose]

Skin: Eyes: Wash skin: Remove: Change: Provide:	Frostbite Frostbite N.R. When wet or contam (liq) N.R. Frostbite	NIOSH 20 ppm: CCRS*/SA* 50 ppm: SA:CF*/PAPRS* 100 ppm: CCRFS/GMFS/PAPRTS*/ SAT:CF*/SCBAF/SAF §: SCBAF:PD,PP/SAF:PD,PP:ASCBA Escape: GMFS/SCBAE	Inh Con	Irrit eyes, nose, throat; rhin; choking, cough; reflex bronchoconstriction; liq: frostbite	Eye: Skin: Breath:	Frostbite Frostbite Resp support	Eyes, skin, resp sys

[Sulfur dioxide]

Skin: Eyes: Wash skin: Remove: Change: Provide:	Frostbite Frostbite N.R. N.R. N.R. Frostbite	TBAL	Inh	Asphy: incr breath rate, pulse rate; slight musc inco, emotional upset; ftg, nau, vomit, convuls	Eye: Skin: Breath:	Frostbite Frostbite Resp support	Resp sys

[Sulfur hexafluoride]

Chemical name, structure/formula, CAS and RTECS Nos., and DOT ID and guide Nos.	Synonyms, trade names, and conversion factors	Exposure limits (TWA unless noted otherwise)	IDLH	Physical description	Chemical and physical properties		Incompatibilities and reactivities	Measurement method (See Table 1)
					MW, BP, SOL Fl.P, IP, Sp, Gr, flammability	VP, FRZ UEL, LEL		
Sulfuric acid H₂SO₄ 7664-93-9 WS5600000 1830 137 1831 137 (fuming) 1832 137 (spent)	Battery acid, Hydrogen sulfate, Oil of vitriol, Sulfuric acid (aqueous)	NIOSH/OSHA 1 mg/m³	15 mg/m³	Colorless to dark-brown, oily, odorless liquid. [Note: Pure compound is a solid below 51°F. Often used in an aqueous solution.]	MW: 98.1 BP: 554°F Sol: Miscible Fl.P: NA IP: ? Sp.Gr: 1.84 (96-98% acid) Noncombustible Liquid, but capable of igniting finely divided combustible materials.	VP: 0.001 mm FRZ: 51°F UEL: NA LEL: NA	Organic materials, chlorates, carbides, fulminates, water, powdered metals [Note: Reacts violently with water with evolution of heat. Corrosive to metals.]	Si gel; NaHCO₃/ Na₂CO₃; IC; IV [#7903, Inorganic Acids]
Sulfur monochloride S₂Cl₂ 10025-67-9 WS4300000 1828 137	Sulfur chloride, Sulfur subchloride, Thiosulfurous dichloride	NIOSH C 1 ppm (6 mg/m³) OSHA† 1 ppm (6 mg/m³) 1 ppm = 5.52 mg/m³	5 ppm	Light-amber to yellow-red, oily liquid with a pungent, nauseating, irritating odor.	MW: 135.0 BP: 280°F Sol: Decomposes Fl.P: 245°F IP: 9.40 eV Sp.Gr: 1.68 Class IIIB Combustible Liquid	VP: 7 mm FRZ: -107°F UEL: ? LEL: ?	Peroxides, oxides of phosphorous, organics, water [Note: Decomposes violently in water to form hydrochloric acid, sulfur dioxide, sulfur, sulfite, thiosulfate, and hydrogen sulfide. Corrosive to metals.]	None available
Sulfur pentafluoride S₂F₁₀ 5714-22-7 WS4480000	Disulfur decafluoride, Sulfur decafluoride	NIOSH C 0.01 ppm (0.1 mg/m³) OSHA† 0.025 pp (0.25 mg/m³) 1 ppm = 10.39 mg/m³	1 ppm	Colorless liquid or gas (above 84°F) with an odor like sulfur dioxide.	MW: 254.1 BP: 84°F Sol: Insoluble Fl.P: NA IP: ? Sp.Gr(32°F): 2.08 RGasD: 8.77 Noncombustible Liquid Nonflammable Gas	VP: 561 mm FRZ: -134°F UEL: NA LEL: NA	None reported	None available
Sulfur tetrafluoride SF₄ 7783-60-0 WT4800000 2418 125	Tetrafluorosulfurane	NIOSH C 0.1 ppm (0.4 mg/m³) OSHA† none 1 ppm = 4.42 mg/m³	N.D.	Colorless gas with an odor like sulfur dioxide. [Note: Shipped as a liquefied compressed gas.]	MW: 108.1 BP: -41°F Sol: Reacts Fl.P: NA IP: 12.63 eV RGasD: 3.78 Nonflammable Gas	VP(70°F): 10.5 atm FRZ: -185°F UEL: NA LEL: NA	Moisture, concentrated sulfuric acid, dioxygen difluoride [Note: Readily hydrolyzed by moisture, forming hydrofluoric acid & thionyl fluoride.]	Bub; NaOH; IC OSHA [#ID110]

Personal protection and sanitation (See Table 3)		Recommendations for respirator selection — maximum concentration for use (MUC) (See Table 4)	Health hazards				
			Route	Symptoms (See Table 5)	First aid (See Table 6)		Target organs (See Table 5)
Skin:	Prevent skin contact	NIOSH/OSHA	Inh	Irrit eyes, skin, nose,	Eye:	Irr immed	Eyes, skin, resp sys,
Eyes:	Prevent eye contact	15 mg/m³: SA:CF‡/PAPRAGHiE‡/	Ing	throat; pulm edema, bron;	Skin:	Water flush immed	teeth
Wash skin:	When contam	CCRFAGHiE/GMFAGHiE/	Con	emphy; conj; stomatis;	Breath:	Resp support	
Remove:	When wet or contam	SCBAF/SAF		dental erosion; trachbronc;	Swallow:	Medical attention	
Change:	N.R.	§: SCBAF:PD,PP/SAF:PD,PP:ASCBA		eye, skin burns; derm		immed	
Provide:	Eyewash (>1%),	Escape: GMFAGHiE/SCBAE					
	Quick drench (>1%)						

[Sulfuric acid]

Skin:	Prevent skin contact	NIOSH/OSHA	Inh	Irrit eyes, skin, muc memb;	Eye:	Irr immed	Eyes, skin, resp sys
Eyes:	Prevent eye contact	5 ppm: CCRFS/GMFS/PAPRS‡/	Ing	lac; cough; eye, skin burns;	Skin:	Water flush immed	
Wash skin:	When contam	SCBAF/SAF	Con	pulm edema	Breath:	Resp support	
Remove:	When wet or contam	§: SCBAF:PD,PP/SAF:PD,PP:ASCBA			Swallow:	Medical attention	
Change:	N.R.	Escape: GMFS/SCBAE				immed	
Provide:	Eyewash, Quick drench						

[Sulfur monochloride]

Skin:	Prevent skin contact	NIOSH	Inh	Irrit eyes, skin, resp sys;	Eye:	Irr immed	Eyes, skin, resp sys,
Eyes:	Prevent eye contact	0.1 ppm: SA	Ing	in animals: pulm edema,	Skin:	Soap wash immed	CNS
Wash skin:	N.R.	0.25 ppm: SA:CF	Con	hemorr	Breath:	Resp support	
Remove:	When wet or contam	0.5 ppm: SAT:CF/SCBAF/SAF			Swallow:	Medical attention	
Change:	N.R.	1 ppm: SA:PD,PP				immed	
Provide:	Eyewash, Quick drench	§: SCBAF:PD,PP/SAF:PD,PP:ASCBA					
		Escape: GMFAG/SCBAE					

[Sulfur pentafluoride]

Skin:	Frostbite	TBAL	Inh	Irrit eyes, muc memb; eye,	Eye:	Frostbite	Eyes, skin, resp sys
Eyes:	Frostbite		Con	skin burns (from SF_4	Skin:	Frostbite	
Wash skin:	N.R.			releasing hydrofluoric	Breath:	Resp support	
Remove:	N.R.			acid on exposure to			
Change:	N.R.			moisture); liq: frostbite;			
Provide:	Frostbite			in animals: dysp, weak,			
				rhin			

[Sulfur tetrafluoride]

Chemical name, structure/formula, CAS and RTECS Nos., and DOT ID and guide Nos.	Synonyms, trade names, and conversion factors	Exposure limits (TWA unless noted otherwise)	IDLH	Physical description	Chemical and physical properties		Incompatibilities and reactivities	Measurement method (See Table 1)
					MW, BP, SOL Fl.P, IP, Sp, Gr, flammability	VP, FRZ UEL, LEL		
Sulfuryl fluoride SO_2F_2 2699-79-8 WT5075000 2191 123	Sulfur difluoride dioxide, Vikane® 1 ppm = 4.18 mg/m³	NIOSH 5 ppm (20 mg/m³) ST 10 ppm (40 mg/m³) OSHA† 5 ppm (20 mg/m³)	200 ppm	Colorless, odorless gas. [insecticide/ fumigant] [Note: Shipped as a liquefied compressed gas.]	MW: 102.1 BP: -68°F Sol(32°F): 0.2% Fl.P: NA IP: 13.04 eV RGasD: 3.72 Nonflammable Gas	VP(70°F): 15.8 atm FRZ: -212°F UEL: NA LEL: NA	None reported	Char; NaOH; IC; Iv [#6012]
Sulprofos $C_{12}H_{19}O_2PS_3$ 35400-43-2 TE4165000 1 ppm = 13.19 mg/m³	Bolstar®, O-Ethyl O-(4-methylthio)-phenyl S-propyl-phosphorodithioate	NIOSH 1 mg/m³ OSHA† none	N.D.	Tan-colored liquid with a sulfide-like odor.	MW: 322.5 BP: ? Sol: Low Fl.P: ? IP: ? Sp.Gr: 1.20	VP: <8 mm FRZ: ? UEL: ? LEL: ?	None reported	OVS-2; Toluene/ Acetone; GC/FPD; IV [#5600, Organo-phosphorus Pesticides]
2,4,5-T $Cl_3C_6H_2OCH_2COOH$ 93-76-5 AJ8400000 2765 152	2,4,5-Trichlorophenoxyacetic acid	NIOSH/OSHA 10 mg/m³	250 mg/m³	Colorless to tan, odorless, crystalline solid. [herbicide]	MW: 255.5 BP: Decomposes Sol(77°F): 0.03% Fl.P: ? IP: ? Sp.Gr: 1.80 Combustible Solid, but burns with difficulty.	VP: <1 x 10⁻⁷ mm MLT: 307°F UEL: ? LEL: ?	None reported	Filter; Methanol; HPLC/UVD; IV [#5001]
Talc (containing no asbestos and less than 1% quartz) $Mg_3Si_4O_{10}(OH)_2$ 14807-96-6 WW2710000	Hydrous magnesium silicate, Steatite talc	NIOSH 2 mg/m³ (resp) OSHA† 20 mppcf	1000 mg/m³	Odorless, white powder.	MW: Varies BP: ? Sol: Insoluble Fl.P: NA IP: NA Sp.Gr: 2.70-2.80 Noncombustible Solid	VP: 0 mm (approx) MLT: 1652-1832°F UEL: NA LEL: NA	None reported	Filter; LTA; XRD; III [P&CAM #355]

Personal protection and sanitation (See Table 3)		Recommendations for respirator selection — maximum concentration for use (MUC) (See Table 4)	Health hazards				
			Route	Symptoms (See Table 5)	First aid (See Table 6)		Target organs (See Table 5)
Skin:	Frostbite	NIOSH/OSHA	Inh	Conj, rhinitis, pharyngitis,	Eye:	Frostbite	Eyes, skin, resp sys,
Eyes:	Frostbite	50 ppm: SA*	Con	pares; liq: frostbite;	Skin:	Frostbite	CNS, kidneys
Wash skin:	N.R.	125 ppm: SA:CF*	(liq)	in animals: narco, tremor,	Breath:	Resp support	
Remove:	N.R.	200 ppm: SCBAF/SAF		convuls; pulm edema; kidney			
Change:	N.R.	§: SCBAF:PD,PP/SAF:PD,PP:ASCBA		inj			
Provide:	Frostbite	Escape: GMFS/SCBAE					

[Sulfuryl fluoride]

Personal protection and sanitation (See Table 3)		Recommendations for respirator selection — maximum concentration for use (MUC) (See Table 4)	Health hazards				
Skin:	Prevent skin contact	TBAL	Inh	Nau, vomit, abdom cramps,	Eye:	Irr immed	Resp sys, CNS, CVS,
Eyes:	N.R.		Ing	diarr, salv; head, gidd,	Skin:	Soap wash immed	blood chol
Wash skin:	When contam			verti, weak; rhin, chest	Breath:	Resp support	
Remove:	When wet or contam			tight; blurred vision,	Swallow:	Medical attention	
Change:	N.R.			miosis; card irreg; musc		immed	
				fasc; dysp			

[Sulprofos]

Personal protection and sanitation (See Table 3)		Recommendations for respirator selection — maximum concentration for use (MUC) (See Table 4)	Health hazards				
Skin:	N.R.	NIOSH/OSHA	Inh	In animals: ataxia; skin	Eye:	Irr immed	Skin, liver, GI
Eyes:	N.R.	50 mg/m^3: DM	Ing	irrit, acne-like rash,	Skin:	Soap wash	tract
Wash skin:	N.R.	100 mg/m^3: DMXSQ/SA	Con	liver damage	Breath:	Resp support	
Remove:	N.R.	250 mg/m^3: SA:CF/HiEF/PAPRDM/			Swallow:	Medical attention	
Change:	N.R.	SCBAF/SAF				immed	
		§: SCBAF:PD,PP/SAF:PD,PP:ASCBA					
		Escape: HiEF/SCBAE					

[2,4,5-T]

Personal protection and sanitation (See Table 3)		Recommendations for respirator selection — maximum concentration for use (MUC) (See Table 4)	Health hazards				
Skin:	N.R.	NIOSH	Inh	Fibrotic pneumoconiosis,	Eye:	Irr immed	Eyes, resp sys, CVS
Eyes:	N.R.	10 mg/m^3: DM	Con	irrit eyes	Breath:	Fresh air	
Wash skin:	N.R.	20 mg/m^3: DMXSQ/SA					
Remove:	N.R.	50 mg/m^3: PAPRDM/SA:CF					
Change:	N.R.	100 mg/m^3: HiEF/SAT:CF/PAPRTHiE/					
		SCBAF/SAF					
		1000 mg/m^3: SA:PD,PP					
		§: SCBAF:PD,PP/SAF:PD,PP:ASCBA					
		Escape: HiEF/SCBAE					

[Talc (containing no asbestos and less than 1% quartz)]

Chemical name, structure/formula, CAS and RTECS Nos., and DOT ID and guide Nos.	Synonyms, trade names, and conversion factors	Exposure limits (TWA unless noted otherwise)	IDLH	Physical description	Chemical and physical properties		Incompatibilities and reactivities	Measurement method (See Table 1)
					MW, BP, SOL Fl.P, IP, Sp, Gr, flammability	VP, FRZ UEL, LEL		
Tantalum (metal and oxide dust, as Ta) Ta (Metal) 7440-25-7 (Metal) WW5505000 (Metal)	Tantalum metal: Tantalum-181 Synonyms of other tantalum dusts (including oxide dusts) vary depending upon the specific compound.	NIOSH 5 mg/m³ ST 10 mg/m³ OSHA 5 mg/m³	2500 mg/m³ (as Ta)	Metal: Steel-blue to gray solid or black, odorless powder.	MW: 180.9 BP: 9797°F Sol: Insoluble Fl.P: NA IP: NA Sp.Gr: 16.65 (Metal) 14.40 (Powder) Metal: Combustible Solid; powder ignites SPONTANEOUSLY in air.	VP: 0 mm (approx) MLT: 5425°F UEL: NA LEL: NA MEC: <200 g/m³	Strong oxidizers, bromine trifluoride, fluorine	Filter; none; Grav; IV [#0500, Particulates NOR (total)]
TEDP [(CH₃CH₂O)₂PS]₂O 3689-24-5 XN4375000 1704 153	Bladafum®, Dithion, Sulfotep, Tetraethyl dithiono-pyrophosphate, Tetraethyl dithiopyro-phosphate, Thiotepp® 1 ppm = 13.18 mg/m³	NIOSH/OSHA 0.2 mg/m³ [skin]	10 mg/m³	Pale-yellow liquid with a garlic-like odor. [Note: A pesticide that may be absorbed on a solid carrier or mixed in a more flammable liquid.]	MW: 322.3 BP: Decomposes Sol: 0.0007% Fl.P: ? IP: ? Sp.Gr(77°F): 1.20 Combustible Liquid	VP: 0.0002 mm FRZ: ? UEL: ? LEL: ?	Strong oxidizers, iron [Note: Corrosive to iron.]	None available
Tellurium Te 13494-80-9 WY2625000	Aurum paradoxum, Metallum problematum	NIOSH*/OSHA* 0.1 mg/m³ [*Note: The REL and PEL also apply to other tellurium compounds (as Te) except Tellurium hexafluoride, and Bismuth telluride.]	25 mg/m³ (as Te)	Odorless, dark-gray to brown, amorphous powder or grayish-white, brittle solid.	MW: 127.6 BP: 1814°F Sol: Insoluble Fl.P: NA IP: NA Sp.Gr: 6.24 Combustible Solid	VP: 0 mm (approx) MLT: 842°F UEL: NA LEL: NA	Oxidizers, chlorine, cadmium	Filter; Acid; ICP; IV [#7300, Elements]
Tellurium hexafluoride TeF₆ 7783-80-4 WY2800000 2195 125	Tellurium fluoride 1 ppm = 9.88 mg/m³	NIOSH/OSHA 0.02 ppm (0.2 mg/m³)	1 ppm	Colorless gas with a repulsive odor.	MW: 241.6 BP: Sublimes Sol: Decomposes Fl.P: NA IP: ? RGasD: 8.34 Nonflammable Gas	VP: >1 atm FRZ: -36°F (Sublimes) UEL: NA LEL: NA	Water [Note: Hydrolyzes slowly in water to telluric acid.]	Char; NaOH; FAAS; II(3) [#S187]

Personal protection and sanitation (See Table 3)		Recommendations for respirator selection — maximum concentration for use (MUC) (See Table 4)	Health hazards			
			Route	Symptoms (See Table 5)	First aid (See Table 6)	Target organs (See Table 5)
Skin:	N.R.	NIOSH/OSHA	Inh	Irrit eyes, skin;	Eye: Irr immed	Eyes, skin, resp sys
Eyes:	N.R.	25 mg/m³: DM^	Con	in animals: pulm irrit	Breath: Resp support	
Wash skin:	N.R.	50 mg/m³: DMXSQ^/DMFu/SA				
Remove:	N.R.	125 mg/m³: SA:CF/PAPRDM^				
Change:	N.R.	250 mg/m³: HiEF/SAT:CF/PAPRTHiE/ SCBAF/SAF				
		2500 mg/m³: SA:PD,PP				
		§: SCBAF:PD,PP/SAF:PD,PP:ASCBA				
		Escape: HiEF/SCBAE				
[Tantalum (metal and oxide dust, as Ta)]						
Skin:	Prevent skin contact	NIOSH/OSHA	Inh	Irrit eyes, skin; eye pain,	Eye: Irr immed	Eyes, skin, resp sys,
Eyes:	Prevent eye contact	2 mg/m³: SA	Abs	blurred vision, lac; rhin;	Skin: Soap wash immed	CNS, CVS, blood chol
Wash skin:	When contam	5 mg/m³: SA:CF	Ing	head; cyan; anor, nau,	Breath: Resp support	
Remove:	When wet or contam	10 mg/m³: SCBAF/SAF	Con	vomit, diarr; local sweat,	Swallow: Medical attention	
Change:	N.R.	§: SCBAF:PD,PP/SAF:PD,PP:ASCBA		weak, twitch, para,	immed	
Provide:	Eyewash, Quick drench	Escape: GMFOVHiE/SCBAE		Cheyne-Stokes respiration,		
				convuls, low BP, card irreg		
[TEDP]						
Skin:	N.R.	NIOSH/OSHA	Inh	Garlic breath, sweat; dry	Eye: Irr immed	Skin, CNS, blood
Eyes:	N.R.	0.5 mg/m³: DM^	Ing	mouth, metallic taste; som;	Skin: Soap wash prompt	
Wash skin:	N.R.	1 mg/m³: DMXSQ^/DMFu/SA	Con	anor, nau, no sweat; derm;	Breath: Resp support	
Remove:	N.R.	2.5 mg/m³: SA:CF/PAPRDM^		in animals: CNS, red	Swallow: Medical attention	
Change:	N.R.	5 mg/m³: HiEF/SAT:CF/PAPRTHiE/ SCBAF/SAF		blood cell effects	immed	
		25 mg/m³: SA:PD,PP				
		§: SCBAF:PD,PP/SAF:PD,PP:ASCBA				
		Escape: HiEF/SCBAE				
[Tellurium]						
Skin:	N.R.	NIOSH/OSHA	Inh	Head; dysp; garlic breath;	Breath: Resp support	Resp sys
Eyes:	N.R.	0.2 ppm: SA		in animals: pulm edema		
Wash skin:	N.R.	0.5 ppm: SA:CF				
Remove:	N.R.	1 ppm: SAT:CF/SCBAF/SAF				
Change:	N.R.	§: SCBAF:PD,PP/SAF:PD,PP:ASCBA				
		Escape: GMFS/SCBAE				
[Tellurium hexafluoride]						

Chemical name, structure/formula, CAS and RTECS Nos., and DOT ID and guide Nos.	Synonyms, trade names, and conversion factors	Exposure limits (TWA unless noted otherwise)	IDLH	Physical description	Chemical and physical properties		Incompatibilities and reactivities	Measurement method (See Table 1)
					MW, BP, SOL Fl.P, IP, Sp, Gr, flammability	VP, FRZ UEL, LEL		
Temephos S[C$_6$H$_4$OP(S)(OCH$_3$)$_2$]$_2$ 3383-96-8 TF6890000	Abate®; Temefos; O,O,O'O'-Tetramethyl O,O'-thiodi-p-phenylene phosphorothioate	NIOSH 10 mg/m^3 (total) 5 mg/m^3 (resp) OSHA† 15 mg/m^3 (total) 5 mg/m^3 (resp)	N.D.	White, crystalline solid or liquid (above 87°F). [insecticide] [Note: Technical grade is a viscous, brown liquid.]	MW: 466.5 BP: 248-257°F (Decomposes) Sol: Insoluble Fl.P: ? IP: ? Sp.Gr: 1.32 Combustible Solid	VP(77°F): 0.00000007 mm MLT: 87°F UEL: ? LEL: ?	None reported	Filter; none; Grav; IV [Particulates NOR: #0500 (total) #0600 (resp)]
TEPP [(CH$_3$CH$_2$O)$_2$PO]$_2$O 107-49-3 UX6825000 2783 152 3018 152 (liquid)	Ethyl pyrophosphate, Tetraethyl pyrophosphate, Tetron® 1 ppm = 11.87 mg/m^3	NIOSH/OSHA 0.05 mg/m^3 [skin]	5 mg/m^3	Colorless to amber liquid with a faint, fruity odor. [insecticide] [Note: A solid below 32°F.]	MW: 290.2 BP: Decomposes Sol: Miscible Fl.P: NA IP: ? Sp.Gr: 1.19 Noncombustible Liquid	VP: 0.00015 mm FRZ: 32°F UEL: NA LEL: NA	Strong oxidizers, alkalis, water [Note: Hydrolyzes quickly in water to form pyrophosphoric acid.]	Chrom-102 (2); Toluene; GC/FPD; IV [#2504, Tetraethyl Pyrophos-phate]
o-Terphenyl C$_6$H$_5$C$_6$H$_4$C$_6$H$_5$ 84-15-1 WZ6472000	o-Diphenylbenzene; 1,2-Diphenylbenzene; 2-Phenylbiphenyl; 1,2-Terphenyl; ortho-Terphenyl; o-Triphenyl 1 ppm = 9.42 mg/m^3	NIOSH C 5 mg/m^3 (0.5 ppm) OSHA† C 9 mg/m^3 (1 ppm)	500 mg/m^3	Colorless or light-yellow solid.	MW: 230.3 BP: 630°F Sol: Insoluble Fl.P(oc): 325°F IP: 7.99 eV Sp.Gr: 1.1 Combustible Solid	VP: Very low MLT: 136°F UEL: ? LEL: ?	None reported	Filter; CS$_2$; GC/FID; IV [#5021]
m-Terphenyl C$_6$H$_5$C$_6$H$_4$C$_6$H$_5$ 92-06-8 WZ6470000	m-Diphenylbenzene; 1,3-Diphenylbenzene; Isodiphenylbenzene; 3-Phenylbiphenyl; 1,3-Terphenyl; meta-Terphenyl; m-Triphenyl 1 ppm = 9.42 mg/m^3	NIOSH C 5 mg/m^3 (0.5 ppm) OSHA† C 9 mg/m^3 (1 ppm)	500 mg/m^3	Yellow solid (needles).	MW: 230.3 BP: 689°F Sol: Insoluble Fl.P(oc): 375°F IP: 8.01 eV Sp.Gr: 1.23 Combustible Solid	VP: Very low MLT: 192°F UEL: ? LEL: ?	None reported	Filter; CS$_2$; GC/FID; IV [#5021]

Personal protection and sanitation (See Table 3)		Recommendations for respirator selection — maximum concentration for use (MUC) (See Table 4)	Route	Symptoms (See Table 5)	First aid (See Table 6)		Target organs (See Table 5)
Skin:	Prevent skin contact	TBAL	Inh	Irrit eyes, blurred vision;	Eye:	Irr immed	Eyes, resp sys, CNS,
Eyes:	Prevent eye contact		Abs	dizz, conf; dysp; salv;	Skin:	Soap wash immed	CVS, blood chol
Wash skin:	When contam		Ing	abdom cramps, nau, diarr,	Breath:	Resp support	
Remove:	When wet or contam		Con	vomit	Swallow:	Medical attention	
Change:	Daily					immed	
[Temephos]							
Skin:	Prevent skin contact	NIOSH/OSHA	Inh	Eye pain, blurred vision,	Eye:	Irr immed	Eyes, resp sys, CNS,
Eyes:	Prevent eye contact	0.5 mg/m^3: SA	Abs	lac; rhin; head, chest tight,	Skin:	Water flush immed	CVS, GI tract,
Wash skin:	When contam	1.25 mg/m^3: SA:CF	Ing	cyan; anor, nau, vomit,	Breath:	Resp support	blood chol
Remove:	When wet or contam	2.5 mg/m^3: SAT:CF/SCBAF/SAF	Con	diarr; weak, twitch, para,	Swallow:	Medical attention	
Change:	N.R.	5 mg/m^3: SA:PD,PP		Cheyne-Stokes respiration,		immed	
Provide:	Eyewash, Quick drench	§: SCBAF:PD,PP/SAF:PD,PP:ASCBA		convuls; low BP, card			
		Escape: GMFOVHiE/SCBAE		irreg; sweat			
[TEPP]							
Skin:	Prevent skin contact	NIOSH	Inh	Irrit eyes, skin, muc memb;	Eye:	Irr immed	Eyes, skin, resp sys,
Eyes:	Prevent eye contact	25 mg/m^3: DM$^£$	Ing	thermal skin burns; head;	Skin:	Water flush immed	liver, kidneys
Wash skin:	When contam	50 mg/m^3: DMXSQ$^£$/SA$^£$	Con	sore throat;	Breath:	Resp support	
Remove:	When wet or contam	125 mg/m^3: SA:CF$^£$/PAPRDM$^£$		in animals: liver, kidney	Swallow:	Medical attention	
Change:	Daily	250 mg/m^3: HiEF/SCBAF/SAF		damage		immed	
Provide:	Eyewash, Quick drench	500 mg/m^3: SAF:PD,PP					
		§: SCBAF:PD,PP/SAF:PD,PP:ASCBA					
		Escape: HiEF/SCBAE					
[o-Terphenyl]							
Skin:	Prevent skin contact	NIOSH	Inh	Irrit eyes, skin, muc memb;	Eye:	Irr immed	Eyes, skin, resp sys,
Eyes:	Prevent eye contact	25 mg/m^3: DM$^£$	Ing	thermal skin burns; head;	Skin:	Water flush immed	liver, kidneys
Wash skin:	When contam	50 mg/m^3: DMXSQ$^£$/SA$^£$	Con	sore throat;	Breath:	Resp support	
Remove:	When wet or contam	125 mg/m^3: SA:CF$^£$/PAPRDM$^£$		in animals: liver, kidney	Swallow:	Medical attention	
Change:	Daily	250 mg/m^3: HiEF/SCBAF/SAF		damage		immed	
Provide:	Eyewash, Quick drench	500 mg/m^3: SAF:PD,PP					
		§: SCBAF:PD,PP/SAF:PD,PP:ASCBA					
		Escape: HiEF/SCBAE					
[m-Terphenyl]							

Chemical name, structure/formula, CAS and RTECS Nos., and DOT ID and guide Nos.	Synonyms, trade names, and conversion factors	Exposure limits (TWA unless noted otherwise)	IDLH	Physical description	Chemical and physical properties		Incompatibilities and reactivities	Measurement method (See Table 1)
					MW, BP, SOL FI.P, IP, Sp, Gr, flammability	VP, FRZ UEL, LEL		
p-Terphenyl $C_6H_5C_6H_4C_6H_5$ 92-94-4 WZ6475000	p-Diphenylbenzene; 1,4-Diphenylbenzene; 4-Phenylbiphenyl; 1,4-Terphenyl; para-Terphenyl; p-Triphenyl 1 ppm = 9.42 mg/m³	NIOSH C 5 mg/m³ (0.5 ppm) OSHA† C 9 mg/m³ (1 ppm)	500 mg/m³	White or light-yellow solid.	MW: 230.3 BP: 761°F Sol: Insoluble FI.P: 405°F IP: 7.78 eV Sp.Gr: 1.23 Combustible Solid	VP: Very low MLT: 415°F UEL: ? LEL: ?	None reported	Filter; CS₂; GC/FID; IV [#5021]
2,3,7,8-Tetrachloro-dibenzo-p-dioxin $C_{12}H_4Cl_4O_2$ 1746-01-6 HP3500000	Dioxin; Dioxine; TCDBD; TCDD; 2,3,7,8-TCDD [Note: Formed during past production of 2,4,5-tri-chlorophenol, 2,4,5-T & 2(2,4,5-trichlorophenoxy)-propionic acid.]	NIOSH Ca See Appendix A OSHA none	Ca [N.D.]	Colorless to white, crystalline solid. [Note: Exposure may occur through contact at previously contaminated worksites.]	MW: 322.0 BP: Decomposes Sol: 0.00000002% FI.P: ? IP: ? Sp.Gr: ?	VP(77°F): 0.000002 mm MLT: 581°F UEL: ? LEL: ?	UV light (decomposes)	None available
1,1,1,2-Tetrachloro-2,2-difluoroethane CCl_3CClF_2 76-11-9 KI1425000	2,2-Difluoro-1,1,1,2-tetrachloroethane; Freon® 112a; Halocarbon 112a; Refrigerant 112a 1 ppm = 8.34 mg/m³	NIOSH/OSHA 500 ppm (4170 mg/m³)	2000 ppm	Colorless solid with a slight, ether-like odor. [Note: A liquid above 105°F.]	MW: 203.8 BP: 197°F Sol: 0.01% FI.P: NA IP: ? Sp.Gr: 1.65 Noncombustible Solid	VP: 40 mm MLT: 105°F UEL: NA LEL: NA	Chemically-active metals such as potassium, beryllium, powdered aluminum, zinc, magnesium, calcium & sodium; acids	Char; CS₂; GC/FID; IV [#1016]
1,1,2,2-Tetrachloro-1,2-difluoroethane CCl_2FCCl_2F 76-12-0 KI1420000	1,2-Difluoro-1,1,2,2-tetrachloroethane; Freon® 112; Halocarbon 112; Refrigerant 112 1 ppm = 8.34 mg/m³	NIOSH/OSHA 500 ppm (4170 mg/m³)	2000 ppm	Colorless solid or liquid (above 77°F) with a slight, ether-like odor.	MW: 203.8 BP: 199°F Sol(77°F): 0.01% FI.P: NA IP: 11.30 eV Sp.Gr: 1.65 Noncombustible Solid	VP: 40 mm MLT: 77°F UEL: NA LEL: NA	Chemically-active metals such as potassium, beryllium, powdered aluminum, zinc, magnesium, calcium & sodium; acids	Char; CS₂; GC/FID; IV [#1016]

Personal protection and sanitation (See Table 3)		Recommendations for respirator selection — maximum concentration for use (MUC) (See Table 4)	Health hazards					
			Route	Symptoms (See Table 5)		First aid (See Table 6)		Target organs (See Table 5)
Skin:	Prevent skin contact	NIOSH	Inh	Irrit eyes, skin, muc memb;	Eye:	Irr immed		Eyes, skin, resp sys,
Eyes:	Prevent eye contact	25 mg/m³: DM£	Ing	thermal skin burns; head;	Skin:	Water flush immed		liver, kidneys
Wash skin:	When contam	50 mg/m³: DMXSQ£/SA£	Con	sore throat;	Breath:	Resp support		
Remove:	When wet or contam	125 mg/m³: SA:CF£/PAPRDM£		in animals: liver, kidney	Swallow:	Medical attention		
Change:	Daily	250 mg/m³: HiEF/SCBAF/SAF		damage		immed		
Provide:	Eyewash, Quick drench	500 mg/m³: SAF:PD,PP						
		§: SCBAF:PD,PP/SAF:PD,PP:ASCBA						
		Escape: HiEF/SCBAE						

[p-Terphenyl]

Skin:	Prevent skin contact	NIOSH	Inh	Irrit eyes; allergic derm,	Eye:	Irr immed		Eyes, skin, liver,
Eyes:	Prevent eye contact	¥: SCBAF:PD,PP/SAF:PD,PP:ASCBA	Abs	chloracne; porphyria; GI	Skin:	Soap flush immed		kidneys, repro sys
Wash skin:	When contam/Daily	Escape: GMFOVHiE/SCBAE	Ing	dist; possible repro,	Breath:	Resp support		[in animals:
Remove:	When wet or contam		Con	terato effects;	Swallow:	Medical attention		tumors at
Change:	Daily			in animals: liver, kidney		immed		many sites]
Provide:	Eyewash, Quick drench			damage; hemorr; [carc]				

[2,3,7,8-Tetrachloro-dibenzo-p-dioxin]

Skin:	Prevent skin contact	NIOSH/OSHA	Inh	Irrit eyes, skin; CNS	Eye:	Irr immed		Eyes, skin, resp sys,
Eyes:	Prevent eye contact	2000 ppm: SA/SCBAF	Ing	depres; pulm edema; drow;	Skin:	Soap wash prompt		CNS
Wash skin:	When contam	§: SCBAF:PD,PP/SAF:PD,PP:ASCBA	Con	dysp	Breath:	Resp support		
Remove:	When wet or contam	Escape: GMFOV/SCBAE			Swallow:	Medical attention		
Change:	N.R.					immed		

[1,1,1,2-Tetrachloro-2,2-difluoroethane]

Skin:	Prevent skin contact	NIOSH/OSHA	Inh	In animals: irrit eyes,	Eye:	Irr immed		Eyes, skin, resp sys,
Eyes:	Prevent eye contact	2000 ppm: SA/SCBAF	Ing	skin; conj; pulm edema;	Skin:	Soap wash prompt		CNS
Wash skin:	When contam	§: SCBAF:PD,PP/SAF:PD,PP:ASCBA	Con	narco	Breath:	Resp support		
Remove:	When wet or contam	Escape: GMFOV/SCBAE			Swallow:	Medical attention		
Change:	N.R.					immed		

[1,1,2,2-Tetrachloro-1,2-difluoroethane]

Chemical name, structure/formula, CAS and RTECS Nos., and DOT ID and guide Nos.	Synonyms, trade names, and conversion factors	Exposure limits (TWA unless noted otherwise)	IDLH	Physical description	Chemical and physical properties		Incompatibilities and reactivities	Measurement method (See Table 1)
					MW, BP, SOL Fl.P, IP, Sp, Gr, flammability	VP, FRZ UEL, LEL		
1,1,1,2-Tetrachloro-ethane CCl_3CH_2Cl 630-20-6 KI8450000 1702 151	None	NIOSH Handle with caution in the workplace. See Appendix C (Chloroethanes) OSHA none	N.D.	Yellowish-red liquid.	MW: 167.9 BP: 267°F Sol: 0.1% Fl.P: ? IP: ? Sp.Gr: 1.54	VP(77°F): 14mm FRZ: -94°F UEL: ? LEL: ?	Potassium; sodium; dinitrogen tetraoxide; potassium hydroxide; nitrogen tetroxide; sodium potassium alloy; 2,4-dinitrophenyl disulfide	None available
1,1,2,2-Tetrachloro-ethane $CHCl_2CHCl_2$ 79-34-5 KI8575000 1702 151	Acetylene tetrachloride, Symmetrical tetrachloro-ethane 1 ppm = 6.87 mg/m³	NIOSH Ca See Appendix A See Appendix C (Chloroethanes) 1 ppm (7 mg/m³) [skin] OSHA† 5 ppm (35 mg/m³) [skin]	Ca [100 ppm]	Colorless to pale-yellow liquid with a pungent, chloroform-like odor.	MW: 167.9 BP: 296°F Sol: 0.3% Fl.P: NA IP: 11.10 eV Sp.Gr(77°F): 1.59 Noncombustible Liquid	VP: 5 mm FRZ: -33°F UEL: NA LEL: NA	Chemically-active metals, strong caustics, fuming sulfuric acid [Note: Degrades slowly when exposed to air.]	Char(pet); CS_2; GC/FID; IV [#1019]
Tetrachloroethylene $Cl_2C=CCl_2$ 127-18-4 KX3850000 1897 160	Perchlorethylene, Perchloroethylene, Perk, Tetrachlorethylene 1 ppm = 6.78 mg/m³	NIOSH Ca See Appendix A Minimize workplace exposure concentrations; limit number of workers exposed. OSHA† 100 ppm C 200 ppm 300 ppm (5-min max peak in any 3 hrs)	Ca [150 ppm]	Colorless liquid with a mild, chloroform-like odor.	MW: 165.8 BP: 250°F Sol: 0.02% Fl.P: NA IP: 9.32 eV Sp.Gr: 1.62 Noncombustible Liquid, but decomposes in a fire to hydrogen chloride and phosgene.	VP: 14 mm FRZ: -2°F UEL: NA LEL: NA	Strong oxidizers; chemically-active metals such as lithium, beryllium & barium; caustic soda; sodium hydroxide; potash	Char; CS_2; GC/FID; IV [#1003, Halogenated Hydrocarbons]
Tetrachloronaphthalene $C_{10}H_4Cl_4$ 1335-88-2 QK3700000	Halowax®, Nibren wax, Seekaway wax	NIOSH/OSHA 2 mg/m³ [skin]	Unknown	Colorless to pale-yellow solid with an aromatic odor.	MW: 265.9 BP: 599-680°F Sol: Insoluble Fl.P(oc): 410°F IP: ? Sp.Gr: 1.59-1.65 Combustible Solid	VP: <1 mm MLT: 360°F UEL: ? LEL: ?	Strong oxidizers	Filter/Bub; none; GC/FID; II(2) [#S130]

Personal protection and sanitation (See Table 3)	Recommendations for respirator selection — maximum concentration for use (MUC) (See Table 4)	Health hazards			
		Route	Symptoms (See Table 5)	First aid (See Table 6)	Target organs (See Table 5)
Skin: Prevent skin contact Eyes: Prevent eye contact Wash skin: When contam Remove: When wet or contam Change: N.R. Provide: Eyewash, Quick drench	TBAL	Inh Ing Con	Irrit eyes, skin; weak, restless, irreg respiration, musc inco; in animals: liver changes	Eye: Irr immed Skin: Soap wash immed Breath: Resp support Swallow: Medical attention immed	Eyes, skin, CNS, liver
[1,1,1,2-Tetrachloroethane]					
Skin: Prevent skin contact Eyes: Prevent eye contact Wash skin: When contam Remove: When wet or contam Change: N.R. Provide: Eyewash, Quick drench	NIOSH ¥: SCBAF:PD,PP/SAF:PD,PP:ASCBA Escape: GMFOV/SCBAE	Inh Abs Ing Con	Nau, vomit, abdom pain; tremor fingers; jaun, hepatitis, liver tend; derm; monocy; kidney damage; [carc]	Eye: Irr immed Skin: Soap wash prompt Breath: Resp support Swallow: Medical attention immed	Skin, liver, kidneys, CNS, GI tract [in animals: liver tumors]
[1,1,2,2-Tetrachloroethane]					
Skin: Prevent skin contact Eyes: Prevent eye contact Wash skin: When contam Remove: When wet or contam Change: N.R. Provide: Eyewash, Quick drench	NIOSH ¥: SCBAF:PD,PP/SAF:PD,PP:ASCBA Escape: GMFOV/SCBAE	Inh Abs Ing Con	Irrit eyes, nose, throat; nau; flush face, neck; verti, dizz, inco; head, som; skin eryt; liver damage; [carc]	Eye: Irr immed Skin: Soap wash prompt Breath: Resp support Swallow: Medical attention immed	Eyes, skin, resp sys, liver, kidneys, CNS [in animals: liver tumors]
[Tetrachloroethylene]					
Skin: Prevent skin contact Eyes: Prevent eye contact Wash skin: When contam Remove: When wet or contam Change: Daily	NIOSH/OSHA 20 mg/m^3: SCBAF/SAF §: SCBAF:PD,PP/SAF:PD,PP:ASCBA Escape: GMFOVHiE/SCBAE	Inh Abs Ing Con	Acne-form derm; head, ftg, anor, verti; jaun, liver inj	Eye: Irr immed Skin: Soap wash immed Breath: Resp support Swallow: Medical attention immed	Liver, skin, CNS
[Tetrachloronaphthalene]					

Chemical name, structure/formula, CAS and RTECS Nos., and DOT ID and guide Nos.	Synonyms, trade names, and conversion factors	Exposure limits (TWA unless noted otherwise)	IDLH	Physical description	Chemical and physical properties		Incompatibilities and reactivities	Measurement method (See Table 1)
					MW, BP, SOL FI.P, IP, Sp, Gr, flammability	VP, FRZ UEL, LEL		
Tetraethyl lead (as Pb) $Pb(C_2H_5)_4$ 78-00-2 TP4550000 1649 131	Lead tetraethyl, TEL, Tetraethylplumbane	NIOSH/OSHA 0.075 mg/m³ [skin]	40 mg/m³ (as Pb)	Colorless liquid (unless dyed red, orange, or blue) with a pleasant, sweet odor. [Note: Main usage is in anti-knock additives for gasoline.]	MW: 323.5 BP: 228°F (Decomposes) Sol: 0.00002% FI.P: 200°F IP: 11.10 eV Sp.Gr: 1.65 Class IIIB Combustible Liquid	VP: 0.2 mm FRZ: -202°F UEL: ? LEL: 1.8%	Strong oxidizers, sulfuryl chloride, rust, potassium permanganate [Note: Decomposes slowly at room temperature and more rapidly at higher temperatures.]	XAD-2; Pentane; GC/PID; IV [#2533]
Tetrahydrofuran C_4H_8O 109-99-9 LU5950000 2056 127	Diethylene oxide; 1,4-Epoxybutane; Tetramethylene oxide; THF 1 ppm = 2.95 mg/m³	NIOSH 200 ppm (590 mg/m³) ST 250 ppm (735 mg/m³) OSHA† 200 ppm (590 mg/m³)	2000 ppm [10%LEL]	Colorless liquid with an ether-like odor.	MW: 72.1 BP: 151°F Sol: Miscible FI.P: 6°F IP: 9.45 eV Sp.Gr: 0.89 Class IB Flammable Liquid	VP: 132 mm FRZ: -163°F UEL: 11.8% LEL: 2%	Strong oxidizers, lithium-aluminum alloys [Note: Peroxides may accumulate upon prolonged storage in presence of air.]	Char; CS₂; GC/FID; IV [#1609]
Tetramethyl lead (as Pb) $Pb(CH_3)_4$ 75-74-1 TP4725000 1649 131	Lead tetramethyl, Tetramethylplumbane, TML	NIOSH/OSHA 0.075 mg/m³ [skin]	40 mg/m³ (as Pb)	Colorless liquid (unless dyed red, orange, or blue) with a fruity odor. [Note: Main usage is in anti-knock additives for gasoline.]	MW: 267.3 BP: 212°F (Decomposes) Sol: 0.002% FI.P: 100°F IP: 8.50 eV Sp.Gr: 2.00 Class II Combustible Liquid	VP: 23 mm FRZ: -15°F UEL: ? LEL: ?	Strong oxidizers such as sulfuryl chloride or potassium permanganate	XAD-2; Pentane; GC/PID; IV [#2534]
Tetramethyl succinonitrile $(CH_3)_2C(CN)C(CN)(CH_3)_2$ 3333-52-6 WN4025000 1 ppm = 5.57 mg/m³	Tetramethyl succino-dinitrile, TMSN	NIOSH/OSHA 3 mg/m³ (0.5 ppm) [skin]	5 ppm	Colorless, odorless solid. [Note: Forms cyanide in the body.]	MW: 136.2 BP: Sublimes Sol: Insoluble FI.P: ? IP: ? Sp.Gr: 1.07 Combustible Solid	VP: ? MLT: 338°F (Sublimes) UEL: ? LEL: ?	Strong oxidizers	Char; CS₂; GC/FID; II(3) [#S155]

Personal protection and sanitation (See Table 3)	Recommendations for respirator selection — maximum concentration for use (MUC) (See Table 4)	Route	Symptoms (See Table 5)	First aid (See Table 6)	Target organs (See Table 5)
Skin: Prevent skin contact (>0.1%) Eyes: Prevent eye contact Wash skin: When contam (>0.1%) Remove: When wet or contam (>0.1%) Change: Daily Provide: Quick drench (>0.1%) [Tetraethyl lead (as Pb)]	NIOSH/OSHA 0.75 mg/m³: SA 1.875 mg/m³: SA:CF 3.75 mg/m³: SAT:CF/SCBAF/SAF 40 mg/m³: SA:PD,PP §: SCBAF:PD,PP/SAF:PD,PP:ASCBA Escape: GMFOV/SCBAE	Inh Abs Ing Con	Insom, lass, anxiety; tremor, hyper-reflexia, spasticity; bradycardia, hypotension, hypothermia, pallor, nau, anor, low-wgt; conf, disorientation, halu, psychosis, mania, convuls, coma; eye irrit	Eye: Irr immed Skin: Soap wash immed Breath: Resp support Swallow: Medical attention immed	CNS, CVS, kidneys, eyes
Skin: Prevent skin contact Eyes: Prevent eye contact Wash skin: When contam Remove: When wet (flamm) Change: N.R. [Tetrahydrofuran]	NIOSH/OSHA 2000 ppm: SA:CF£/CCRFOV/GMFOV/ PAPROV£/SCBAF/SAF §: SCBAF:PD,PP/SAF:PD,PP:ASCBA Escape: GMFOV/SCBAE	Inh Ing Con	Irrit eyes, upper resp sys; nau, dizz, head, CNS depres	Eye: Irr immed Skin: Water flush prompt Breath: Resp support Swallow: Medical attention immed	Eyes, resp sys, CNS
Skin: Prevent skin contact (>0.1%) Eyes: Prevent eye contact Wash skin: When contam (>0.1%) Remove: When wet or contam (>0.1%) Change: Daily Provide: Quick drench (>0.1%) [Tetramethyl lead (as Pb)]	NIOSH/OSHA 0.75 mg/m³: SA 1.875 mg/m³: SA:CF 3.75 mg/m³: SAT:CF/SCBAF/SAF 40 mg/m³: SA:PD,PP §: SCBAF:PD,PP/SAF:PD,PP:ASCBA Escape: GMFOV/SCBAE	Inh Abs Ing Con	Insom, bad dreams, restless, anxious; hypotension; nau, anor; delirium, mania, convuls; coma	Eye: Irr immed Skin: Soap wash immed Breath: Resp support Swallow: Medical attention immed	CNS, CVS, kidneys
Skin: Prevent skin contact Eyes: Prevent eye contact Wash skin: When contam Remove: When wet or contam Change: Daily [Tetramethyl succinonitrile]	NIOSH/OSHA 28 mg/m³: SA/SCBAF §: SCBAF:PD,PP/SAF:PD,PP:ASCBA Escape: GMFOVHiE/SCBAE	Inh Abs Ing Con	Head, nau; convuls, coma; liver, kidney, GI effects	Eye: Irr immed Skin: Soap wash prompt Breath: Resp support Swallow: Medical attention immed	CNS, liver, kidneys, GI tract

Chemical name, structure/formula, CAS and RTECS Nos., and DOT ID and guide Nos.	Synonyms, trade names, and conversion factors	Exposure limits (TWA unless noted otherwise)	IDLH	Physical description	Chemical and physical properties		Incompatibilities and reactivities	Measurement method (See Table 1)
					MW, BP, SOL Fl.P, IP, Sp, Gr, flammability	VP, FRZ UEL, LEL		
Tetranitromethane $C(NO_2)_4$ 509-14-8 PB4025000 1510 143	Tetan, TNM 1 ppm = 8.02 mg/m³	NIOSH/OSHA 1 ppm (8 mg/m³)	4 ppm	Colorless to pale-yellow liquid or solid (below 57°F) with a pungent odor.	MW: 196.0 BP: 259°F Sol: Insoluble Fl.P: ? IP: ? Sp.Gr: 1.62 Combustible Liquid, but difficult to ignite.	VP: 8 mm FRZ: 57°F UEL: ? LEL: ?	Hydrocarbons, alkalis, metals, oxidizers, aluminum, toluene, cotton [Note: Combustible material wet with tetranitromethane may be highly explosive.]	Imp/Ethyl Acetate none; GC/FID IV [#3513]
Tetrasodium pyrophosphate $Na_4P_2O_7$ 7722-88-5 UX7350000	Pyrophosphate, Sodium pyrophosphate, Tetrasodium diphosphate, Tetrasodium pyrophosphate (anhydrous), TSPP	NIOSH 5 mg/m³ OSHA† none	N.D.	Odorless, white powder or granules. [Note: The decahydrate ($Na_4P_2O_7 \cdot 10H_2O$) is in the form of colorless, transparent crystals.]	MW: 265.9 BP: Decomposes Sol(77°F): 7% IP: NA Sp.Gr: 2.45 Noncombustible Solid	VP: 0 mm (approx) MLT: 1810°F UEL: NA LEL: NA	Strong acids	Filter; none; Grav; IV [#0500, Particulates NOR (total)]
Tetryl $(NO_2)_3C_6H_2N(NO_2)CH_3$ 479-45-8 BY6300000	N-Methyl-N,2,4,6-tetranitroaniline; Nitramine; 2,4,6-Tetryl; 2,4,6-Trinitrophenyl-N-methylnitramine	NIOSH/OSHA 1.5 mg/m³ [skin]	750 mg/m³	Colorless to yellow, odorless, crystalline solid.	MW: 287.2 BP: 356-374°F (Explodes) Sol: 0.02% Fl.P: Explodes IP: ? Sp.Gr: 1.57 Combustible Solid (Class A Explosive)	VP: <1 mm MLT: 268°F UEL: ? LEL: ?	Oxidizable materials, hydrazine	Filter; Reagent; Vis; II(3) [#S225]
Thallium (soluble compounds, as Tl) 1707 151 (compounds, n.o.s.)	Synonyms vary depending upon the specific soluble thallium compound.	NIOSH/OSHA 0.1 mg/m³ [skin]	15 mg/m³ (as Tl)	Appearance and odor odor vary depending upon the specific soluble thallium compound.	Properties vary depending upon the specific soluble thallium compound.		Varies	Filter; Acid; ICP; IV [#7300, Elements]

Personal protection and sanitation (See Table 3)		Recommendations for respirator selection — maximum concentration for use (MUC) (See Table 4)	Health hazards			
			Route	Symptoms (See Table 5)	First aid (See Table 6)	Target organs (See Table 5)
Skin: Eyes: Wash skin: Remove: Change: Provide:	Prevent skin contact Prevent eye contact When contam When wet (flamm) Daily Eyewash	NIOSH/OSHA 4 ppm: SA:CF£/CCRFS4/GMFS4/ PAPRS£/SCBAF/SAF §: SCBAF:PD,PP/SAF:PD,PP:ASCBA Escape: GMFS4/SCBAE	Inh Ing Con	Irrit eyes, skin, nose, throat; dizz, head; chest pain, dysp; methemo, cyan; skin burns	Eye: Irr immed Skin: Soap wash prompt Breath: Resp support Swallow: Medical attention immed	Eyes, skin, resp sys, blood, CNS
[Tetranitromethane]						
Skin: Eyes: Wash skin: Remove: Change: Provide:	Prevent skin contact Prevent eye contact When contam When wet or contam Daily Eyewash (soln)	TBAL	Inh Ing Con	Irrit eyes, skin, nose, throat; derm	Eye: Irr immed Skin: Water wash prompt Breath: Resp support Swallow: Medical attention immed	Eyes, skin, resp sys
[Tetrasodium pyrophosphate]						
Skin: Eyes: Wash skin: Remove: Change:	Prevent skin contact Prevent eye contact When contam/Daily When wet or contam Daily	NIOSH/OSHA 7.5 mg/m³: DM 15 mg/m³: DMXSQ*/SA* 37.5 mg/m³: SA:CF*/PAPRDM* 75 mg/m³: HiEF/SCBAF/SAF 750 mg/m³: SAF:PD,PP §: SCBAF:PD,PP/SAF:PD,PP:ASCBA Escape: HiEF/SCBAE	Inh Abs Ing Con	Sens derm, itch, eryt; edema on nasal folds, cheeks, neck; kera; sneez; anemia; ftg; cough, coryza; irrity; mal, head, lass, insom; nau, vomit; liver, kidney damage	Eye: Irr immed Skin: Soap wash prompt Breath: Resp support Swallow: Medical attention immed	Eyes, skin, resp sys, CNS, liver, kidneys
[Tetryl]						
Skin: Eyes: Wash skin: Remove: Change:	Prevent skin contact Prevent eye contact When contam When wet or contam Daily	NIOSH/OSHA 0.5 mg/m³: DM^ 1 mg/m³: DMXSQ^/SA 2.5 mg/m³: SA:CF/PAPRDM^ 5 mg/m³: HiEF/SAT:CF/PAPRTHiE/ SCBAF/SAF 15 mg/m³: SAF:PD,PP §: SCBAF:PD,PP/SAF:PD,PP:ASCBA Escape: HiEF/SCBAE	Inh Abs Ing Con	Nau, diarr, abdom pain, vomit; ptosis, strabismus; peri neuritis, tremor; retster tight, chest pain, pulm edema; sez, chorea, psychosis; liver, kidney damage; alopecia; pares legs	Eye: Irr immed Skin: Water flush prompt Breath: Resp support Swallow: Medical attention immed	Eyes, resp sys, CNS, liver, kidneys, GI tract, body hair
[Thallium (soluble compounds, as Tl)]						

Chemical name, structure/formula, CAS and RTECS Nos., and DOT ID and guide Nos.	Synonyms, trade names, and conversion factors	Exposure limits (TWA unless noted otherwise)	IDLH	Physical description	Chemical and physical properties		Incompatibilities and reactivities	Measurement method (See Table 1)
					MW, BP, SOL Fl.P, IP, Sp, Gr, flammability	VP, FRZ UEL, LEL		
4,4'-Thiobis(6-tert-butyl-m-cresol) [CH₃(OH)C₆H₂C(CH₃)₃]₂S 96-69-5 GP3150000	4,4'-Thiobis(3-methyl-6-tert-butylphenol); 1,1'-Thiobis(2-methyl-4-hydroxy-5-tert-butylbenzene)	NIOSH 10 mg/m³ (total) 5 mg/m³ (resp) OSHA† 15 mg/m³ (total) 5 mg/m³ (resp)	N.D.	Light-gray to tan powder with a slightly aromatic odor.	MW: 358.6 BP: ? Sol: 0.08% Fl.P: 420°F IP: ? Sp.Gr. 1.10 Combustible Solid	VP: 0.0000006 mm MLT: 302°F UEL: NA LEL: NA	None reported	Filter; none; Grav; IV [Particulates NOR: #0500 (total) #0600 (resp)]
Thioglycolic acid HSCH₂COOH 68-11-1 AI5950000 1940 153	Acetyl mercaptan, Mercaptoacetate, Mercaptoacetic acid, 2-Mercaptoacetic acid, 2-Thioglycolic acid, Thiovanic acid 1 ppm = 3.77 mg/m³	NIOSH 1 ppm (4 mg/m³) [skin] OSHA† none	N.D.	Colorless liquid with a strong, disagreeable odor characteristic of mercaptans. [Note: Olfactory fatigue may occur after short exposures.]	MW: 92.1 BP: ? Sol: Miscible Fl.P: >230°F IP: ? Sp.Gr. 1.32 Class IIIB Combustible Liquid	VP(64°F): 10mm FRZ: 2°F UEL: ? LEL: 5.9%	Air, strong oxidizers, bases, active metals (e.g., sodium potassium, magnesium, calcium) [Note: Readily oxidized by air.]	None available
Thionyl chloride SOCl₂ 7719-09-7 XM5150000 1836 137	Sulfinyl chloride, Sulfur chloride oxide, Sulfurous dichloride, Sulfurous oxychloride, Thionyl dichloride 1 ppm = 4.87 mg/m³	NIOSH C 1 ppm (5 mg/m³) OSHA† none	N.D.	Colorless to yellow to reddish liquid with a pungent odor like sulfur dioxide. [Note: Fumes form when exposed to moist air.]	MW: 119.0 BP: 169°F Sol: Reacts Fl.P: NA IP: ? Sp.Gr. 1.64 Noncombustible Liquid	VP(70°F): 100mm FRZ: -156°F UEL: NA LEL: NA	Water, acids, alkalis, ammonia, chloryl perchlorate [Note: Reacts violently with water to form sulfur dioxide & hydrogen chloride.]	None available
Thiram C₆H₁₂N₂S₄ 137-26-8 JO1400000 2771 151	bis(Dimethylthiocarbamoyl) disulfide, Tetramethylthiuram disulfide [(CH₃)₂NC(S)SSC(S)N(CH₃)₂]	NIOSH/OSHA 5 mg/m³	100 mg/m³	Colorless to yellow, crystalline solid with a characteristic odor. [Note: Commercial pesticide products may be dyed blue.]	MW: 240.4 BP: Decomposes Sol: 0.003% Fl.P: ? IP: ? Sp.Gr. 1.29 Combustible Solid	VP: 0.000008 mm MLT: 312°F UEL: ? LEL: ?	Strong oxidizers, strong acids, oxidizable materials	Filter; CH₃CN; HPLC/UVD; IV [#5005]

Personal protection and sanitation (See Table 3)		Recommendations for respirator selection — maximum concentration for use (MUC) (See Table 4)	Health hazards				
			Route	Symptoms (See Table 5)	First aid (See Table 6)		Target organs (See Table 5)
Skin:	N.R.	TBAL	Inh	Irrit eyes, skin, resp sys	Eye:	Irr immed	Eyes, skin, resp sys
Eyes:	N.R.		Ing		Breath:	Fresh air	
Wash skin:	N.R.		Con		Swallow:	Medical attention	
Remove:	N.R.					immed	
Change:	N.R.						

[4,4'-Thiobis(6-tert-butyl-m-cresol)]

Skin:	Prevent skin contact	TBAL	Inh	Irrit eyes, skin, nose,	Eye:	Irr immed	Eyes, skin, resp sys
Eyes:	Prevent eye contact		Abs	throat; lac, corn damage;	Skin:	Water flush immed	
Wash skin:	When contam		Ing	skin burns, blisters;	Breath:	Resp support	
Remove:	When wet or contam		Con	in animals: weak; gasping	Swallow:	Medical attention	
Change:	N.R.			respirations; convuls		immed	
Provide:	Eyewash, Quick drench						

307

[Thioglycolic acid]

Skin:	Prevent skin contact	TBAL	Inh	Irrit eyes, skin, muc memb;	Eye:	Irr immed	Eyes, skin, resp sys
Eyes:	Prevent eye contact		Ing	eye, skin burns	Skin:	Water flush immed	
Wash skin:	When contam		Con		Breath:	Resp support	
Remove:	When wet or contam		Con		Swallow:	Medical attention	
Change:	N.R.					immed	
Provide:	Eyewash, Quick drench						

[Thionyl chloride]

Skin:	Prevent skin contact	NIOSH/OSHA	Inh	Irrit eyes, skin, muc memb;	Eye:	Irr immed	Eyes, skin, resp sys,
Eyes:	Prevent eye contact	50 mg/m³: CCROVDMFu*/SA*	Ing	derm; Antabuse-like effects	Skin:	Soap wash prompt	CNS
Wash skin:	When contam	100 mg/m³: SA:CF*/CCRFOVHiE/	Con		Breath:	Resp support	
Remove:	When wet or contam	GMFOVHiE/PAPROVDMFu*/			Swallow:	Medical attention	
Change:	Daily	SCBAF/SAF				immed	
		§: SCBAF:PD,PP/SAF:PD,PP:ASCBA					
		Escape: GMFOVHiE/SCBAE					

[Thiram]

Chemical name, structure/formula, CAS and RTECS Nos., and DOT ID and guide Nos.	Synonyms, trade names, and conversion factors	Exposure limits (TWA unless noted otherwise)	IDLH	Physical description	Chemical and physical properties		Incompatibilities and reactivities	Measurement method (See Table 1)
					MW, BP, SOL Fl.P, IP, Sp, Gr, flammability	VP, FRZ UEL, LEL		
Tin Sn 7440-31-5 XP7320000	Metallic tin, Tin flake, Tin metal, Tin powder	NIOSH*/OSHA* 2 mg/m³ [*Note: The REL and PEL also apply to other inorganic tin compounds (as Sn) except tin oxides.]	100 mg/m³	Gray to almost silver-white, ductile, malleable, lustrous solid.	MW: 118.7 BP: 4545°F Sol: Insoluble Fl.P: NA IP: NA Sp.Gr: 7.28 Noncombustible Solid, but powdered form may ignite.	VP: 0 mm (approx) MLT: 449°F UEL: NA LEL: NA	Chlorine, turpentine, acids, alkalis	Filter; Acid; ICP; IV [#7300, Elements]
Tin (organic compounds, as Sn)	Synonyms vary depending upon the specific organic tin compound. [Note: Also see specific listing for Cyhexatin.]	NIOSH* 0.1 mg/m³ [skin] [*Note: The REL applies to all organic tin compounds except cyhexatin.] OSHA† 0.1 mg/m³	25 mg/m³ (as Sn)	Appearance and odor vary depending upon the specific organic tin compound.	Properties vary depending upon the specific organic tin compound.		Varies	Filter/ XAD-2; Acetic acid/ CH₃CN; HPLC/GFAAS; IV [#5504]
Tin(II) oxide (as Sn) SnO 21651-19-4	Stannous oxide, Tin protoxide [Note: Also see specific listing for Tin(IV) oxide (as Sn).]	NIOSH 2 mg/m³ OSHA† none	N.D.	Brownish-black powder.	MW: 134.7 BP: Decomposes Sol: Insoluble Fl.P: NA IP: NA Sp.Gr: 6.3	VP: 0 mm (approx) MLT(600 mmHg): 1976°F (Decomposes) UEL: NA LEL: NA	None reported	Filter; Acids; ICP; IV [#7300, Elements]
Tin(IV) oxide (as Sn) SnO₂ 18282-10-5 XQ4000000	Stannic dioxide, Stannic oxide, White tin oxide [Note: Also see specific listing for Tin(II) oxide (as Sn).]	NIOSH 2 mg/m³ OSHA† none	N.D.	White or slightly gray powder.	MW: 150.7 BP: Decomposes Sol: Insoluble Fl.P: NA IP: NA Sp.Gr: 6.95	VP: 0 mm (approx) MLT: 2966°F (Decomposes) UEL: ? LEL: ?	Chlorine trifluoride	Filter; Acids; ICP; IV [#7300, Elements]

Personal protection and sanitation (See Table 3)	Recommendations for respirator selection — maximum concentration for use (MUC) (See Table 4)	Health hazards			
		Route	Symptoms (See Table 5)	First aid (See Table 6)	Target organs (See Table 5)
Skin: N.R. Eyes: N.R. Wash skin: N.R. Remove: N.R. Change: N.R.	NIOSH/OSHA 10 mg/m³: DM* 20 mg/m³: DMXSQ^*/SA* 50 mg/m³: SA:CF*/PAPRDM^* 100 mg/m³: HiEF/SCBAF/SAF §: SCBAF:PD,PP/SAF:PD,PP:ASCBA Escape: HiEF/SCBAE	Inh Ccn	Irrit eyes, skin, resp sys; in animals: vomit, diarr, para with musc twitch	Eye: Irr immed Skin: Soap wash immed Breath: Resp support Swallow: Medical attention immed	Eyes, skin, resp sys
[Tin]					
Recommendations vary depending upon the specific compound.	NIOSH/OSHA 1 mg/m³: CCROVDM/SA 2.5 mg/m³: SA:CF/PAPROVDM 5 mg/m³: CCRFOVHiE/GMFOVHiE/ PAPRTOVHiE/SAT:CF/ SCBAF/SAF 25 mg/m³: SAF:PD,PP §: SCBAF:PD,PP/SAF:PD,PP:ASCBA Escape: GMFOVHiE/SCBAE	Inh Abs Ing Con	Irrit eyes, skin; resp sys; head, verti; psycho-neurologic dist; sore throat, cough; abdom pain, vomit; urine retention; paresis, focal anes; skin burns, pruritus; in animals: hemolysis; hepatic nec; kidney damage	Eye: Irr immed Skin: Water flush immed Breath: Resp support Swallow: Medical attention immed	Eyes, skin, resp sys, CNS, liver, kidneys, urinary tract, blood
[Tin (organic compounds, as Sn)					
Skin: N.R. Eyes: N.R. Wash skin: N.R. Remove: N.R. Change: N.R.	TBAL	Inh Con	Stannosis (benign pneumoconiosis): dysp, decr pulm func	Eye: Irr immed Breath: Fresh air	Resp sys
[Tin(II) oxide (as Sn)]					
Skin: N.R. Eyes: N.R. Wash skin: N.R. Remove: N.R. Change: N.R.	TBAL	Inh Con	Stannosis (benign pneumoconiosis): dysp, decr pulm func	Eye: Irr immed Breath: Fresh air	Resp sys
[Tin(IV) oxide (as Sn)]					

Chemical name, structure/formula, CAS and RTECS Nos., and DOT ID and guide Nos.	Synonyms, trade names, and conversion factors	Exposure limits (TWA unless noted otherwise)	IDLH	Physical description	Chemical and physical properties		Incompatibilities and reactivities	Measurement method (See Table 1)
					MW, BP, SOL Fl.P, IP, Sp, Gr, flammability	VP, FRZ UEL, LEL		
Titanium dioxide TiO_2 13463-67-7 XR2275000	Rutile, Titanium oxide, Titanium peroxide	NIOSH Ca See Appendix A OSHA† 15 mg/m³	Ca [5000 mg/m³]	White, odorless powder.	MW: 79.9 BP: 4532- 5432°F Sol: Insoluble Fl.P: NA IP: NA Sp.Gr: 4.26 Noncombustible Solid	VP: 0 mm (approx) MLT: 3326- 3362°F UEL: NA LEL: NA	None reported	Filter; Acid; FAAS; II(3) [#S385]
o-Tolidine $C_{14}H_{16}N_2$ 119-93-7 DD1225000	4,4'-Diamino-3,3'-dimethyl-biphenyl; Diaminoditolyl; 3,3'-Dimethylbenzidine; 3,3'-Dimethyl-4,4'-diphenyl-diamine; 3,3'-Tolidine	NIOSH Ca See Appendix A See Appendix C C 0.02 mg/m³ [60-min] [skin] OSHA See Appendix C	Ca [N.D.]	White to reddish crystals or powder. [Note: Darkens on exposure to air. Often used in paste or wet cake form. Used as a basis for many dyes.]	MW: 212.3 BP: 572°F Sol: 0.1% Fl.P: ? IP: ? Sp.Gr: ? Combustible Solid	VP: ? MLT: 264°F UEL: ? LEL: ?	Strong oxidizers	Filter; Water; HPLC/UVD; IV [#5013, Dyes]
Toluene $C_6H_5CH_3$ 108-88-3 XS5250000 1294 130	Methyl benzene, Methyl benzol, Phenyl methane, Toluol 1 ppm = 3.77 mg/m³	NIOSH 100 ppm (375 mg/m³) ST 150 ppm (560 mg/m³) OSHA† 200 ppm C 300 ppm 500 ppm (10-min max peak)	500 ppm	Colorless liquid with a sweet, pungent, benzene-like odor.	MW: 92.1 BP: 232°F Sol(74°F): 0.07% Fl.P: 40°F IP: 8.82 eV Sp.Gr: 0.87 Class IB Flammable Liquid	VP: 21 mm FRZ: -139°F UEL: 7.1% LEL: 1.1%	Strong oxidizers	Char; CS_2; GC/FID; IV [#1500, Hydro-carbons] [Also #4000, #1501]
Toluenediamine $CH_3C_6H_3(NH_2)_2$ 25376-45-8 95-80-7 (2,4-TDA) XS9445000 XS9625000 (2,4-TDA) 1709 181	Diaminotoluene, Methylphenylene diamine, TDA, Tolylenediamine	NIOSH Ca (all isomers) See Appendix A OSHA none	Ca [N.D.]	Colorless to brown, needle-shaped crystals or powder. [Note: Tends to darken on storage & exposure to air. Properties given are for 2,4-TDA.]	MW: 122.2 BP: 558°F Sol: Soluble Fl.P: 300°F IP: ? Sp.Gr: 1.05 (Liquid at 212°F) Combustible Solid	VP(224°F): 1mm MLT: 210°F UEL: ? LEL: ?	None reported	Imp; Reagent; HPLC/UVD; IV [#5516]

Personal protection and sanitation (See Table 3)		Recommendations for respirator selection — maximum concentration for use (MUC) (See Table 4)	Health hazards				
			Route	Symptoms (See Table 5)	First aid (See Table 6)		Target organs (See Table 5)
Skin:	N.R.	NIOSH	Inh	Lung fib; [carc]	Breath:	Resp support	Resp sys [in animals: lung tumors]
Eyes:	N.R.	¥: SCBAF:PD,PP/SAF:PD,PP:ASCBA					
Wash skin:	N.R.	Escape: HiEF/SCBAE					
Remove:	N.R.						
Change:	Daily						

[Titanium dioxide]

Skin:	Prevent skin contact	NIOSH	Inh	Irrit eyes, nose;	Eye:	Irr immed	Eyes, resp sys,
Eyes:	Prevent eye contact	¥: SCBAF:PD,PP/SAF:PD,PP:ASCBA	Abs	in animals: liver, kidney	Skin:	Soap flush immed	liver, kidneys
Wash skin:	When contam/Daily	Escape: GMFOVHiE/SCBAE	Ing	damage; [carc]	Breath:	Resp support	[in animals:
Remove:	When wet or contam		Con		Swallow:	Medical attention	liver, bladder &
Change:	Daily					immed	mammary gland
Provide:	Eyewash, Quick drench						tumors]

311

[o-Tolidine]

Skin:	Prevent skin contact	NIOSH	Inh	Irrit eyes, nose; ftg, weak,	Eye:	Irr immed	Eyes, skin, resp sys,
Eyes:	Prevent eye contact	500 ppm: CCROV*/PAPROV*/GMFOV/	Abs	conf, euph, dizz, head;	Skin:	Soap wash prompt	CNS, liver, kidneys
Wash skin:	When contam	SA*/SCBAF	Ing	dilated pupils, lac; ner,	Breath:	Resp support	
Remove:	When wet (flamm)	§: SCBAF:PD,PP/SAF:PD,PP:ASCBA	Con	musc ftg, insom; pares;	Swallow:	Medical attention	
Change:	N.R.	Escape: GMFOV/SCBAE		derm; liver, kidney damage		immed	

[Toluene]

Skin:	Prevent skin contact	NIOSH	Inh	Irrit eyes, skin, nose,	Eye:	Irr immed	Eyes, skin, resp sys,
Eyes:	Prevent eye contact	¥: SCBAF:PD,PP/SAF:PD,PP:ASCBA	Abs	throat; derm; ataxia, tacar,	Skin:	Water flush immed	blood, CVS, liver,
Wash skin:	When contam/Daily	Escape: GMFOV/SCBAE	Ing	nau, vomit, convuls, resp	Breath:	Resp support	CNS
Remove:	When wet or contam		Con	depres; methemo, cyan, head,	Swallow:	Medical attention	[in animals: liver,
Change:	Daily			ftg, dizz, bluish skin;		immed	skin & mammary
Provide:	Eyewash, Quick drench			liver inj; [carc]			gland tumors]

[Toluenediamine]

Chemical name, structure/formula, CAS and RTECS Nos., and DOT ID and guide Nos.	Synonyms, trade names, and conversion factors	Exposure limits (TWA unless noted otherwise)	IDLH	Physical description	Chemical and physical properties		Incompatibilities and reactivities	Measurement method (See Table 1)
					MW, BP, SOL Fl.P, IP, Sp, Gr, flammability	VP, FRZ UEL, LEL		
Toluene-2,4-diisocyanate $CH_3C_6H_3(NCO)_2$ 584-84-9 CZ6300000 2078 156	TDI; 2,4-TDI; 2,4-Toluene diisocyanate 1 ppm = 7.13 mg/m^3	NIOSH Ca See Appendix A OSHA† C 0.02 ppm (0.14 mg/m^3)	Ca [2.5 ppm]	Colorless to pale-yellow solid or liquid (above 71°F) with a sharp, pungent odor.	MW: 174.2 BP: 484°F Sol: Insoluble Fl.P: 260°F IP: ? Sp.Gr: 1.22 Class IIIB Combustible Liquid	VP(77°F): 0.05 mm MLT: 71°F UEL: 9.5% LEL: 0.9%	Strong oxidizers, water, acids, bases & amines (may cause foam & spatter); alcohols [Note: Reacts slowly with water to form carbon dioxide and polyureas.]	Coated glass wool; Methanol; HPLC/UVD; IV [#2535]
o-Toluidine $CH_3C_6H_4NH_2$ 95-53-4 XU2975000 1708 153	o-Aminotoluene, 2-Aminotoluene, 1-Methyl-2-aminobenzene, o-Methylaniline, 2-Methylaniline, ortho-Toluidine 1 ppm = 4.38 mg/m^3	NIOSH Ca See Appendix A [skin] OSHA 5 ppm (22 mg/m^3) [skin]	Ca [50 ppm]	Colorless to pale-yellow liquid with an aromatic, aniline-like odor.	MW: 107.2 BP: 392°F Sol: 2% Fl.P: 185°F IP: 7.44 eV Sp.Gr: 1.01 Class IIIA Combustible Liquid	VP: 0.3 mm FRZ: 6°F UEL: ? LEL: ?	Strong oxidizers, nitric acid, bases	Si gel; Ethanol; GC/FID; IV [#2002, Aromatic Amines]
m-Toluidine $CH_3C_6H_4NH_2$ 108-44-1 XU2800000 1708 153	3-Amino-1-methylbenzene, 1-Aminophenylmethane, m-Aminotoluene, 3-Methylaniline, 3-Methylbenzenamine, 3-Toluidine, m-Tolylamine	NIOSH See Appendix D OSHA† none	N.D.	Colorless to light-yellow liquid with an aromatic, amine-like odor. [Note: Used as a basis for many dyes.]	MW: 107.2 BP: 397°F Sol: 2% Fl.P: 187°F IP: 7.50 eV Sp.Gr: 0.999 Class IIIA Combustible Liquid	VP(106°F): 1mm FRZ: -23°F UEL: ? LEL: ?	Oxidizers, acids	Si gel; Ethanol; GC/FID; IV [#2002, Aromatic Amines]
p-Toluidine $CH_3C_6H_4NH_2$ 106-49-0 XU3150000 1708 153	4-Aminotoluene, 4-Methylaniline, 4-Methylbenzenamine, 4-Toluidine, Tolylamine	NIOSH Ca See Appendix A OSHA† none	Ca [N.D.]	White solid with an aromatic odor. [Note: Used as a basis for many dyes.]	MW: 107.2 BP: 393°F Sol: 0.7% Fl.P: 188°F IP: 7.50 eV Sp.Gr: 1.05 Combustible Solid	VP(108°F): 1mm MLT: 111°F UEL: ? LEL: ?	Oxidizers, acids	Si gel; Ethanol; GC/FID; IV [#2002, Aromatic Amines]

Personal protection and sanitation (See Table 3)		Recommendations for respirator selection — maximum concentration for use (MUC) (See Table 4)	Health hazards				
			Route	Symptoms (See Table 5)	First aid (See Table 6)		Target organs (See Table 5)
Skin: Eyes: Wash skin: Remove: Change: Provide:	Prevent skin contact Prevent eye contact When contam/Daily When wet or contam Daily Eyewash, Quick drench	NIOSH ¥: SCBAF:PD,PP/SAF:PD,PP:ASCBA Escape: GMFOV/SCBAE	Inh Ing Con	Irrit eyes, skin, nose, throat; choke, paroxysmal cough; chest pain, retster soreness; nau, vomit, abdom pain; bron, bronchospasm, pulm edema; dysp, asthma; conj, lac; derm, skin sens; [carc]	Eye: Skin: Breath: Swallow:	Irr immed Soap wash immed Resp support Medical attention immed	Eyes, skin, resp sys [in animals: pancreas, liver, mammary gland, circulatory sys & skin tumors]

[Toluene-2,4-diisocyanate]

Skin: Eyes: Wash skin: Remove: Change: Provide:	Prevent skin contact Prevent eye contact When contam When wet or contam N.R. Eyewash, Quick drench	NIOSH ¥: SCBAF:PD,PP/SAF:PD,PP:ASCBA Escape: GMFOV/SCBAE	Inh Abs Ing Con	Irrit eyes; anoxia, head, cyan; weak, dizz, drow; micro hema, eye burns; derm; [carc]	Eye: Skin: Breath: Swallow:	Irr immed Soap wash immed Resp support Medical attention immed	Eyes, skin, blood kidneys, liver, CVS [bladder cancer]

[o-Toluidine]

Skin: Eyes: Wash skin: Remove: Change:	Prevent skin contact Prevent eye contact When contam When wet or contam N.R.	TBAL	Inh Abs Ing Con	Irrit eyes, skin; hema, methemo; cyan, nau, vomit, low BP, convuls; anemia, weak	Eye: Skin: Breath: Swallow:	Irr immed Soap wash immed Resp support Medical attention immed	Eyes, skin, blood CVS

[m-Toluidine]

Skin: Eyes: Wash skin: Remove: Change: Provide:	Prevent skin contact Prevent eye contact When contam/Daily When wet or contam Daily Eyewash, Quick drench	NIOSH ¥: SCBAF:PD,PP/SAF:PD,PP:ASCBA Escape: GMFOVHiE/SCBAE	Inh Abs Ing Con	Irrit eyes, skin; derm; hema, methemo; cyan, nau, vomit, low BP, convuls; anemia, weak; [carc]	Eye: Skin: Breath: Swallow:	Irr immed Soap wash immed Resp support Medical attention immed	Eyes, skin, blood, CVS [in animals: liver tumors]

[p-Toluidine]

Chemical name, structure/formula, CAS and RTECS Nos., and DOT ID and guide Nos.	Synonyms, trade names, and conversion factors	Exposure limits (TWA unless noted otherwise)	IDLH	Physical description	Chemical and physical properties		Incompatibilities and reactivities	Measurement method (See Table 1)
					MW, BP, SOL Fl.P, IP, Sp, Gr, flammability	VP, FRZ UEL, LEL		
Tributyl phosphate $(CH_3[CH_2]_3O)_3PO$ 126-73-8 TC7700000 1 ppm = 10.89 mg/m³	Butyl phosphate, TBP, Tributyl ester of phosphoric acid, Tri-n-butyl phosphate	NIOSH 0.2 ppm (2.5 mg/m³) OSHA† 5 mg/m³	30 ppm	Colorless to pale-yellow, odorless liquid.	MW: 266.3 BP: 552°F (Decomposes) Sol: 0.6% Fl.P(oc): 295°F IP: ? Sp.Gr: 0.98 Class IIIB Combustible Liquid	VP(77°F): 0.004 mm FRZ: -112°F UEL: ? LEL: ?	Alkalis, oxidizers, water, moist air	Filter; Diethyl ether; GC/FPD; IV [#5034]
Trichloroacetic acid CCl_3COOH 76-03-9 AJ7875000 1839 153 (solid) 2564 153 (solution)	TCA, Trichloroethanoic acid	NIOSH 1 ppm (7 mg/m³) OSHA† none 1 ppm = 6.68 mg/m³	N.D.	Colorless to white, crystalline solid with a sharp, pungent odor.	MW: 163.4 BP: 388°F Sol: Miscible Fl.P: NA IP: ? Sp.Gr: 1.62 Noncombustible Solid	VP(124°F): 1mm MLT: 136°F UEL: NA LEL: NA	Moisture, iron, zinc, aluminum, strong oxidizers [Note: Decomposes on heating to form phosgene & hydrogen chloride. Corrosive to metals.]	None available
1,2,4-Trichlorobenzene $C_6H_3Cl_3$ 120-82-1 DC2100000none 2321 153 (liquid)	unsym-Trichlorobenzene; 1,2,4-Trichlorobenzol	NIOSH C 5 ppm (40 mg/m³) OSHA† 1 ppm = 7.42 mg/m³	N.D.	Colorless liquid or crystalline solid (below 63°F) with an aromatic odor. 2.5%	MW: 181.4 BP: 416°F Sol: 0.003% Fl.P: 222°F IP: ? Sp.Gr: 1.45 Class IIIB Combustible Liquid Combustible Solid	VP: 1 mm FRZ: 63°F UEL(302°F): 6.6% LEL(302°F):	Acids, acid fumes, oxidizers, steam	Filter/ XAD-2; Hexane; GC/ECD; IV [#5517, Poly-chloro-benzenes]
1,1,2-Trichloroethane $CHCl_2CH_2Cl$ 79-00-5 KJ3150000 1 ppm = 5.46 mg/m³	Ethane trichloride, ß-Trichloroethane, Vinyl trichloride	NIOSH Ca See Appendix A See Appendix C (Chloroethanes) 10 ppm (45 mg/m³) [skin] OSHA 10 ppm (45 mg/m³) [skin]	Ca [100 ppm]	Colorless liquid with a sweet, chloroform-like odor.	MW: 133.4 BP: 237°F Sol: 0.4% Fl.P: ? IP: 11.00 eV Sp.Gr: 1.44 Combustible Liquid, forms dense soot.	VP: 19mm FRZ: -34°F UEL: 15.5% LEL: 6%	Strong oxidizers & caustics; chemically-active metals (such as aluminum, magnesium powders, sodium & potassium)	Char; CS₂; GC/FID; IV [#1003, Haloge-nated Hydro-carbons]

314

Personal protection and sanitation (See Table 3)		Recommendations for respirator selection — maximum concentration for use (MUC) (See Table 4)	Health hazards					
			Route	Symptoms (See Table 5)		First aid (See Table 6)		Target organs (See Table 5)

Personal protection and sanitation (See Table 3)		Recommendations for respirator selection (MUC) (See Table 4)	Route	Symptoms (See Table 5)	First aid (See Table 6)		Target organs (See Table 5)
Skin:	Prevent skin contact	NIOSH	Inh	Irrit eyes, skin, resp sys;	Eye:	Irr immed	Eyes, skin, resp sys
Eyes:	Prevent eye contact	2 ppm: SA	Ing	head; nau	Skin:	Soap wash prompt	
Wash skin:	When contam	5 ppm: SA:CF	Con		Breath:	Resp support	
Remove:	When wet or contam	10 ppm: SCBAF/SAF			Swallow:	Medical attention	
Change:	N.R.	30 ppm: SAF:PD,PP				immed	
		§: SCBAF:PD,PP/SAF:PD,PP:ASCBA					
		Escape: GMFOVHiE/SCBAE					

[Tributyl phosphate]

Personal protection and sanitation (See Table 3)		Recommendations for respirator selection (MUC) (See Table 4)	Route	Symptoms (See Table 5)	First aid (See Table 6)		Target organs (See Table 5)
Skin:	Prevent skin contact	TBAL	Inh	Irrit eyes, skin, nose,	Eye:	Irr immed	Eyes, skin, resp sys,
Eyes:	Prevent eye contact		Ing	throat, resp sys; cough,	Skin:	Water flush immed	GI tract
Wash skin:	When contam		Con	dysp, delayed pulm edema;	Breath:	Resp support	
Remove:	When wet or contam			eye, skin burns; derm;	Swallow:	Medical attention	
Change:	Daily			salv, vomit, diarr		immed	
Provide:	Eyewash, Quick drench						

[Trichloroacetic acid]

Personal protection and sanitation (See Table 3)		Recommendations for respirator selection (MUC) (See Table 4)	Route	Symptoms (See Table 5)	First aid (See Table 6)		Target organs (See Table 5)
Skin:	Prevent skin contact	TBAL	Inh	Irrit eyes, skin, muc memb;	Eye:	Irr immed	Eyes, skin, resp sys,
Eyes:	Prevent eye contact		Abs	in animals: liver, kidney	Skin:	Soap wash	liver, repro sys
Wash skin:	When contam		Ing	damage; possible terato	Breath:	Resp support	
Remove:	When wet or contam		Con	effects	Swallow:	Medical attention	
Change:	N.R.					immed	

[1,2,4-Trichlorobenzene]

Personal protection and sanitation (See Table 3)		Recommendations for respirator selection (MUC) (See Table 4)	Route	Symptoms (See Table 5)	First aid (See Table 6)		Target organs (See Table 5)
Skin:	Prevent skin contact	NIOSH	Inh	Irrit eyes, nose; CNS	Eye:	Irr immed	Eyes, resp sys, CNS,
Eyes:	Prevent eye contact	¥: SCBAF:PD,PP/SAF:PD,PP:ASCBA	Abs	depres; liver, kidney	Skin:	Soap wash prompt	liver, kidneys
Wash skin:	When contam	Escape: GMFOV/SCBAE	Ing	damage; derm; [carc]	Breath:	Resp support	[in animals:
Remove:	When wet or contam		Con		Swallow:	Medical attention	liver cancer]
Change:	N.R.					immed	
Provide:	Eyewash, Quick drench						

[1,1,2-Trichloroethane]

Chemical name, structure/formula, CAS and RTECS Nos., and DOT ID and guide Nos.	Synonyms, trade names, and conversion factors	Exposure limits (TWA unless noted otherwise)	IDLH	Physical description	Chemical and physical properties		Incompatibilities and reactivities	Measurement method (See Table 1)
					MW, BP, SOL Fl.P, IP, Sp, Gr, flammability	VP, FRZ UEL, LEL		
Trichloroethylene CICH=CCl₂ 79-01-6 KX4550000 1710 160	Ethylene trichloride, TCE, Trichloroethene, Trilene 1 ppm = 5.37 mg/m³	NIOSH Ca See Appendix A See Appendix C OSHA† 100 ppm C 200 ppm 300 ppm (5-min max peak in any 2 hrs)	Ca [1000 ppm]	Colorless liquid (unless dyed blue) with a chloroform-like odor.	MW: 131.4 BP: 189°F Sol: 0.1% Fl.P: ? IP: 9.45 eV Sp.Gr: 1.46 Combustible Liquid, but burns with difficulty.	VP: 58 mm FRZ: -99°F UEL(77°F): 10.5% LEL(77°F): 8%	Strong caustics & alkalis; chemically-active metals (such as barium, lithium, sodium, magnesium, titanium & beryllium)	Char; CS₂; GC/FID; IV [#1022]
Trichloronaphthalene C₁₀H₅Cl₃ 1321-65-9 QK4025000	Halowax®, Nibren wax, Seekay wax	NIOSH/OSHA 5 mg/m³ [skin]	Unknown	Colorless to pale-yellow solid with an aromatic odor.	MW: 231.5 BP: 579-669°F Sol: Insoluble Fl.P(oc): 392°F IP: ? Sp.Gr: 1.58 Combustible Solid	VP: <1 mm MLT: 199°F UEL: ? LEL: ?	Strong oxidizers	Filter/Bub; none; GC/FID; II(2) [#S128]
1,2,3-Trichloropropane CH₂ClCHClCH₂Cl 96-18-4 TZ9275000	Allyl trichloride, Glycerol trichlorohydrin, Glyceryl trichlorohydrin, Trichlorohydrin 1 ppm = 6.03 mg/m³	NIOSH Ca See Appendix A 10 ppm (60 mg/m³) [skin] OSHA† 50 ppm (300 mg/m³)	Ca [100 ppm]	Colorless liquid with a chloroform-like odor.	MW: 147.4 BP: 314°F Sol: 0.1% Fl.P: 160°F IP: ? Sp.Gr: 1.33 Class IIIA Combustible Liquid	VP: 3 mm FRZ: 6°F UEL(302°F): 12.6% LEL(248°F): 3.2%	Chemically-active metals, strong caustics & oxidizers	Char; CS₂; GC/FID; IV [#1003, Halogenated Hydrocarbons]
1,1,2-Trichloro-1,2,2-trifluoroethane CCl₂FCClF₂ 76-13-1 KJ4000000	Chlorofluorocarbon-113, CFC-113, Freon® 113, Genetron® 113, Halocarbon 113, Refrigerant 113, TTE 1 ppm = 7.67 mg/m³	NIOSH 1000 ppm (7600 mg/m³) ST 1250 ppm (9500 mg/m³) OSHA† 1000 ppm (7600 mg/m³)	2000 ppm	Colorless to water-white liquid with an odor like carbon tetrachloride at high concentrations. [Note: A gas above 118°F.]	MW: 187.4 BP: 118°F Sol(77°F): 0.02% Fl.P: ? IP: 11.99 eV Sp.Gr(77°F): 1.56 Noncombustible Liquid at ordinary temperatures, but the gas will ignite and burn weakly at 1256°F.	VP: 285 mm FRZ: -31°F UEL: ? LEL: ?	Chemically-active metals such as calcium, powdered aluminum, zinc, magnesium & beryllium [Note: Decomposes if in contact with alloys containing >2% magnesium.]	Char; CS₂; GC/FID; IV [#1020]

Personal protection and sanitation (See Table 3)		Recommendations for respirator selection — maximum concentration for use (MUC) (See Table 4)	Health hazards				
			Route	Symptoms (See Table 5)	First aid (See Table 6)		Target organs (See Table 5)
Skin:	Prevent skin contact	NIOSH	Inh	Irrit eyes, skin; head,	Eye:	Irr immed	Eyes, skin, resp sys,
Eyes:	Prevent eye contact	¥: SCBAF:PD,PP/SAF:PD,PP:ASCBA	Abs	verti; vis dist, ftg, gidd,	Skin:	Soap wash prompt	heart, liver, CNS
Wash skin:	When contam	Escape: GMFOV/SCBAE	Ing	tremor, som, nau, vomit;	Breath:	Resp support	[in animals:
Remove:	When wet or contam		Con	derm; card arrhy, pares;	Swallow:	Medical attention	liver & kidney
Change:	N.R.			liver inj; [carc]		immed	cancer]
Provide:	Eyewash, Quick drench						

[Trichloroethylene]

Skin:	Prevent skin contact	NIOSH/OSHA	Inh	Anor, nau; verti; jaun,	Eye:	Irr immed	Liver
Eyes:	Prevent eye contact	50 mg/m³: SCBAF/SAF	Abs	liver inj	Skin:	Soap wash	
Wash skin:	When contam	§: SCBAF:PD,PP/SAF:PD,PP:ASCBA	Ing		Breath:	Resp support	
Remove:	When wet or contam	Escape: GMFOVHiE/SCBAE	Con		Swallow:	Medical attention	
Change:	Daily					immed	

317

[Trichloronaphthalene]

Skin:	Prevent skin contact	NIOSH	Inh	Irrit eyes, nose, throat;	Eye:	Irr immed	Eyes, skin, resp sys,
Eyes:	Prevent eye contact	¥: SCBAF:PD,PP/SAF:PD,PP:ASCBA	Abs	CNS depres;	Skin:	Soap wash	CNS, liver, kidneys
Wash skin:	When contam	Escape: GMFOV/SCBAE	Ing	in animals: liver, kidney	Breath:	Resp support	[in animals:
Remove:	When wet or contam		Con	inj; [carc]	Swallow:	Medical attention	forestomach,
Change:	N.R.					immed	liver & mammary
Provide:	Eyewash, Quick drench						gland cancer]

[1,2,3-Trichloropropane]

Skin:	Prevent skin contact	NIOSH/OSHA	Inh	Irrit skin, throat;	Eye:	Irr immed	Skin, heart, CNS, CVS
Eyes:	Prevent eye contact	2000 ppm: SA/SCBAF	Ing	drow; derm; CNS depres;	Skin:	Soap wash prompt	
Wash skin:	When contam	§: SCBAF:PD,PP/SAF:PD,PP:ASCBA	Con	in animals: card arrhy,	Breath:	Resp support	
Remove:	When wet or contam	Escape: GMFOV/SCBAE		narco	Swallow:	Medical attention	
Change:	N.R.					immed	

[1,1,2-Trichloro-1,2,2-trifluoroethane]

Chemical name, structure/formula, CAS and RTECS Nos., and DOT ID and guide Nos.	Synonyms, trade names, and conversion factors	Exposure limits (TWA unless noted otherwise)	IDLH	Physical description	Chemical and physical properties		Incompatibilities and reactivities	Measurement method (See Table 1)
					MW, BP, SOL Fl.P, IP, Sp, Gr, flammability	VP, FRZ UEL, LEL		
Triethylamine (C₂H₅)₃N 121-44-8 YEO175000 1296 132	TEA 1 ppm = 4.14 mg/m³	NIOSH See Appendix D OSHA† 25 ppm (100 mg/m³)	200 ppm	Colorless liquid with a strong, ammonia-like odor.	MW: 101.2 BP: 193°F Sol: 2% Fl.P: 20°F IP: 7.50 eV Sp.Gr. 0.73 Class IB Flammable Liquid	VP: 54 mm FRZ: -175°F UEL: 8.0% LEL: 1.2%	Strong oxidizers, strong acids, chlorine, hypochlorite, halogenated compounds	Bub; NaOH; GC/FID; II(3) [#S152]
Trifluorobromomethane CBrF₃ 75-63-8 PA5425000 1009 126	Bromotrifluoromethane, Fluorocarbon 1301, Freon® 13B1, Halocarbon 13B1, Halon® 1301, Monobromotrifluoromethane, Refrigerant 13B1, Trifluoromonobromomethane 1 ppm = 6.09 mg/m³	NIOSH/OSHA 1000 ppm (6100 mg/m³)	40,000 ppm	Colorless, odorless gas. [Note: Shipped as a liquefied compressed gas.]	MW: 148.9 BP: -72°F Sol: 0.03% Fl.P: NA IP: 11.78 eV RGasD: 5.14 Nonflammable Gas	VP: >1 atm FRZ: -267°F UEL: NA LEL: NA	Chemically-active metals (such as calcium, powdered aluminum, zinc & magnesium)	Char(2); CH₂Cl₂; GC/FID; IV [#1017]
Trimellitic anhydride C₉H₄O₅ 552-30-7 DC2050000	1,2,4-Benzenetricarboxylic anhydride; 4-Carboxyphthalic anhydride; TMA; TMAN; Trimelic acid anhydride [Note: TMA is also a synonym for Trimethylamine.] 1 ppm = 7.86 mg/m³	NIOSH 0.005 ppm (0.04 mg/m³) Should be handled in the workplace as an extremely toxic substance. OSHA† none	N.D.	Colorless solid.	MW: 192.1 BP: ? Sol: ? Fl.P: NA IP: ? Sp.Gr: ? Combustible Solid	VP: 0.000004 mm MLT: 322°F UEL: NA LEL: NA	None reported	Filter; Methanol; GC/FID; IV [#5036]
Trimethylamine (CH₃)₃N 75-50-3 PA0350000 1083 118 (anhydrous) 1297 132 (aqueous soln.)	N,N-Dimethylmethanamine; TMA [Note: May be used in an aqueous solution (typically 25%, 30%, or 40% TMA.] 1 ppm = 2.42 mg/m³	NIOSH 10 ppm (24 mg/m³) ST 15 ppm (36 mg/m³) OSHA† none	N.D.	Colorless gas with a fishy, amine odor. [Note: A liquid below 37°F. Shipped as a liquefied compressed gas.]	MW: 59.1 BP: 37°F Sol(86°F): 48% Fl.P: NA (Gas 20°F (Liq) IP: 7.82 eV RGasD: 2.09 Flammable Gas Class IA Flammable Liquid	VP(70°F): 1454 mm FRZ: -179°F UEL: 11.6% LEL: 2.0%	Strong oxidizers (including bromine), ethylene oxide, nitrosating agents (e.g., sodium nitrite), mercury, strong acids [Note: Corrosive to many metals (e.g., zinc, brass, aluminum, copper).]	None available

Personal protection and sanitation (See Table 3)	Recommendations for respirator selection — maximum concentration for use (MUC) (See Table 4)	Health hazards			
		Route	Symptoms (See Table 5)	First aid (See Table 6)	Target organs (See Table 5)
Skin: Prevent skin contact Eyes: Prevent eye contact Wash skin: When contam Remove: When wet (flamm) Change: N.R. Provide: Eyewash (>1%), Quick drench (>1%)	OSHA 200 ppm: SA:CF^E/SCBAF/SAF §: SCBAF:PD,PP/SAF:PD,PP:ASCBA Escape: GMFS/SCBAE	Inh Abs Ing Con	Irrit eyes, skin, resp sys; in animals: myocardial, kidney, liver damage	Eye: Irr immed Skin: Soap wash immed Breath: Resp support Swallow: Medical attention immed	Eyes, skin, resp sys, CVS, liver, kidneys
[Triethylamine]					
Skin: Frostbite Eyes: Frostbite Wash skin: N.R. Remove: N.R. Change: N.R. Provide: Frostbite	NIOSH/OSHA 10,000 ppm: SA 25,000 ppm: SA:CF 40,000 ppm: SAT:CF/SCBAF/SAF §: SCBAF:PD,PP/SAF:PD,PP:ASCBA Escape: GMFOV/SCBAE	Inh Con (liq)	Li-head; card arrhy; liq: frostbite	Eye: Frostbite Skin: Frostbite Breath; Resp support	CNS, heart
[Trifluorobromomethane]					
Skin: Prevent skin contact Eyes: Prevent eye contact Wash skin: When contam Remove: When wet or contam Change: Daily	TBAL	Inh Ing Con	Irrit eyes, skin, nose, resp sys; pulm edema, resp sens; rhinitis, asthma, cough, wheez, dysp, mal, fever, musc aches, sneez	Eye: Irr immed Skin: Soap wash Breath: Resp support Swallow: Medical attention immed	Eyes, skin, resp sys
[Trimellitic anhydride]					
Skin: Prevent skin contact (liq/soln)/Frostbite Eyes: Prevent eye contact (liq/soln)/Frostbite Wash skin: When contam (soln) Remove: When wet (flamm) Change: N.R. Provide: Eyewash (liq/soln), Quick drench (liq/soln), Frostbite	TBAL	Inh Ing (soln) Con	Irrit eyes, skin, nose, throat, resp sys; cough, dysp, delayed pulm edema; blurred vision, corn nec; skin burns; liq: frostbite	Eye: Irr immed (liq/soln)/Frostbite Skin: Water flush immed (liq/soln)/Frostbite Breath: Resp support Swallow: Medical attention immed (soln)	Eyes, skin, resp sys
[Trimethylamine]					

Chemical name, structure/formula, CAS and RTECS Nos., and DOT ID and guide Nos.	Synonyms, trade names, and conversion factors	Exposure limits (TWA unless noted otherwise)	IDLH	Physical description	Chemical and physical properties		Incompatibilities and reactivities	Measurement method (See Table 1)
					MW, BP, SOL Fl.P, IP, Sp, Gr, flammability	VP, FRZ UEL, LEL		
1,2,3-Trimethylbenzene $C_6H_3(CH_3)_3$ 526-73-8 DC3300000	Hemellitol [Note: Hemimellitene is a mixture of the 1,2,3-isomer with up to 10% of related aromatics such as the 1,2,4-isomer.] 1 ppm = 4.92 mg/m³	NIOSH 25 ppm (125 mg/m³) OSHA† none	N.D.	Clear, colorless liquid with a distinctive, aromatic odor.	MW: 120.2 BP: 349°F Sol: Low Fl.P: ? IP: 8.48 eV Sp.Gr: 0.89 Flammable Liquid	VP(62°F): 1 mm FRZ: -14°F UEL: 6.6% LEL: 0.8%	Oxidizers, nitric acid	None available
1,2,4-Trimethylbenzene $C_6H_3(CH_3)_3$ 95-63-6 DC3325000	Assymetrical trimethyl-benzene, psi-Cumene, Pseudocumene [Note: Hemimellitene is a mixture of the 1,2,3-isomer with up to 10% of related aromatics such as the 1,2,4-isomer.] 1 ppm = 4.92 mg/m³	NIOSH 25 ppm (125 mg/m³) OSHA† none	N.D.	Clear, colorless liquid with a distinctive, aromatic odor.	MW: 120.2 BP: 337°F Sol: 0.006% Fl.P: 112°F IP: 8.27 eV Sp.Gr: 0.88 Class II Flammable Liquid	VP(56°F): 1 mm FRZ: -77°F UEL: 6.4% LEL: 0.9%	Oxidizers, nitric acid	None available
1,3,5-Trimethylbenzene $C_6H_3(CH_3)_3$ 108-67-8 OX6825000 2325 129	Mesitylene, Symmetrical trimethyl-benzene, sym-Trimethylbenzene 1 ppm = 4.92 mg/m³	NIOSH 25 ppm (125 mg/m³) OSHA† none	N.D.	Clear, colorless liquid with a distinctive, aromatic odor.	MW: 120.2 BP: 329°F Sol: 0.002% Fl.P: 122°F IP: 8.39 eV Sp.Gr: 0.86 Class II Flammable Liquid	VP: 2 mm FRZ: -49°F UEL: ? LEL: ?	Oxidizers, nitric acid	None available
Trimethyl phosphite $(CH_3O)_3P$ 121-45-9 TH1400000 2329 129	Methyl phosphite, Trimethoxyphosphine 1 ppm = 5.08 mg/m³	NIOSH 2 ppm (10 mg/m³) OSHA† none	N.D.	Colorless liquid with a distinctive, pungent odor.	MW: 124.1 BP: 232°F Sol: Reacts Fl.P: 82°F IP: ? Sp.Gr: 1.05 Class IC Flammable Liquid	VP(77°F): 24 mm FRZ: -108°F UEL: ? LEL: ?	Magnesium perchlorate, water [Note: Reacts (hydrolyzes) with water.]	None available

Personal protection and sanitation (See Table 3)		Recommendations for respirator selection — maximum concentration for use (MUC) (See Table 4)	Health hazards					
			Route	Symptoms (See Table 5)	First aid (See Table 6)		Target organs (See Table 5)	
Skin:	Prevent skin contact	TBAL	Inh	Irrit eyes, skin, nose,	Eye:	Irr immed	Eyes, skin, resp sys,	
Eyes:	Prevent eye contact		Ing	throat, resp sys; bron;	Skin:	Soap wash	CNS, blood	
Wash skin:	When contam		Con	hypochromic anemia, head,	Breath:	Resp support		
Remove:	When wet or contam			drow, ftg, dizz, nau, inco;	Swallow:	Medical attention		
Change:	N.R.			vomit, conf; chemical pneu		immed		
				(aspir liq)				

[1,2,3-Trimethylbenzene]

Personal protection and sanitation		Recommendations	Route	Symptoms	First aid		Target organs	
Skin:	Prevent skin contact	TBAL	Inh	Irrit eyes, skin, nose,	Eye:	Irr immed	Eyes, skin, resp sys,	
Eyes:	Prevent eye contact		Ing	throat, resp sys; bron;	Skin:	Soap wash	CNS, blood	
Wash skin:	When contam		Con	hypochromic anemia, head,	Breath:	Resp support		
Remove:	When wet or contam			drow, ftg, dizz, nau, inco;	Swallow:	Medical attention		
Change:	N.R.			vomit, conf; chemical pneu		immed		
				(aspir liq)				

[1,2,4-Trimethylbenzene]

Skin:	Prevent skin contact	TBAL	Inh	Irrit eyes, skin, nose,	Eye:	Irr immed	Eyes, skin, resp sys,	
Eyes:	Prevent eye contact		Ing	throat, resp sys; bron;	Skin:	Soap wash	CNS, blood	
Wash skin:	When contam		Con	hypochromic anemia, head,	Breath:	Resp support		
Remove:	When wet or contam			drow, ftg, dizz, nau, inco;	Swallow:	Medical attention		
Change:	N.R.			vomit, conf; chemical pneu		immed		
				(aspir liq)				

[1,3,5-Trimethylbenzene]

Skin:	Prevent skin contact	TBAL	Inh	Irrit eyes, skin, upper	Eye:	Irr immed	Eyes, skin, resp sys,	
Eyes:	Prevent eye contact		Ing	resp sys; derm;	Skin:	Soap flush immed	repro sys	
Wash skin:	When contam		Con	in animals: terato effects	Breath:	Resp support		
Remove:	When wet (flamm)				Swallow:	Medical attention		
Change:	N.R.					immed		
Provide:	Quick drench							

[Trimethyl phosphite]

Chemical name, structure/formula, CAS and RTECS Nos., and DOT ID and guide Nos.	Synonyms, trade names, and conversion factors	Exposure limits (TWA unless noted otherwise)	IDLH	Physical description	Chemical and physical properties		Incompatibilities and reactivities	Measurement method (See Table 1)
					MW, BP, SOL Fl.P, IP, Sp, Gr, flammability	VP, FRZ UEL, LEL		
2,4,6-Trinitrotoluene $CH_3C_6H_2(NO_2)_3$ 118-96-7 XU0175000 1356 113 (wet)	1-Methyl-2,4,6-trinitrobenzene; TNT; Trinitrotoluene; sym-Trinitrotoluene; Trinitrotoluol	NIOSH 0.5 mg/m³ [skin] OSHA† 1.5 mg/m³ [skin]	500 mg/m³	Colorless to pale-yellow, odorless solid or crushed flakes.	MW: 227.1 BP: 464°F (Explodes) Sol(77°F): 0.01% Fl.P: ? (Explodes) IP: 10.59 eV Sp.Gr: 1.65 Combustible Solid (Class A Explosive)	VP: 0.0002 mm MLT: 176°F UEL: ? LEL: ?	Strong oxidizers, ammonia, strong alkalis, combustible materials, heat [Note: Rapid heating will result in detonation.]	Tenax GC; Acetone; GC/TEA-EAP; OSHA [#44]
Triorthocresyl phosphate $(CH_3C_6H_4O)_3PO$ 78-30-8 TD0350000 2574 151	TCP, TOCP, Tri-o-cresyl ester of phosphoric acid, Tri-o-cresyl phosphate	NIOSH 0.1 mg/m³ [skin] OSHA† 0.1 mg/m³	40 mg/m³	Colorless to pale-yellow, odorless liquid or solid (below 52°F).	MW: 368.4 BP: 770°F (Decomposes) Sol: Slight Fl.P: 437°F IP: ? Sp.Gr: 1.20 Class IIIB Combustible Liquid	VP(77°F): 0.00002 mm FRZ: 52°F UEL: ? LEL: ?	Oxidizers	Filter; Diethyl ether; GC/FPD; IV [#5037]
Triphenylamine $(C_6H_5)_3N$ 603-34-9 YK2680000	N,N-Diphenylaniline; N,N-Diphenylbenzenamine	NIOSH 5 mg/m³ OSHA† none	N.D.	Colorless solid.	MW: 245.3 BP: 689°F Sol: Insoluble Fl.P: ? IP: 7.60 eV Sp.Gr: 0.77	VP: ? MLT: 261°F UEL: ? LEL: ?	None reported	None available
Triphenyl phosphate $(C_6H_5O)_3PO$ 115-86-6 TC8400000	Phenyl phosphate, TPP, Triphenyl ester of phosphoric acid	NIOSH/OSHA 3 mg/m³	1000 mg/m³	Colorless, crystalline powder with a phenol-like odor.	MW: 326.3 BP: 776°F Sol(129°F): 0.002% Fl.P: 428°F IP: ? Sp.Gr: 1.29 Combustible Solid	VP(380°F): 1mm MLT: 120°F UEL: ? LEL: ?	None reported	Filter; Diethyl ether; GC/FPD; IV [#5038]

Personal protection and sanitation (See Table 3)		Recommendations for respirator selection — maximum concentration for use (MUC) (See Table 4)	Health hazards				
			Route	Symptoms (See Table 5)	First aid (See Table 6)		Target organs (See Table 5)

Personal protection and sanitation		Recommendations for respirator selection — MUC	Route	Symptoms	First aid	Target organs
Skin: Eyes: Wash skin: Remove: Change:	Prevent skin contact Prevent eye contact When contam/Daily When wet or contam Daily	NIOSH 5 mg/m³: SA* 12.5 mg/m³: SA:CF* 25 mg/m³: SCBAF/SAF 500 mg/m³: SAF:PD,PP §: SCBAF:PD,PP/SAF:PD,PP:ASCBA Escape: GMFOVHiE/SCBAE	Inh Abs Ing Con	Irrit skin, muc memb; liver damage, jaun; cyan; sneez; cough, sore throat; peri neur, musc pain; kidney damage; cataract; sens derm; leucyt; anemia; card irreg	Eye: Skin: Breath: Swallow:	Irr immed Soap wash prompt Resp support Medical attention immed	Eyes, skin, resp sys, blood, liver, CVS, CNS, kidneys
[2,4,6-Trinitrotoluene]							
Skin: Eyes: Wash skin: Remove: Change:	Prevent skin contact N.R. When contam When wet or contam N.R.	NIOSH/OSHA 0.5 mg/m³: DM 1 mg/m³: DMXSQ/SA 2.5 mg/m³: SA:CF/PAPRDM 5 mg/m³: HiEF/SAT:CF/PAPRTHiE/ SCBAF/SAF 40 mg/m³: SA:PD,PP §: SCBAF:PD,PP/SAF:PD,PP:ASCBA Escape: HiEF/SCBAE	Inh Abs Ing Con	GI dist; peri neur; cramps in calves, pares in feet or hands; weak feet, wrist drop, para	Eye: Skin: Breath: Swallow:	Irr immed Soap wash immed Resp support Medical attention immed	PNS, CNS
[Triorthocresyl phosphate]							
Skin: Eyes: Wash skin: Remove: Change:	Prevent skin contact Prevent eye contact Daily N.R. Daily	TBAL	Inh Ing Con	In animals: irrit skin	Eye: Skin: Breath: Swallow:	Irr immed Soap wash Resp support Medical attention immed	Skin
[Triphenylamine]							
Skin: Eyes: Wash skin: Remove: Change:	N.R. N.R. N.R. N.R. N.R.	NIOSH/OSHA 15 mg/m³: D 30 mg/m³: HiE/DXSQ/SA 75 mg/m³: SA:CF/PAPRDM 150 mg/m³: HiEF/SAT:CF/PAPRTHiE/ SCBAF/SAF 1000 mg/m³: SA:PD,PP §: SCBAF:PD,PP/SAF:PD,PP:ASCBA Escape: HiEF/SCBAE	Inh Ing	Minor changes in blood enzymes; in animals: musc weak, para	Breath: Swallow:	Resp support Medical attention immed	Blood, PNS
[Triphenyl phosphate]							

Chemical name, structure/formula, CAS and RTECS Nos., and DOT ID and guide Nos.	Synonyms, trade names, and conversion factors	Exposure limits (TWA unless noted otherwise)	IDLH	Physical description	Chemical and physical properties		Incompatibilities and reactivities	Measurement method (See Table 1)
					MW, BP, SOL Fl.P, IP, Sp, Gr, flammability	VP, FRZ UEL, LEL		
Tungsten W 7440-33-7 YO7175000	Tungsten metal, Wolfram	NIOSH* 5 mg/m³ ST 10 mg/m³ [*Note: The REL also applies to other insoluble tungsten compounds (as W).] OSHA† none	N.D.	Hard, brittle, steel-gray to tin-white solid.	MW: 183.9 BP: 10,701°F Sol: Insoluble Fl.P: NA IP: NA Sp.Gr: 19.3 Combustible in the form of finely divided powder; may ignite spontaneously.	VP: 0 mm (approx) MLT: 6170°F UEL: NA LEL: NA	Bromine trifluoride, chlorine trifluoride, fluorine, iodine pentafluoride	Filter; Acid; FAAS; IV [#7074]
Tungsten (soluble compounds, as W)	Synonyms vary depending upon the specific soluble tungsten compound.	NIOSH 1 mg/m³ ST 3 mg/m³ OSHA† none	N.D.	Appearance and odor vary depending upon the specific soluble tungsten compound.	Properties vary depending upon the specific soluble tungsten compound.		Varies	Filter; Acid; FAAS; IV [#7074]
Tungsten carbide (cemented) WC/Co/Ni/Ti 1: 11107-01-0 2: 12718-69-3 3: 37329-49-0 1: Y07350000 2: Y07525000 3: YO7700000	Cemented tungsten carbide, Cemented WC, Hard metal [Note: The tungsten carbide (WC) content is generally 85-95% & the cobalt content is generally 5-15%.] [1: 85% WC, 15% Co 2: 92% WC, 8% Co 3: 78% WC, 14% Co, 8% Ti]	NIOSH See Appendix C OSHA† See Appendix C	N.D.	A mixture of tungsten carbide, cobalt, and sometimes other metals & metal oxides or carbides.	Properties vary depending upon the specific mixture.		Tungsten carbide: Fluorine, chlorine trifluoride, oxides of nitrogen, lead dioxide	None available
Turpentine C₁₀H₁₆ (approx) 8006-64-2 YO8400000 1299 128	Gumspirits, Gum turpentine, Spirits of turpentine, Steam distilled turpentine, Sulfate wood turpentine, Turps, Wood turpentine 1 ppm 5.56 mg/m³ (approx)	NIOSH/OSHA 100 ppm (560 mg/m³)	800 ppm	Colorless liquid with a characteristic odor.	MW: 136(approx) BP: 309-338°F Sol: Insoluble Fl.P: 95°F IP: ? Sp.Gr: 0.86 Class IC Flammable Liquid	VP: 4 mm FRZ: -58 to -76°F UEL: ? LEL: 0.8%	Strong oxidizers, chlorine, chromic anhydride, stannic chloride, chromyl chloride	Char; CS₂; GC/FID; IV [#1551]

$C_{10}H_{16}$

Personal protection and sanitation (See Table 3)	Recommendations for respirator selection — maximum concentration for use (MUC) (See Table 4)	Health hazards			
		Route	Symptoms (See Table 5)	First aid (See Table 6)	Target organs (See Table 5)
Skin: N.R. Eyes: N.R. Wash skin: N.R. Remove: N.R. Change: N.R. [Tungsten]	NIOSH 50 mg/m³: HiE/SA/SCBAF §: SCBAF:PD,PP/SAF:PD,PP:ASCBA Escape: HiEF/SCBAE	Inh Ing Con	Irrit eyes, skin, resp sys; diffuse pulm fib; loss of appetite, nau, cough; blood changes	Eye: Irr immed Skin: Soap wash Breath: Fresh air Swallow: Medical attention immed	Eyes, skin, resp sys, blood
Recommendations vary depending upon the specific compound. [Tungsten (soluble compounds, as W)]	NIOSH 10 mg/m³: HiE/SA 25 mg/m³: SA:CF 50 mg/m³: HiEF/SCBAF/SAF §: SCBAF:PD,PP/SAF:PD,PP:ASCBA Escape: HiEF/SCBAE	Inh Ing Con	Irrit eyes, skin, resp sys; in animals: CNS disturbances; diarr; resp failure; behavior, body weight, blood changes	Eye: Irr immed Skin: Water wash Breath: Resp support Swallow: Medical attention immed	Eyes, skin, resp sys, CNS, GI tract
Skin: Prevent skin contact Eyes: Prevent eye contact Wash skin: When contam/Daily (Ni) Remove: When wet or contam Change: Daily [Tungsten carbide (cemented)]	NIOSH 0.25 mg Co/m³: DM^ 0.5 mg Co/m³: DMXSQ*^/DMFu*/SA* 1.25 mg Co/m³: SA:CF*/PAPRDM*^/PAPRDMFu* 2.5 mg Co/m³: HiEF/SCBAF/SAF 20 mg Co/m³: SAF:PD,PP §: SCBAF:PD,PP/SAF:PD,PP:ASCBA Escape: HiEF/SCBAE	Inh Ing Con	Irrit eyes, skin, resp sys; possible skin sens to cobalt, nickel; diffuse pulm fib; loss of appetite, nau, cough; blood changes Tungsten carbide (cemented) containing NICKEL NIOSH ¥: SCBAF:PD,PP/SAF:PD,PP:ASCBA Escape: HiEF/SCBAE	Eye: Irr immed Skin: Soap wash Breath: Fresh air Swallow: Medical attention immed	Eyes, skin, resp sys, blood
Skin: Prevent skin contact Eyes: Prevent eye contact Wash skin: When contam Remove: When wet (flamm) Change: N.R. [Turpentine]	NIOSH/OSHA 800 ppm: SA:CFᴱ/PAPROVᴱ/CCRFOV/GMFOV/SCBAF/SAF §: SCBAF:PD,PP/SAF:PD,PP:ASCBA Escape: GMFOV/SCBAE	Inh Abs Ing Con	Irrit eyes, skin, nose, throat; head, verti, convuls; skin sens; hema, album; kidney damage; abdom pain, nau, vomit, diarr; chemical pneu (aspir liq)	Eye: Irr immed Skin: Soap wash prompt Breath: Resp support Swallow: Medical attention immed	Eyes, skin, resp sys, CNS, kidneys

Chemical name, structure/formula, CAS and RTECS Nos., and DOT ID and guide Nos.	Synonyms, trade names, and conversion factors	Exposure limits (TWA unless noted otherwise)	IDLH	Physical description	Chemical and physical properties		Incompatibilities and reactivities	Measurement method (See Table 1)
					MW, BP, SOL Fl.P, IP, Sp, Gr, flammability	VP, FRZ UEL, LEL		
1-Undecanethiol $CH_3(CH_2)_{10}SH$ 5332-52-5 1228 131	Undecyl mercaptan 1 ppm = 7.71 mg/m³	NIOSH C 0.5 ppm (3.9 mg/m³) [15-min] OSHA none	N.D.	Liquid.	MW: 188.4 BP: 495°F Sol: Insoluble Fl.P: ? IP: ? Sp.Gr: 0.84 Combustible Liquid	VP: ? FRZ: 27°F UEL: ? LEL: ?	Oxidizers, reducing agents, strong acids & bases, alkali metals	None available
Uranium (insoluble compounds, as U) U (Metal) 7440-61-1 (Metal) YR3490000 (Metal) 2979 162 (Metal, pyrophoric)	Uranium metal: Uranium I Synonyms of other insoluble uranium compounds vary depending upon the specific compound.	NIOSH Ca See Appendix A 0.2 mg/m³ ST 0.6 mg/m³ OSHA† 0.25 mg/m³	Ca [10 mg/m³ (as U)]	Metal: Silver-white, malleable, ductile lustrous solid. [Note: Weakly radioactive.]	MW: 238.0 BP: 6895°F Sol: Insoluble Fl.P: NA IP: NA Sp.Gr: 19.05 (Metal) Metal: Combustible Solid, especially turnings and powder.	VP: 0 mm (approx) MLT: 2097°F UEL: NA LEL: NA MEC: 60 g/m³	Carbon dioxide, carbon tetrachloride, nitric acid, fluorine [Note: Complete coverage of uranium metal scrap with oil is essential for prevention of fire.]	None available
Uranium (soluble compounds, as U)	Synonyms vary depending upon the specific soluble uranium compound.	NIOSH Ca See Appendix A 0.05 mg/m³ OSHA 0.05 mg/m³	Ca [10 mg/m³ (as U)]	Appearance and odor vary depending upon the specific soluble uranium compound.	Properties vary depending upon the specific soluble uranium compound. Uranium hexafluoride:		Uranyl nitrate: combustibles Uranium hexafluoride: water	None available
n-Valeraldehyde $CH_3(CH_2)_3CHO$ 110-62-3 YV3600000 2058 129	Amyl aldehyde, Pentanal, Valeral, Valeraldehyde, Valeric aldehyde 1 ppm = 3.53 mg/m³	NIOSH 50 ppm (175 mg/m³) See Appendix C (Aldehydes) OSHA† none	N.D.	Colorless liquid with a strong, acrid, pungent odor.	MW: 86.2 BP: 217°F Sol: Slight Fl.P: 54°F IP: 9.82 eV Sp.Gr: 0.81 Class IB Flammable Liquid	VP: 26 mm FRZ: -133°F UEL: ? LEL: ?	None reported	XAD-2*; Toluene; GC/FID; IV [#2536]

Personal protection and sanitation (See Table 3)	Recommendations for respirator selection — maximum concentration for use (MUC) (See Table 4)	Health hazards			
		Route	Symptoms (See Table 5)	First aid (See Table 6)	Target organs (See Table 5)
Skin: Prevent skin contact Eyes: Prevent eye contact Wash skin: When contam Remove: When wet (flamm) Change: N.R.	NIOSH 5 ppm: CCROV/SA 12.5 ppm: SA:CF/PAPROV 25 ppm: CCRFOV/GMFOV/PAPRTOV/ SCBAF/SAF §: SCBAF:PD,PP/SAF:PD,PP:ASCBA Escape: GMFOV/SCBAE	Inh Abs Ing Con	Irrit eyes, skin, resp sys; conf, dizz, head, drow, nau, vomit, weak, convuls	Eye: Irr immed Skin: Soap wash Breath: Resp support Swallow: Medical attention immed	Eyes, skin, resp sys, CNS
[1-Undecanethiol]					
Skin: Prevent skin contact Eyes: Prevent eye contact Wash skin: When contam/Daily Remove: When wet or contam Change: Daily Provide: Eyewash	NIOSH ¥: SCBAF:PD,PP/SAF:PD,PP:ASCBA Escape: HiEF/SCBAE	Inh Ing Con	Derm; kidney damage; blood changes; in animals: lung, lymph node damage Potential for cancer is a result of alpha-emitting properties & radioactive decay products (e.g., radon).	Eye: Irr immed Skin: Soap wash prompt Breath: Resp support Swallow: Medical attention immed	Skin, kidneys, bone marrow, lymphatic sys [lung cancer]
[Uranium (insoluble compounds, as U)]					
Skin: Prevent skin contact Eyes: Prevent eye contact Wash skin: When contam/Daily Remove: When wet or contam Change: Daily Provide: Eyewash (UF₆), Quick drench	NIOSH ¥: SCBAF:PD,PP/SAF:PD,PP:ASCBA Escape(Halides): GMFAGHiE/SCBAE Escape(Non-halides): HiEF/SCBAE	Inh Ing Con	Lac, conj; short breath, cough, chest rales; nau, vomit; skin burns; RBC, casts in urine; album; high BUN; [carc] Potential for cancer is a result of alpha-emitting properties & radioactive decay products (e.g., radon).	Eye: Irr immed Skin: Water flush immed Breath: Resp support Swallow: Medical attention immed	Resp sys, blood, liver, kidneys, lymphatics sys, skin, bone marrow [lung cancer]
[Uranium (soluble, compounds as U)]					
Skin: Prevent skin contact Eyes: Prevent eye contact Wash skin: When contam Remove: When wet (flamm) Change: N.R. Provide: Eyewash, Quick drench	TBAL	Inh Ing Con	Irrit eyes, skin, nose, throat	Eye: Irr immed Skin: Soap flush immed Breath: Resp support Swallow: Medical attention immed	Eyes, skin, resp sys
[n-Valeraldehyde]					

Chemical name, structure/formula, CAS and RTECS Nos., and DOT ID and guide Nos.	Synonyms, trade names, and conversion factors	Exposure limits (TWA unless noted otherwise)	IDLH	Physical description	Chemical and physical properties		Incompatibilities and reactivities	Measurement method (See Table 1)
					MW, BP, SOL FI.P, IP, Sp, Gr, flammability	VP, FRZ UEL, LEL		
Vanadium dust V_2O_5 1314-62-1 YW2450000 2862 151	Divanadium pentoxide, Vanadic anhydride, Vanadium oxide, Vanadium pentaoxide Other synonyms vary depending upon the specific vanadium compound.	NIOSH* C 0.05 mg V/m^3 [15-min] [*Note: The REL applies to all vanadium compounds except Vanadium metal & Vanadium carbide (see Ferrovanadium dust).] OSHA† C 0.5 mg V_2O_5/m^3 (resp)	35 mg/m^3 (as V)	Yellow-orange powder or dark gray, odorless flakes dispersed in air.	MW: 181.9 BP: 3182°F (Decomposes) Sol: 0.8% FI.P: NA IP: NA Sp.Gr: 3.36 Noncombustible Solid, but may increase intensity of fire when in contact with combustible materials.	VP: 0 mm (approx) MLT: 1274°F UEL: NA LEL: NA	Lithium, chlorine trifluoride	Filter; THF; XRD; IV [#7504] [Also #7300, Elements]
Vanadium fume V_2O_5 1314-62-1 YW2460000 2862 151	Divanadium pentoxide, Vanadic anhydride, Vanadium oxide, Vanadium pentaoxide Other synonyms vary depending upon the specific vanadium compound.	NIOSH* C 0.05 mg V/m^3 [15-min] OSHA† C 0.1 mg V_2O_5/m^3	35 mg/m^3 (as V)	Finely divided particulate dispersed in air.	MW: 181.9 BP: 3182°F (Decomposes) Sol: 0.8% FI.P: NA IP: NA Sp.Gr: 3.36 Noncombustible Solid	VP: 0 mm (approx) MLT: 1274°F UEL: NA LEL: NA	Lithium, chlorine trifluoride	Filter; THF; XRD; IV [#7504] [Also #7300, Elements]
Vegetable oil mist 68956-68-3 YX1850000	Vegetable mist	NIOSH 10 mg/m^3 (total) 5 mg/m^3 (resp) OSHA 15 mg/m^3 (total) 5 mg/m^3 (resp)	N.D.	An oil extracted from the seeds, fruit, or nuts of vegetables or other plant matter.	MW: varies BP: ? Sol: Insoluble FI.P: 323-540°F IP: ? Sp.Gr: 0.91-0.95 Combustible Liquid	VP: ? FRZ: ? UEL: ? LEL: ?	None reported	Filter; none; Grav; IV [Particulates NOR: #0500 (total), #0600 (resp)]
Vinyl acetate $CH_2=CHOOCCH_3$ 108-05-4 AK0875000 1301 129P	1-Acetoxyethylene, Ethenyl acetate, Ethenyl ethanoate, VAC, Vinyl acetate monomer, Vinyl ethanoate 1 ppm = 3.52 mg/m^3	NIOSH C 4 ppm (15 mg/m^3) [15-min] OSHA† none	N.D.	Colorless liquid with a pleasant, fruity odor. [Note: Raw material for many poly-vinyl resins.]	MW: 86.1 BP: 162°F Sol: 2% FI.P: 18°F IP: 9.19 eV Sp.Gr: 0.93 Class IB Flammable Liquid	VP: 83 mm FRZ: -136°F UEL: 13.4% LEL: 2.6%	Acids, bases, silica gel, alumina, oxidizers, azo compounds, ozone [Note: Usually contains a stabilizer (e.g., hydroquinone or diphenylamine) to prevent polymerization.]	Carbon mol sieve; CH_2Cl_2/Methanol; GC/FID; IV [#1453]

Personal protection and sanitation (See Table 3)		Recommendations for respirator selection — maximum concentration for use (MUC) (See Table 4)	Health hazards			
			Route	Symptoms (See Table 5)	First aid (See Table 6)	Target organs (See Table 5)
Skin:	Prevent skin contact	NIOSH (as V)	Inh	Irrit eyes, skin, throat;	Eye: Irr immed	Eyes, skin, resp sys
Eyes:	Prevent eye contact	0.5 mg/m³: HiE*/SA*	Ing	green tongue, metallic	Skin: Soap wash prompt	
Wash skin:	When contam	1.25 mg/m³: SA:CF*/PAPRHiE*	Con	taste, eczema; cough; fine	Breath: Resp support	
Remove:	When wet or contam	2.5 mg/m³: HiEF/PAPRTHiE*/		rales, wheez, bron, dysp	Swallow: Medical attention	
Change:	N.R.	SCBAF/SAF			immed	
		35 mg/m³: SAF:PD,PP				
		§: SCBAF:PD,PP/SAF:PD,PP:ASCBA				
		Escape: HiEF/SCBAE				

[Vanadium dust]

Personal protection and sanitation (See Table 3)		Recommendations for respirator selection — maximum concentration for use (MUC) (See Table 4)	Health hazards			
			Route	Symptoms (See Table 5)	First aid (See Table 6)	Target organs (See Table 5)
Skin:	N.R.	NIOSH (as V)	Inh	Irrit eyes, throat; green	Breath: Resp support	Eyes, skin, resp sys
Eyes:	N.R.	0.5 mg/m³: HiE*/SA*	Con	tongue, metallic taste;		
Wash skin:	N.R.	1.25 mg/m³: SA:CF*/PAPRHiE*		cough, fine rales, wheez,		
Remove:	N.R.	2.5 mg/m³: HiEF/PAPRTHiE*/		bron, dysp; eczema		
Change:	N.R.	SCBAF/SAF				
		35 mg/m³: SAF:PD,PP				
		§: SCBAF:PD,PP/SAF:PD,PP:ASCBA				
		Escape: HiEF/SCBAE				

[Vanadium fume]

Personal protection and sanitation (See Table 3)		Recommendations for respirator selection — maximum concentration for use (MUC) (See Table 4)	Health hazards			
			Route	Symptoms (See Table 5)	First aid (See Table 6)	Target organs (See Table 5)
Skin:	N.R.	TBAL	Inh	Irrit eyes, skin, resp sys; lac	Eye: Irr immed	Eyes, skin, resp sys
Eyes:	N.R.		Con		Breath: Fresh air	
Wash skin:	N.R.					
Remove:	N.R.					
Change:	N.R.					

[Vegetable oil mist]

Personal protection and sanitation (See Table 3)		Recommendations for respirator selection — maximum concentration for use (MUC) (See Table 4)	Health hazards			
			Route	Symptoms (See Table 5)	First aid (See Table 6)	Target organs (See Table 5)
Skin:	Prevent skin contact	NIOSH	Inh	Irrit eyes, skin, nose,	Eye: Irr immed	Eyes, skin, resp sys
Eyes:	Prevent eye contact	40 ppm: CCROV*/SA*	Ing	throat; hoarseness, cough;	Skin: Soap flush immed	
Wash skin:	When contam	100 ppm: SA:CF*/PAPROV*	Con	loss of smell; eye burns,	Breath: Resp support	
Remove:	When wet or contam	200 ppm: CCRFOV/GMFOV/PAPRTOV*/		skin blisters	Swallow: Medical attention	
Change:	N.R.	SCBAF/SAF			immed	
Provide:	Eyewash, Quick drench	4000 ppm: SA:PD,PP*				
		§: SCBAF:PD,PP/SAF:PD,PP:ASCBA				
		Escape: GMFOV/SCBAE				

[Vinyl acetate]

Chemical name, structure/formula, CAS and RTECS Nos., and DOT ID and guide Nos.	Synonyms, trade names, and conversion factors	Exposure limits (TWA unless noted otherwise)	IDLH	Physical description	Chemical and physical properties		Incompatibilities and reactivities	Measurement method (See Table 1)
					MW, BP, SOL Fl.P, IP, Sp, Gr, flammability	VP, FRZ UEL, LEL		
Vinyl bromide CH$_2$=CHBr 593-60-2 KU8400000 1085 116P	Bromoethene, Bromoethylene 1 ppm = 4.38 mg/m^3	NIOSH Ca See Appendix A OSHA† none	Ca [N.D.]	Colorless gas or liquid (below 60°F) with a pleasant odor. [Note: Shipped as a liquefied compressed gas with 0.1% phenol added to prevent polymerization.]	MW: 107.0 BP: 60°F Sol: Insoluble Fl.P: NA (Gas) IP: 9.80 eV RGasD: 3.79 Sp.Gr: 1.49 (Liquid at 60°F) Flammable Gas Class IA Flammable Liquid	VP: 1.4 atm FRZ: -219°F UEL: 15% LEL: 9%	Strong oxidizers [Note: May polymerize in sunlight.]	Char; Ethanol; GC/FID; IV [#1009]
Vinyl chloride CH$_2$=CHCl 75-01-4 KU9625000 1086 116P	Chloroethene, Chloroethylene, Ethylene monochloride, Monochloroethene, Monochloroethylene, VC, Vinyl chloride monomer (VCM) 1 ppm = 2.56 mg/m^3	NIOSH Ca See Appendix A [Use 1910.1017] OSHA[1910.1017] 1 ppm C 5 ppm [15-min]	Ca [N.D.]	Colorless gas or liquid (below 7°F) with a pleasant odor at high concentrations. [Note: Shipped as a liquefied compressed gas.]	MW: 62.5 BP: 7°F Sol(77°F): 0.1% Fl.P: NA (Gas) IP: 9.99 eV RGasD: 2.21 Flammable Gas	VP: 3.3 atm FRZ: -256°F UEL: 33.0% LEL: 3.6%	Copper, oxidizers, aluminum, peroxides, iron, steel [Note: Polymerizes in air, sunlight, or heat unless stabilized by inhibitors such as phenol. Attacks iron & steel in presence of moisture.]	Char(2); CS$_2$; GC/FID; IV [#1007]
Vinyl cyclohexene dioxide C$_8$H$_{12}$O$_2$ 106-87-6 RN8640000 1 ppm = 5.73 mg/m^3	1-Epoxyethyl-3,4-epoxy-cyclohexane; 4-Vinylcyclohexene diepoxide; 4-Vinyl-1-cyclohexene dioxide	NIOSH Ca Appendix A 10 ppm (60 mg/m^3) [skin] OSHA† none	Ca [N.D.]	Colorless liquid.	MW: 140.2 BP: 441°F Sol: High Fl.P(oc): 230°F IP: ? Sp.Gr: 1.10 Class IIIB Combustible Liquid	VP: 0.1 mm FRZ: -164°F UEL: ? LEL: ?	Alcohols, amines, water [Note: Slowly hydrolyzes in water.]	None available
Vinyl fluoride CH$_2$=CHF 75-02-5 YZ7351000 1860 116P	Fluoroethene, Fluoroethylene, Monofluoroethylene, Vinyl fluoride monomer 1 ppm = 1.89 mg/m^3	NIOSH 1 ppm C 5 ppm [use 1910.1017] OSHA none	N.D.	Colorless gas with a faint, ethereal odor. [Note: Shipped as a liquefied compressed gas.]	MW: 46.1 BP: -98°F Sol: Insoluble Fl.P: NA (Gas) IP: 10.37 eV RGasD: 1.60 Flammable Gas	VP: 25.2 atm FRZ: -257°F UEL: 21.7% LEL: 2.6%	None reported [Note: Inhibited with 0.2% terpenes to prevent polymerization.]	None available

Personal protection and sanitation (See Table 3)	Recommendations for respirator selection — maximum concentration for use (MUC) (See Table 4)	Route	Symptoms (See Table 5)	First aid (See Table 6)	Target organs (See Table 5)
Skin: Prevent skin contact (liq) Eyes: Prevent eye contact (liq) Wash skin: When contam (liq) Remove: When wet (flamm) Change: N.R.	NIOSH ¥: SCBAF:PD,PP/SAF:PD,PP:ASCBA Escape: GMFOV/SCBAE	Inh Ing (liq) Con (liq)	Irrit eyes, skin; dizz, conf, inco, narco, nau, vomit; liq: frostbite; [carc]	Eye: Irr immed (liq) Skin: Water flush immed (liq) Breath: Resp support Swallow: Medical attention immed (liq)	Eyes, skin, CNS, liver [in animals: liver & lymph node tumors]
[Vinyl bromide]					
Skin: Frostbite Eyes: Frostbite Wash skin: N.R. Remove: When wet (flamm) Change: N.R. Provide: Frostbite	NIOSH ¥: SCBAF:PD,PP/SAF:PD,PP:ASCBA Escape: GMFS/SCBAE	Inh Con (liq)	Weak; abdom pain, GI bleeding; enlarged liver; pallor or cyan of extremities; liq: frostbite; [carc]	Eye: Frostbite Skin: Frostbite Breath: Resp support	Liver, CNS, blood, resp sys, lymphatic sys [liver cancer]
[Vinyl chloride]					
Skin: Prevent skin contact Eyes: Prevent eye contact Wash skin: When contam Remove: When wet or contam Change: N.R. Provide: Eyewash, Quick drench	NIOSH ¥: SCBAF:PD,PP/SAF:PD,PP:ASCBA Escape: GMFOV/SCBAE	Inh Abs Ing Con	In animals: irrit eyes, skin, resp sys; testicular atrophy; leupen; nec thymus; skin sens; [carc]	Eye: Irr immed Skin: Water wash immed Breath: Resp support Swallow: Medical attention immed	Eyes, skin, resp sys, blood, thymus, repro sys [in animals: skin tumors]
[Vinyl cyclohexene dioxide]					
Skin: Frostbite Eyes: Frostbite Wash skin: N.R. Remove: When wet (flamm) Change: N.R. Provide: Frostbite	NIOSH 10 ppm: CCROV/SA 25 ppm: SA:CF/PAPROV 50 ppm: CCRFOV/GMFOV/PAPRTOV/ SCBAF/SAF 200 ppm: SAF:PD,PP §: SCBAF:PD,PP/SAF:PD,PP:ASCBA Escape: GMFOV/SCBAE	Inh Con (liq)	Head, dizz, conf, inco, narco, nau, vomit; liq: frostbite	Eye: Frostbite Skin: Frostbite Breath: Resp support	CNS
[Vinyl fluoride]					

Chemical name, structure/formula, CAS and RTECS Nos., and DOT ID and guide Nos.	Synonyms, trade names, and conversion factors	Exposure limits (TWA unless noted otherwise)	IDLH	Physical description	Chemical and physical properties		Incompatibilities and reactivities	Measurement method (See Table 1)
					MW, BP, SOL FI.P, IP, Sp, Gr, flammability	VP, FRZ UEL, LEL		
Vinylidene chloride CH$_2$=CCl$_2$ 75-35-4 KV9275000 1303 129P	1,1-DCE; 1,1-Dichloroethene; 1,1-Dichloroethylene; VDC; Vinylidene chloride monomer; Vinylidene dichloride	NIOSH Ca See Appendix A OSHA† none	Ca [N.D.]	Colorless liquid or gas (above 89°F) with a mild, sweet, chloroform-like odor.	MW: 96.9 BP: 89°F Sol: 0.04% FI.P: -2°F IP: 10.00 eV Sp.Gr: 1.21 Class IA Flammable Liquid	VP: 500 mm FRZ: -189°F UEL: 15.5% LEL: 6.5%	Aluminum, sunlight, air, copper, heat [Note: Polymerization may occur if exposed to oxidizers, chlorosulfonic acid, nitric acid, or oleum. Inhibitors such as the monomethyl ether of hydroquinone are added to prevent polymerization.]	Char; CS$_2$; GC/FID; IV [#1015]
Vinylidene fluoride CH$_2$=CF$_2$ 75-38-7 KW0560000 1959 116P	Difluoro-1,1-ethylene; 1,1-Difluoroethane; 1,1-Difluoroethylene; Halocarbon 1132A; VDF; Vinylidene difluoride 1 ppm = 2.62 mg/m^3	NIOSH 1 ppm C 5 ppm [use 1910.1017] OSHA none	N.D.	Colorless gas with a faint, ethereal odor. [Note: Shipped as a liquefied compressed gas.]	MW: 64.0 BP: -122°F Sol: Insoluble FI.P: NA (Gas) IP: 10.29 eV RGasD: 2.21 Flammable Gas	VP: 35.2 atm FRZ: -227°F UEL: 21.3% LEL: 5.5%	Oxidizers, aluminum chloride [Note: Violent reaction with hydrogen chloride when heated under pressure.]	None available
Vinyl toluene CH$_2$=CHC$_6$H$_4$CH$_3$ 25013-15-4 WL5075000 2618 130P	Ethenylmethylbenzene, Methylstyrene, Tolyethylene 1 ppm = 4.83 mg/m^3	NIOSH/OSHA 100 ppm (480 mg/m^3)	400 ppm	Colorless liquid with a strong, disagreeable odor.	MW: 118.2 BP: 339°F Sol: 0.009% FI.P: 127°F IP: 8.20 eV Sp.Gr: 0.89 Class II Combustible Liquid	VP: 1 mm FRZ: -106°F UEL: 11.0% LEL: 0.8%	Oxidizers, peroxides, strong acids, iron or aluminum salts [Note: Usually inhibited with tert-butyl catechol to prevent polymerization.]	Char; CS$_2$; GC/FID; IV [#1501, Aromatic Hydro-carbons]
VM & P Naphtha 8032-32-4 OI6180000 1271 128	Ligroin, Painters naphtha, Petroleum ether, Petroleum spirit, Refined solvent naphtha, Varnish makers' & painters' naphtha	NIOSH 350 mg/m^3 C 1800 mg/m^3 [15-min] OSHA† none	N.D.	Clear to yellowish liquid with a pleasant, aromatic odor.	MW: 87-114 (approx) BP: 203-320°F Sol: Insoluble FI.P: 20-55°F IP: ? Sp.Gr(60°F): 0.73-0.76 Class IB Flammable Liquid	VP: 2-20 mm FRZ: ? UEL: 6.0% LEL: 1.2%	None reported [Note: VM&P Naphtha is a refined petroleum solvent predominantly C$_7$-C$_{11}$ which is typically 55% paraffins, 30% mono-cycloparaffins, 2% dicyclo-paraffins & 12% alkylbenzenes.]	Char; CS$_2$; GC/FID; IV [#1550, Naphthas]

Personal protection and sanitation (See Table 3)	Recommendations for respirator selection — maximum concentration for use (MUC) (See Table 4)	Route	Symptoms (See Table 5)	First aid (See Table 6)	Target organs (See Table 5)
Skin: Prevent skin contact Eyes: Prevent eye contact Wash skin: When contam Remove: When wet (flamm) Change: N.R. Provide: Eyewash, Quick drench	NIOSH ¥: SCBAF:PD,PP/SAF:PD,PP:ASCBA Escape: GMFOV/SCBAE	Inh Abs Ing Con	Irrit eyes, skin, throat; dizz, head, nau; dysp; liver, kidney dysfunc; pneuitis; [carc]	Eye: Irr immed Skin: Water flush immed Breath: Resp support Swallow: Medical attention immed	Eyes, skin, resp sys, CNS, liver, kidneys [in animals: liver & kidney tumors]
[Vinylidene chloride]					
Skin: Frostbite Eyes: Frostbite Wash skin: N.R. Remove: When wet (flamm) Change: N.R. Provide: Frostbite	NIOSH 10 ppm: CCROV/SA 25 ppm: SA:CF/PAPROV 50 ppm: CCRFOV/GMFOV/PAPRTOV/ SCBAF/SAF 200 ppm: SAF:PD,PP §: SCBAF:PD,PP/SAF:PD,PP:ASCBA Escape: GMFOV/SCBAE	Inh Con (liq)	Dizz, head, nau; liq: frostbite	Eye: Frostbite Skin: Frostbite Breath: Resp support	CNS
[Vinylidene fluoride]					
Skin: Prevent skin contact Eyes: Prevent eye contact Wash skin: When contam Remove: When wet or contam Change: N.R.	NIOSH/OSHA 400 ppm: CCROV*/PAPROV*/GMFOV/ SA*/SCBAF §: SCBAF:PD,PP/SAF:PD,PP:ASCBA Escape: GMFOV/SCBAE	Inh Ing Con	Irrit eyes, skin, upper resp sys; drow; in animals: narco	Eye: Irr immed Skin: Soap flush prompt Breath: Resp support Swallow: Medical attention immed	Eyes, resp sys, CNS
[Vinyl toluene]					
Skin: Prevent skin contact Eyes: Prevent eye contact Wash skin: When contam Remove: When wet (flamm) Change: N.R.	NIOSH 3500 mg/m^3: CCROV/SA 8750 mg/m^3: SA:CF/PAPROV 17,500 mg/m^3: CCRFOV/GMFOV/ PAPRTOV/SCBAF/SAF §: SCBAF:PD,PP/SAF:PD,PP:ASCBA Escape: GMFOV/SCBAE	Inh Ing Con	Irrit eyes, upper resp sys; derm, CNS depres; chemical pneu (aspir liq)	Eye: Irr immed Skin: Soap wash prompt Breath: Resp support Swallow: Medical attention immed	Eyes, skin, resp sys, CNS
[VM & P naphtha]					

Chemical name, structure/formula, CAS and RTECS Nos., and DOT ID and guide Nos.	Synonyms, trade names, and conversion factors	Exposure limits (TWA unless noted otherwise)	IDLH	Physical description	Chemical and physical properties		Incompatibilities and reactivities	Measurement method (See Table 1)
					MW, BP, SOL Fl.P, IP, Sp.Gr, flammability	VP, FRZ UEL, LEL		
Warfarin $C_{19}H_{16}O_4$ 81-81-2 GN4550000	3-(α-Acetonyl)-benzyl-4-hydroxycoumarin, 4-Hydroxy-3-(3-oxo-1-phenyl butyl)-2H-1-benzopyran-2-one, WARF	NIOSH/OSHA 0.1 mg/m³	100 mg/m³	Colorless, odorless, crystalline powder. [rodenticide]	MW: 308.3 BP: Decomposes Sol: 0.002% Fl.P: ? IP: ? Sp.Gr: ? Combustible Solid	VP(71°F): 0.09 mm MLT: 322°F UEL: ? LEL: ?	Strong oxidizers	Filter; Methanol; HPLC/UVD; IV [#5002]
Welding fumes ZC2550000	Synonyms vary depending upon the specific component of the welding fumes.	NIOSH Ca See Appendix A OSHA† none	Ca [N.D.]	Fumes generated by the process of joining or cutting pieces of metal by heat, pressure, or both.	Properties vary depending upon the specific component of the welding fumes.		Varies	Filter; Acid; ICP; IV [#7300, Elements]
Wood dust ZC9850000	Hard wood dust, Soft wood dust, Western red cedar dust	NIOSH Ca See Appendix A 1 mg/m³ OSHA† 15 mg/m³ (total) 5 mg/m³ (resp)	Ca [N.D.]	Dust from various types of wood.	MW: varies BP: NA Sol: ? Fl.P: NA IP: NA Sp.Gr: ? Combustible Solid	VP: 0 mm (approx) MLT: NA UEL: NA LEL: NA	None reported	Filter; none; Grav; IV [#0500, Particulates NOR (total)]
o-Xylene $C_6H_4(CH_3)_2$ 95-47-6 ZE2450000 1307 130	1,2-Dimethylbenzene; ortho-Xylene; o-Xylol 1 ppm = 4.34 mg/m³	NIOSH 100 ppm (435 mg/m³) ST 150 ppm (655 mg/m³) OSHA† 100 ppm (435 mg/m³)	900 ppm	Colorless liquid with an aromatic odor.	MW: 106.2 BP: 292°F Sol: 0.02% Fl.P: 90°F IP: 8.56 eV Sp.Gr: 0.88 Class IC Flammable Liquid	VP: 7 mm FRZ: -13°F UEL: 6.7% LEL: 0.9%	Strong oxidizers, strong acids	Char; CS₂; GC/FID; IV [#1501, Aromatic Hydro- carbons]

Personal protection and sanitation (See Table 3)		Recommendations for respirator selection — maximum concentration for use (MUC) (See Table 4)	Route	Symptoms (See Table 5)	First aid (See Table 6)		Target organs (See Table 5)
Skin:	Prevent skin contact	NIOSH/OSHA	Inh	Hema, back pain; hematoma	Eye:	Irr immed	Blood, CVS
Eyes:	N.R.	0.5 mg/m^3: DM	Abs	arms, legs; epis;	Skin:	Soap wash prompt	
Wash skin:	When contam	1 mg/m^3: DMXSQ/SA	Ing	bleeding lips, muc memb	Breath:	Resp support	
Remove:	When wet or contam	2.5 mg/m^3: SA:CF/PAPRDM	Con	hemorr; abdom pain,	Swallow:	Medical attention	
Change:	Daily	5 mg/m^3: HiEF/SAT:CF/PAPRTHiE/		vomit, fecal blood;		immed	
		SCBAF/SAF		petechial rash; abnor			
		100 mg/m^3: SA:PD,PP		hematologic indices			
		§: SCBAF:PD,PP/SAF:PD,PP:ASCBA					
		Escape: HiEF/SCBAE					
[Warfarin]							
Skin:	N.R.	NIOSH	Inh	Symptoms vary depending	Eye:	Irr immed	Eyes, skin, resp sys,
Eyes:	N.R.	¥: SCBAF:PD,PP/SAF:PD,PP:ASCBA	Con	upon the specific	Skin:	Soap wash	CNS
Wash skin:	N.R.	Escape: GMFOVHiE/SCBAE		component of the welding	Breath:	Resp support	[lung cancer]
Remove:	N.R.			fumes; metal fume fever:			
Change:	N.R.			flu-like symptoms, dysp,			
				cough, musc pain, fever,			
				chills; interstitial pneu;			
				[carc]			
[Welding fumes]							
Skin:	N.R.	NIOSH	Inh	Irrit eyes; epis; derm;	Eye:	Irr immed	Eyes, skin, resp sys
Eyes:	N.R.	¥: SCBAF:PD,PP/SAF:PD,PP:ASCBA	Con	resp hypersensitivity;	Skin:	Soap wash	[nasal cancer]
Wash skin:	N.R.	Escape: HiEF/SCBAE		granulomatous pneuitis;	Breath:	Fresh air	
Remove:	N.R.			asthma; cough, wheez,			
Change:	N.R.			sinusitis; prolonged colds;			
				[carc]			
[Wood dust]							
Skin:	Prevent skin contact	NIOSH/OSHA	Inh	Irrit eyes, skin, nose,	Eye:	Irr immed	Eyes, skin, resp sys,
Eyes:	Prevent eye contact	900 ppm: CCROV*/PAPROV*/SA*/SCBAF	Abs	throat; dizz, excitement,	Skin:	Soap wash prompt	CNS, GI tract, blood,
Wash skin:	When contam	§: SCBAF:PD,PP/SAF:PD,PP:ASCBA	Ing	drow, inco, staggering	Breath:	Resp support	liver, kidneys
Remove:	When wet (flamm)	Escape: GMFOV/SCBAE	Con	gait; corn vacuolization;	Swallow:	Medical attention	
Change:	N.R.			anor, nau, vomit, abdom		immed	
				pain; derm			
[o-Xylene]							

Chemical name, structure/formula, CAS and RTECS Nos., and DOT ID and guide Nos.	Synonyms, trade names, and conversion factors	Exposure limits (TWA unless noted otherwise)	IDLH	Physical description	Chemical and physical properties		Incompatibilities and reactivities	Measurement method (See Table 1)
					MW, BP, SOL Fl.P, IP, Sp, Gr, flammability	VP, FRZ UEL, LEL		
m-Xylene $C_6H_4(CH_3)_2$ 108-38-3 ZE2275000 1307 130	1,3-Dimethylbenzene; meta-Xylene; m-Xylol 1 ppm = 4.34 mg/m³	NIOSH 100 ppm (435 mg/m³) ST 150 ppm (655 mg/m³) OSHA† 100 ppm (435 mg/m³)	900 ppm	Colorless liquid with an aromatic odor.	MW: 106.2 BP: 282°F Sol: Slight Fl.P: 82°F IP: 8.56 eV Sp.Gr. 0.86 Class IC Flammable Liquid	VP: 9 mm FRZ: -54°F UEL: 7.0% LEL: 1.1%	Strong oxidizers, strong acids	Char; CS₂; GC/FID; IV [#1501, Aromatic Hydro- carbons]
p-Xylene $C_6H_4(CH_3)_2$ 106-42-3 ZE2625000 1307 130	1,4-Dimethylbenzene; para-Xylene; p-Xylol 1 ppm = 4.34 mg/m³	NIOSH 100 ppm (435 mg/m³) ST 150 ppm (655 mg/m³) OSHA† 100 ppm (435 mg/m³)	900 ppm	Colorless liquid with an aromatic odor. [Note: A solid below 56°F.]	MW: 106.2 BP: 281°F Sol: 0.02% Fl.P: 81°F IP: 8.44 eV Sp.Gr. 0.86 Class IC Flammable Liquid	VP: 9 mm FRZ: 56°F UEL: 7.0% LEL: 1.1%	Strong oxidizers, strong acids	Char; CS₂; GC/FID; IV [#1501, Aromatic Hydro- carbons]
m-Xylene α, α'-diamine $C_6H_4(CH_2NH_2)_2$ 1477-55-0 PF8970000	1,3-bis(Aminomethyl)benzene; 1,3-Benzenedimethanamine; MXDA; m-Phenylenebis(methylamine); m-Xylylenediamine	NIOSH C 0.1 mg/m³ [skin] OSHA† none	N.D.	Colorless liquid.	MW: 136.2 BP: 477°F Sol: Miscible Fl.P: 243°F IP: ? Sp.Gr. 1.032 Class IIIB Combustible Liquid	VP(77°F): 0.03 mm FRZ: 58°F UEL: ? LEL: ?	None reported	None available
Xylidine $(CH_3)_2C_6H_3NH_2$ 1300-73-8 ZE8575000 1711 151	Aminodimethylbenzene, Aminoxylene, Dimethylaminobenzene, Dimethylaniline, Xylidine isomers (e.g., 2,4-Dimethylaniline) [Note: Dimethylaniline is also used as a synonym for N,N-Dimethylaniline.] 1 ppm = 4.96 mg/m³	NIOSH 2 ppm (10 mg/m³) [skin] OSHA† 5 ppm (25 mg/m³) [skin]	50 ppm	Pale-yellow to brown liquid with a weak, aromatic, amine-like odor.	MW: 121.2 BP: 415-439°F Sol: Slight Fl.P: 206°F (2,3-) IP: 7.65 eV (2,4-) 7.30 eV (2,6-) Sp.Gr. 0.98 Class IIIB Combustible Liquid (2,3-)	VP: <1 mm FRZ: -33°F UEL: ? LEL: 1.0% (2,3-)	Strong oxidizers, hypochlorite salts	Si gel; Ethanol; GC/FID; IV [#2002]

Personal protection and sanitation (See Table 3)		Recommendations for respirator selection — maximum concentration for use (MUC) (See Table 4)	Route	Symptoms (See Table 5)	First aid (See Table 6)		Target organs (See Table 5)
Skin: Eyes: Wash skin: Remove: Change:	Prevent skin contact Prevent eye contact When contam When wet (flamm) N.R.	NIOSH/OSHA 900 ppm: CCROV*/PAPROV*/SA*/SCBAF §: SCBAF:PD/SAF:PD,PP:ASCBAF Escape: GMFOV/SCBAE	Inh Abs Ing Con	Irrit eyes, skin, nose, throat; dizz, excitement, drow, inco, staggering gait; corn vacuolization; anor, nau, vomit, abdom pain; derm	Eye: Skin: Breath: Swallow:	Irr immed Soap wash prompt Resp support Medical attention immed	Eyes, skin, resp sys, CNS, GI tract, blood, liver, kidneys
[m-Xylene]							
Skin: Eyes: Wash skin: Remove: Change:	Prevent skin contact Prevent eye contact When contam When wet (flamm) N.R.	NIOSH/OSHA 900 ppm: CCROV*/PAPROV*/SA*/SCBAF §: SCBAF:PD,PP/SAF:PD,PP:ASCBA Escape: GMFOV/SCBAE	Inh Abs Ing Con	Irrit eyes, skin, nose, throat; dizz, excitement, drow, inco, staggering gait; corn vacuolization; anor, nau, vomit, abdom pain; derm	Eye: Skin: Breath: Swallow:	Irr immed Soap wash prompt Resp support Medical attention immed	Eyes, skin, resp sys, CNS, GI tract, blood, liver, kidneys
[p-Xylene]							
Skin: Eyes: Wash skin: Remove: Change: Provide:	Prevent skin contact Prevent eye contact When contam When wet or contam N.R. Eyewash, Quick drench,	TBAL	Inh Abs Ing Con	In animals: irrit eyes, skin; liver, kidney, lung damage	Eye: Skin: Breath: Swallow:	Irr immed Water flush immed Resp support Medical attention immed	Eyes, skin, resp sys, liver, kidneys
[m-Xylene α, α'-diamine]							
Skin: Eyes: Wash skin: Remove: Change: Provide:	Prevent skin contact Prevent eye contact When contam When wet or contam N.R. Eyewash, Quick drench	NIOSH 20 ppm: CCROV/SA 50 ppm: SA:CF/CCRFOV/GMFOV/ PAPRCV/SCBAF/SAF §: SCBAF:PD,PP/SAF:PD,PP:ASCBA Escape: GMFOV/SCBAE	Inh Abs Ing Con	Anoxia, cyan, methemo; lung, liver, kidney damage	Eye: Skin: Breath: Swallow:	Irr immed Soap wash immed Resp support Medical attention immed	Resp sys, blood, liver, kidneys, CVS
[Xylidine]							

Chemical name, structure/formula, CAS and RTECS Nos., and DOT ID and guide Nos.	Synonyms, trade names, and conversion factors	Exposure limits (TWA unless noted otherwise)	IDLH	Physical description	Chemical and physical properties		Incompatibilities and reactivities	Measurement method (See Table 1)
					MW, BP, SOL Fl.P, IP, Sp, Gr, flammability	VP, FRZ UEL, LEL		
Yttrium Y 7440-65-5 ZG2980000	Yttrium metal	NIOSH*/OSHA* 1 mg/m³ [*Note: The REL and PEL also apply to other yttrium compounds (as Y).]	500 mg/m³ (as Y)	Dark-gray to black, odorless solid.	MW: 88.9 BP: 5301°F Sol: Soluble in hot H₂O Fl.P: NA IP: NA Sp.Gr: 4.47 Noncombustible Solid in bulk form.	VP: 0 mm (approx) MLT: 2732°F UEL: NA LEL: NA	Oxidizers	Filter; Acid; ICP; IV [#7300, Elements]
Zinc chloride fume ZnCl₂ 7646-85-7 ZH1400000	Zinc dichloride fume	NIOSH 1 mg/m³ ST 2 mg/m³ OSHA† 1 mg/m³	50 mg/m³	White particulate dispersed in air.	MW: 136.3 BP: 1350°F Sol(70°F): 435% Fl.P: NA IP: NA Sp.Gr: 2.91 Noncombustible Solid	VP: 0 mm (approx) MLT: 554°F UEL: NA LEL: NA	Potassium	Filter; Water; FAAS; OSHA [#ID121]
Zinc oxide ZnO 1314-13-2 ZH4810000 1516 143	Zinc peroxide	NIOSH 5 mg/m³ (fume/dust) ST 10 mg/m³ (fume) C 15 mg/m³ (dust) OSHA† 5 mg/m³ (fume) 15 mg/m³ (total dust) 5 mg/m³ (resp dust)	500 mg/m³	White, odorless solid.	MW: 81.4 BP: ? Sol(64°F): 0.0004% Fl.P: NA IP: NA Sp.Gr: 5.61 Noncombustible Solid	VP: 0 mm (approx) MLT: 3587°F UEL: NA LEL: NA	Chlorinated rubber (at 419°F), water [Note: Slowly decomposed by water.]	Filter; none; XRD; IV [#7502]
Zinc stearate Zn(C₁₈H₃₅O₂)₂ 557-05-1 ZH5200000	Dibasic zinc stearate, Zinc distearate, Zinc salt of stearic acid	NIOSH 10 mg/m³ (total) 5 mg/m³ (resp) OSHA† 15 mg/m³ (total) 5 mg/m³ (resp)	N.D.	Soft, white powder with a slight, characteristic odor.	MW: 632.4 BP: ? Sol: Insoluble Fl.P(oc): 530°F IP: NA Sp.Gr: 1.10 Combustible Solid	VP: 0 mm (approx) MLT: 266°F UEL: ? LEL: ? MEC: 20 g/m³	Oxidizers, dilute acids [Note: Hydrophobic (i.e., repels water).]	Filter; none; Grav; IV [Particulates NOR: #0500 (total), #0600 (resp)]

Personal protection and sanitation (See Table 3)		Recommendations for respirator selection — maximum concentration for use (MUC) (See Table 4)	Health hazards			
			Route	Symptoms (See Table 5)	First aid (See Table 6)	Target organs (See Table 5)
Skin:	N.R.	NIOSH/OSHA	Inh	Irrit eyes;	Eye: Irr immed	Eyes, resp sys,
Eyes:	N.R.	5 mg/m³: DM	Ing	in animals: pulm irrit;	Skin: Soap wash prompt	liver
Wash skin:	N.R.	10 mg/m³: DMXSQ/SA	Con	eye inj; possible liver	Breath: Resp support	
Remove:	N.R.	25 mg/m³: SA:CF/PAPRDM		damage	Swallow: Medical attention	
Change:	N.R.	50 mg/m³: HiEF/SAT:CF/PAPRTHiE/			immed	
		SCBAF/SAF				
		500 mg/m³: SA:PD,PP				
		§: SCBAF:PD,PP/SAF:PD,PP:ASCBA				
		Escape: HiEF/SCBAE				
[Yttrium]						
Skin:	N.R.	NIOSH/OSHA	Inh	Irrit eyes, skin, nose,	Breath: Resp support	Eyes, skin, resp sys,
Eyes:	N.R.	10 mg/m³: DMFu*/SA*	Con	throat; conj; cough,		CVS
Wash skin:	N.R.	25 mg/m³: SA:CF*/PAPRDMFu*		copious sputum; dysp,		
Remove:	N.R.	50 mg/m³: HiEF/PAPRTHiE*/		chest pain, pulm edema,		
Change:	N.R.	SCBAF/SAF		broncopneu; pulm fib, cor		
		§: SCBAF:PD,PP/SAF:PD,PP:ASCBA		pulmonale; fever; cyan;		
		Escape: HiEF/SCBAE		tachypnea; skin burns		
[Zinc chloride fume]						
Skin:	N.R.	NIOSH/OSHA	Inh	Metal fume fever: chills,	Breath: Resp support	Resp sys
Eyes:	N.R.	50 mg/m³: DMFu/SA		musc ache, nau, fever,		
Wash skin:	N.R.	125 mg/m³: SA:CF/PAPRDMFu		dry throat, cough, weak,		
Remove:	N.R.	250 mg/m³: HiEF/SAT:CF/PAPRTHiE		lass; metallic taste;		
Change:	N.R.	SCBAF/SAF		head; blurred vision;		
		500 mg/m³: SA:PD,PP		low back pain; vomit; ftg;		
		§: SCBAF:PD,PP/SAF:PD,PP:ASCBA		mal; tight chest, dysp,		
		Escape: HiEF/SCBAE		rales, decr pulm func		
[Zinc oxide]						
Skin:	N.R.	TBAL	Inh	Irrit eyes, skin, upper	Eye: Irr immed	Eyes, skin, resp sys
Eyes:	N.R.		Ing	resp sys; cough	Skin: Soap wash	
Wash skin:	N.R.		Con		Breath: Fresh air	
Remove:	N.R.				Swallow: Medical attention	
Change:	N.R.				immed	
[Zinc stearate]						

Chemical name, structure/formula, CAS and RTECS Nos., and DOT ID and guide Nos.	Synonyms, trade names, and conversion factors	Exposure limits (TWA unless noted otherwise)	IDLH	Physical description	Chemical and physical properties		Incompatibilities and reactivities	Measurement method (See Table 1)
					MW, BP, SOL Fl.P, IP, Sp, Gr, flammability	VP, FRZ UEL, LEL		
Zirconium compounds (as Zr) Zr (Metal) 7440-67-7 (Metal) ZH7070000 (Metal) 1358 170 (powder, wet) 1932 135 (scrap) 2008 135 (powder, dry)	Zirconium metal: Zirconium Synonyms of other zirconium compounds vary depending upon the specific compound.	NIOSH* 5 mg/m³ ST 10 mg/m³ [*Note: The REL applies to all zirconium compounds (as Zr) except Zirconium tetrachloride.] OSHA† 5 mg/m³	50 mg/m³ (as Zr)	Metal: Soft, malleable, ductile, solid or gray to gold, amorphous powder.	MW: 91.2 BP: 6471°F Sol: Insoluble Fl.P: NA IP: NA Sp.Gr: 6.51 (Metal) Metal: Combustible, but solid form is difficult to ignite; however, powder form may ignite SPONTANEOUSLY and can continue burning under water.	VP: 0 mm (approx) MLT: 3375°F UEL: NA LEL: NA	Potassium nitrate, oxidizers [Note: Fine powder may be stored completely immersed in water.]	Filter; Acid; ICP; IV [#7300, Elements]

Personal protection and sanitation (See Table 3)	Recommendations for respirator selection — maximum concentration for use (MUC) (See Table 4)	Health hazards				
		Route	Symptoms (See Table 5)	First aid (See Table 6)		Target organs (See Table 5)
Recommendations vary depending upon the specific compound.	NIOSH/OSHA 25 mg/m³: DM 50 mg/m³: DMXSQ/PAPRDM/HiEF/SA/ SCBAF §: SCBAF:PD,PP/SAF:PD,PP:ASCBA Escape: HiEF/SCBAE	Inh Con	Skin, lung granulomas; in animals: irrit skin, muc memb; X-ray evidence of retention in lungs	Eye: Skin: Breath: Swallow:	Irr immed Soap wash Resp support Medical attention immed	Skin, resp sys
[Zirconium compounds (as Zr)]						

APPENDICES

343

APPENDIX A — NIOSH POTENTIAL OCCUPATIONAL CARCINOGENS

New Policy

For the past 20 plus years, NIOSH has subscribed to a carcinogen policy that was published in 1976 by Edward J. Fairchild, II, Associate Director for Cincinnati Operations, which called for "no detectable exposure levels for proven carcinogenic substances" (Annals of the New York Academy of Sciences, 271:200-207, 1996). This was in response to a generic OSHA rulemaking on carcinogens. Because of advances in science and in approaches to risk assessment and risk management, NIOSH has adopted a more inclusive policy. NIOSH recommended exposure limits (RELs) will be based on risk evaluations using human or animal health effects data, and on an assessment of what levels can be feasibly achieved by engineering controls and measured by analytical techniques. To the extent feasible, NIOSH will project not only a no-effect exposure, but also exposure levels at which there may be residual risks. This policy applies to all workplace hazards, including carcinogens, and is responsive to Section 20(a)(3) of the Occupational Safety and Health Act of 1970, which charges NIOSH to ". . .describe exposure levels that are safe for various periods of employment, including but not limited to the exposure levels at which no employee will suffer impaired health or functional capacities or diminished life expectancy as a result of his work experience."

The effect of this new policy will be the development, whenever possible, of quantitative RELs that are based on human and/or animal data, as well as on the consideration of technological feasibility for controlling workplace exposures to the REL. Under the old policy, RELs for most carcinogens were non-quantitative values labeled "lowest feasible concentration (LFC)." [Note: There are a few exceptions to LFC RELs for carcinogens (e.g., RELs for asbestos, formaldehyde, benzene, and ethylene oxide are quantitative values based primarily on analytical limits of detection or technological feasibility). Also, in 1989, NIOSH adopted several quantitative RELs for carcinogens from OSHA's permissible exposure limit (PEL) update.]

Under the new policy, NIOSH will also recommend the complete range of respirators (as determined by the *NIOSH Respirator Decision Logic*) for carcinogens with quantitative RELs. In this way, respirators will be consistently recommended regardless of whether a substance is a carcinogen or a non-carcinogen.

Old Policy

In the past, NIOSH identified numerous substances that should be treated as potential occupational carcinogens even though OSHA might not have identified them as such. In determining their carcinogenicity, NIOSH used the OSHA classification outlined in 29 CFR 1990.103, which states in part:

> Potential occupational carcinogen means any substance, or combination or mixture of substances, which causes an increased incidence of benign and/or malignant neoplasms, or a substantial decrease in the latency period between exposure and onset of neoplasms in humans or in one or more experimental mammalian species as the result of any oral, respiratory or dermal exposure, or

any other exposure which results in the induction of tumors at a site other than the site of administration. This definition also includes any substance which is metabolized into one or more potential occupational carcinogens by mammals.

When thresholds for carcinogens that would protect 100% of the population had not been identified, NIOSH usually recommended that *__occupational exposures to carcinogens be limited to the lowest feasible concentration__*. To ensure maximum protection from carcinogens through the use of respiratory protection, NIOSH also recommended that only the most reliable and protective respirators be used. These respirators include (1) a self-contained breathing apparatus (SCBA) that has a full facepiece and is operated in a positive-pressure mode, or (2) a supplied-air respirator that has a full facepiece and is operated in a pressure-demand or other positive-pressure mode in combination with an auxiliary SCBA operated in a pressure-demand or other positive-pressure mode.

Recommendations to be Revised

The RELs and respirator recommendations for carcinogens listed in this edition of the *Pocket Guide* still reflect the old policy. This edition, which contains other updated information, is long overdue; hence, it is published now rather than later. Changes in the RELs and respirator recommendations that reflect the new policy will be included in future editions.

APPENDIX B — THIRTEEN OSHA-REGULATED CARCINOGENS

Without establishing PELs, OSHA promulgated standards in 1974 to regulate the industrial use of 13 chemicals identified as potential occupational carcinogens (2-acetylaminofluorene, 4-aminodiphenyl, benzidine, bis-chloromethyl ether, 3,3'-dichlorobenzidine, 4-dimethylaminoazobenzene, ethyleneimine, meth-yl chloromethyl ether, alpha-naphthylamine, beta-naphthylamine, 4-nitrobiphenyl, N-nitrosodimeth-ylamine, and beta-propiolactone). Exposures of workers to these 13 chemicals are to be controlled through the required use of engineering controls, work practices, and personal protective equipment, including respirators. See 29 CFR 1910.1003-1910.1016 for specific details of these requirements.

Respirator selections in the *Pocket Guide* are based on NIOSH policy, which considers the 13 chemicals to be potential occupational carcinogens.

APPENDIX C — SUPPLEMENTARY EXPOSURE LIMITS

Aldehydes (Low-Molecular-Weight)

Exposure to acetaldehyde has produced nasal tumors in rats and laryngeal tumors in hamsters, and exposure to malonaldehyde has produced thyroid gland and pancreatic islet cell tumors in rats. NIOSH therefore recommends that acetaldehyde and malonaldehyde be considered potential occupational carcinogens in conformance with the OSHA carcinogen policy. Testing has not been completed to determine the carcinogenicity of acrolein, butyraldehyde (CAS#: 123-72-8), crotonaldehyde, glutaraldehyde, glyoxal (CAS#: 107-22-2), paraformaldehyde (CAS#: 30525-89-4), propiolaldehyde (CAS#: 624-67-9), propionaldehyde (CAS#: 123-38-6), and n-valeraldehyde, nine related low-molecular-weight-aldehydes. However, the limited studies to date indicate that these substances have chemical reactivity and mutagenicity similar to acetaldehyde and malonaldehyde. Therefore, NIOSH recommends that careful consideration should be given to reducing exposures to these nine related aldehydes. Further information can be found in the "NIOSH Current Intelligence Bulletin 55: Carcinogenicity of Acetaldehyde and Malonaldehyde, and Mutagenicity of Related Low-Molecular-Weight Aldehydes" [DHHS (NIOSH) Publication No. 91-112.]

Asbestos

NIOSH considers asbestos (i.e., actinolite, amosite, anthophyllite, chrysotile, crocidolite, and tremolite) to be a potential occupational carcinogen and recommends that exposures be reduced to the lowest possible concentration. For asbestos fibers >5 micrometers in length, NIOSH recommends a REL of 100,000 fibers per cubic meter of air (100,000 fibers/m^3), which is equal to 0.1 fiber per cubic centimeter of air (0.1 fiber/cm^3), as determined by a 400-liter air sample collected over 100 minutes and NIOSH Analytical Method #7400.

APPENDIX C — SUPPLEMENTARY EXPOSURE LIMITS (Continued)

As found in 29 CFR 1910.1001, the OSHA PEL for asbestos fibers (i.e., actinolite asbestos, amosite, anthophyllite asbestos, chrysotile, crocidolite, and tremolite asbestos) is an 8-hour TWA airborne concentration of 0.1 fiber (longer than 5 micrometers and having a length-to-diameter ratio of at least 3 to 1) per cubic centimeter of air (0.1 fiber/cm³), as determined by the membrane filter method at approximately 400X magnification with phase contrast illumination. No worker should be exposed in excess of 1 fiber/cm³ (excursion limit) as averaged over a sampling period of 30 minutes.

Benzidine-, o-Tolidine, and o-Dianisidine-based Dyes

In December 1980, OSHA and NIOSH jointly published the Health Hazard Alert: Benzidine-, o-Tolidine, and o-Dianisidine-based Dyes. In this Alert, OSHA and NIOSH concluded that benzidine and benzidine-based dyes were potential occupational carcinogens and recommended that worker exposure be reduced to the lowest feasible level. OSHA and NIOSH further concluded that o-tolidine and o-dianisidine (and dyes based on them) may present a cancer risk to workers and should be handled with caution and exposure minimized.

APPENDIX C — SUPPLEMENTARY EXPOSURE LIMITS (Continued)

Carbon Black

NIOSH considers "Carbon Black" to be the material consisting of more than 80% elemental carbon in the form of near-spherical colloidal particles and coalesced particle aggregates of colloidal size that is obtained by the partial combustion or thermal decomposition of hydrocarbons. The NIOSH REL (10-hour TWA) for carbon black is 3.5 mg/m^3. Polycyclic aromatic hydrocarbons (PAHs), particulate polycyclic organic material (PPOM), and polynuclear aromatic hydrocarbons (PNAs) are terms frequently used to describe various petroleum-based substances that NIOSH considers to be potential occupational carcinogens. Since some of these aromatic hydrocarbons may be formed during the manufacture of carbon black (and become adsorbed on the carbon black), the NIOSH REL (10-hour TWA) for carbon black in the presence of PAHs is also 0.1 mg PAHs/m^3 (measured as the cyclohexane-extractable fraction). The OSHA PEL (8-hour TWA) for carbon black is 3.5 mg/m^3.

Chloroethanes

NIOSH considers ethylene dichloride; hexachloroethane; 1,1,2,2-tetrachloroethane; and 1,1,2-trichloroethane; to be potential occupational carcinogens. Additionally, NIOSH recommends that the other five chloroethane compounds: 1,1-dichloroethane; ethyl chloride; methyl chloroform; pentachloroethane; and 1,1,1,2-tetrachloroethane be treated in the workplace with caution because of their structural similarity to the four chloroethanes shown to be carcinogenic in animals.

APPENDIX C — SUPPLEMENTARY EXPOSURE LIMITS (Continued)

Chromic Acid and Chromates (as CrO₃), Chromium(II) and Chromium(III) Compounds (as Cr), and Chromium Metal (as Cr)

The NIOSH REL (10-hour TWA) is 0.001 mg Cr(VI)/m³ for all hexavalent chromium [Cr(VI)] compounds. NIOSH considers all Cr(VI) compounds (including chromic acid, tert-butyl chromate, zinc chromate, and chromyl chloride) to be potential occupational carcinogens. The NIOSH REL (8-hour TWA) is 0.5 mg Cr/m³ for chromium metal and chromium(II) and chromium(III) compounds.

The OSHA PEL is 0.1 mg CrO₃/m³ (ceiling) for chromic acid and chromates (including tert-butyl chromate with a "skin" designation and zinc chromate); 0.5 mg Cr/m³ (8-hour TWA) for chromium(II) and chromium(III) compounds; and 1 mg Cr/m³ (8-hour TWA) for chromium metal and insoluble salts.

Coal Tar Pitch Volatiles

NIOSH considers coal tar products (i.e., coal tar, coal tar pitch, or creosote) to be potential occupational carcinogens; the NIOSH REL (10-hour TWA) for coal tar products is 0.1 mg/m³ (cyclohexane-extractable fraction).

The OSHA PEL (8-hour TWA) for coal tar pitch volatiles is 0.2 mg/m³ (benzene-soluble fraction). OSHA defines "coal tar pitch volatiles" in 29 CFR 1910.1002 as the fused polycyclic hydrocarbons that volatilize from the distillation residues of coal, petroleum (excluding asphalt), wood, and other organic matter and includes substances such as anthracene, benzo(a)pyrene (BaP), phenanthrene, acridine, chrysene, pyrene, etc.

APPENDIX C — SUPPLEMENTARY EXPOSURE LIMITS (Continued)

Coke Oven Emissions

The production of coke by the carbonization of bituminous coal leads to the release of chemically-complex emissions from coke ovens that include both gases and particulate matter of varying chemical composition. The emissions include coal tar pitch volatiles (e.g., particulate polycyclic organic matter [PPOM], polycyclic aromatic hydrocarbons [PAHs], and polynuclear aromatic hydrocarbons [PNAs]), aromatic compounds (e.g., benzene and β-naphthylamine), trace metals (e.g., arsenic, beryllium, cadmium, chromium, lead, and nickel), and gases (e.g., nitric oxides and sulfur dioxide).

Cotton Dust (raw)

NIOSH recommends reducing exposures to cotton dust to the lowest feasible concentration to reduce the prevalence and severity of byssinosis; the REL is <0.200 mg/m³ (as lint-free cotton dust).

As found in OSHA Table Z-1 (29 CFR 1910.1000), the PEL for cotton dust (raw) is 1 mg/m³ for the cotton waste processing operations of waste recycling (sorting, blending, cleaning, and willowing) and garnetting. PELs for other sectors (as found in 29 CFR 1910.1043) are 0.200 mg/m³ for yarn manufacturing and cotton washing operations, 0.500 mg/m³ for textile mill waste house operations or for dust from "lower grade washed cotton" used during yarn manufacturing, and 0.750 mg/m³ for textile slashing and weaving operations. The OSHA standard in 29 CFR 1910.1043 does not apply to cotton harvesting, ginning, or the handling and processing of woven or knitted materials and washed cotton. All PELs for cotton dust are mean concentrations of lint-free, respirable cotton dust collected by the vertical elutriator or an equivalent method and averaged over an 8-hour period.

APPENDIX C — SUPPLEMENTARY EXPOSURE LIMITS (Continued)

Lead

NIOSH considers "Lead" to mean metallic lead, lead oxides, and lead salts (including organic salts such as lead soaps but excluding lead arsenate). The NIOSH REL for lead (10-hour TWA) is 0.100 mg/m³; air concentrations should be maintained so that worker blood lead remains less than 0.060 mg Pb/100 g of whole blood.

OSHA considers "Lead" to mean metallic lead, all inorganic lead compounds (lead oxides and lead salts), and a class of organic compounds called soaps; all other lead compounds are excluded from this definition. The OSHA PEL (8-hour TWA) is 0.050 mg/m³; other OSHA requirements can be found in 29 CFR 1910.1025. The OSHA PEL (8-hour TWA) for lead in "non-ferrous foundries with less than 20 employees" is 0.075 mg/m³.

Mineral Dusts

These OSHA PELS for "mineral dusts" listed below are from Table Z-3 of 29 CFR 1910.1000. The OSHA PEL (8-hour TWA) for crystalline silica (as respirable quartz) is either 250 mppcf divided by the value "%SiO_2 + 5" or 10 mg/m³ divided by the value "%SiO_2 + 2". The OSHA PEL (8-hour TWA) for crystalline silica (as total quartz) is 30 mg/m³ divided by the value "%SiO_2 + 2". The OSHA PELs (8-hour TWAs) for cristobalite and tridymite are ½ the values calculated above using the count or mass formulae for quartz.

The OSHA PEL (8-hour TWA) for amorphous silica (including diatomaceous earth) is either 80 mg/m³ divided by the value "%SiO_2", or 20 mppcf.

The OSHA PELs (8-hour TWAs) for mica, soapstone, and talc (not containing asbestos) are 20 mppcf.

APPENDIX C — SUPPLEMENTARY EXPOSURE LIMITS (Continued)

The OSHA PEL (8-hour TWA) for Portland cement is 50 mppcf. The OSHA PEL (8-hour TWA) for graphite (natural) is 15 mppcf.

The OSHA PEL (8-hour TWA) for coal dust (as the respirable fraction) containing less than 5% SiO_2 is 2.4 mg/m³ divided by the value "%SiO_2 + 2". The OSHA PEL (8-hour TWA) for coal dust (as the respirable fraction) containing greater than 5% SiO_2 is 10 mg/m³ divided by the value "%SiO_2 + 2".

NIAX® Catalyst ESN

In May 1978, OSHA and NIOSH jointly published the Current Intelligence Bulletin (CIB) 26: NIAX® Catalyst ESN. In this CIB, OSHA and NIOSH recommended that occupational exposure to NIAX® Catalyst ESN, its components, dimethylaminopropionitrile and bis(2-(dimethylamino)ethyl)ether, as well as formulations containing either component, be minimized. Exposures should be limited to as few workers as possible, while minimizing workplace exposure concentrations with effective work practices and engineering controls. Exposed workers should be carefully monitored for potential disorders of the nervous and genitourinary system. Although substitution is a possible control measure, alternatives to NIAX® Catalyst ESN or its components should be carefully evaluated with regard to possible adverse health effects.

Trichloroethylene

NIOSH considers trichloroethylene (TCE) to be a potential occupational carcinogen and recommends a REL of 2 ppm (as a 60-minute ceiling) during the usage of TCE as an anesthetic agent and 25 ppm (as a 10-hour TWA) during all other exposures.

APPENDIX C — SUPPLEMENTARY EXPOSURE LIMITS (Continued)

Tungsten Carbide (Cemented)

"Cemented tungsten carbide" or "hard metal" refers to a mixture of tungsten carbide, cobalt, and sometimes metal oxides or carbides and other metals (including nickel). When the cobalt (Co) content exceeds 2%, its contribution to the potential hazard is judged to exceed that of tungsten carbide. Therefore, the NIOSH REL (10-hour TWA) for cemented tungsten carbide containing >2% Co is 0.05 mg Co/m^3; the applicable OSHA PEL is 0.1 mg Co/m^3 (8-hour TWA). Nickel (Ni) may sometimes be used as a binder rather than cobalt. NIOSH considers cemented tungsten carbide containing nickel to be a potential occupational carcinogen and recommends a REL of 0.015 mg Ni/m^3 (10-hour TWA). The OSHA PEL for Insoluble Nickel (i.e., a 1 mg Ni/m^3 8-hour TWA) applies to mixtures of tungsten carbide and nickel.

APPENDIX D — SUBSTANCES WITH NO ESTABLISHED RELs

After reviewing available published literature, NIOSH provided comments to OSHA on August 1, 1988, regarding the "Proposed Rule on Air Contaminants" (29 CFR 1910, Docket No. H-020). In these comments, NIOSH questioned whether the PELs proposed (and listed below) for the following substances included in the *Pocket Guide* were adequate to protect workers from recognized health hazards: acetylene tetrabromide [TWA 1 ppm], chlorobenzene [TWA 75 ppm], coal dust (<5% SiO_2) [2 mg/m³ (as the respirable dust fraction)], coal dust (≥ 5% SiO_2) [0.1 mg/m³ (as the respirable quartz fraction)], ethyl bromide [TWA 200 ppm; STEL 250 ppm], ethylene glycol [Ceiling 50 ppm], ethyl ether [TWA 400 ppm; STEL 500 ppm], fenthion [TWA 0.2 mg/m³ (skin)], furfural [TWA 2 ppm (skin)], 2-isopropoxyethanol [TWA 25 ppm], isopropyl acetate [TWA 250 ppm; STEL 310 ppm], isopropylamine [TWA 5 ppm; STEL 10 ppm], manganese tetroxide (as Mn) [TWA 1 mg/m³], molybdenum (soluble compounds as Mo) [TWA 5 mg/m³], nitromethane [TWA 100 ppm], m-toluidine [TWA 2 ppm (skin)], and triethylamine [TWA 10 ppm; STEL 15 ppm].

At that time, NIOSH also conducted a limited evaluation of the literature and concluded that the documentation cited by OSHA was inadequate to support the proposed PEL (as an 8-hour TWA) of 10 mg/m³ for α-alumina, benomyl, emery, glycerine (mist), graphite (synthetic), magnesium oxide fume, molybdenum (insoluble compounds as Mo), particulates not otherwise regulated, picloram, and rouge.

APPENDIX E—RESPIRATOR RECOMMENDATIONS FOR SELECTED CHEMICALS

Mercury compounds [except (organo) alkyls]

Mercury vapor:
 NIOSH
 0.5 mg/m³: CCRS†/SA
 1.25 mg/m³: SA:CF/PAPRS†(canister)
 2.5 mg/m³: CCRFS†/GMFS†/SAT:CF/
         PAPRTS†(canister)/
         SCBAF/SAF
 10 mg/m³: SA:PD,PP
 §: SCBAF:PD,PP/SAF:PD,PP:ASCBA
 Escape: GMFS†/SCBAE

Other non (organo) alkyl mercury compounds:
 NIOSH/OSHA
 1 mg/m³: CCRS†/SA
 2.5 mg/m³: SA:CF/PAPRS†(canister)
 5 mg/m³: CCRFS†/GMFS†/SAT:CF/
         PAPRTS†(canister)/
         SCBAF/SAF
 10 mg/m³: SA:PD,PP
 §: SCBAF:PD,PP/SAF:PD,PP:ASCBA
 Escape: GMFS†/SCBAE

357

APPENDIX F—MISCELLANEOUS NOTES

Benzene: The final OSHA Benzene standard in 1910.1028 applies to all occupational exposures to benzene except some subsegments of industry where exposures are consistently under the action level (i.e., distribution and sales of fuels, sealed containers and pipelines, coke production, oil and gas drilling and production, natural gas processing, and the percentage exclusion for liquid mixtures); for the excepted subsegments, the benzene limits in Table Z-2 apply (i.e., an 8-hour TWA of 10 ppm, an acceptable ceiling of 25 ppm, and 50 ppm for a maximum duration of 10 minutes as an acceptable maximum peak above the acceptable ceiling).

APPENDIX G—VACATED 1989 OSHA PELs

Acetaldehyde:	TWA 100 ppm (180 mg/m³) ST 150 ppm (270 mg/m³)
Acetic anhydride:	C 5 ppm (20 mg/m³)
Acetone:	TWA 750 ppm (1800 mg/m³) ST 1000 ppm (2400 mg/m³)
Acetonitrile:	TWA 40 ppm (70 mg/m³) ST 60 ppm (105 mg/m³)
Acetylsalicyclic acid:	TWA 5 mg/m³
Acrolein:	TWA 0.1 ppm (0.25 mg/m³) ST 0.3 ppm (0.8 mg/m³)
Acrylamide:	TWA 0.03 mg/m³ [skin]
Acrylic acid:	TWA 10 ppm (30 mg/m³) [skin]
Allyl alcohol:	TWA 2 ppm (5 mg/m³) ST 4 ppm (10 mg/m³) [skin]
Allyl chloride:	TWA 1 ppm (3 mg/m³) ST 2 ppm (6 mg/m³)
Allyl glycidyl ether:	TWA 5 ppm (22 mg/m³) ST 10 ppm (44 mg/m³)
Allyl propyl disulfide:	TWA 2 ppm (12 mg/m³) ST 3 ppm (18 mg/m³)
α-Alumina:	TWA 10 mg/m³ (total) TWA 5 mg/m³ (resp)
Aluminum (pyro powders & welding fumes, as Al):	TWA 5 mg/m³
Aluminum (soluble salts & alkyls, as Al):	TWA 2 mg/m³
Amitrole:	TWA 0.2 mg/m³
Ammonia:	ST 35 ppm (27 mg/m³)
Ammonium chloride fume:	TWA 10 mg/m³ ST 20 mg/m³
Ammonium sulfamate:	TWA 10 mg/m³ (total) TWA 5 mg/m³ (resp)
Aniline (and homologs):	TWA 2 ppm (8 mg/m³) [skin]
Atrazine:	TWA 5 mg/m³
Barium sulfate:	TWA 10 mg/m³ (total) TWA 5 mg/m³ (resp)

Benomyl:	TWA 10 mg/m³ (total)
	TWA 5 mg/m³ (resp)
Benzenethiol:	TWA 0.5 ppm (2 mg/m³)
Bismuth telluride (doped with selenium sulfide, as Bi_2Te_3):	TWA 5 mg/m³
Borates, tetra, sodium salts (Anhydrous):	TWA 10 mg/m³
Borates, tetra, sodium salts (Decahydrate):	TWA 10 mg/m³
Borates, tetra, sodium salts (Pentahydrate):	TWA 10 mg/m³
Boron oxide:	TWA 10 mg/m³
Boron tribromide:	C 1 ppm (10 mg/m³)
Bromacil:	TWA 1 ppm (10 mg/m³)
Bromine:	TWA 0.1 ppm (0.7 mg/m³)
	ST 0.3 ppm (2 mg/m³)
Bromine pentafluoride:	TWA 0.1 ppm (0.7 mg/m³)
n-Butane:	TWA 800 ppm (1900 mg/m³)
2-Butanone:	TWA 200 ppm (590 mg/m³)
	ST 300 ppm (885 mg/m³)
2-Butoxyethanol:	TWA 25 ppm (120 mg/m³) [skin]
n-Butyl acetate:	TWA 150 ppm (710 mg/m³)
	ST 200 ppm (950 mg/m³)
Butyl acrylate:	TWA 10 ppm (55 mg/m³)
n-Butyl alcohol:	C 50 ppm (150 mg/m³) [skin]
sec-Butyl alcohol:	TWA 100 ppm (305 mg/m³)
tert-Butyl alcohol:	TWA 100 ppm (300 mg/m³)
	ST 150 ppm (450 mg/m³)
n-Butyl glycidyl ether:	TWA 25 ppm (135 mg/m³)
n-Butyl lactate:	TWA 5 ppm (25 mg/m³)
n-Butyl mercaptan:	TWA 0.5 ppm (1.5 mg/m³)
o-sec-Butylphenol:	TWA 5 ppm (30 mg/m³) [skin]
p-tert-Butyltoluene:	TWA 10 ppm (60 mg/m³)
	ST 20 ppm (120 mg/m³)
Calcium cyanamide:	TWA 0.5 mg/m³

Caprolactam:	Dust: TWA 1 mg/m³ ST 3 mg/m³ Vapor: TWA 5 ppm (20 mg/m³) ST 10 ppm (40 mg/m³)	Cesium hydroxide:	TWA 2 mg/m³
		Chlorinated camphene:	TWA 0.5 mg/m³ ST 1 mg/m³ [skin]
Captafol:	TWA 0.1 mg/m³	Chlorine:	TWA 0.5 ppm (1.5 mg/m³) ST 1 ppm (3 mg/m³)
Captan:	TWA 5 mg/m³		
Carbofuran:	TWA 0.1 mg/m³	Chlorine dioxide:	TWA 0.1 ppm (0.3 mg/m³) ST 0.3 ppm (0.9 mg/m³)
Carbon dioxide:	TWA 10,000 ppm (18,000 mg/m³) ST 30,000 ppm (54,000 mg/m³)	Chloroacetyl chloride:	TWA 0.05 ppm (0.2 mg/m³)
Carbon disulfide:	TWA 4 ppm (12 mg/m³) ST 12 ppm (36 mg/m³) [skin]	o-Chlorobenzylidene malononitrile:	C 0.05 ppm (0.4 mg/m³) [skin]
		Chlorodifluoromethane:	TWA 1000 ppm (3500 mg/m³)
Carbon monoxide:	TWA 35 ppm (40 mg/m³) C 200 ppm (229 mg/m³)	Chloroform:	TWA 2 ppm (9.78 mg/m³)
		1-Chloro-1-nitropropane:	TWA 2 ppm (10 mg/m³)
Carbon tetrabromide:	TWA 0.1 ppm (1.4 mg/m³) ST 0.3 ppm (4 mg/m³)	Chloropentafluoroethane:	TWA 1000 ppm (6320 mg/m³)
Carbon tetrachloride:	TWA 2 ppm (12.6 mg/m³)	ß-Chloroprene:	TWA 10 ppm (35 mg/m³) [skin]
Carbonyl fluoride:	TWA 2 ppm (5 mg/m³) ST 5 ppm (15 mg/m³)	o-Chlorostyrene:	TWA 50 ppm (285 mg/m³) ST 75 ppm (428 mg/m³)
Catechol:	TWA 5 ppm (20 mg/m³) [skin]	o-Chlorotoluene:	TWA 50 ppm (250 mg/m³)

APPENDIX G—VACATED 1989 OSHA PELs (Continued)

Chlorpyrifos:	TWA 0.2 mg/m³ [skin]	Cyhexatin:	TWA 5 mg/m³
Coal dust:	TWA 2 mg/m³ (<5% SiO₂) (resp dust) TWA 0.1 mg/m³ (≥5% SiO₂) (respquartz)	Decaborane:	TWA 0.3 mg/m³ (0.05 ppm) ST 0.9 mg/m³ (0.15 ppm) [skin]
Cobalt metal dust & fume, as Co):	TWA 0.05 mg/m³	Diazinon®:	TWA 0.1 mg/m³ [skin]
Cobalt carbonyl (as Co):	TWA 0.1 mg/m³	2-N-Dibutylaminoethanol:	TWA 2 ppm (14 mg/m³)
Cobalt hydrocarbonyl (as Co):	TWA 0.1 mg/m³	Dibutyl phosphate:	TWA 1 ppm (5 mg/m³) ST 2 ppm (10 mg/m³)
Crag® herbicide:	TWA 10 mg/m³ (total) TWA 5 mg/m³ (resp)	Dichloroacetylene:	C 0.1 ppm (0.4 mg/m³)
Crufomate:	TWA 5 mg/m³	p-Dichlorobenzene:	TWA 75 ppm (450 mg/m³) ST 110 ppm (675 mg/m³)
Cyanamide:	TWA 2 mg/m³		
Cyanogen:	TWA 10 ppm (20 mg/m³)	1,3-Dichloro-5,5- dimethylhydantoin:	TWA 0.2 mg/m³ ST 0.4 mg/m³
Cyanogen chloride:	C 0.3 ppm (0.6 mg/m³)		
Cyclohexanol:	TWA 50 ppm (200 mg/m³) [skin]	Dichloroethyl ether:	TWA 5 ppm (30 mg/m³) ST 10 ppm (60 mg/m³) [skin]
Cyclohexanone:	TWA 25 ppm (100 mg/m³) [skin]	Dichloromonofluoromethane:	TWA 10 ppm (40 mg/m³)
Cyclohexylamine:	TWA 10 ppm (40 mg/m³)	1,1-Dichloro-1-nitroethane:	TWA 2 ppm (10 mg/m³)
Cyclonite:	TWA 1.5 mg/m³ [skin]	1,3-Dichloropropene:	TWA 1 ppm (5 mg/m³) [skin]
Cyclopentane:	TWA 600 ppm (1720 mg/m³)		

2,2-Dichloropropionic acid:	TWA 1 ppm (6 mg/m³)
Dicrotophos:	TWA 0.25 mg/m³ [skin]
Dicyclopentadiene:	TWA 5 ppm (30 mg/m³)
Dicyclopentadienyl iron:	TWA 10 mg/m³ (total) TWA 5 mg/m³ (resp)
Diethanolamine:	TWA 3 ppm (15 mg/m³)
Diethylamine:	TWA 10 ppm (30 mg/m³) ST 25 ppm (75 mg/m³)
Diethylenetriamine:	TWA 1 ppm (4 mg/m³)
Diethyl ketone:	TWA 200 ppm (705 mg/m³)
Diethyl phthalate:	TWA 5 mg/m³
Diglycidyl ether:	TWA 0.1 ppm (0.5 mg/m³)
Diisobutyl ketone:	TWA 25 ppm (150 mg/m³)
N,N-Dimethylaniline:	TWA 5 ppm (25 mg/m³) ST 10 ppm (50 mg/m³) [skin]
Dimethyl-1,2-dibromo-2,2-dichlorethyl phosphate:	TWA 3 mg/m³ [skin]
Dimethyl sulfate:	TWA 0.1 ppm (0.5 mg/m³) [skin]
Dinitolmide:	TWA 5 mg/m³
Di-sec octyl phthalate:	TWA 5 mg/m³ ST 10 mg/m³
Dioxane:	TWA 25 ppm (90 mg/m³) [skin]
Dioxathion:	TWA 0.2 mg/m³ [skin]
Diphenylamine:	TWA 10 mg/m³
Dipropylene glycol methyl ether:	TWA 100 ppm (600 mg/m³) ST 150 ppm (900 mg/m³) [skin]
Dipropyl ketone:	TWA 50 ppm (235 mg/m³)
Diquat (Diquat dibromide):	TWA 0.5 mg/m³
Disulfiram:	TWA 2 mg/m³
Disulfoton:	TWA 0.1 mg/m³ [skin]
2,6-Di-tert-butyl-p-cresol:	TWA 10 mg/m³
Diuron:	TWA 10 mg/m³
Divinyl benzene:	TWA 10 ppm (50 mg/m³)

364

Emery:	TWA 10 mg/m³ (total) TWA 5 mg/m³ (resp)	Ethyl ether:	TWA 400 ppm (1200 mg/m³) ST 500 ppm (1500 mg/m³)
Endosulfan:	TWA 0.1 mg/m³ [skin]	Ethylidene norbornene:	C 5 ppm (25 mg/m³)
Epichlorohydrin:	TWA 2 ppm (8 mg/m³) [skin]	Ethyl mercaptan:	TWA 0.5 ppm (1 mg/m³)
Ethanolamine:	TWA 3 ppm (8 mg/m³) ST 6 ppm (15 mg/m³)	N-Ethylmorpholine:	TWA 5 ppm (23 mg/m³) [skin]
Ethion:	0.4 mg/m³ [skin]	Ethyl silicate:	TWA 10 ppm (85 mg/m³)
Ethyl acrylate:	TWA 5 ppm (20 mg/m³) ST 25 ppm (100 mg/m³) [skin]	Fenamiphos:	TWA 0.1 mg/m³ [skin]
		Fensulfothion:	TWA 0.1 mg/m³
Ethyl benzene:	TWA 100 ppm (435 mg/m³) ST 125 ppm (545 mg/m³)	Fenthion:	TWA 0.2 mg/m³ [skin]
		Ferbam:	TWA 10 mg/m³
Ethyl bromide:	TWA 200 ppm (890 mg/m³) ST 250 ppm (1110 mg/m³)	Ferrovanadium dust:	TWA 1 mg/m³ ST 3 mg/m³
Ethylene chlorohydrin:	C 1 ppm (3 mg/m³) [skin]	Fluorotrichloromethane:	C 1000 ppm (5600 mg/m³)
Ethylene dichloride:	TWA 1 ppm (4 mg/m³) ST 2 ppm (8 mg/m³)	Fonofos:	TWA 0.1 mg/m³ [skin]
		Formamide:	TWA 20 ppm (30 mg/m³) ST 30 ppm (45 mg/m³)
Ethylene glycol:	C 50 ppm (125 mg/m³)		
Ethylene glycol dinitrate:	ST 0.1 mg/m³ [skin]	Furfural:	TWA 2 ppm (8 mg/m³) [skin]

APPENDIX G—VACATED 1989 OSHA PELs (Continued)

Furfuryl alcohol:	TWA 10 ppm (40 mg/m³) ST 15 ppm (60 mg/m³) [skin]
Gasoline:	TWA 300 ppm (900 mg/m³) ST 500 ppm (1500 mg/m³)
Germanium tetrahydride:	TWA 0.2 ppm (0.6 mg/m³)
Glutaraldehyde:	C 0.2 ppm (0.8 mg/m³)
Glycerin (mist):	TWA 10 mg/m³ (total) TWA 5 mg/m³ (resp)
Glycidol:	TWA 25 ppm (75 mg/m³)
Graphite (natural):	TWA 2.5 mg/m³ (resp)
Graphite (synthetic):	TWA 10 mg/m³ (total) TWA 5 mg/m³ (resp)
n-Heptane:	TWA 400 ppm (1600 mg/m³) ST 500 ppm (2000 mg/m³)
Hexachlorobutadiene:	TWA 0.02 ppm (0.24 mg/m³)
Hexachlorocyclopentadiene:	TWA 0.01 ppm (0.1 mg/m³)
Hexafluoroacetone:	TWA 0.1 ppm (0.7 mg/m³) [skin]
n-Hexane:	TWA 50 ppm (180 mg/m³)
Hexane isomers (except n-Hexane):	TWA 500 ppm (1800 mg/m³) ST 1000 ppm (3600 mg/m³)
2-Hexanone:	TWA 5 ppm (20 mg/m³)
Hexone:	TWA 50 ppm (205 mg/m³) ST 75 ppm (300 mg/m³)
Hexylene glycol:	C 25 ppm (125 mg/m³)
Hydrazine:	TWA 0.1 ppm (0.1 mg/m³) [skin]
Hydrogenated terphenyls:	TWA 0.5 ppm (5 mg/m³)
Hydrogen bromide:	C 3 ppm (10 mg/m³)
Hydrogen cyanide:	ST 4.7 ppm (5 mg/m³) [skin]
Hydrogen fluoride (as F):	TWA 3 ppm ST 6 ppm
Hydrogen sulfide:	TWA 10 ppm (14 mg/m³) ST 15 ppm (21 mg/m³)
2-Hydroxypropyl acrylate:	TWA 0.5 ppm (3 mg/m³) [skin]
Indene:	TWA 10 ppm (45 mg/m³)

APPENDIX G—VACATED 1989 OSHA PELs (Continued)

Indium:	TWA 0.1 mg/m³
Iodoform:	TWA 0.6 ppm (10 mg/m³)
Iron pentacarbonyl (as Fe):	TWA 0.1 ppm (0.8 mg/m³) ST 0.2 ppm (1.6 mg/m³)
Iron salts (soluble, as Fe):	TWA 1 mg/m³
Isoamyl alcohol (primary & secondary):	TWA 100 ppm (360 mg/m³) ST 125 ppm (450 mg/m³)
Isobutane:	TWA 800 ppm (1900 mg/m³)
Isobutyl alcohol:	TWA 50 ppm (150 mg/m³)
Isooctyl alcohol:	TWA 50 ppm (270 mg/m³) [skin]
Isophorone:	TWA 4 ppm (23 mg/m³)
Isophorone diisocyanate:	TWA 0.005 ppm ST 0.02 ppm [skin]
2-Isopropoxyethanol:	TWA 25 ppm (105 mg/m³)
Isopropyl acetate:	TWA 250 ppm (950 mg/m³) ST 310 ppm (1185 mg/m³)

Isopropyl alcohol:	TWA 400 ppm (980 mg/m³) ST 500 ppm (1225 mg/m³)
Isopropylamine:	TWA 5 ppm (12 mg/m³) ST 10 ppm (24 mg/m³)
N-Isopropylaniline:	TWA 2 ppm (10 mg/m³) [skin]
Isopropyl glycidyl ether:	TWA 50 ppm (240 mg/m³) ST 75 ppm (360 mg/m³)
Kaolin:	TWA 10 mg/m³ (total) TWA 5 mg/m³ (resp)
Ketene:	TWA 0.5 ppm (0.9 mg/m³) ST 1.5 ppm (3 mg/m³)
Magnesium oxide fume:	TWA 10 mg/m³
Malathion:	TWA 10 mg/m³ [skin]
Manganese compounds and fume (as Mn):	Compounds: C 5 mg/m³ Fume: TWA 1 mg/m³ ST 3 mg/m³
Manganese cyclopentadienyl tricarbonyl (as Mn):	TWA 0.1 mg/m³ [skin]

Manganese tetroxide (as Mn):	TWA 1 mg/m³
Mercury compounds, as Hg [except(organo) alkyls]:	Hg Vapor: TWA 0.05 mg/m³ [skin] Non-alkyl compounds: C 0.1 mg/m³ [skin]
Mercury (organo) alkyl compounds (as Hg):	TWA 0.01 mg/m³ ST 0.03 mg/m³ [skin]
Mesityl oxide:	TWA 15 ppm (60 mg/m³) ST 25 ppm (100 mg/m³)
Methacrylic acid:	TWA 20 ppm (70 mg/m³) [skin]
Methomyl:	TWA 2.5 mg/m³
Methoxychlor:	TWA 10 mg/m³
4-Methoxyphenol:	TWA 5 mg/m³
Methyl acetate:	TWA 200 ppm (610 mg/m³) ST 250 ppm (760 mg/m³)
Methyl acetylene-propadiene mixture	TWA 1000 ppm (1800 mg/m³) ST 1250 ppm (2250 mg/m³)
Methylacrylonitrile:	TWA 1 ppm (3 mg/m³) [skin]
Methyl alcohol:	TWA 200 ppm (260 mg/m³) ST 250 ppm (325 mg/m³) [skin]
Methyl bromide:	TWA 5 ppm (20 mg/m³) [skin]
Methyl chloride:	TWA 50 ppm (105 mg/m³) ST 100 ppm (210 mg/m³)
Methyl chloroform:	TWA 350 ppm (1900 mg/m³) ST 450 ppm (2450 mg/m³)
Methyl-2-cyanoacrylate:	TWA 2 ppm (8 mg/m³) ST 4 ppm (16 mg/m³)
Methylcyclohexane:	TWA 400 ppm (1600 mg/m³)
Methylcyclohexanol:	TWA 50 ppm (235 mg/m³)
o-Methylcyclohexanone:	TWA 50 ppm (230 mg/m³) ST 75 ppm (345 mg/m³) [skin]
Methyl cyclopentadienyl manganese tricarbonyl (as Mn):	TWA 0.2 mg/m³ [skin]
Methyl demeton:	TWA 0.5 mg/m³ [skin]

APPENDIX G—VACATED 1989 OSHA PELs (Continued)

4,4'-Methylenebis(2-chloroaniline):	TWA 0.02 ppm (0.22 mg/m³) [skin]
Methylene bis(4-cyclo- hexylisocyanate):	C 0.01 ppm (0.11 mg/m³) [skin]
Methyl ethyl ketone peroxide:	C 0.7 ppm (5 mg/m³)
Methyl formate:	TWA 100 ppm (250 mg/m³) ST 150 ppm (375 mg/m³)
Methyl iodide:	TWA 2 ppm (10 mg/m³) [skin]
Methyl isoamyl ketone:	TWA 50 ppm (240 mg/m³)
Methyl isobutyl carbinol:	TWA 25 ppm (100 mg/m³) ST 40 ppm (165 mg/m³) [skin]
Methyl isopropyl ketone:	TWA 200 ppm (705 mg/m³)
Methyl mercaptan:	TWA 0.5 ppm (1 mg/m³)
Methyl parathion:	TWA 0.2 mg/m³ [skin]
Methyl silicate:	TWA 1 ppm (6 mg/m³)
α-Methyl styrene:	TWA 50 ppm (240 mg/m³) ST 100 ppm (485 mg/m³)
Metribuzin:	TWA 5 mg/m³

Mica:	TWA 3 mg/m³ (resp)
Molybdenum (insoluble compounds, as Mo):	TWA 10 mg/m³
Monocrotophos:	TWA 0.25 mg/m³
Monomethyl aniline:	TWA 0.5 ppm (2 mg/m³) [skin]
Morpholine:	TWA 20 ppm (70 mg/m³) ST 30 ppm (105 mg/m³) [skin]
Naphthalene:	TWA 10 ppm (50 mg/m³) ST 15 ppm (75 mg/m³)
Nickel metal & other compounds (as Ni):	Metal & insoluble compounds: TWA 1 mg/m³ Soluble compounds: TWA 0.1 mg/m³
Nitric acid:	TWA 2 ppm (5 mg/m³) ST 4 ppm (10 mg/m³)
p-Nitroaniline:	TWA 3 mg/m³ [skin]
Nitrogen dioxide:	ST 1 ppm (1.8 mg/m³)
Nitroglycerine:	ST 0.1 mg/m³) [skin]
2-Nitropropane:	TWA 10 ppm (35 mg/m³)

368

APPENDIX G—VACATED 1989 OSHA PELs (Continued)

Nitrotoluene (o-, m-, p-isomers):	TWA 2 ppm (11 mg/m³) [skin]	Pentaerythritol:	TWA 10 mg/m³ (total) TWA 5 mg/m³ (resp)
Nonane:	TWA 200 ppm (1050 mg/m³)	n-Pentane:	TWA 600 ppm (1800 mg/m³) ST 750 ppm (2250 mg/m³)
Octachloronaphthalene:	TWA 0.1 mg/m³ ST 0.3 mg/m³ [skin]	2-Pentanone:	TWA 200 ppm (700 mg/m³) ST 250 ppm (875 mg/m³)
Octane:	TWA 300 ppm (1450 mg/m³) ST 375 ppm (1800 mg/m³)	Perchloryl fluoride:	TWA 3 ppm (14 mg/m³) ST 6 ppm (28 mg/m³)
Osmium tetroxide (as Os):	TWA 0.002 mg/m³ (0.0002 ppm) ST 0.006 mg/m³ (0.0006 ppm)	Petroleum distillates (naphtha):	TWA 400 ppm (1600 mg/m³)
Oxalic acid:	TWA 1 mg/m³ ST 2 mg/m³	Phenothiazine:	TWA 5 mg/m³ [skin]
Oxygen difluoride:	C 0.05 ppm (0.1 mg/m³)	Phenyl glycidyl ether:	TWA 1 ppm (6 mg/m³)
Ozone:	TWA 0.1 ppm (0.2 mg/m³) ST 0.3 ppm (0.6 mg/m³)	Phenylhydrazine:	TWA 5 ppm (20 mg/m³) ST 10 ppm (45 mg/m³) [skin]
Paraffin wax fume:	TWA 2 mg/m³	Phenylphosphine:	C 0.05 ppm (0.25 mg/m³)
Paraquat:	TWA 0.1 mg/m³ (resp) [skin]	Phorate:	TWA 0.05 mg/m³ ST 0.2 mg/m³ [skin]
Pentaborane:	TWA 0.005 ppm (0.01 mg/m³) ST 0.015 ppm (0.03 mg/m³)	Phosdrin:	TWA 0.01 ppm (0.1 mg/m³) ST 0.03 ppm (0.3 mg/m³) [skin]

APPENDIX G—VACATED 1989 OSHA PELs (Continued)

370

Phosphine:	TWA 0.3 ppm (0.4 mg/m³) ST 1 ppm (1 mg/m³)
Phosphoric acid:	TWA 1 mg/m³ ST 3 mg/m³
Phosphorus oxychloride:	TWA 0.1 ppm (0.6 mg/m³)
Phosphorus pentasulfide:	TWA 1 mg/m³ ST 3 mg/m³
Phosphorus trichloride:	TWA 0.2 ppm (1.5 mg/m³) ST 0.5 ppm (3 mg/m³)
Phthalic anhydride:	TWA 6 mg/m³ (1 ppm)
m-Phthalodinitrile:	TWA 5 mg/m³ TWA 10 mg/m³ (total)
Picloram:	TWA 5 mg/m³ (resp)
Piperazine dihydrochloride:	TWA 5 mg/m³
Platinum metal (as Pt):	TWA 1 mg/m³
Portland cement:	TWA 10 mg/m³ (total) TWA 5 mg/m³ (resp)
Potassium hydroxide:	TWA 2 mg/m³
Propargyl alcohol:	TWA 1 ppm (2 mg/m³) [skin]
Propionic acid:	TWA 10 ppm (30 mg/m³)
Propoxur:	TWA 0.5 mg/m³
n-Propyl acetate:	TWA 200 ppm (840 mg/m³) ST 250 ppm (1050 mg/m³)
n-Propyl alcohol:	TWA 200 ppm (500 mg/m³) ST 250 ppm (625 mg/m³)
Propylene dichloride:	TWA 75 ppm (350 mg/m³) ST 110 ppm (510 mg/m³)
Propylene glycol dinitrate:	TWA 0.05 ppm (0.3 mg/m³)
Propylene glycol monomethyl ether:	TWA 100 ppm (360 mg/m³) ST 150 ppm (540 mg/m³)
Propylene oxide:	TWA 20 ppm (50 mg/m³)
n-Propyl nitrate:	TWA 25 ppm (105 mg/m³) ST 40 ppm (170 mg/m³)
Resorcinol:	TWA 10 ppm (45 mg/m³) ST 20 ppm (90 mg/m³)
Ronnel:	TWA 10 mg/m³

Rosin core solder, pyrolysis products (as formaldehyde):	TWA 0.1 mg/m³
Rouge:	TWA 10 mg/m³ (total) TWA 5 mg/m³ (resp)
Silica, amorphous:	TWA 6 mg/m³ TWA 0.1 mg/m³ (fused)
Silica, crystalline (as respirable dust):	TWA 0.05 mg/m³ (cristobalite) TWA 0.05 mg/m³ (tridymite) TWA 0.1 mg/m³ (quartz) TWA 0.1 mg/m³ (tripoli)
Silicon:	TWA 10 mg/m³ (total) TWA 5 mg/m³ (resp)
Silicon carbide:	TWA 10 mg/m³ (total) TWA 5 mg/m³ (resp)
Silicon tetrahydride:	TWA 5 ppm (7 mg/m³)
Soapstone:	TWA 6 mg/m³ (total) TWA 3 mg/m³ (resp)

Sodium azide:	C 0.1 ppm (as HN_3) [skin] C 0.3 mg/m³ (as NaN_3) [skin]
Sodium bisulfite:	TWA 5 mg/m³
Sodium fluoroacetate:	TWA 0.05 mg/m³ ST 0.15 mg/m³ [skin]
Sodium hydroxide:	C 2 mg/m³
Sodium metabisulfite:	TWA 5 mg/m³
Stoddard solvent:	TWA 525 mg/m³ (100 ppm)
Styrene:	TWA 50 ppm (215 mg/m³) ST 100 ppm (425 mg/m³)
Subtilisins:	ST 0.00006 mg/m³ [60-minute]
Sulfur dioxide:	TWA 2 ppm (5 mg/m³) ST 5 ppm (13 mg/m³)
Sulfur monochloride:	C 1 ppm (6 mg/m³)
Sulfur pentafluoride:	C 0.01 ppm (0.1 mg/m³)
Sulfur tetrafluoride:	C 0.1 ppm (0.4 mg/m³)

APPENDIX G—VACATED 1989 OSHA PELs (Continued)

Sulfuryl fluoride:	TWA 5 ppm (20 mg/m^3) ST 10 ppm (40 mg/m^3)
Sulprofos:	TWA 1 mg/m^3
Talc:	TWA 2 mg/m^3 (resp)
Temephos:	TWA 10 mg/m^3 (total) TWA 5 mg/m^3 (resp)
Terphenyl (o-, m-, p-isomers):	C 5 mg/m^3 (0.5 ppm)
1,1,2,2-Tetrachloroethane:	TWA 1 ppm (7 mg/m^3) [skin]
Tetrachloroethylene:	TWA 25 ppm (170 mg/m^3)
Tetrahydrofuran:	TWA 200 ppm (590 mg/m^3) ST 250 ppm (735 mg/m^3)
Tetrasodium pyrophosphate:	TWA 5 mg/m^3
4,4'-Thiobis(6-tert-butyl-m-cresol):	TWA 10 mg/m^3 (total) TWA 5 mg/m^3 (resp)
Thioglycolic acid:	TWA 1 ppm (4 mg/m^3) [skin]
Thionyl chloride:	C 1 ppm (5 mg/m^3)
Tin (organic compounds, as Sn):	TWA 0.1 mg/m^3 [skin]
Tin(II) oxide (as Sn):	TWA 2 mg/m^3
Tin(IV) oxide (as Sn):	TWA 2 mg/m^3
Titanium dioxide:	TWA 10 mg/m^3
Toluene:	TWA 100 ppm (375 mg/m^3) ST 150 ppm (560 mg/m^3)
Toluene-2,4-diisocyanate:	TWA 0.005 ppm (0.04 mg/m^3) ST 0.02 ppm (0.15 mg/m^3)
m-Toluidine:	TWA 2 ppm (9 mg/m^3) [skin]
p-Toluidine:	TWA 2 ppm (9 mg/m^3) [skin]
Tributyl phosphate:	TWA 0.2 ppm (2.5 mg/m^3)
Trichloroacetic acid:	TWA 1 ppm (7 mg/m^3)
1,2,4-Trichlorobenzene:	C 5 ppm (40 mg/m^3)
Trichloroethylene:	TWA 50 ppm (270 mg/m^3) ST 200 ppm (1080 mg/m^3)
1,2,3-Trichloropropane:	TWA 10 ppm (60 mg/m^3)
1,1,2-Trichloro-1,2,2-trifluoroethane:	TWA 1000 ppm (7600 mg/m^3) ST 1250 ppm (9500 mg/m^3)

Triethylamine:	TWA 10 ppm (40 mg/m³) ST 15 ppm (60 mg/m³)
Trimellitic anhydride:	TWA 0.005 ppm (0.04 mg/m³)
Trimethylamine:	TWA 10 ppm (24 mg/m³) ST 15 ppm (36 mg/m³)
1,2,3-Trimethylbenzene:	TWA 25 ppm (125 mg/m³)
1,2,4-Trimethylbenzene:	TWA 25 ppm (125 mg/m³)
1,3,5-Trimethylbenzene:	TWA 25 ppm (125 mg/m³)
Trimethyl phosphite:	TWA 2 ppm (10 mg/m³)
2,4,6-Trinitrotoluene:	TWA 0.5 mg/m³ [skin]
Triorthocresyl phosphate:	TWA 0.1 mg/m³ [skin]
Triphenylamine:	TWA 5 mg/m³
Tungsten (insoluble compounds, as W):	TWA 5 mg/m³ ST 10 mg/m³
Tungsten (soluble compounds, as W):	TWA 1 mg/m³ ST 3 mg/m³
Tungsten carbide (cemented):	TWA 5 mg/m³ (as W) ST 10 mg/m³ (as W) TWA 0.05 mg/m³ (as Co) TWA 1 mg/m³ (as Ni)
Uranium (insoluble compounds, as U):	TWA 0.2 mg/m³ ST 0.6 mg/m³
n-Valeraldehyde:	TWA 50 ppm (175 mg/m³)
Vanadium dust:	TWA 0.05 mg V₂O₅/m³ (resp)
Vanadium fume:	C 0.05 mg V₂O₅/m³
Vinyl acetate:	TWA 10 ppm (30 mg/m³) ST 20 ppm (60 mg/m³)
Vinyl bromide:	TWA 5 ppm (20 mg/m³)
Vinyl cyclohexene dioxide:	TWA 10 ppm (60 mg/m³) [skin]
Vinylidene chloride:	TWA 1 ppm (4 mg/m³)
VM & P Naphtha:	TWA 1350 mg/m³ (300 ppm) ST 1800 mg/m³ (400 ppm)
Welding fumes:	TWA 5 mg/m³

APPENDIX G—VACATED 1989 OSHA PELs (Continued)

Wood dust (all wood dusts except Western red cedar):	TWA 5 mg/m³ ST 10 mg/m³	Zinc oxide:	TWA 5 mg/m³ (fume) ST 10 mg/m³ (fume) TWA 10 mg/m³ (total dust) TWA 5 mg/m³ (resp dust)
Wood dust (Western red cedar):	TWA 2.5 mg/m³		
Xylene (o-, m-, p-isomers):	TWA 100 ppm (435 mg/m³) ST 150 ppm (655 mg/m³)	Zinc stearate:	TWA 10 mg/m³ (total) TWA 5 mg/m³ (resp)
m-Xylene α,α'-diamine:	C 0.1 mg/m³ [skin]	Zirconium compounds (as Zr):	TWA 5 mg/m³ ST 10 mg/m³
Xylidine:	TWA 2 ppm (10 mg/m³) [skin]		
Zinc chloride fume:	TWA 1 mg/m³ ST 2 mg/m³		

INDICES

CAS NUMBER INDEX

376

377

CAS NUMBER INDEX

CAS NUMBER INDEX

379

CAS NUMBER INDEX

CAS NUMBER INDEX

381

CAS NUMBER INDEX

382

CAS NUMBER INDEX

383

DOT ID NUMBER INDEX

DOT ID NUMBER INDEX

DOT ID NUMBER INDEX

DOT ID NUMBER INDEX

387

DOT ID NUMBER INDEX

388

SYNONYM AND TRADE NAME INDEX

389

392

396

SYNONYM AND TRADE NAME INDEX (Continued)

399

400

402

403

404

406

407

410

411

413

414

415

416

417

420

421

422

423

424

425

426

428

429

430

433

434

435

436

437

438

440

☆ U.S. GOVERNMENT PRINTING OFFICE: 1997 J551-571